D1616813

Bayesian statistics for social scientists

Lawrence D Phillips

Brunel University

Bayesian statistics
for social scientists

THOMAS Y. CROWELL COMPANY
New York · Established 1834

Library of Congress Cataloging in Publication Data

Phillips, Lawrence D
  Bayesian statistics for social scientists.

  Includes bibliographical references.
  1. Statistics.   2. Bayesian statistical decision
theory.   3. Social sciences—Statistical methods.
I. Title.
HA29.P518 1973   519.5   73-3208
ISBN 0-690-00137-1

First published in the United States of America 1974
Copyright © 1973 by Lawrence D. Phillips
Illustrations © 1973 by Thomas Nelson & Sons Ltd.

Manufactured in the United States of America
1 2 3 4 5 6 7 8 9 10

Contents

Preface

Over the past few years I have been encouraged by colleagues and students who knew of my interest in Bayesian statistics to write a book that would explain the Bayesian approach in reasonably simple language, and would serve as a practical guide to carrying out Bayesian analyses. This book is the result. It attempts to introduce Bayesian statistics to the professional psychologist, sociologist, educational researcher, or economist who seeks alternatives to significance tests, who wishes to find out more than that his results are not due to chance and who wants to know how likely his statistical hypotheses are now that the data are in. The book should also be of interest to the student of the social sciences who has had some exposure to statistics and who is interested in learning the Bayesian viewpoint. But the reader I mainly had in mind when writing this book is the social science student new to statistics. Thus, it assumes that the reader has no previous acquaintance with statistics, and has perhaps half-forgotten his school mathematics. Depending on the pace of the course, this book could serve as a textbook for a statistics class for which the total number of timetabled hours is at least 45.

Though I am a hearty advocate of the Bayesian viewpoint, I have tried to provide sufficient explanation of non-Bayesian approaches to enable the reader to understand non-Bayesian analyses, which still predominate in the social sciences literature. Enough information is given for the reader to give an exact or approximate Bayesian interpretation to most parametric tests of significance that would be encountered in the literature. In addition, the rationale behind current practice employing confidence intervals, significance tests and hypothesis testing is explained.

Chapter 1 provides a general introduction to the key ideas of Bayesian inference. The five chapters that follow (Part 1) lay the foundations: probability theory, Bayes theorem, and distribution theory. In Part 2 I discuss measurement, collecting data and the usual descriptive statistics, including correlation and regression. Part 3 deals entirely with inferential statistics. Chapters 11 and 12 concentrate mainly on estimation, Chapter 13 presents non-Bayesian methods, while Chapter 14 concludes with Bayesian approaches to hypothesis testing.

My initial contact with Bayesian statistics came about when I was a Ph.D. student at the University of Michigan in the early sixties. I had excellent teachers:

William L. Hays, Harold Lindman and especially Ward Edwards to whom I owe a deep and lasting debt. I have learned much from the writings of L. J. Savage, Howard Raiffa, Robert Schlaifer and Harold Jeffreys, while the books by Dennis Lindley (1965) and Samuel Schmitt (1969) have provided much of the material in Chapters 11 and 12.

Many people have contributed directly to this book. In particular Dennis Lindley has read and commented on most of an earlier version, and I am most grateful for his wise and helpful suggestions and for correcting a number of errors. A. D. Lovie and E. W. Kelley read the entire manuscript and provided many useful suggestions. Brendan McGuinness and Patrick Humphreys have helped me in learning to teach Bayesian statistics. To all these people I give my thanks. They share whatever merits this book has; I alone take responsibility for any remaining errors.

I am particularly grateful to the first-year social science students at Brunel University who attended my Bayesian statistics courses from 1968 to 1972. Each year I learned a little more about how to teach Bayesian ideas, and much of this experience is contained between these covers. I also owe a great debt to Patrick Humphreys who wrote the computer programs for two of the tables in the Appendix, a task that turned out to be more complex than we had anticipated. Other tables have been reproduced with kind permission from Novick and Jackson (1974), Pearson and Hartley (1966), and Fisher and Yates (1963). I am also grateful to Addison-Wesley for permission to reproduce Figs 11–4 and 12–4.

Many people generously gave support, encouragement and help during the writing of this book. I am very grateful to them all, especially to my wife Maryann.

LAWRENCE D. PHILLIPS

1 · Introduction

'Did you hear about the man who lived in a room so small that he had to sleep with his head in the oven and his feet in the refrigerator? On the average he was very comfortable.' That old story well illustrates the distrust many people feel about statistics. Sometimes that distrust is justified, as when we hear the exhortation to buy a particular brand of toothpaste because it reduces tooth decay by 60%, or when a television announcer claims that his product is 40% more effective than brand X. The political party in office produces figures to prove that national unemployment is at an all-time low, while the opposition party uses the same figures in a different way to show that unemployment is rapidly increasing. The smooth-talking salesman honestly tells you that his product has an average life of five years, but he does not tell you that quality control during manufacture is so poor that some of the products can be expected to wear out after only six months' use, while others may last for nine or ten years. Surely anything can be proved with statistics.

Another criticism of statistics comes from people who feel that the ineffable aspects of human behaviour are what make us uniquely human. They insist that people and societies cannot be reduced to numbers, that something essential is lost by the social scientist who in his fervour to classify, count, and measure misses the subtleties of human behaviour and interaction. At best, statistics can only express the obvious; at worst they hide the truly important aspects of human experience.

Both these criticisms are, to some extent, justified. Statistics can be misused to prove just about anything. But this is hardly an argument for abandoning statistics; rather it argues for the intelligent use of statistics, for educating the reader so he can tell when statistics are being used properly and when they are being used inappropriately, and for educating the user of statistics so he will not mislead his readers.

The second criticism, that statistics obscure the subtle and complex aspects of human and societal behaviour, is taken very seriously by social scientists. Anyone who has tried to reduce data to numbers feels that he has lost something in the translations. Again, this is not an argument for avoiding statistics; it points to the necessity for understanding the limitations of statistics. Let me amplify this point.

The physicist is interested in, for example, temperature, voltage, weight, and length; he has developed instruments for measuring these, thermometers, voltmeters, scales, and metre-sticks. Some of these devices measure directly as a metre-stick measures length, but others measure only indirectly as the height of a column of liquid in a glass tube indicates temperature, or as the deflection of a pointer indicates voltage. These last two examples are instances of *derived* measurement, the former of *fundamental* measurement. Fundamental measurements are made in terms of themselves, for example, length is measured in terms of length, weight in terms of a standard weight on a balance. Derived measurements are related to the quantity being measured only through some law; temperature relates to the height of the column of liquid through the operation of laws describing the expansion and contraction of liquids and solids brought about by changes in temperature, and voltage is related to the needle's deflection through the operation of laws describing the amount and interaction of electromagnetic forces set up in a coil by the passage of current through the coil.

The social sciences are in the unfortunate position of having to rely solely on derived measurements with little underlying theory and fewer laws than would allow the scientist to relate the measurements he is making to the real subject of his investigation. Nobody has found a way to measure directly anxiety, love, aggressiveness, conflict, hope, and all the aspects of the behaviour of people and societies that we feel are important. Rather than measure anxiety directly, we measure amount of sweating, increase in heartbeat, change in breathing rate, change in chemical composition of the blood, or any of many other indices of anxiety. Not only are these measurements indirect, but we do not even know for sure how they relate to anxiety. Sweating may indicate a state of anxiety or it may be caused by an increase in the room temperature; changes in heartbeat or in the chemical composition of the blood may be caused by fear or anger. So without a satisfactory theory relating anxiety to these physiological changes, we cannot be sure that a measurable change in one of the indices reflects a change in the anxiety of the person being studied.

More will be said about this dilemma in Chapter 7. For now the important point is that the meaninglessness of some statistics is often not a problem in statistics, but a problem in measurement. If a social scientist carelessly attaches numbers to his observations or to his data, no amount of sophisticated statistical manipulation of those numbers will make them any more meaningful than the original assignment. What comes out of the statistical mill is no better than what goes in.

The emphasis in this book is on the intelligent use of statistics; the conditions under which particular statistical analyses are appropriate or inappropriate will be stressed. If statistics are used appropriately, and if measurements are meaningful, then statistical results can be intelligently interpreted in a useful and meaningful way. Cold, impersonal numbers may or may not obscure the meaning behind the numbers—that is up to the scientist. Used intelligently, statistics can illuminate meaning, even magnify and enrich it.

1.1   Scope of the book

Purposes

This book is intended primarily for undergraduate students who are taking a first course in statistics. But it should also serve to satisfy the curiosity of the post-graduate student or the professional social scientist who has heard of

Bayesian statistics, wants to know what it is about, but whose limited mathematical background does not permit his reading presently available Bayesian treatises, nearly all of which require intermediate to advanced level mathematics.

By the time you have finished this book, you should be able to

carry out simple statistical analyses of data;
recognize when a particular analysis is appropriate and when it is not;
understand simple statistical analyses reported in the literature.

You will not meet these objectives merely by reading the text; doing the exercises at the end of each chapter is essential to a full understanding of the material in the chapter. Also, you will find that even though you have understood a chapter, it will require periodic review, for most students find that statistical topics have a strange tendency to slip away or suddenly to become unclear. The summaries at the end of the chapters will help you in your reviews.

Mathematical background needed

This book assumes only very modest mathematical ability on the part of the reader. You should feel comfortable with fractions, decimals, percentages, and simple algebra. You should be able to handle positive and negative numbers, and you should be able to deal with logarithms. If you are not sure of your abilities in any of these areas, you can brush up with the help of either of two books. If you like programmed texts, get *A First Program in Mathematics* by Arthur Heywood, Belmont, California: Dickenson Publishing Company, 1967 (distributed in Great Britain by Prentice-Hall). This text contains diagnostic tests which you can use to spot your mathematical weaknesses. The tests guide you to only those programmes in the book which you need. The programmes are written in non-trivial frames and employ both linear and branching techniques. The book does not, however, contain sections on positive and negative numbers or on logarithms. If you do not like programmed texts, try Helen Walker's *Mathematics Essential for Elementary Statistics*, New York: Holt, Rinehart and Winston, 1957. This text also contains diagnostic tests; each chapter begins with a test, and if you pass the test you do not need to read the chapter.

1.2   Key ideas of Bayesian statistics

What is statistics?

Perhaps I should say, 'What are statistics?' Most of us are familiar with statistics in the plural sense. Average amounts of rainfall, mean incomes of residents in a particular suburb, rise in the gross national product, rate of change in the cost of living, proportions of people preferring this candidate to that one, all these are statistics. Numbers attached to data, these are statistics. On the other hand, statistics in the singular sense refers to a body of knowledge whose application enables the scientist to make sense out of the data he has collected In particular, he is interested in going beyond the data he has collected so that he can make a generalization. He is not interested so much in the data at hand as in the wider meaning of that data. The sociologist is only marginally interested in the behaviour of the working-class families he has observed; he would really like to generalize his findings at least to the wider community his families came from. The psychologist studying memory does not wish to confine his findings to the people he has observed; he is looking at the behaviour of a few people in his search for general laws governing the operation of memory.

Statistics that summarize data, that enable whole masses of data to be communicated with a few numbers, are called *descriptive statistics*. These will be treated only briefly in this book because the main topic of interest is *inferential statistics*, the making of generalizations or inferences beyond the data immediately at hand. You must know something about both these kinds of statistics in order to read the literature in your field, and you must know how to use statistics if you are to complete the laboratory and applied aspects of your course successfully.

Controversies in statistics

Most statistics texts and courses give the impression that there is little controversy among statisticians about statistical methods. That simply is not true. A heated dialogue continues among statisticians about the very foundations of their subject, and the controversy is far from being resolved. This book takes the more controversial point of view, usually referred to as the Bayesian school. The battle lines have been too clearly drawn between the Bayesians and the 'traditionalists', but just as the traditionalists do not speak with a single voice, so the Bayesians find differences among themselves. The differences among the Bayesians are sufficiently small that this book need not bother much with them, but I will occasionally suggest that the last word on a particular topic has not yet been heard. Readers who are acquainted with 'traditional' statistics, if such a subject exists, will find much that is familiar in this book. Often the Bayesians arrive at the same end point as the traditionalists, but the route is very different. What the Bayesian does when he is making statistical calculations is often identical to what the traditionalist does, only the meaning is different. There are times when the two points of view differ, however, and these will be mentioned.

I have kept in mind that the reader will want to be able to read the literature in his discipline and to understand the meaning of non-Bayesian statistical analyses. The points of agreement between the two schools make it possible for you to understand the results of traditional analyses, even though you have learned only Bayesian statistics. Rather than explain the traditional approach to the analysis in question, I have given the Bayesian interpretation of the traditional analysis. You will not learn how to do traditional statistical analyses but you will be able to see what assumptions and procedures would lead a Bayesian to the traditional results. In all fairness I should warn you that not all traditional procedures have Bayesian counterparts, at least not yet. The traditionalists have had a head start of several decades, so the traditional methods are more extensively developed. However, Bayesian methods are appearing with increasing frequency in the statistician's journals, so the gap will become narrower within the next few years. Enough is now known about Bayesian procedures to justify writing this book.

As with any controversial point of view, the Bayesians find they have vociferous detractors. You will undoubtedly come across some. I do not propose here to answer the critics; most of the common criticisms are answered, sometimes implicitly, sometimes explicitly, in the chapters to follow. Bayesian statistical procedures are as defensible as (and I think more than) any traditional procedures. This book merely presents some of the Bayesian methods. The decision to become a 'traditionalist' or a 'Bayesian' is left to you.

Elements of Bayesian Statistics

One theme occurs throughout this book: revision of opinion in the light of new information. The Bayesian statistician is concerned first with expressing his opinions about some theoretical matter in an open, public way, then with collecting data that bear on this opinion, and finally with using Bayes' theorem to revise his prior opinion in the light of the data. His revised opinion is then taken as his current opinion, which he can communicate to others, or which he can modify after the collection of more data. For example, suppose that an unscrupulous gambler places his biased coin in his pocket. From past experience with this coin, he knows that it has a bias in favour of 'heads'. Later, as he takes it out of his pocket, he discovers another identically appearing coin; one of the two coins is the biased one, but the other is fair, for it is the change he received earlier. How can he decide which coin is which?

A Bayesian statistician might approach the problem in the following manner. First, he would say, examine the coins to see if you can get any clue as to which is biased. Suppose there is no clue, so you arbitrarily choose one of the coins. Then what is your current opinion about whether or not you have chosen the biased coin? If you have no reason to think it is one coin or the other, you might say that your current opinion is equally divided between the two possibilities. You are as certain that it is biased as unbiased, or there is a 50–50 chance of it being biased. You might also say that if you placed a bet on whether or not the coin was biased, you would be utterly indifferent between betting on the coin being biased or betting on it being unbiased. Your prior opinion leads you to give even odds on the coin being biased.

Next, the statistician would conduct a simple experiment; he would toss the coin a few times. Suppose he tosses it 10 times, and it comes up heads 8 times. The data from the experiment are '8 heads out of 10 tosses'. He would then combine these data with your prior opinion, using Bayes' theorem, to arrive at the revised or posterior odds. In Chapter 4 Bayes' theorem will be introduced, and its application to this example will be given. For now, it is enough to say that the posterior opinion would be expressed in probabilities or odds, just as the prior opinion was. The posterior opinion might now be 75–25 or odds of 3 to 1 in favour of the coin being biased. The actual posterior opinion would depend on whether or not the gambler knew the degree of bias, and if so, what it actually was.

Opinions are expressed in probabilities, data are collected, and these data change the prior probabilities, through the operation of Bayes' theorem, to yield posterior probabilities.

That is the essence of Bayesian methods.

This key idea has dictated the organization of the book. In Part I, we learn how to quantify prior opinion. Part II is concerned entirely with describing data. Bayesian methods for combining prior opinions and data form the subject of Part III.

It is easy to lose your way when learning statistics. You will be less likely to if you remember that the entire book is an expansion of the key idea:

Prior opinions are changed by data to yield posterior opinions.

That is what Bayesian statistics is all about.

1.3   Problems to be covered

I have already said that this book is mainly concerned with making inferences. But inferences about what? Two sorts of inferences dominate the experimental literature in the social sciences:

inferences about uncertain quantities;
inferences about hypotheses or events.

Inferences about one uncertain quantity

What proportion of the population approves of the way the president (or prime minister) is handling governmental affairs? What is the average score of machinists on a particular test of mechanical aptitude? How much variation in I.Q. from one person to the next can be expected from college students? None of these questions can be answered with certainty because it simply is not possible to ask *all* people their opinion of the capability of their country's leader, or to test *all* machinists, or to measure the I.Q.'s of *all* college students.

From our point of view, the proportion of all people, the average score of all machinists, and the variation in I.Q. of all college students are all uncertain quantities. We suppose that they exist as single values, but we are uncertain of those values. We may have a vague idea, or even a fairly precise notion, as to the values, but as scientists we would like to collect data to enable us to be more confident of the values of those uncertain quantities. The best we can do is take a representative sample of people from the larger group and then let the data from this sample be applied against our prior opinions, using Bayes' theorem, to give us our new, posterior opinions about the uncertain quantity.

These three examples illustrate the sorts of uncertain quantities we will be dealing with in this book:

proportions   averages   variations

You should know what proportions and averages are, but you probably do not know very precisely what is meant by variation. Later, in Chapter 9, we will show how variation can be expressed as a single number.

Inferences about two uncertain quantities

Just as a scientist may want to make inferences about some uncertain quantity, so he may wish to know whether or not two uncertain quantities are different from one another. Is the proportion of people in Kansas approving the president's activities different from the proportion approving in California? Do machinists and clerks differ in their scores on the mechanical aptitude test? Is the variation in I.Q. amongst English college students different from the variation in America? To answer these questions, the scientist must collect data from representative samples of people and use these data to revise his prior opinions about the uncertain differences.

We could go on to examine differences among more than two uncertain quantities; such inferences are possible but beyond the scope of this book. Here we shall deal with no more than two uncertain quantities.

Inferences about the relationships between quantities

The social sciences are still in their infancy and so a great deal of experimental effort is spent in trying to discover what goes with what. Does the level of a person's achievement motivation have any relationship to whether or not the person is engaged in an entrepreneurial profession? Is the age of a child when the mother begins toilet training related to the mother's social class? Is there any relationship between creative ability and neurosis? Statistics can help us to make inferences about whether or not two quantities are related.

Increasingly, social scientists are interested in the *degree* to which one quantity goes with another one, or the *degree* of relationship between two quantities. To what extent is approval of the president's (or prime minister's) behaviour related to the age of the respondent? What is the degree of relationship between scores on the mechanical aptitude test and ratings of success as a machinist? To what extent are I.Q. and grades at university related? In the social sciences, relationships are seldom perfect; we can rarely say that when one quantity increases, a related quantity will increase in direct proportion, but we can say that as one quantity increases the other tends to increase also. If the tendency is weak, that is, there are many exceptions to the rule, then we say that the degree of relationship is weak, but if there are few exceptions then the relationship is strong. The social scientist learns to formulate statements like this last one in a precise manner through the use of statistics. He can use Bayesian methods to revise prior opinions about the uncertain degree of relationship.

Since one of the aims of science is prediction, it follows that scientists often try to formulate the *rule* for predicting one quantity from knowledge of another, related quantity. I can come closer, on the average, to predicting your true weight if I know your height than if I do not know it. Height and weight are related quantities; even though the relationship is not perfect, I can use knowledge of one to help in predicting the other.

In this book we will discuss one particular type of rule, and will learn how our prior uncertainty about that rule can be modified with data to give us posterior opinions about the rule.

Inferences about hypotheses and events

Scientists are often interested in testing their theories. Whatever the scientist's statistical persuasion, he first derives from theory specific, testable hypotheses. sometimes called *statistical hypotheses*, only one of which could be true. The Bayesian will then express prior opinions about the relative truth of those hypotheses, collect data which bear on the truth, and then use Bayes' theorem to revise the prior opinions. The resulting posterior opinions give the scientist's judgement, in the light of the data, about which hypothesis is more likely to be true than the others. Usually social scientists formulate hypotheses which are not capable of conclusive proof or disproof, but which are sufficiently different that the data can be expected to favour one or the other.

For example, one theory about children of normal intelligence who are having difficulty in learning to read relates the reading disability to an emotionally-taxing experience, such as divorce of the parents, that the child has recently experienced. From that theory, one might derive this statistical hypothesis: A higher proportion of recently-broken homes will be found among children with reading problems than among children who are learning to read without difficulty. A second, alternative, hypothesis, derived from the notion that reading problems are not associated with emotionally-taxing experiences, would state that the proportions of broken homes for the two groups of children would show no difference other than one attributable to chance. The investigator collects data on say, 50 reading-problem children and 50 non-reading problem children, all of normal intelligence, and finds that broken homes occur twice as frequently among families of reading-problem children than the families of the other children. Obviously these data do not conclusively prove or disprove either theory, but the data could be used to revise the investigator's opinions held before the data were collected so that now his posterior opinions express his judgement about the relative likelihood of the truth of the two hypotheses.

Hypothesis testing has become one of the hallmarks of social science and is very much in vogue these days amongst social scientists. Students often come to believe that unless an experiment tests an hypothesis it is not really scientific. One reason is that conventional methods of statistical inference lay heavy emphasis on hypothesis testing, so that the scientist using conventional statistics is forced to formulate his experiment in terms of hypotheses to be tested.

Bayesian methods, on the other hand, place more emphasis on inferences about unknown quantities than on hypothesis testing. In the example just given, one might look at the difference between the proportion of broken homes among reading-problem children and the proportion among normal children. Bayesian methods could be applied to make an inference about the difference between those proportions. If that difference were found to be very small, then one could conclude that breaking up of the home has little influence. But the point is that by focussing interest directly on the difference between proportions the scientist is conveying more information and information which is more useful than he would if he confined his attention solely to the hypotheses. After all, if he had concluded that home background did make a difference, the next reasonable question to ask would be, 'Yes, but how much of a difference?' To answer that he would have to make an inference about the difference in proportions of broken homes, so why not start with that question in the first place.

In practice, Bayesian statisticians make rather more inferences about hypotheses than they would like, but they often do so for the sake of mathematical convenience, not because the logic of the experiment or statistical method demands it. There are times, however, when inferences about hypotheses are entirely appropriate. This is especially true when the scientist is concerned with predicting events.

Events which have already occurred but whose outcomes are still unknown to us and events that have yet to occur may be the subject of a scientist's predictions or inferences. Will this patient commit suicide? Is this person brain-damaged or functionally ill? Will the next toss of this coin result in 'heads' or 'tails'? Is this the person who committed the crime? As you can see from these examples, events are a special type of hypothesis, for, after all, I can talk of a patient's committing suicide as either an event that has not yet happened or an hypothesis about the patient's future behaviour. Also, none of these examples involves an uncertain quantity. It is the event itself which is of interest and about which we wish to make an inference. Particularly in Chapter 4 we will be making inferences about events, while in later chapters interest will centre mainly on uncertain quantities, though we will show how inferences can be made about hypotheses based on uncertain quantities.

1.4   Decision theory and statistics

Suppose that a new drug is being tested. How great must the posterior odds favouring the drug's effectiveness be before the drug is put on the market? Odds of 2 to 1 may be great enough if the drug will be used to treat a dying cancer patient, while odds of 100 to 1 may not be enough if the drug is to be administered to a baby suffering from a minor ailment that can be treated by other, possibly less effective but proven, drugs. The decision to use the drug or not will be influenced not only by the odds, but also by the benefit to be gained from making a correct decision and the possible loss from making the wrong one.

Posterior probabilities are relevant to the decision, but alone they do not solve the decision problem. You would have to know something about the relative values of being right or wrong, and you would have to know the formal rules for combining these values with the probabilities of being right or wrong. Theories of decision making exist for this purpose, but this book will not discuss them. Here we will confine our attention to making inferences, and to revising these inferences in the light of new information. What you learn from this book is part of what the decision theorist does: to learn the rest you could hardly do better than to read either Schlaifer (1969), who provides an elementary yet thorough grounding in the basics of decision making, Raiffa (1968), who covers roughly the same ground from a more theoretical point of view, or Lindley (1971).

1.5   Summary

This book emphasizes the intelligent use of statistics. Its purpose is to enable you to carry out simple Bayesian analyses, to recognize the conditions under which a particular analysis is appropriate, and to understand simple statistical analyses appearing in the literature. Your mathematical ability can be very modest indeed, yet you should find the book comprehensible.

Two major points of view about statistics are current. I have adopted the more controversial, the Bayesian school. While you will learn only Bayesian methods in this book, you will be able to understand traditional statistical analyses, which are still far more frequently found in the social science literature.

Bayesians believe that a scientist should quantify his opinions as probabilities before performing an experiment, then do the experiment so as to collect data bearing on those opinions, and then use Bayes' theorem formally to revise those prior probabilities to yield new, posterior probabilities. These posterior probabilities are taken as the scientist's revised opinions in the light of the information provided by the data. That is the key idea behind all Bayesian methods, and it is the major theme of this book.

Variations on the theme will include making inferences about one or two uncertain quantities, where the uncertain quantities are either proportions, averages, or measures of variation. I will also include methods for making inferences about the relationships between quantities and inferences about hypotheses and events. The book will not be concerned with decision making.

Part 1
Quantifying prior opinion

2 · Probability

Probabilities quantify opinion. This chapter shows how uncertainty about events and hypotheses can be expressed in the form of probabilities. By the time you have finished the chapter, and that includes doing the problems at the end, you should understand

what a probability is;
how to measure probability;
the difference between Bayesian and 'traditional' views of probability;
how odds and probabilities are related.

If you understand these points, you should be able to assign meaningful probabilities to any events or hypotheses, and your probabilities should be consistent with one another.

2.1 Meaning of probability

Probability defined

The unique feature of Bayesian statistics that distinguishes it from the traditional approach is the definition of a probability. (The traditional view will be discussed under the section headed 'Relative Frequency' in this chapter.) For a Bayesian,

a probability is a degree of belief held by a person about some hypothesis, event, or uncertain quantity.

By convention, we restrict probabilities to numbers between 0 and 1. The bigger the number, the greater the degree of belief. I think there is a 0·55 chance that some form of extra-sensory perception is possible by some people, a 0·6 chance that I will someday own a television receiver so flat it can be hung on the wall, a 0·7 chance that a person convicted of a crime in England is under 21 years of age rather than 21 or older, a 0·85 chance that people in entrepreneurial occupations generally take more risks than people who work in bureaucratic organizations, and a 0·99 chance that a man will set foot on one of the planets before the end of this century.

Each of these statements is a degree of belief that says something about me as well as about the event, hypothesis, or uncertain quantity in question. You may disagree with some of the probabilities I have assigned. Nothing in Bayesian statistics says your probability is any better than mine. When prior opinions differ, then prior probabilities should be different. When two people disagree it is because the past experience and information on which they base their probabilities are different. The point is not whose probability to believe but rather that differing probabilities reflect differences in information on which the probabilities are based.

As new evidence becomes available, and as data are collected, two scientists with divergent prior probabilities will come to share common information. These new data serve to revise the prior opinions, more data will allow further revision, and so forth. An important point about Bayesian statistics is this:

Initially divergent opinions will be brought more and more into agreement through the successive application of Bayes' theorem as more and more data are gathered.

For a Bayesian, a scientific 'truth' is established when most scientists come to share a common belief.

The definition of probability given in this section does not tell you how to assign numbers to your feelings of uncertainty, so in the next two sections methods of measuring probability will be presented.

Events

Before I discuss methods for measuring probability, it will be necessary to introduce the concept of a simple experiment. This idea will not only lead us to a simple method for quantifying opinion, it will also allow me in later sections and chapters to use examples in which all readers would assign the same probabilities. This has the advantage that you can check your answers against mine; unless we both use the same probabilities you would have a difficult time knowing if you were correct in your use of the probabilities.

First, let us be clear about the meaning of a simple experiment.

A simple experiment is any procedure that leads to a single, well-defined, public outcome.

I am using 'public' in the sense that anyone observing the procedure would agree about the outcome. Tossing a coin, rolling a die, selecting a card at random, choosing a slip of paper from a hatful of different papers, drawing straws, and selecting a person at random from a class of students are examples of simple experiments. Remember that only a single outcome is permissible. Complex, inter-related outcomes cannot be considered, as would be the case in the experiment 'switch off the electricity to the building'.

The next concept is that of an elementary event.

An elementary event is the outcome of a simple experiment.

If I choose a student at random from my statistics class, then the person I actually get is an elementary event. Obviously, there are as many elementary events in this example as there are students in the classroom. Two elementary events are possible if a coin is flipped (assuming that the coin cannot stand on its edge), and one of six elementary events can occur when a die is rolled.

Usually the scientist is not interested in elementary events; he wants to make statements about event classes.

An event class, or more simply, an event, is a collection of elementary events, all of which have a given shared property.

If I draw a person at random from the statistics class, getting a particular person is an elementary event, but getting a blond person is an event. Other events might be getting a man, getting someone with flat feet, selecting someone under six feet in height. Consider the simple experiment of selecting a card from a pack of cards. There are 52 elementary events; 26 of these form the event class denoted by 'red card', 13 fall into the event class 'heart', and 4 fall into the event class 'queen'. If any one of the elementary events making up an event class occurs as the outcome of a simple experiment, we say that the event has occurred. The event 'red card' is said to occur when a single red card is drawn, even though the other 25 elementary events in the event class did not occur.

Exercise 2–1

For the simple experiment of rolling an unbiased, six-sided die:

a   List the elementary events.

b   How many elementary events are there in the event class 'an even number comes up'?

c   How many elementary events are there in the event class 'the number that comes up is 4 or less'?

d   How many elementary events are there in the event class 'the number that comes up is greater than 5'?

e   How many elementary events are there in the event class 'the number that comes up is less than 1'?

Answers

a   1, 2, 3, 4, 5, 6. An elementary event can be a number.

b   Three: 2, 4, 6.

c   Four: 4, 3, 2, 1.

d   One: 6.

e   None: An event class that contains no elementary events is called an 'empty event'.

Now consider the case of a simple experiment in which all the elementary events are equally likely to be chosen. By 'equally likely' I mean that if you had to place a bet on the occurrence of any one particular elementary event, you would be indifferent about the one on which you actually placed your money. Suppose, for example, I have two identical balls in an urn, one red and one blue. One of the balls is to be drawn, blind. If it comes up one colour, I pay you a valuable prize, but if it comes up the other colour, you pay me the prize. Now, do you care which colour ball is associated with paying you the prize? If you do not, then we say that the drawing is just as likely to result in one colour as the other. The events are equally likely.

The only trouble with this definition of 'equally likely' is that, for the example just given, it does not admit of any colour preferences you may have. But that is not a fundamental flaw in the definition, for I could find some other way of distinguishing the otherwise identical balls, a way that would not involve preferences which are not really relevant to the simple experiment. Perhaps I could find two colours neither one of which you prefer to the other, or possibly I could identify the balls with two equally preferred numbers. We might call such an event a 'neutral' event. The main point to remember is that the notion of 'equally likely' is defined in terms of your indifference among neutral events. My example for just two events can easily be extended to any number of events.

If we take all the elementary events to be equally likely, then we can agree on a basis for assigning probabilities to events. For example, in drawing a card from a well-shuffled pack, what is the probability of getting a red card? Since 26 of the 52 elementary events belong to the event class 'red card', we form the ratio $26/52 = \frac{1}{2}$ to determine the probability of 'red card'. The probability of getting a heart is $13/52 = \frac{1}{4}$, and the probability of getting a queen is $4/52 = 1/13$. In general:

In a simple experiment where the elementary events are equally likely to be chosen the probability of an event can be assumed to be equal to the proportion of elementary events in the event class,

where

$$\begin{array}{l}\text{proportion of elementary} \\ \text{events in an event class}\end{array} = \left(\begin{array}{l}\text{number of elementary} \\ \text{events in an event class}\end{array}\right) \div \left(\begin{array}{l}\text{total number of} \\ \text{elementary events}\end{array}\right)$$

Exercise 2–2

For the simple experiment of rolling an unbiased, six-sided die, what is the probability of getting:

a   An even number?
b   A 4 or less?
c   Greater than a 5?
d   Less than a 1?

Answers

a $3/6 = 1/2$.
b $4/6 = 2/3$.
c $1/6$.
d $0/6 = 0$. The probability of the empty event is 0.

2.2   Measuring probabilities

When dealing with events, you will often find that your degrees of belief are identical to the proportion of elementary events in an event class. Indeed, if you had not determined the proportion but had relied solely on your intuition in arriving at a probability, you would most likely change your assessment to conform to the actual proportion if someone pointed out to you the numbers of elementary events involved. For simple experiments the logic leading to a probability assessment is clear and compelling. Many of the examples and exercises in this chapter and the next are based on simple experiments, and the experiments social scientists conduct can often be looked at from the viewpoint of simple experiments. The outcome of an experiment is data for the scientist. Because of this close link between simple experiments and the experiments performed by scientists, elementary events can form the basis for assessing probabilities of data observed in experiments. More will be said about this in Section 4.5 of Chapter 4.

Unfortunately, counting elementary events will rarely prove to be useful as a means of arriving at probabilities of hypotheses or uncertain quantities. The reason for this is that it will rarely be obvious what the elementary events are that should be counted; the concepts of elementary events and event classes just do not seem relevant. Elementary events are used in conjunction with the

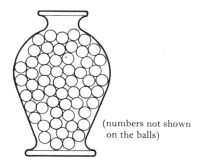

(numbers not shown
on the balls)

Fig. 2–1
Standard urn for measuring probability

idea of a simple experiment, and simple experiments do not have much to do with assessing degrees of belief in hypotheses or uncertain quantities.

At all costs, I wish to avoid the notion that one kind of probability applies to events and another kind to hypotheses or uncertain quantities. Probabilities are degrees of belief, whether we are talking about events, hypotheses or uncertain quantities. It may be easier to arrive at a probability in one situation rather than another, but it is not necessary to have one kind of probability for easy situations and another for difficult ones. Instead, what we shall next do is develop a standard device which will allow us to 'measure' degrees of belief in any situation. This standard device will form our measuring instrument for probabilities in much the same manner as a thermometer is the measuring instrument for temperature.

Our standard device is an urn filled with 100 identically-shaped balls (Fig. 2–1). (Sometimes 1000 balls are used if measurement is to be made more precisely.) Each ball is identified by a number, from 1 to 100. The simple experiment of drawing, blind, one ball from the urn is to be performed.

To see how the standard device can be used to measure degrees of belief we must consider two bets, one involving the event whose probability you wish to assess, and one involving the standard device. Suppose, for example, you want to determine the probability that a manned landing will be made on Mars before the end of 1985. Imagine that the following bet has been offered to you:

Bet A $\begin{cases}$ If a man has set foot on Mars by the end of 1985 you win £5. \\ If there is no landing by the end of 1985 you win nothing. $\end{cases}$

If you win, you will be paid on January 1st, 1986.

The tree diagram of Fig. 2–2(a) is a convenient representation of this bet.

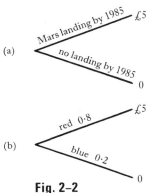

(a)

(b)

Fig. 2–2
Tree diagrams for the Mars bet and for the reference bet

Now imagine that balls 1 to 80 in the standard urn have been painted red while the remaining 20 balls have been coloured blue. The balls are thoroughly mixed, and one is to be drawn on the first day of 1986 by a blindfolded observer. Now consider this bet.

Bet B $\begin{cases}$ If the ball drawn is red you win £5. \\ If the ball is blue you win nothing. $\end{cases}$

This bet is shown in Fig. 2–2(b). We would all agree that the probabilities of drawing a red or a blue ball are 0·8 and 0·2 respectively, and these probabilities are shown on the branches of the tree. Remember, we are trying to find out what probabilities should be shown on the branches of the tree representing the Mars bet.

Consider both bets. Which do you prefer, A or B? Remember that neither bet pays off until January 1st, 1986. Suppose you prefer B. Then I assume you must think there is a better chance for you to win £5 with bet B than with A. From this I infer you think the probability of getting a red ball is greater than the probability of a Mars landing by 1985. In other words, the probability of a Mars landing by 1985 is, in your judgement, less than 0·8.

Now suppose I change the composition of the urn to 70 red balls and 30 blue ones; the chance of winning £5 with bet B is reduced to 0·7. Do you still prefer bet B to A? If you do, then I will continue to reduce the proportion of red balls in the urn, until I find some mix of red and blue balls that causes you to be indifferent between playing either bet A or B. You will actually find several acceptable mixes which are similar, for the indifference region is usually a bit fuzzy. You might find it difficult to distinguish between mixes of 67–33, 68–32, 69–31, 70–30, and 71–29; perhaps they all yield bets of type **B** which feel about the same as bet A. This fuzziness of the indifference region is common, but need not be worrying. The region will become narrower as you gain experience in expressing uncertainty in the form of probabilities, and in any event you can use the middle of the region as your assessment, in this case 69–31.

When you find a mix that makes you indifferent between the two bets, then we are justified in assigning the same probability to the event 'red' as we are to the event 'Mars landing by 1985'. If a 0·69 chance of drawing a red ball makes you indifferent between bet A and bet B, then we can say that you must feel there is a 0·69 chance of a Mars landing by 1985 (see Fig. 2–3).

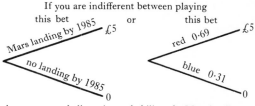

If you are indifferent between playing
this bet   or   this bet

Mars landing by 1985   £5

red 0·69   £5

no landing by 1985   0

blue 0·31   0

then you must believe the probability of a Mars landing by 1985 to be equal to 0·69

Fig. 2–3
Determining the probability of an event

Once you have understood the logic of this example, you can use the standard device directly to assess the probability you would associate with a hypothesis or event. Perhaps the easiest method is to adjust, mentally, the proportion of red balls in the urn until you find that the uncertainty associated with drawing a red ball in a simple experiment is identical with your uncertainty about some hypothesis. If you have adjusted the proportion of red balls correctly, you should be indifferent between betting on the truth of the hypothesis and betting (the same amount) on the draw of a red ball from the urn.

Exercise 2–3

Use the standard device of balls in an urn to help you assess probabilities for each of the following hypotheses:

a   The next person to greet you will be smoking a cigarette.
b   The first person to call you by name tomorrow will be under 30 years of age.
c   A cure for cancer will be found within 15 years.
d   Someday the Pope will sanction the Pill.

Answers

There are no correct or true probabilities for these hypotheses. The values you assign are acceptable as long as they meet certain consistency requirements which are discussed in Chapter 3.

If you are assessing the probabilities of more than two hypotheses, then you will need to put in the urn balls of as many different colours as there are different hypotheses. If you wish to consider these hypotheses:

a   that the manned landing on Mars will occur before 1985;
b   that the manned landing on Mars will occur between 1985 and 2000;
c   that the manned landing on Mars will occur after 2000;

then you will need balls of three colours. As before, the proportion of each colour represents the probability you assign to the associated hypothesis.

Although the urn and balls is a device that will be most generally helpful in assessing probabilities, other devices are useful, too. Suppose, for example, that you have just assigned 0·5–0·5 prior probabilities to two hypotheses; you consider the hypotheses equally likely. Is your uncertainty about these hypotheses exactly the same as your uncertainty about the toss of a fair coin? The fair coin is the standard device—heads and tails are equally likely. You should assign equal probabilities to the two outcomes of the toss of the coin, and you should associate probabilities of 0·5–0·5 to *any* two equally likely events or

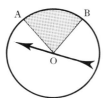

Fig. 2–4
The spinner, a standard device to which
probabilities can be compared

hypotheses. A die is a convenient standard device to which you can compare probability estimates of 1/6. You should ask yourself this question: 'Is my uncertainty about this hypothesis exactly the same as my uncertainty about whether, say, a six will come up when I roll a fair die?' If your uncertainty about the hypothesis is the same as your uncertainty about the outcome of the roll of the die, then you should assign a probability of 1/6 to the hypothesis.

A device similar to the urn and balls is a spinner, shown in Fig. 2–4. The relative sizes of the white and shaded sectors represent the probabilities associated with two hypotheses. If the sectors are of equal size, then the device represents probabilities of 0·5–0·5. If the shaded sector is one quarter the size of the whole circle, then probabilities of 0·25–0·75 are represented.

In general, the probability represented by the shaded sector is given by

Number of degrees in angle AOB ÷ 360 degrees in whole circle

Suppose you think the probability of some hypothesis is 0·2. To see how this would look on the spinner, you multiply 360 by 0·2 to get 72 degrees for the angle of the shaded sector. If you draw the spinner, it should look like Fig. 2–5.

If you could spin the pointer, there would be a 0·2 chance of the arrow coming to rest over the shaded sector. Do you feel that this device accurately portrays your feeling of uncertainty about the two hypotheses? If it does not, then you should change the sizes of the sectors until you arrive at a representation that is satisfactory. You could then measure the angle of the shaded sector, divide by 360, and the result is the probability of the less likely hypothesis.

The spinner can be used for more than two hypotheses by adding more sectors. Five hypotheses would require five sectors, and the ratio of the angle of each sector to 360 will give the probabilities you associate with each hypothesis.

The use of standard devices as an aid in arriving at probabilities is based on the idea that probabilities can be compared. Probabilities are different from one another only in their values; we do not have one kind of probability for events and another kind for hypotheses; we do not have different kinds of probability for events involving people than for events involving things. Probabilities for unique events can be compared with probabilities for repeated events because the probabilities are different only in value, not in kind. With apologies to Gertrude Stein, a probability is a probability is a probability.

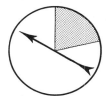

Fig. 2–5
Spinner for probabilities of 0·8 and 0·2

The trouble with using standard devices is that even these simple mechanical analogues to probability are not as simple, psychologically, as they seem. A person may say that a coin is equally likely to come up heads as tails, but when you ask that person to bet on the outcome for many flips of the coin, he will probably act as though he had a slight bias favouring either heads or tails. In other words, his verbal report does not quite correspond with his feelings about the outcomes. Davidson, Suppes and Siegel (1957), for example, experimented for a long time before they found two events that were truly equally likely for the subjects in their experiments. One of their devices was a six-sided die, three sides of which had ZOJ printed on them, and three sides had ZEJ. To most people, ZOJ is just as likely as ZEJ to come up on a toss of the die. They found other nonsense syllables that worked just as well.

Similar criticisms apply to the spinner device; the subjective size of the shaded sector may depend for some people on its position on the spinner. For the urn a colour bias may operate to cause you to add or subtract a small amount of probability because the balls are your favourite colour. One way to check for these biases is to reverse the association between the events represented by the standard device and the hypotheses or events whose probabilities are being assessed. In the Mars-landing example we originally associated the red balls with the hypothesis. We can check for bias in our estimates by associating the blue balls with the hypothesis, and then seeing what proportion of blue balls is required. If we arrive at the same answer as before, 0·69, then we can be reasonably sure no bias is operating.

Relative frequencies

Suppose you have what looks like a fair coin and you want to find out the probability of its landing heads when you toss it. So you perform a little experiment: you toss it 10 times. It comes up heads 6 times, but you conclude that that is close enough to 5 to warrant your assigning the probability of heads as 0·5. Just to make sure, you toss the coin 100 times, and it comes up heads 46 times. Again, 0·5 seems a reasonable assessment. But to make really certain, you toss the coin 1000 times. It comes up heads 489 times, and now you are quite sure that the probability of heads is $\frac{1}{2}$. Why did you do this? After all, the proportion of heads on the first experiment was 0·6, on the second 0·46, and on the third 0·489. You might have noticed that the proportion got closer to 0·5 in each of the experiments, and you assumed that if you flipped the coin an infinite number of times, an experiment that is possible in theory only, obviously, then it would turn up heads *exactly* half of the time. This notion forms the basis of *the* definition of probability for the traditional statistician. For him probabilities are objective because they are related to observable events through the limit of a relative frequency. He defines a probability as the relative frequency of occurrence of an event after an infinite number of similar trials has occurred. Now this is not a very useful definition for it says nothing about how to arrive at probabilities short of making an infinite number of trials. Fortunately, James Bernoulli in the eighteenth century proved a theorem which says, in essence, that *in the long run, the relative frequency of an event approaches its probability*. This theorem is the mathematical equivalent of most people's intuitive notion of the *law of averages*, that in the long run events occur with relative frequencies that are very close to their 'true' probabilities. In practice you never have to observe a great many trials; 100, even 50, or 30 may suffice. The relative frequencies observed for even a modest number of trials may come very close to the long-run relative frequencies. And even if you do not count the relative frequencies, just observing the events will enable you to make very good probability estimates. A number of experiments, reviewed by Peterson and Beach (1967), have shown that people can judge relative frequencies and proportions very accurately, and, as you would expect, with increasing accuracy as the number of trials increases.

There are two major troubles with using relative frequencies as the sole basis for prior probabilities. In the first place, relative frequencies of past events may not be entirely applicable to future events. In the relative frequency definition of probability note that I included the requirement of 'similar trials'. Identical trials would be absurd, for then the outcome of each trial would be the same. If each flip of the coin were precisely identical, then the flip would always result in a heads, or a tails. So to avoid getting all heads or all tails, the trials must be slightly different. But just how slightly is left undefined, and so a subjective element enters into this supposedly 'objective' definition.

The second trouble with relative frequencies is that they cannot apply to unique events. If an event can only happen once, it makes little sense to enquire about its past history or even an imagined repetition of trials on which it could occur. Horse races, football games, sporting events of all kinds, are unique events. Yet it seems reasonable to assign degrees of belief to the outcomes of these games. Scientific hypotheses have this characteristic. If you consider them as events, they either occur or they do not, that is, they are either true or not true. Accordingly, the believer in relative frequencies would assign probabilities to scientific hypotheses of either 1 or 0. The traditional statistician, who accepts the notion that probabilities are identified with relative frequencies, never talks about the probability of a hypothesis, he only talks about the probability of data given the truth of a hypothesis. Data can be repeated. Do the experiment again, and you should get the same, or nearly the same, data. Relative frequencies make sense in terms of repeated observations in which data can occur, so it makes sense to talk about the probability of data. The Bayesian is willing to attach probabilities to both data and hypotheses, for it is meaningful for him to assign probabilities to the occurrence of data as well as to the truth of hypotheses.

Whether you view probabilities as relative frequencies or as degrees of belief can make a practical difference. For example, many social scientists feel that clinical diagnoses are best left to intuitive, judgemental processes, while others maintain that statistical methods are superior to intuitive ones. The clinician frequently makes the complaint that statistics are based on past occurrences and so do not apply to the unique case that is about to be diagnosed; for him, the present 'trial' is not 'similar enough' to past trials. The statistician, on the other hand, goes on demonstrating that these past cases are relevant to the unique one about to be considered, that the trials *are* sufficiently similar.

Those on both sides of this argument have in mind a relative frequency definition of probability. For example, a statistician may consult the hospital's records before advising a clinical psychologist about the diagnosis of a patient as either brain-damaged or functionally ill. The statistician is interested in determining the relative frequencies with which functional illness and brain damage occurred in that hospital in the past. He finds that 90% of the patients were functionally ill, and he uses this relative frequency as the basis for his prior probabilities. But suppose that the hospital has been operating for ten years, and that in the past three months a new hospital has opened that specializes in brain-damaged patients. You would expect that the number of brain-damaged patients referred to the old hospital to have decreased, making the previous relative frequency data of little use. In more general terms, the 'trials' are too dissimilar; the cases before the opening of the new hospital are not similar to those after the opening. The clinician feels that he can often detect these dissimilarities between trials and either make use of them in his diagnosis, or discard them as irrelevant. In some cases the past relative frequencies may be adjusted slightly, by using your good judgement, to reflect more accurately your current assessment of the situation. But this procedure only makes sense if you believe that probabilities are degrees of belief, which may or may not be based on relative frequencies, or on modified relative frequencies.

An attempt to resolve this controversy concerning clinical versus statistical prediction has been given by Pankoff and Roberts (1968). They adopt a Bayesian point of view.

2.3   Odds

Odds defined

Some readers may have experience in quantifying their opinions about uncertain events not in the form of probabilities but of betting odds. Why, since odds are more familiar than probabilities to many people, did I not use them?

The difficulty with betting odds is, as those of you who frequent betting shops know, that the odds you are offered there reflect not only the events you are betting on, but also how heavy the betting has been. Odds given in betting shops are not good estimates of the odds on the event itself, though they do bear some relationship. Your intuition about odds is contaminated by the betting habits of other people, so you should be wary of expressing your uncertainty in the form of betting odds.

Another difficulty is that the odds *you* estimate might be influenced by the amount of money you have available or by the value you place on the money you might win, and research has shown that that value is seldom in perfect correspondence with the amount of money. These are insurmountable difficulties, so we will not attempt to quantify our uncertainty as betting odds.

However, odds (without the 'betting' connotation) will occasionally be useful. To talk of one event being twice as likely as another is sometimes convenient. Odds will always refer to an event, E, and its complement, $\bar{E}$ (read 'not-E'). When we say E is twice as likely as $\bar{E}$, we mean that the probability of E is twice as large as that of $\bar{E}$, that the odds are 2 to 1 *favour* of E (note the discrepancy from betting-shop parlance).

Let us use the Greek letter omega, Ω, to represent odds. The odds favouring E over $\bar{E}$ will be written $\Omega(E)$. The relationship between the probability of E, $p(E)$, and the odds favouring E is

$$\Omega(E) = \frac{p(E)}{1 - p(E)}$$

or, conversely,

$$p(E) = \frac{\Omega(E)}{1 + \Omega(E)}$$

As an example, if E is twice as likely as $\bar{E}$, then $\Omega(E) = 2$. We find the probability of E as follows:

$$p(E) = \frac{2}{1+2} = \frac{2}{3} = 0.67$$

You can check this by turning the probability back to odds:

$$\Omega(E) = \frac{0.67}{1 - 0.67} = \frac{0.67}{0.33} = 2$$

Exercise 2–4

a   What are the probabilities that correspond to these odds statements?

  i   She is three times as likely to succeed as to fail.
  ii   The letter is 4·5 times as likely to .be delivered tomorrow as later than tomorrow.
  iii   He is 10 times more likely to marry than to remain single.

b   What are the odds that correspond to these probability statements?

  i   The probability he will be promoted within a year is 0·6.
  ii   The probability is 0·8 that this hypothesis is true.
  iii   There is a 0·9 chance of a totally successful cure.

Answers

a i $3/4 = 0·75$.
    ii $4·5/5·5 = 0·82$.
    iii $10/11 = 0·91$.
b i $0·6/0·4 = 1·5$.
    ii $0·8/0·2 = 4$.
    iii $0·9/0·1 = 9$.

Odds are usually expressed as numbers equal to or greater than one. What do you do, then, if $p(E) = 0·2$, for example? This gives $\Omega(E) = 0·2/0·8 = 0·25$! The answer is simple: give the resulting odds for $\overline{E}$ rather than E. For the example, we would find $\Omega(\overline{E}) = 0·8/0·2 = 4$.

The probability–odds scale

The correspondence between probability and odds is shown by the scale in Fig. 2–6. With this you can translate odds to probabilities, or probabilities to odds without having to solve the formulae above. I suggest you study this carefully; many people are surprised to find what odds correspond to a particular probability, or vice versa. Repeat Exercise 2–4 using the probability–odds scale.

2.4 Summary

A probability is a degree of belief held by a person about some hypothesis, event, or uncertain quantity. This definition of probability contrasts to the more traditional view in which a probability is seen as the limit of a relative frequency. The 'personalist' rather than the 'relative frequency' view is adopted in this book.

The 'personalist' definition of probability does not lead to a subjective view of statistics, however. Before any data have been observed, opinions will, naturally, differ. But after data have been collected, it is possible to apply Bayes' theorem, and then the revised probabilities will be in closer agreement. With enough data, initially divergent opinions will become nearly indistinguishable. It is the revision of opinion that is linked to observations.

As a basis for agreeing about probabilities, the concept of a simple experiment was introduced. In a simple experiment where the elementary events are equally likely to be chosen, the probability of an event can be taken as equal to the proportion of elementary events in the event class. This fundamental notion allows examples to be constructed in which all readers will have identical probabilities, and will form the basis in later chapters for determining the probability of data occurring.

To measure probabilities it is necessary to consider a standard measuring device, an urn filled with 100 balls. The number of balls of different colours should be adjusted so that the uncertainty associated with drawing a ball of a certain colour is the same as the uncertainty of the event whose probability you are trying to measure. The proportion of balls of that colour represents, then, the probability of the event. Other standard measuring devices, such as a spinner, can be helpful, too.

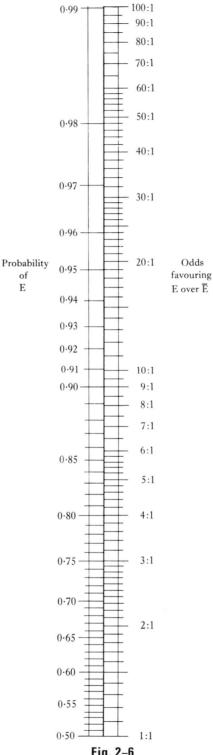

Fig. 2–6
Probability–odds scale

Sometimes it is useful to express opinion in odds rather than probabilities, but identification with betting odds must be avoided. Odds are particularly useful when only two hypotheses or events are being considered.

Problems

2–1 Three students who carried out a postal survey of attitudes to traffic were able to classify their respondents on the basis of occupation into the following social classes:

Social class	Number of replies
1	76
2	136
3 non-manual	80
3 manual	60
4	26
5	7

If someone were chosen at random from this group, what is the probability that the person will be

a in social class 3?
b in the top social class (1)?
c classed as both belonging to class 1 and to class 3?

2–2 A survey of a rural district shows that 100 families live in the area. The number of children in the families is shown in the following table.

Number of children X	Number of families with X children
0	20
1	25
2	30
3	15
4 or more	10

If a family is selected at random from the district, what is the probability that the family will have

a at least two children?
b exactly three children?
c either two or three children?
d at most two children?

2–3 Four of the florins in my pocket are 10p pieces (which show an older Queen Elizabeth), 3 are 2-shilling pieces depicting a younger Queen Elizabeth, 2 show King George VI and 1 shows King George V. If I choose a coin at random what is the probability that it

a is a new coin?
b shows a portrait of Queen Elizabeth?

2–4 Use one of the standard devices mentioned in the chapter to assess your and some of your friends' uncertainty about these events or hypotheses:

a The Pope will sanction the Pill in this century.
b The smoking of marijuana will be legalized in your country within the next ten years.

c   A woman will be elected president (or prime minister) of your country sometime this century.

Or invent your own event or hypothesis.

2–5   Carry out a class experiment to compare the two main standard devices discussed in the chapter: the balls in the urn, and the spinner. Let half the class use one device, the remaining half the other. Carry out measurements on friends, ensuring that the same person is not assessed twice. Bring the data back to class and compare measurements to the same questions obtained by the different devices. Your instructor will help organize the experiment, and will assist in the analysis of the data. Keep the results and analyze them again after you have completed Chapter 12, for then you will be able to carry out a more extensive analysis of the data.

2–6   250 people are classified as follows:

Protestant	75
Roman Catholic	100
Other religious affiliation	50
No religious affiliation	25
TOTAL	250

a   If one person is to be chosen at random, what is the probability that the person will have some religious affiliation?

b   What is the probability that the person chosen will be either a Protestant or a Roman Catholic?

3 · Probability laws

Up to now we have been concerned only with showing that probability is the language of uncertainty, and some methods have been explained which should help you to use the language. Now it is time to learn the grammar. There are restrictions on probabilities that must be clearly understood; these restrictions are called probability laws.

There are two reasons for knowing these laws. In the first place, the laws impose requirements of internal consistency on the probabilities you assign to events that are related. You must ensure that your assessments conform to the limitations of the laws. Thus, you can use the laws to check on the internal consistency of the probabilities you assign to related events.

In the second place, some of the laws show how the probabilities of simple events are related to complex events made up of combinations of the simple events. You will find occasions when your intuition is clearest about simple events, yet you are primarily interested in complex events. The probability laws will enable you to use your probabilities for the simple events as a basis for *calculating* the probabilities of the complex events. At other times you will find that your experience bears only indirectly on the events involved in a particular problem, so you have no easy way of assessing probabilities. In these circumstances you will find that you can make assessments about events that are directly related to your experience and then use the laws to transform those probabilities into probabilities of events involved in the problem.

I should warn you that this is a difficult chapter. Do not read it all in one sitting; keep coming back to it, work through the exercises, and eventually it will fall into place. The grammar of probability does not come easily to most people, so do not become discouraged if you fail to understand a point on first reading. Gradually you will begin to feel comfortable with the limitations imposed by the probability laws.

Before we go on to the laws, it is necessary to introduce some standard terminology.

3.1 Nomenclature

When we talk about the probability of an event it will often be convenient to talk of probabilities in general rather than any specific probability. A probability assessment says something about the event or hypothesis and also something about the person making it and the information he had available to him. We might use this symbol for a probability:

$p(E|P, I)$

The E stands for the event, the P for the person making the estimate and the I for the information available. The symbol is read 'the probability of E given the person P and the information I'. The vertical line stands for 'given'. Note that the symbol does *not* mean *p* times E divided by P or I. The short way of referring to the symbol is 'the probability of E given P and I'. *This is a conditional probability.* Strictly speaking, every probability is conditional; it is conditional on the person assigning the probability and on the information.

In most statistical analyses, the person and the information available before collecting any data remain constant throughout the analysis. When this is the case, it is convenient to drop the 'given P and I' part of the notation. Then the probability of an event becomes simply

$p(E)$

Always remember when you see this notation that the conditional person and information available to the person are understood.

Now we can turn to the probability laws. Each law is stated in terms of probabilities for events, but remember that there is only one kind of probability, so all the laws are applicable for hypotheses and uncertain quantities as well.

3.2   First law

If I told you that the probability of some event was 1·3, or minus 0·6 you should object. We have already met the restrictions that probabilities cannot be negative or greater than 1. If I told you that a 'sure thing' had a probability of 0·8, you should also object. A 'sure thing' implies a probability of 1.

First law   **Probabilities cannot be less than zero nor greater than one, and the probability of the sure event is 1. Put mathematically,**

$0 \leq p(E) \leq 1$ and $p(\text{sure event}) = 1$

The symbol $\leq$ is read 'less than or equal to'. The first law is read 'zero is less than or equal to the probability of E which is less than or equal to 1'. In other words, the probability of an event lies between 0 and 1 inclusive. The 'sure event' is an event that, in your judgement, is bound to happen. The coin must come up either heads or tails, so the event 'heads or tails' is a sure event. When I select a student from the class, the event that I get a person is a sure event.

This law gives the first restrictions on probabilities, and its application is obvious: be sure your probabilities fall between 0 and 1, inclusive, and assign a probability of 1 to any event you think is certain to occur.

3.3   Second law

This law and the next are concerned with the relationships between events. It is these laws that show how probabilities assigned to individual events should be related to probabilities of combinations of events.

The second law deals with events that are *mutually exclusive*, a term which we define as follows:

Events on a list are mutually exclusive if the occurrence of any one event on the list means that none of the others can occur.

If a coin comes up heads it cannot also come up tails on the same toss. Heads and tails are mutually exclusive events. Suppose I select someone from the statistics class. Are the events on this list mutually exclusive?

a man   a woman   a blond   a brunette

Man and woman are themselves mutually exclusive, but blond and man (or blond and woman) are not. It is possible to get both a man and a blond, or both a woman and a blond, etc. To make the events mutually exclusive, it is necessary to alter the events:

blond man   blond woman   brunette man   brunette woman

That list qualifies as containing mutually exclusive events. This example also shows how an event need not be limited to a single descriptor. 'Man' may be an event, but so also may 'blond man' or 'blond man with flat feet' or 'blond man under the age of 25 who is married with two children, both of whom are blond and have flat feet'.

You cannot just look at a list of events to decide whether or not they are mutually exclusive, you must also consider the simple experiment. Consider this list:

heads   tails

Those events are mutually exclusive for the simple experiment 'toss a coin', but they are not mutually exclusive for the experiment 'toss two coins'. Since one coin could come up heads and the other tails, both heads and tails can occur as the result of the simple experiment. You would, of course, be correct in saying that the outcome of this simple experiment is not completely described by just the two events heads and tails, that four events are necessary for a complete description:

1st coin		*2nd coin*
heads	and	tails
heads	and	heads
tails	and	heads
tails	and	tails

Notice that these four events are mutually exclusive for the simple experiment 'toss two coins'. If, for example, we get 'heads and heads', then none of the other events can also have occurred as the result of that toss.

The first statement of the second law deals with any two mutually exclusive events. We will distinguish these events by using a subscript notation; the two events will be referred to as E_1 and E_2. They could be any two events on a list of mutually exclusive events.

Now we turn to the second law. It will be given first for two events, later for any number.

Second law **The probability of either of two mutually exclusive events occurring is equal to the sum of their individual probabilities. In mathematical notation,**

$$p(E_1 \text{ or } E_2) = p(E_1) + p(E_2)$$

The probability of either E_1 or E_2 occurring is equal to the probability of E_1 plus the probability of E_2. Let us use the concept of the simple experiment to arrive at mutually agreed-upon probabilities that can be used in some examples. Consider a fair die. It has six sides, so there are six elementary events possible. The die is fair, so we can assume that each elementary event is as likely to occur as any other. Thus, the probability of any one side must be 1/6. Now, what is the probability of getting a 1 or a 2? By the second law,

$$p(1 \text{ or } 2) = p(1) + p(2) = 1/6 + 1/6 = 1/3$$

Or, consider an even more obvious example. What is the probability of getting either a head or a tail when a coin is tossed? Assuming the coin is fair and that it will not land on its edge, we would probably agree that the two alternatives each have a probability of 1/2. By the second law,

$$p(\text{head or tail}) = p(\text{head}) + p(\text{tail}) = 1/2 + 1/2 = 1$$

The probability of getting one or the other is a certainty.

Exercise 3–1

As you are about to park your car in an illegal spot you see in the distance a man in uniform. Based on the few cues you can make out at such a distance and on your knowledge of people likely to be in the area, you quickly assess these probabilities:

Event	*Probability of the event*
man is a policeman	0·3
man is a traffic warden	0·4
man is a bus conductor	0·2
other possibility	0·1

What is the probability that the man is

a either a policeman or a traffic warden?
b either a bus conductor or someone not on the list?

Answers

a By the second law,
$p(\text{policeman or traffic warden}) = p(\text{policeman}) + p(\text{traffic warden}) = 0\cdot3 + 0\cdot4 = 0\cdot7.$

b Also by the second law,
$p(\text{bus conductor or someone else}) = p(\text{bus conductor}) + p(\text{someone else}) = 0\cdot2 + 0\cdot1 = 0\cdot3.$

The second law can be extended to more than two events. Suppose we wish to consider n mutually exclusive events, where n can be any number. The first event we wish to consider is E_1, the second E_2, and so forth to the last event, E_n.

Second law The probability of any one event occurring from among *n* mutually exclusive events is equal to the sum of the probabilities of the individual events. In mathematical notation,

$$p(E_1 \text{ or } E_2 \text{ or } \ldots \text{ or } E_n) = p(E_1) + p(E_2) + \ldots + p(E_n)$$

Here the three dots mean 'and so forth on up to'. The probability of E_1 or of E_2 and so forth on up to E_n is equal to the probability of E_1 plus the probability of E_2 and so forth on up to E_n. More neatly, the probability of any one of *n* events is equal to the sum of their individual probabilities. Remember that this law only applies to mutually exclusive events. The law is sometimes referred to as the 'addition law'.

We will frequently have occasion to refer to the sum of the probabilities of several events. Rather than write each time

$$p(E_1) + p(E_2) + \ldots + p(E_n)$$

a short-cut notation will be used. The Greek letter sigma or $\sum$ will be used to indicate 'the sum of'.

$$\sum p(E_i) = p(E_1) + p(E_2) + \ldots + p(E_n)$$

Now the second law can be written:

$$p(E_1 \text{ or } E_2 \text{ or } \ldots \text{ or } E_n) = \sum p(E_i)$$

Exercise 3–2

You and your partner are playing duplicate bridge with five other teams. Assuming that ties are impossible, you assign the following probabilities to each team to indicate your degrees of belief about which team will be top scorer for the evening:

Team	Probability
1(yours)	0·3
2	0·25
3	0·15
4	0·1
5	0·1
6	0·1

What is the probability that the winner will be:

a   Either team 1, 2, or 3?
b   An even numbered team?

Answers

a   By the second law
$$p(\text{team 1 or team 2 or team 3}) = p(\text{team 1}) + p(\text{team 2}) + p(\text{team 3})$$
$$= 0\cdot3 + 0\cdot25 + 0\cdot15 = 0\cdot7.$$
b $p(2 \text{ or } 4 \text{ or } 6) = p(2) + p(4) + p(6) = 0\cdot25 + 0\cdot1 + 0\cdot1 = 0\cdot45.$

First corollary to the second law

The first and second laws can be put together to form new laws which are called 'corollaries'. In this section we will look at one very useful corollary.

Suppose we have some event like 'rain tomorrow'. The complement of that event, 'no rain tomorrow', is itself an event. Now, it will either rain tomorrow or it will not, so the event 'rain tomorrow or no rain tomorrow' is the sure event, which we saw from the first law must have a probability of 1.

p(rain tomorrow or no rain tomorrow) = 1

Let the event 'rain tomorrow' be designated by E and its complement 'no rain tomorrow' by $\overline{E}$. The bar above the E means 'the complement of E'. Then by the first law,

$p(E \text{ or } \overline{E}) = 1$

But by the second law we know that the probability of either E or $\overline{E}$ is equal to the sum of their individual probabilities.

$p(E \text{ or } \overline{E}) = p(E) + p(\overline{E})$

So it follows that

$p(E) + p(\overline{E}) = 1$

or, by rearrangement,

$p(E) = 1 - p(\overline{E})$

This result is the corollary.

First corollary to the second law **The probability of an event is equal to 1 minus the probability of the complement of the event.**

The probability of heads, on the toss of a coin, is equal to 1 minus the probability of tails. For the toss of a fair die, the probability of rolling a 1, 2, 3, 4, or 5 is equal to 1 minus the probability of a six:

$p(1 \text{ or } 2 \text{ or } 3 \text{ or } 4 \text{ or } 5) = 1 - p(6) = 1 - 1/6 = 5/6$

That agrees with the result you obtain by applying the second law:

$$p(1 \text{ or } 2 \text{ or } 3 \text{ or } 4 \text{ or } 5) = p(1) + p(2) + p(3) + p(4) + p(5)$$
$$= 1/6 + 1/6 + 1/6 + 1/6 + 1/6 = 5/6$$

Exercise 3–3

Use the first corollary to the second law to compute the probability of some team other than your own winning the evening of bridge. Use the probability assignments from Exercise 3–2. Check your answer by direct application of the second law.

Answer

$$p(\text{other than team 1 winning}) = 1 - p(\text{team 1 winning})$$
$$= 1 - 0\cdot3 = 0\cdot7.$$

Check:

$$p(\text{other than team 1 winning}) = p(2) + p(3) + p(4) + p(5) + p(6)$$
$$= 0\cdot25 + 0\cdot15 + 0\cdot1 + 0\cdot1 + 0\cdot1 = 0\cdot7.$$

Second corollary to the second law

The second corollary to the second law is especially useful. It deals with a list of events which are not only mutually exclusive but also collectively exhaustive. By 'collectively exhaustive' we mean that the list is to be considered complete; one of the events *must* happen. This list

rain all day tomorrow
snow all day tomorrow
sunny all day tomorrow

contains events which are mutually exclusive (if one occurs the others cannot) but *not* exhaustive (something not on the list may occur). I can think of other reasonable possibilities to add to the list.

The decision about whether a list is exhaustive is usually made by stopping short of events whose probabilities are near zero. Considering the toss of a coin, this list is usually considered exhaustive:

heads   tails

But if I am standing over an open grating, and I do not catch flipped coins very well, then the list could be lengthened:

heads   tails   falls through grating so result cannot be observed

If the coin is flipped before the beginning of a football game on to the ground, you would prefer this list:

heads   tails   stands on edge

Many other events could be included, such as 'coin disintegrates in mid-air', but we do not usually include events whose probabilities of occurrence are very low.

If the events on the list are mutually exclusive and exhaustive, then the event 'some event occurs' is the sure event and has probability 1. But the probability of 'some event occurs' is equal to the sum of the individual probabilities, by the second law. Therefore, the sum of the individual probabilities must be 1.

Second corollary to the second law   The sum of the probabilities of individual events which are mutually exclusive and collectively exhaustive is 1. In mathematical notation,

$$\sum p(E_i) = 1$$

Suppose I examine a coin and decide it is slightly biased in favour of heads. If I assign $p(\text{heads}) = 0\cdot52$ and $p(\text{tails}) = 0\cdot5$, I have violated the second corollary because the two probabilities do not sum to 1. Noting this, I could apply the first corollary to arrive at

$$p(\text{tails}) = 1 - p(\text{heads}) = 1 - 0\cdot52 = 0\cdot48$$

Note that the events in Exercise 3–2 form a mutually exclusive and collectively exhaustive list, and that the six individual probabilities sum to 1.

The next exercise will show you how the second law and its corollaries can be used to check on the consistency of your probability assignments.

Exercise 3–4

Assign probabilities to the following four mutually exclusive and collectively exhaustive hypotheses:

A man will set foot on Mars for the first time. . .

H_1 in this decade (the 70s).
H_2 in the next decade (the 80s).
H_3 in the last decade of this century (the 90s).
H_4 sometime later than this century.

a   Check the consistency of your assignments by applying the second corollary.
b   On the basis of your assignments, compute the probability that a man will set foot on Mars:

i   sometime this century;
ii   sometime other than this decade (the 70s).

c   Check the probabilities computed in (b) with your intuition. If there is any discrepancy, you will have to change your original assignments.

Answers

I assigned the following probabilities, though yours may be different:

$p(H_1) = 0.35$
$p(H_2) = 0.6$
$p(H_3) = 0.03$
$p(H_4) = 0.02$

a   By the second corollary these four probabilities should sum to 1. They do, so that consistency check is met.
b   By the second law,

$$p(70s \text{ or } 80s \text{ or } 90s) = p(70s) + p(80s) + p(90s)$$
$$= p(H_1) + p(H_2) + p(H_3)$$
$$= 0.35 + 0.6 + 0.03 = 0.98$$

$$p(80s \text{ or } 90s \text{ or later}) = p(80s) + p(90s) + p(later)$$
$$= p(H_2) + p(H_3) + p(later)$$
$$= 0.6 + 0.03 + 0.02 = 0.65$$

I could have used the first corollary:

$$p(70s \text{ or } 80s \text{ or } 90s) = 1 - p(later) = 1 - 0.02 = 0.98$$
$$p(80s \text{ or } 90s \text{ or later}) = 1 - p(70s) = 1 - 0.35 = 0.65$$

c   Is the probability, for me, 0.98 that a man will set foot on Mars before the last decade? Yes, that seems reasonable. But a probability of 0.65 does not seem large enough for the proposition that the landing will occur after the 70s. In looking again at my original assignments I think I did not give enough probability to H_2 and I gave too much to H_1. So, I will add 0.1 to H_2 and, to keep the sum equal to 1, I will take away 0.1 from H_1. My new assignments are:

$p(H_1) = 0.25$
$p(H_2) = 0.70$
$p(H_3) = 0.03$
$p(H_4) = 0.02$
———
sum $= 1.00$

Now, by the first corollary,

p(70s or 80s or 90s) = 1 − 0·02 = 0·98
p(80s or 90s or later) = 1 − 0·25 = 0·75

Those values seem intuitively reasonable, so I now feel content with my new assignments and their implications.

3.4 Third law

Assigning a probability to an event can be difficult when you find that the probability depends on whether or not the occurrence of some other event is known to you. An example will clarify this problem.

Suppose that a student is contemplating a long trip in his not-so-new automobile. He has had a number of accidents in his few years of driving and feels that if he has one more his insurance company will drop him and he will be unable to get any other company to insure him. He tries to estimate the probability of his having an accident, but finds that it depends on whether or not he has a breakdown of his car. The probability of an accident is less if the car does not break down, and is more if it does. How, then, can he arrive at a reasonable probability of having an accident?

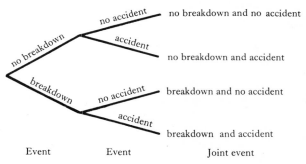

Event   Event   Joint event

Fig. 3–1
Event tree for the student's driving problem

We can begin to tackle this problem by drawing the event tree shown in Fig. 3–1. The tree is read from left to right, so that tracing through the various branches of the tree gives us the four *joint events* described at the right of the tree. The events are drawn in the order you wish to consider them, and this order may or may not correspond to the actual order of occurrence. In this case the student could not think about the probability of having an accident without first considering the chance of a breakdown, so the possibility of having a breakdown is shown first.

The next step is to assign probabilities to the two branches of the first fork. If the student gives a probability of 0·2 to his having a breakdown, then the probability of no breakdown must be 0·8. Now we go to the upper right fork and assign probabilities to 'no accident' and 'accident' *assuming* that no breakdown has occurred. The student decides that if he does not have a breakdown his chance of an accident is only 0·03. Thus, the probability of no accident given that the car remains operating is $1 - 0.03 = 0.97$. Now we go to the lower right fork and assign probabilities *assuming* that a breakdown has occurred. This time the student figures he has a 0.3 chance of an accident if the car breaks down, for the breakdown could be serious enough to lead to a crash. That leaves a 0.7 probability of no accident, again assuming a breakdown. These probabilities are shown under the events in Fig. 3–2. Notice that although the events on the upper right-hand fork are the same as the lower right-hand fork, the probabilities are different. This is because the probabilities assigned on the right-hand forks are *conditional* on the events in the left-hand fork, so the probabilities are called *conditional probabilities*. These are not a different kind of probability, rather a different kind of event. We should, strictly speaking, not talk of 'conditional probabilities'; instead we should refer to the 'probabilities of conditional events'.

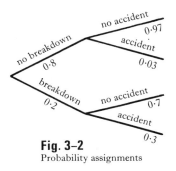

Fig. 3–2
Probability assignments

We have run across conditional probabilities earlier in the chapter when the statement was made that all probabilities were conditional on the person making the assignment and the information available at the time. Now we are saying that it will often be useful to talk of probabilities of events *given* knowledge of other events. For these conditional probabilities we use the notation $p(F|E)$, which reads 'the probability of event F given event E'.

In this example we have two lists of events:

1st List	*2nd List*
E_1: no breakdown	F_1: no accident
E_2: breakdown	F_2: accident

In this problem we have four conditional probabilities:

$$p(F_1|E_1) = p(\text{no accident}|\text{no breakdown}) = 0.97$$

$$p(F_2|E_1) = p(\text{accident}|\text{no breakdown}) = 0.03$$

$$p(F_1|E_2) = p(\text{no accident}|\text{breakdown}) = 0.7$$

$$p(F_2|E_2) = p(\text{accident}|\text{breakdown}) = 0.3$$

The remaining two probabilities are called *unconditional* probabilities because they were determined without specifying anything about the occurrence or non-occurrence of any other events in the event tree (although they are, strictly speaking, conditional on the person doing the assessing and on the information available to him about events other than those on the event tree). These two unconditional probabilities are

$$p(E_1) = p(\text{no breakdown}) = 0.8$$

$$p(E_2) = p(\text{breakdown}) = 0.2$$

Recall that our student's original problem was to find the unconditional probability of an accident, $p(\text{accident})$. How can this be determined from the probabilities assessed so far? The first step, whose reason will be obvious to you in a moment, is to compute the probabilities of the four joint events shown in Fig. 3–1. The rationale for doing this will be easier to see by introducing a standard device which is analogous to the event structure of the student's problem.

Imagine that I have taken an urn containing 1000 balls and labelled 200 of them with the word 'breakdown' and the remaining 800 with 'no breakdown'. Now if I mix the balls and perform a simple experiment, the probability of drawing a 'breakdown' ball is $200/1000 = 0.2$, the same as on the first fork of the event tree in Fig. 3–2. Suppose further that I take all the balls labelled 'no breakdown' and add a second label, 'no accident' to 0.97 of them and 'accident' to 0.03 of them. Then I take all 200 of the 'breakdown' balls and add the label 'no accident' to 0.7 of them and 'accident' to 0.3 of them.

Now we can compute the number of balls that have different double labels. How many balls are labelled 'no breakdown, no accident'? We know that 800 balls show a 'no breakdown' label and that 0.97 of these also have a 'no accident' label, so $800 \times 0.97 = 776$ balls must bear the double label. In similar fashion the number of balls bearing each double label can be found:

Label	Number of balls	
no breakdown, no accident	$800 \times 0.97 =$	776
no breakdown, accident	$800 \times 0.03 =$	24
breakdown, no accident	$200 \times 0.7 =$	140
breakdown, accident	$200 \times 0.3 =$	60

Total number of balls $= 1000$

Performing a simple experiment with this urn will result in a joint event (a ball with two labels) whose probability of occurrence is exactly the same as the probability of the corresponding joint event shown in Fig. 3–1! So to find the probabilities of the student's joint events we have only to compute the corresponding probabilities for the standard device. This can be done easily; simply divide the number of each type of ball by 1000.

Joint event	Probability
no breakdown, no accident	0.776
no breakdown, accident	0.024
breakdown, no accident	0.14
breakdown, accident	0.06

Sum $= 1.000$

Now look back at Fig. 3–2. You will see that you could have computed the above probabilities directly, without counting balls, by simply multiplying the probabilities on the branches of the event tree. For example, the probability of the joint event 'no breakdown and no accident' is $0.8 \times 0.97 = 0.776$. Finally we have arrived at the third probability law:

Third law **The probability of both E and F occurring is equal to the probability of E times the probability of F given E. In mathematical notation,**

$$p(\text{E and F}) = p(\text{E}) \times p(\text{F}|\text{E})$$

This is the calculation that was made to find the probabilities of the joint events now shown in the completed diagram of Fig. 3–3. For example, for the joint event (E_1 and F_1), you must find

$$p(E_1 \text{ and } F_1) = p(E_1) \times p(F_1|E_1)$$

By substituting the appropriate probabilities you get

$$p(E_1 \text{ and } F_1) = 0.8 \times 0.97 = 0.776$$

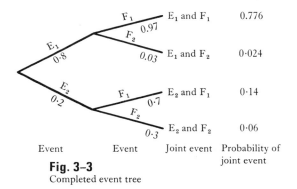

| Event | Event | Joint event | Probability of joint event |

Fig. 3–3
Completed event tree

For the next calculation,

$$p(E_1 \text{ and } F_2) = p(E_1) \times p(F_2|E_1)$$
$$= 0.8 \times 0.03 = 0.024$$

and so forth for the other two joint events.

First Corollary to the third law

We still have not found the unconditional probabilities of accident and no accident. To do this we will need a corollary to the third law. Let me develop it intuitively before stating it formally.

Suppose you were not given the original event tree and its associated probabilities but were given *only* the probabilities of the joint events in Fig. 3–3 and you were asked to compute the probability of breakdown. You might observe that 'breakdown' appears in the bottom two joint events, so you figure that if either of those two events occurs, a breakdown has occurred. Now the second law says that the probability of either of two events occurring is equal to the sum of their individual probabilities, so you add the two probabilities to get the probability of a breakdown:

$$p(\text{breakdown}) = 0{\cdot}14 + 0{\cdot}06 = 0{\cdot}2$$

The correctness of your reasoning can be verified by checking this probability against the probability of breakdown that was originally assigned and that appears in the lower branch of the first fork, 0·2.

You should see now how to compute the probability of an accident. Find the two joint events in which the word 'accident' appears, and add their probabilities:

$$p(\text{accident}) = 0{\cdot}024 + 0{\cdot}06 = 0{\cdot}084$$

And, of course, the probability of no accident can be obtained in the same way,

$$p(\text{no accident}) = 0{\cdot}776 + 0{\cdot}14 = 0{\cdot}916$$

or it can be computed by finding 1 minus the probability of accident,

$$p(\text{no accident}) = 1 - p(\text{accident}) = 1 - 0{\cdot}084 = 0{\cdot}916$$

Notice that this result was obtained by using both the second and third laws.

First corollary to the third law   **The unconditional probability of F is equal to the probability of E times the probability of F given E, plus the probability of $\bar{\text{E}}$ times the probability of F given $\bar{\text{E}}$. In mathematical notation,**

$$p(\text{F}) = p(\text{E}) \times p(\text{F}|\text{E}) + p(\bar{\text{E}}) \times p(\text{F}|\bar{\text{E}})$$

In this form the corollary looks forbidding, but if you will always draw an event tree and follow the assignments and calculations logically, you should find it easy to compute the unconditional probability of an event. In applying this corollary we are finding the probability of an event, F, by extending our analysis to include opinion about another event, E, and opinion about the relationship between F and E. Consequently, we can say that applying the corollary allows us to determine our uncertainty about a single, unconditional event by 'extending the conversation'.

You can test your understanding of the corollary with this exercise.

Exercise 3–5

An artist wishes to determine the probability that his next painting, not yet started, will sell. He decides that he cannot really assess that probability directly, for the chance of a sale depends on how well the painting turns out. He knows from past experience that when he feels good about one of his completed works, he has a 0·7 chance of selling it, but when he feels the work is bad, the chance of a sale is only about 0·1. In the past, about 0·35 of his paintings have been, in his opinion, good, but he is reluctant to use this figure as the probability of producing a good painting because he has lately been going through a difficult transition period in his career where the quality of his work has been rather poor. He settles for a probability of only 0·2 as reflecting the chance that his next painting will turn out well.

a   Draw an event tree for the artist's problem, labelling the branches with the names of the events and their corresponding probabilities.

b   Calculate the probability of a sale.

Answer

a   The event tree should look like this (Fig.3-4):

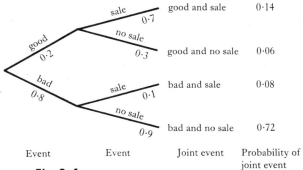

Fig. 3–4
Event tree for the artist problem

b   The probability of a sale is found by adding the two probabilities of joint events that include 'sale' as part of their description.

$$p(\text{sale}) = p(\text{good, sale}) + p(\text{bad, sale}) = 0.14 + 0.08 = 0.22$$

Suppose the artist in this example felt that the chance of selling a painting could be assessed more accurately by considering a slightly more refined judgement of the painting's quality. Instead of just 'good' or 'bad' he prefers to consider the events 'good', 'bad', and 'indifferent'. He might also be hardpressed for cash and so is interested in the event 'immediate sale' as well as 'later sale' and 'no sale'. The first fork on his event tree would have three branches. How does the first corollary to the third law apply when an event tree contains forks of more than two branches?

The general principles embodied in the third law and its corollary apply no matter how many branches in each fork. The next exercise will illustrate this point.

Exercise 3–6

An English scientist wishes to measure, in a particular community, the strength of opinion favouring the return of capital punishment. He feels that an adequate measure is represented by the probability that a person selected at random from the community would favour the proposition. He plans to interview a sample of people in the community so he can obtain data which will be used to revise his prior opinions. For now, let us concentrate on those prior opinions. He finds his prior opinions are rather vague concerning the probability that a person would favour the return of capital punishment, but he feels in a better position to quantify his opinions if he considers the person's political beliefs. If a person considers himself a Conservative, then the scientist thinks the probability is 0·8 that the person would favour the return of capital punishment. He feels the chance is about 0·55 for a Labourite, 0·15 for a Liberal, and 0·25 for a person who would not associate himself with those three political parties. The scientist completes the task of quantifying his prior opinion by looking up figures on the proportions of people affiliated with the different parties (party records, recent surveys, voting records of the last election, etc.), and using this information along with his knowledge of recent social and political trends, to arrive at the following probabilities:

p(Conservative) = 0·35
p(Labour)   = 0·45
p(Liberal)   = 0·08
p(Other)   = 0·12

Sum = 1·00

a   Draw and label the scientist's event tree.
b   Find the probability that a person would favour the return of capital punishment.

Answers

a   Here is the event tree:

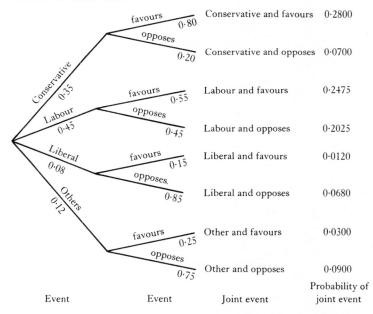

| Event | Event | Joint event | Probability of joint event |

You can see that the probabilities of the joint events are determined by applying the third law: each conditional probability on a branch of a right fork is multiplied by the unconditional probability on the preceding branch of the left fork.

b   The probabilities of four joint events must be added to obtain the required probability.

p(favours) = p(Conservative, favours) + p(Labour, favours)
                      + p(Liberal, favours) + p(other, favours)
        = 0·28 + 0·2475 + 0·012 + 0·03
        = 0·5695

So, before gathering any data, the scientist believes there is about a 0·57 chance that a person in the community would favour the return of capital punishment.

Occasionally your prior opinion may depend on more than one conditional event. The scientist in the previous example may feel that the probability of favouring the proposition depends on the individual's political preference, that his data on political preference are unreliable and that his opinions depend on the person's sex. Now we have three lists:

List 1	*List 2*	*List 3*
male	Conservative	favours
female	Labour	opposes
	Liberal	
	Other	

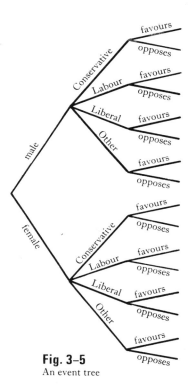

Fig. 3–5
An event tree

The event tree is shown in Fig. 3–5. The probabilities on the first fork are unconditional, $p(E)$. Probabilities on the second set of forks are conditional on the event from the first list: $p(F|E)$. Third-fork probabilities are conditional on events from both first and second lists: $p(G|F, E)$. In general, probabilities on any branch are assessed keeping in mind that events on the path from the origin to the present branch have already occurred.

Joint probabilities are computed as before, by multiplying probabilities along the paths. In general, the probability of the joint event E, F, G is given by

$$p(E, F, G) = p(E) \times p(F|E) \times p(G|F, E)$$

Unconditional probabilities are then found by adding the probabilities of all joint events that include the event whose probability is desired, the same procedure as before.

Second corollary to the third law

Imagine two urns, the first containing 700 white and 300 black balls, the second containing 600 red and 400 green balls. Suppose I perform the simple experiment of drawing a ball from the first urn, then one from the second urn. The possible outcomes of this two-stage experiment are shown in Fig. 3–6.

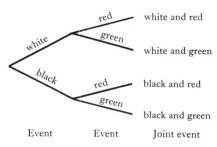

Event   Event   Joint event

Fig. 3–6
Event tree for the two-urn experiment

Now let us use the third law to find the probabilities of the joint events. First we must assign probabilities to each of the branches of the event tree. The branches of the first fork should give no trouble; we assign probabilities equal to the proportions of white and black balls.

$$p(\text{white}) = 0 \cdot 7$$
$$p(\text{black}) = 0 \cdot 3$$
$$\overline{\phantom{p(\text{white}) =}\,1 \cdot 0}$$

Next consider the upper right fork. Remember that the probabilities we place on these branches are for *conditional* events; we do not assess $p(\text{red})$ and $p(\text{green})$, we determine $p(\text{red}|\text{white})$ and $p(\text{green}|\text{white})$. In other words, we must find the probabilities of red and green *given* that a white ball has been drawn from the first urn. Probabilities on the lower right fork must also be for conditional events; we want to find the probabilities of drawing a red or a green ball from the second urn *given* that the ball drawn from the first urn was black.

In the student's car problem and in the artist's problem the probabilities on the branches of the two right forks depended on the preceding event. The artist assigned a higher probability to 'sale' given that he felt good about his painting than if he felt badly. Here we are saying that when we evaluate the probability of green or the probability of red we must take into account the results of the first draw.

If you are feeling a bit confused at this point because you cannot see why the probability of drawing a green ball should be affected in the slightest by the results of the first draw, do not worry, you are correct. Clearly the draws from the separate urns cannot influence one another unless, perhaps, the first ball drawn is coated with an instantaneously acting deadly poison, so that the second ball never is drawn. If the draws cannot influence each other then it seems reasonable that the probability you assign to green conditional on the outcome of the first draw will be the same whether a black or a white ball is drawn first.

Another way to look at this is to imagine that I have made both draws. I ask you, 'What is the probability I have drawn a green ball?' You will probably note the proportion of green balls and reply, '0·6'. Now I say, 'Ah, but I'm willing to tell you the result of the draw from the first urn. If I tell you it was black, will you wish to make a new estimate of the probability I have drawn a green ball?' Your answer would be, 'No'. I reply, 'Well, it was not black anyway, it was white. Now what do you think the probability of green is?' Again you would be uninfluenced by this information because it does not tell you a thing about the second draw, so you answer, 'Still 0·6'.

In general, if you find when you are assessing the probability of an event that your opinion is unaffected by knowing whether or not some other event has occurred, then we say the two events are *independent*.

Two events are independent if

$$p(F|E) = p(F)$$

Event F is independent of event E if the probability of F given E equals the probability of F. Independence is a symmetric notion; if F is independent of E, then E is independent of F. Thus, it is also true that $p(E|F) = p(E)$.

Now let us use this definition to simplify the computation required to find the probabilities of the joint events in the two-urn example. Recall that the third law gives us the rule we should apply:

$$p(E \text{ and } F) = p(E) \times p(F|E)$$

But we have just seen that for independent events,

$$p(F|E) = p(F)$$

So if we substitute this last equation into that for the third law, we get

$$p(E \text{ and } F) = p(E) \times p(F)$$

This is the second corollary to the third law.

Second corollary to the third law   **For independent events, the probability of both E and F occurring is equal to the probability of E times the probability of F. In mathematical notation,**

$$p(E \text{ and } F) = p(E) \times p(F)$$

This corollary is sometimes called the 'multiplication law'.

To apply this corollary to the two-urn problem we follow the same procedure as in the student's car problem: multiply the probabilities on the paths through the tree. The only difference for the two-urn problem is that by recognizing that the two draws are independent, we can put the same probabilities on the lower right fork as on the upper right fork, in this case 0·6 and 0·4. The complete tree is shown in Fig. 3–7.

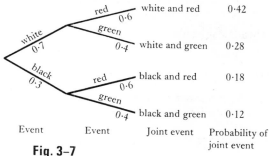

Fig. 3–7

Complete event tree for the two-urn experiment

We will make frequent use of this corollary so be sure you understand it. Remember that it is nothing more than the third law with a simplification for independent events. You can use it *only* for independent events, so to apply the corollary you must first decide whether the events are independent. Of course if you draw a decision tree and find that your probability assessments for the right forks are the same from one fork to the next whatever the first event, then you have as a matter of course found the events to be independent.

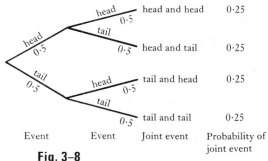

Fig. 3–8

Event tree for two flips of a fair coin

However, sometimes independence is more conveniently recognized not by assessing probabilities, but by noting that knowledge of one event cannot possibly influence knowledge of the other. Then it is only necessary to assess the unconditional probabilities of the events and multiply them to obtain the probability of the joint event. For example, what is the probability that two successive tosses of a coin judged to be fair will result in a head on the first toss and a head on the second? Obviously the first and second tosses are unrelated; the coin does not have a memory! The outcome of the second toss has nothing to do with the outcome of the first toss, so the two tosses are independent. Since we would assign a probability of 0·5 to a head coming up on one toss of a coin, we can find the probability of two heads on two tosses by applying the second corollary to the third law. We could draw the event tree of Fig. 3–8 or we could solve the problem algebraically:

$$p(\text{head and head}) = p(\text{head}) \times p(\text{head})$$
$$= 0{\cdot}5 \times 0{\cdot}5$$
$$= 0{\cdot}25$$

Notice that doing it algebraically saves drawing the whole tree.

See if you understand this corollary by trying the next two exercises.

Exercise 3–7

I toss a coin and roll a die, both judged to be fair. What is the probability of getting:

a   A head and a four?
b   A head and an even number?
c   A head and either a 1, 2, or 3?

Answers

You could draw an event tree and assess probabilities for the relevant branches, then multiply along the corresponding paths. In the process of assessing probabilities you would discover that the probabilities you assigned to the outcomes of the roll of the die were unaffected by knowledge that the coin came up heads or tails. Or, you could proceed by recognizing that the toss and the roll are unrelated, so the corresponding events must be independent. Then, the algebraic approach is simple.

a $p(\text{head and four}) = p(\text{head}) \times p(\text{four})$
   $= 1/2 \times 1/6 = 1/12$

b $p(\text{head and even number}) = p(\text{head}) \times p(\text{even number})$
   $= p(\text{head}) \times p(\text{2 or 4 or 6})$

Note that at this point you must bring in the second law to find $p(\text{2 or 4 or 6})$. Since

$$p(\text{2 or 4 or 6}) = p(2) + p(4) + p(6) = 1/6 + 1/6 + 1/6 = 3/6 = 1/2,$$

$$p(\text{head and even number}) = 1/2 \times 1/2 = 1/4$$

c $p(\text{head and either 1, 2, or 3}) = p(\text{head}) \times p(\text{1, or 2, or 3})$
   $= p(\text{head}) \times \{p(1) + p(2) + p(3)\}$
   $= 1/2 \times (1/6 + 1/6 + 1/6) = 1/2 \times 1/2 = 1/4$

Exercise 3–8

A psychologist notes that an untrained rat placed in a T-maze has a tendency to turn right rather than left at the junction of the runways. He estimates the probability of turning right on any one trial to be 0·6. What probabilities should the psychologist assign to the following events?

a   The rat turns right on each of the next two trials.
b   The rat turns left on the next trial and right on the one after that.
c   The rat turns right on the next trial and left on the one after that.

Answers

a First we must find out if turning right on the next trial and turning right on the following one are independent events. We should ask the psychologist, 'I noticed that the rat turned *right* on the last trial. In light of that information would you still say that his chance of turning right on the next trial is 0·6?' In other words, if we let

E_1 represent right turn on first trial
F_1 represent right turn on second trial

then we are asking the psychologist if he thinks $p(F_1) = p(F_1|E_1)$. If he were to say yes then we can conclude that he believes the events to be independent and so we are justified in applying the second corollary to the third law to this problem. But if he says no, then we must ask him for his estimate of $p(F_1|E_1)$ so we can use the third law itself.

Let us suppose he says the result of the previous trial has no bearing on his judgement of the chances of turning right on the next trial, that is, $p(F_1) = p(F_1|E_1) = 0.6$.

Then the probability of two successive right turns is

$$p(\text{right then right}) = p(\text{right}) \times p(\text{right})$$
$$= 0.6 \times 0.6$$
$$= 0.36$$

b Now ask the psychologist if he would change his probability of a right turn knowing that the rat turned *left* on the previous trial. You are asking him if he thinks $p(F_1) = p(F_1|E_2)$ where E_2 represents left turn on the first trial.

If he says he would stick to 0·6 even if he did know the rat turned left the last time, then he is saying that F_1 and E_2 are independent. Again, you should apply the second corollary to the third law.

$$p(\text{left then right}) = p(\text{left}) \times p(\text{right})$$
$$= \{1 - p(\text{right})\} \times p(\text{right})$$
$$= 0.4 \times 0.6$$
$$= 0.24$$

Notice that we also had to apply the first corollary to the second law to find the probability of a left turn.

c Now we let E_2 represent left turn on first trial and ask the psychologist if

$$p(F_2) = p(F_2|E_2).$$

If he says they are equal then we conclude that F_2 and E_2 are independent. We apply the second corollary to the third law:

$$p(\text{right then left}) = p(\text{right}) \times p(\text{left})$$
$$= p(\text{right}) \times \{1 - p(\text{right})\}$$
$$= 0.6 \times 0.4$$
$$= 0.24$$

That is the same answer as in the preceding problem where you had to find $p(\text{left then right})$. From this similarity you would be correct in inferring that the probability of a sequence of independent events does not depend on their order of occurrence.

Our method of solving this problem was a bit clumsy because we had to keep asking whether the two events in question were independent. We could have simplified the task by asking the psychologist whether the *trials* were independent. In the language we are using here a trial is really a simple experiment, and the rat turning right or left on the trial is the outcome of the simple experiment; it is an event. If we say that the trials are independent, we are really saying that knowing the outcomes of the second trial cannot influence opinion about the outcomes of the first trial and vice versa. That more general statement implies that all of the second-trial events are independent of all of the first-trial events.

In other words, the general statement that *trials* are independent implies the specific statements that *events* are independent from one trial to the next. If the psychologist had said the trials are independent we could have concluded, without further questioning, that

$$p(F_1) = p(F_1|E_1)$$
$$p(F_1) = p(F_1|E_2)$$
$$p(F_2) = p(F_2|E_1)$$
$$p(F_2) = p(F_2|E_2)$$

Then we could have applied the second corollary to the third law with no further ado.

The notion of independence plays an important part in statistical inference. The scientist is frequently interested in knowing whether 'things go together', whether knowing something about one thing will help to predict something else. Especially in the social sciences, where we are not even agreed about which aspects of human and societal behaviour are the right ones to measure, much experimental work is devoted to finding out whether or not something makes a difference to, has an effect on, or influences something else. Are race and intelligence related? Is there a connection between social class and level of education? Is the taking of soft drugs independent of damage to chromosomes? The statistician may use tests of independence on the data derived from experiments addressed to these questions. We will see how to do this in Chapter 14.

Try the next exercise to see if you know when to use the third law and when to use the second corollary to the third law.

Exercise 3–9

a   What is the probability that some time in the next eight hours someone will offer to buy you a beer and someone (not necessarily the same person) will offer you a cigarette?

b   What is the probability that it will rain tomorrow and you will be in a grouchy mood?

c   What is the probability that tomorrow you will receive a letter bearing a foreign postmark and that someone will offer to buy you a beer?

d   What is the probability that the next person to call you by name will be a woman and that the next post will bring a letter bearing a foreign postmark?

e   What is the probability that the next two (different) people to call you by name are both women?

Answers

The safest way to tackle these problems is to start by assuming you will apply the third law. When you assess $p(F|E)$ you may find that it is the same as $p(F)$, in which case the third law turns into the second corollary. But if you find $p(F|E)$

is not the same as $p(F)$, then you know events E and F are not independent, so you must use the third law.

a First assess the probability that someone will offer you a beer in the next eight hours. Suppose you feel 0·05 is about right. Now ask yourself if the probability of being offered a cigarette is different depending on whether or not someone offers to buy you a beer. For me, the chance of being offered a cigarette is low, say 0·01, but it is higher if someone has offered to buy me a beer for I would most likely be in a bar with several friends, one of whom may not know I do not smoke and so would offer me a cigarette. Let me say, then, that p(offer of cigarette|offer of beer) = 0·10. Applying the third law gives

p(offers of beer and cigarette)
= p(offer of beer) × p(offer of cigarette|offer of beer)
= 0·05 × 0·10
= 0·005

It would have been inappropriate to use the second corollary to the third law because the events are not independent. We saw this when we found that p(offer of cigarette) was not equal to p(offer of cigarette|offer of beer).

b These are obviously not independent events for me. I'm more likely to feel grouchy on a rainy day than, say, a sunny day. My mood is not independent of the weather, so if the same is true for you, you must assess p(rain) and p(grouchy|rain), and use the third law, not the second corollary.

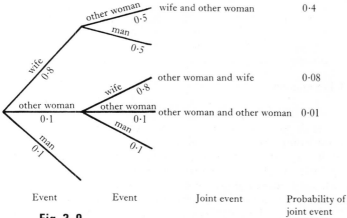

| Event | Event | Joint event | Probability of joint event |

Fig. 3–9
Event tree for the 'two-women' problem

c At first glance these would seem to be independent events, but look again. Suppose the foreign letter brought unexpected good news. Is it not possible that you would tell your friends, one of whom might offer to buy you a beer, to celebrate? But perhaps that is so unlikely for you that, for practical purposes, the events can be treated as independent. If you think so, then use the second corollary to the third law.

d Now here are two events that seem to me completely unrelated, though I suppose some reader will find a situation where they are not independent. If the events are independent for you, use the second corollary to the third law.

e This is a difficult problem to discuss in general terms because the judgement about independence of the events depends very much on where you are as you read this. As I write this at home I am almost certain that my wife will call me by my name before the evening is over. But who would the other person be? Perhaps someone will phone, and call me by my name even if they want to speak to my wife. That seems fairly likely, but if it does not happen, then when I go in to University tomorrow someone is bound to call me by name, and I am equally no more certain the person will be a man than a woman. Of course either a man or a woman may phone this evening before my wife calls me by name. The events that could happen are sufficiently numerous that an event tree may be helpful. Mine is shown in Fig. 3–9. The branches of the left fork represent the possible people, one of whom may be the first to call me by my name, and the numbers below the branches are my probability assignments to those possibilities. The branches of the right fork show the people who might be second. The upper right fork does not contain a 'wife' branch because the problem stated the two people must not be the same person, and the branch that precedes the upper right fork already has 'wife' on it. The middle right fork contains all three possibilities, it being understood that 'other woman' on this fork signifies a different person than 'other woman' on the middle branch of the left fork. I have written out only the joint events of relevance to this problem; the probabilities of the joint events are obtained by applying the third law. To find the probability that the next two people to call me by name will be women, I apply the second law, i.e. add the three relevant joint probabilities.

$$p(\text{woman and woman}) = p(\text{wife and other woman})$$
$$+ p(\text{other woman and wife})$$
$$+ p(\text{other woman and other woman})$$
$$= 0{\cdot}40 + 0{\cdot}08 + 0{\cdot}01$$
$$= 0{\cdot}49$$

3.5   Quantifying opinion

Opinion about complex events

The last part of the previous exercise, the 'two-women problem, illustrates a very important point about quantifying opinion: do not do it for complex events. I found it very difficult to express my opinion about the possibility that the next two people to call me by name will be women, but I discovered that my task was easier if I broke the problem down into simpler events as illustrated in Fig. 3–9. I felt more comfortable quantifying my opinions about those simple events, and I used the probability laws to put those opinions together to give my opinion about the complex event.

A major point in introducing the third law and its corollaries was to enable you to quantify your opinion about complex events. We saw in the capital punishment problem, in the artist's problem, and in this last problem that an event about which opinion was vague could be broken down into simpler events, and that opinions about these simple events could be expressed with some confidence. Then opinions about the original events could be found by combining the probabilities of the simple events through application of the probability laws, particularly the third and its corollaries.

But why bother? Why not directly express opinion about the complex events? The answer to these questions comes from a considerable body of research aimed at finding out how good people are at quantifying opinion in the form of probabilities. A repeated finding of this research is that the probabilities people assign to simple events are quite consistent with each other in that they obey the probability laws, but that probabilities assigned to complex events are not very consistent. (Summaries of this research can be found in Peterson and Beach, 1967, and in Edwards, 1968.)

Many statisticians have been reluctant to adopt Bayesian ideas because they feel that prior opinion is vague and incapable of being quantified. Even if you could quantify it, they argue, the probabilities are largely meaningless. I think this criticism should be taken seriously, for it may reflect an accurate intuitive appreciation of the inconsistencies in our judgements about complex events. The mathematician and the experimentalist may be saying similar things in different words. But the research findings suggest a way out of the pessimism of the traditional statistician. By recognizing that this difficulty may frequently be caused by our inability to handle complex events, we can try to decompose the complex events into simpler ones, and then exercise judgement about the simple events. This we can do with some confidence, and then we reassemble the pieces by using the probability laws. Indeed, several authors have devised procedures, even complex man–computer systems, for this decomposition–judgement–reassembly procedure (Raiffa, 1968; Schlaifer, 1969; Edwards, Phillips, Hays and Goodman, 1968).

It is also worth pointing out that some of the difficulty people have in trying to assess probabilities is simply a matter of inexperience. As I said earlier in this chapter, probabilities are the language of uncertainty, and the probability laws are the grammar of that language. When you have gained some experience in using the language, you will feel more confident that your probability assessments are meaningful.

3.6 Summary

In this chapter we have seen that probabilities are the language of uncertainty, and that the probability laws are the grammar of that language. Uncertainty about events, hypotheses or uncertain quantities can be expressed numerically in the form of probabilities.

The probability laws impose certain constraints on the probabilities we may assess: the first law restricts probabilities to numbers between 0 and 1, inclusive, while the second and third laws, and their corollaries, specify the consistencies that must exist between probabilities we assign to events and those we assign to combinations of the events.

Here are the probability laws:

First law: $\quad\quad\quad\quad 0 \leq p(E) \leq 1$ and $p(\text{sure event}) = 1$

Second law: $\quad\quad\quad p(E_1 \text{ or } E_2) = p(E_1) + p(E_2)$
for mutually exclusive events

First corollary to
the second law: $\quad\quad p(E) = 1 - p(\overline{E})$

Second corollary to
the second law: $\quad\quad \sum p(E_i) = 1$
for mutually exclusive and exhaustive events

Third law: $p(\text{E and F}) = p(\text{E}) \times p(\text{F}|\text{E})$

*First corollary to
the third law:* $p(\text{F}) = p(\text{E}) \times p(\text{F}|\text{E}) + p(\bar{\text{E}}) \times p(\text{F}|\bar{\text{E}})$

*Second corollary to
the third law:* $p(\text{E and F}) = p(\text{E}) \times p(\text{F})$
                         for independent events

Usually your probabilities should be assigned only to simple events. If your real interest lies in complex events, then you should decompose the complex event into simple ones, assess probabilities for the simple events, then use the probability laws to find the probability for the complex event.

Problems

3–1   In a class of 30 men and 20 women, each student writes on a 3-in by 5-in card whether he or she is left-handed, right-handed, or ambidextrous (three mutually exclusive and exhaustive categories). Five of the men and 4 of the women are left-handed and one man is ambidextrous. Suppose the cards are collected and mixed, and then 3 cards are selected at random with replacement (that is, after selecting a card and noting what is written on it, the card is returned to the collection before the next one is selected). What is the probability that

a   the first card will say 'left-handed', the second will say 'right-handed', and the third will say 'left-handed'.
b   all three cards will say 'left-handed'.

3–2   A student considering a simple experiment which can result in one of three mutually exclusive and collectively exhaustive events assigns the following probabilities to the first two events:

$$p(\text{E}_1) = 0{\cdot}7 \quad p(\text{E}_2) = 0{\cdot}2$$

Complete these statements:

a $p(\text{E}_3) =$ c $p(\text{E}_1 \text{ and E}_2) =$
b $p(\text{E}_1 \text{ or E}_2) =$ d $p(\bar{\text{E}}_3) =$

3–3   A man has mislaid his wallet. He thinks there is a $0{\cdot}4$ chance that the wallet is somewhere in his bedroom, a $0{\cdot}1$ chance it is in the kitchen, a $0{\cdot}2$ chance it is in the bathroom, and a $0{\cdot}15$ chance it is in the living room. What is the probability that the wallet is

a   somewhere else?
b   in either the bedroom or the kitchen?

3–4   Before leaving for a dice game, an unscrupulous gambler places a loaded die in his pocket. From past experience, he knows that the die comes up a 3 more often than a fair die. His probabilities for the six possible outcomes are:

$$p(1) = 0{\cdot}15 \quad p(2) = 0{\cdot}15 \quad p(3) = 0{\cdot}30 \quad p(4) = 0{\cdot}1$$
$$p(5) = 0{\cdot}15 \quad p(6) = 0{\cdot}15$$

During the game he reaches for the die but discovers another one, indistinguishable in appearance, in his pocket. All he knows is that one die is a fair one, while the other is the loaded one. He chooses one at random and surreptitiously introduces it into the game. What is the probability that the next throw of that die will result in a three?

3–5   Suppose that the gambler from the previous problem finds out he has the loaded die. What is the probability that on the next three throws of the die it will come up

a   any number other than a 3 on each throw?

b   a 3 on at least one of the throws?

c   a 3 on at least two of the throws?

3–6   A student figures his chance of passing a history exam is about 0·9 if a question on the origins of the First World War appears. Otherwise his chance of passing is only about 0·7. He thinks there is a 0·6 chance that the question will appear. What is the probability of passing the exam?

3–7   A man driving to a distant city wishes to arrive as quickly as possible. He considers taking the shortest route—through the mountains. Since it is winter, there is some possibility that it will snow hard enough to block the road; he will not get through if it snows *and* the mountain road is blocked. He estimates the probability of it snowing as 0·2 and the probability of the road staying open given that it snows as 0·6. What is the probability that he will get through if he takes the mountain road?

3–8   I am behind schedule and reckon that I am 3 times as likely to catch the next underground as to miss it. If I miss it, I am sure to catch the second train that leaves 15 minutes later. If I get the first train, I reckon that possible delays in my journey leave me with a 0·7 chance of arriving on time for an appointment. If I miss the first train, then I assess the odds in favour of my missing the appointment as 10 to 1. What is the probability that I will be late?

3–9   A scientist about to conduct an experiment figures there is about a 0·9 chance of observing result X if Theory A is true, and about a 0·3 chance of observing X if Theory B is true. He feels that Theory A is about twice as likely to be true as Theory B. If theories A and B are the only reasonable contenders, what is the probability that the scientist will observe X when he carries out the experiment?

4 · Revising opinion

The present chapter is the most important in this book. If you understand the logic of this chapter, you will find the rest of the book makes sense, for most of the remaining material is a variant of the theme developed in this chapter.

You have met the theme before:

Prior opinions are changed by data, through the operation of Bayes' theorem, to yield posterior opinions.

In this chapter we see how Bayes' theorem operates. The previous two chapters showed how an individual's uncertainty can be quantified as probabilities and how these probabilities are governed by the probability laws. Now we are ready to see how the probability we assign to an event should be revised when we learn of the occurrence of a related event. In other words, we consider how our uncertainty about the world changes as we systematically collect data. The key to this process is given by Bayes' theorem.

When you have completed this chapter you should

be thoroughly familiar with the operation of Bayes' theorem and be able to apply it for a simple datum or for a string of data;

understand the ways in which intuitive revision of opinion is different from that prescribed by Bayes' theorem;

have an understanding of the way in which prior opinion contributes to posterior opinion;

know how to determine the probabilities that go into Bayes' theorem;

understand the logic of hypothesis testing from a Bayesian point of view.

4.1 Bayes' theorem

In this section I am going to develop Bayes' theorem out of the 'student's driving' example in the previous chapter, then I shall state the theorem formally, and finally show several ways of calculating it.

Extension of the student's driving problem

Suppose our student sets out on the trip but never reaches his destination. Instead, he wakes up in a hospital and has no recollection of how he got there. A nurse confirms only that he has had an accident resulting in a nasty blow on the head and a broken leg. Eventually he becomes accustomed to the headache and to the cast on his leg, and, as boredom sets in, he tries to recollect the events of the accident, to no avail. He is particularly curious to know if his car broke down before the accident. He knows that even if his car had broken down, it may or may not have led to an accident, and that the cause of his accident may have been an event other than a breakdown. So, how can he determine the probability of breakdown *given* that he knows an accident has occurred?

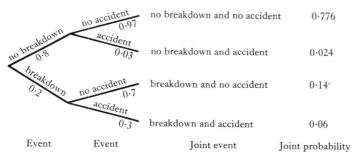

| Event | Event | Joint event | Joint probability |

Fig. 4–1
Event tree for the 'car breakdown' problem

First, let us reconstruct the original event tree we developed in the previous chapter; it is shown in Fig. 4–1. Let us pick up the development of the problem at the point where we introduced a standard device which is analogous to the real problem. That, you recall, was an urn filled with 1000 balls, each ball showing a double label, as follows:

Label	Number of balls
no breakdown, no accident	776
no breakdown, accident	24
breakdown, no accident	140
breakdown, accident	60

The student knows only that he has had an accident. That is equivalent to my drawing a ball at random, finding that it has an 'accident' label on it, and telling you only this information. What, now, is the probability that it has 'breakdown' written on it? If you can answer that question you have solved the student's problem, for your uncertainty is an exact analogue of his.

If we go back to first principles, the probability can be found easily. What is the total number of elementary events we should consider? It is the number of balls with 'accident' on them, that is $24+60 = 84$. How many of these elementary events are in the event class 'breakdown', that is, how many of the 84 balls have 'breakdown' written on them? The answer, of course, is 60.

And so, the probability of breakdown *given* that an accident has occurred is given by the proportion 60/84.

$$p(\text{breakdown}|\text{accident}) = \frac{60}{84} = 0.715$$

That was Bayes' theorem, in informal guise. Here it is more formally:

$$p(\text{breakdown}|\text{accident}) = \frac{p(\text{breakdown and accident})}{p(\text{accident})}$$

The probability in the numerator is a joint probability, found at the right of the event tree. The probability in the denominator is the sum of two joint probabilities; recall that we have been through this before in Chapter 3 when we developed the first corollary to the third law. Although I did not actually state it there, we found that

$$p(\text{accident}) = p(\text{no breakdown and accident})$$
$$+ \; p(\text{breakdown and accident})$$

in other words, the sum of two joint probabilities. Using this result, we can write Bayes' theorem as shown in Fig. 4–2.

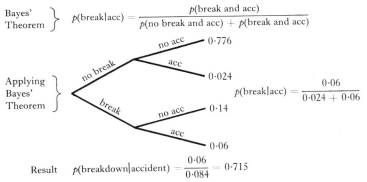

Fig. 4–2
Joint probabilities in Bayes' theorem

A more convenient form of Bayes' theorem can be obtained by applying the third law to each of the joint probabilities, so that the probability of each joint event is given by the product of an unconditional and a conditional probability. You can see how this works by studying Fig. 4–3.

Bayes' theorem for two hypotheses

To generalize, first consider just two events about which we are uncertain; call them H_1 and H_2. For the student's driving problem H_1 is 'breakdown' and H_2 is 'no breakdown'. I have used the symbols H_1 and H_2 because it will be convenient to refer to these particular events as hypotheses. For example, the occurrence of a breakdown can be treated as a hypothesis; it is an event which, from the student's point of view, may or may not have occurred—it is

From Fig. 4–2: $p(\text{break}|\text{acc}) = \dfrac{0{\cdot}06}{0{\cdot}024 + 0{\cdot}06}$

Breaking down the joint probabilities

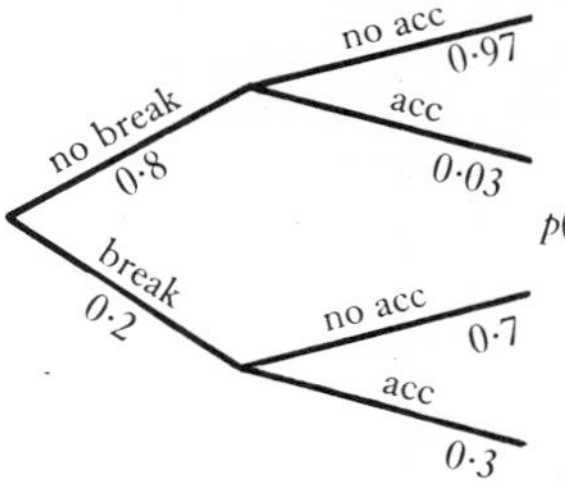

$p(\text{break}|\text{acc}) = \dfrac{0{\cdot}2 \times 0{\cdot}3}{(0{\cdot}8 \times 0{\cdot}03) + (0{\cdot}2 \times 0{\cdot}3)}$

Bayes' theorem: $p(\text{break}|\text{acc}) = \dfrac{p(\text{break})p(\text{acc}|\text{break})}{p(\text{no break})p(\text{acc}|\text{no break}) + p(\text{break})p(\text{acc}|\text{break})}$

Fig. 4–3
Another form of Bayes' theorem

an hypothesis. Note that H_1 and H_2 are competing hypotheses in the sense that one must be true and both cannot be true.

Generalizing further, we recognize that an event has occurred which bears on our uncertainty about the hypotheses. Call this event a datum, and designate it by D. The student knows he has had an accident. That is an item of data, so we let 'accident' be designated by D.

Now we can write Bayes' theorem for two hypotheses. Here it is for H_1:

$$p(H_1|D) = \frac{p(H_1)p(D|H_1)}{p(H_2)p(D|H_2) + p(H_1)p(D|H_1)}$$

And, again, for H_2:

$$p(H_2|D) = \frac{p(H_2)p(D|H_2)}{p(H_2)p(D|H_2) + p(H_1)p(D|H_1)}$$

The probabilities in Bayes' theorem are given names. The unconditional probabilities $p(H_1)$ and $p(H_2)$ are called *prior probabilities* because they represent opinion *before* any data are observed. On the other hand, $p(H_1|D)$ and $p(H_2|D)$ are said to be *posterior probabilities*; they indicate opinion that has been revised in the light of the datum, opinion *after* observing D. Finally, $p(D|H_1)$ and $p(D|H_2)$ are called *likelihoods*. They are the probabilities associated with a particular datum given that event H_1 or that event H_2 has occurred (see Fig. 4–4).

$$\overbrace{p(H_1|D)}^{\text{posterior probability}} = \frac{\overbrace{p(H_1)}^{\text{prior probability}} \times \overbrace{p(D|H_1)}^{\text{likelihood}}}{\underbrace{p(H_2)}_{\text{prior}} \times \underbrace{p(D|H_2)}_{\text{likelihood}} + \underbrace{p(H_1)}_{\text{prior}} \times \underbrace{p(D|H_1)}_{\text{likelihood}}}$$

Fig. 4–4
Names of the probabilities that make up Bayes' theorem

Bayes' theorem looks rather forbidding, but it is not really, if you look closely. Consider it, written for two hypotheses, in Fig. 4–5. First, note that the denominators are identical; each is the sum of two products. If you look closely at the two products, you will see that one appears in the numerator of the first equation, and the other appears in the numerator of the other equation.

Those similarities can be exploited to make computations involving Bayes' theorem quite simple. We turn to that next.

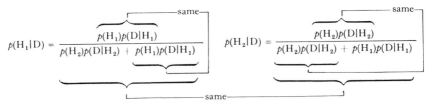

Fig. 4–5
Similarities in Bayes' theorem for two hypotheses

Tabular form of Bayes' theorem

In applying Bayes' theorem, you will be aided by setting out your calculations in tabular form and following the steps shown in Fig. 4–6. Compare these steps to the operations shown in Fig. 4–3 to make sure you understand why each step is carried out.

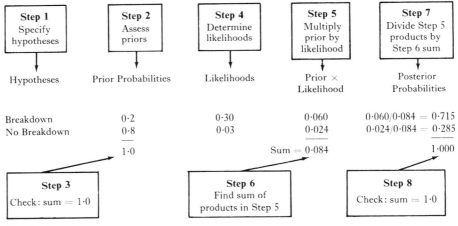

Fig. 4–6
Steps in calculating posterior probabilities by applying Bayes' theorem

What do the calculations mean? Notice that before setting out on the trip the student thought the chance of a breakdown was only 0·2; that was his prior probability. But now he has some data—he was in an accident. His prior opinion has been changed, through the operation of Bayes' theorem, so that now the chance of a breakdown is 0·715. That is his posterior opinion. This revision of opinion in the light of new information is the heart of Bayesian statistics, so be sure you understand how the theorem operates. Try this example.

Exercise 4–1

Page, Rakita, Kaplan and Smith (1957) have used the Archimedes spiral after-effect illusion to diagnose brain damage. The spiral shown below is rotated and the patient is asked to stare fixedly at it for a time; it appears to be shrinking or expanding, depending on the direction of rotation. When it is stopped it seems to rotate in the opposite direction. There is a sense of movement, yet

there is no actual motion. That is the illusion as seen by most people. However, Page *et al.* found that while 85% of people who are functionally ill reported seeing the illusion, only 40% of brain-damaged people reported seeing it.

Suppose that a psychiatrist makes a preliminary diagnosis of a patient as either functionally ill or brain-damaged, and that he is about equally sure of either diagnosis. He shows the rotating spiral to the patient, stops it, and the patient reports he sees the reverse motion. What degrees of belief should the psychiatrist now assign to the two possible diagnoses?

Answer

First let us solve this using the equation form of Bayes' theorem, then the tabular form.

We can consider the two possible diagnoses as hypotheses. Let

H_1 = functional illness and H_2 = brain damage.

The datum is that the patient saw the illusion, so let

D = patient saw illusion.

We wish to find the probability that the patient is functionally ill given that he reported seeing the illusion, and also the probability he is brain-damaged given that he reported seeing the illusion. In other words, we wish to find

$p(H_1|D)$ and $p(H_2|D)$

We use Bayes' theorem to do this. A more easily remembered notation will help. Let H_1 be replaced by F to denote functional illness, H_2 by B to denote brain damage, and D by I to indicate 'saw illusion'. Now we want to find

$p(F|I)$ and $p(B|I)$,

that is, the probability of functional illness given the patient reported seeing the illusion and the probability of brain damage given that he saw the illusion. Writing Bayes' theorem twice in this more mnemonic notation gives

$$p(F|I) = \frac{p(F)p(I|F)}{p(B)p(I|B) + p(F)p(I|F)},$$

and

$$p(B|I) = \frac{p(B)p(I|B)}{p(B)p(I|B) + p(F)p(I|F)}.$$

There are really only four quantities on the right sides of those equations, two prior probabilities, $p(F)$ and $p(B)$, and two likelihoods, $p(I|F)$ and $p(I|B)$. Once we know those values we have almost solved the problem.

Let us start with the prior probabilities. What values could be assigned? The problem states that the psychiatrist is about equally sure of the two diagnoses, so values of 0·5–0·5 would appear reasonable. We assign

$$p(F) = 0·5 \quad \text{and} \quad p(B) = 0·5$$

Now consider the likelihoods. First, $p(I|F)$, the probability that a patient who is functionally ill will report seeing the illusion. Page *et al.* report that about 85% of the functionally-ill subjects in their study reported seeing the illusion, so let us take this percentage as our probability. That is, let

$$p(I|F) = 0·85$$

Those investigators also reported that 40% of their brain-damaged patients reported seeing the illusion, so let

$$p(I|B) = 0·4$$

Now we can apply Bayes' theorem:

$$p(F|I) = \frac{0·5(0·85)}{0·5(0·4) + 0·5(0·85)} = 0·68$$

$$p(B|I) = \frac{0·5(0·4)}{0·5(0·4) + 0·5(0·85)} = 0·32$$

After seeing the test result, the psychiatrist is 68% sure the patient is functionally ill and 32% sure of brain damage. Prior uncertainty of 0·5–0·5 has changed to posterior uncertainty of 0·68–0·32. Or, to say the same thing in odds, the psychiatrist is a little more than twice as sure that the patient is functionally ill as brain damaged.

Next we turn to the tabular form. Follow the steps indicated in Fig. 4–6.

Hypotheses	Priors	Likelihoods	Priors × Likelihoods	Posteriors
Functional illness	0·5	0·85	0·425	$\frac{0·425}{0·625} = 0·68$
Brain damage	0·5	0·4	0·2	$\frac{0·2}{0·625} = 0·32$
	1·0		Sum = 0·625	Sum = 1·00

Some readers may prefer the algebraic form to the tabular, while others may prefer the tabular form.

Comments on Bayes' theorem

Many students find initial difficulty in distinguishing $p(H|D)$ from $p(D|H)$. The first is a posterior probability, the latter a likelihood. As applied to the previous example, one is the probability of functional illness *given* that the patient reports seeing the illusion, while the other is the probability that a functionally ill patient will report seeing the illusion. These are quite distinct probabilities and you cannot get one from the other without also considering the prior probabilities and another likelihood. This is an important point that has implications for scientific inference generally, and we will return to the topic in the last section of this chapter.

Because Bayes' theorem enables us to determine $p(H|D)$ from $p(D|H)$, it is sometimes called the 'theorem of inverse probability' in the literature.

It is worth noting that Bayes' theorem is *not* controversial, for it is derived from the probability laws. To see this, note that the third law,

$$p(E \text{ and } F) = p(E) \times p(F|E)$$

can also be written as

$$p(F \text{ and } E) = p(F) \times p(E|F)$$

The probability of E and F occurring is exactly the same as the probability of F and E; the order of stating the events makes no difference. Thus, the right sides of the two equations above are equal to each other:

$$p(E) \times p(F|E) = p(F) \times p(E|F)$$

Slight rearrangement gives Bayes' theorem:

$$p(F|E) = \frac{p(F) \times p(E|F)}{p(E)}$$

Replacing F by H and E by D gives this general form:

$$p(H|D) = \frac{p(H) \times p(D|H)}{p(D)}$$

I leave it as an exercise for the reader to show that this general form of Bayes' theorem is equivalent to the form given in the section 'Bayes' theorem for two hypotheses'.

Since Bayes' theorem is a consequence of the probability laws discussed in the previous chapter, and since statisticians of all persuasions accept those laws, they also accept Bayes' theorem. It is the interpretation of probability that is controversial; if a statistician accepts the personalist view then he makes heavy use of Bayes' theorem, but if he does not then Bayes' theorem is only occasionally helpful. For a Bayesian, prior probabilities and likelihoods are degrees of belief; both are the results of human judgement. And since all inferential procedures in statistics are variations on the general theme of revision of opinion in the light of new information, Bayes' theorem plays a central role. But for the statistician who takes a relative frequency view of probability it is rare that he can give a relative frequency interpretation to a prior probability, so he makes little use of Bayes' theorem.

General form of Bayes' theorem

You should note that Bayes' theorem is not limited to just two hypotheses. Here it is in general form:

$$p(H_i|D) = \frac{p(H_i)\,p(D|H_i)}{\sum p(H_j)\,p(D|H_j)}$$

The index i can be 1, 2, ..., depending on which hypothesis you are considering. The index j is also 1, 2, ..., and takes on as many values as there are hypotheses. If you have four hypotheses you will write Bayes' theorem four times, and the denominator will contain four products, the product of the prior and likelihood for each of the four hypotheses. In tabular form, the solution will require four hypotheses in the first column, four priors (which must sum to 1) in the second, four likelihoods in the third, four products (whose sum you must find) in the fourth, and, finally, four posteriors. The steps are the same, the table is just longer.

Revision of opinion after several items of data

Suppose you have not just one item of data, but a whole list of data. How should Bayes' theorem be applied then? Let us use the example of the unscrupulous gambler (Chapter 1) to show the application. Recall that he is holding a coin which might be fair or it might be biased toward 'heads'; he is equally unsure of those two possibilities. He tosses the coin ten times and it comes up heads eight times. (The actual sequence is HHTHHHHHTH.) How sure should he be now?

For the moment, let us restrict attention to just the first two flips. What posterior opinion should the gambler hold after he has observed two heads? There are two ways to approach this problem; both arrive at the same end result.

The first approach is to consider the two heads as a single datum, so we start with some opinion prior to observing any flips, then we observe the outcome of two flips and revise opinions in the light of two 'heads'. The second approach is to consider the outcome of each flip as a separate datum, so that prior opinion is revised by the single outcome 'heads', and the posterior opinion resulting from the first flip is taken as the opinion prior to the second flip. Posterior opinion after the first observation is used as prior opinion for the second observation. The posterior probabilities following the second flip then become the opinions in the light of both flips.

Here is how these methods work. We will start with the first one, where 'heads, heads' is treated as a single datum.

Step 1: List the hypotheses. They are 'coin is fair' and 'coin is biased', H_1 and H_2, respectively.

Step 2: Determine priors; say they are 0·5 and 0·5.

Step 3: Check that sum equals one.

Step 4: Determine likelihoods. How likely are two heads *given* that they were the result of flipping the *fair* coin? We want to find

p(H and H|fair coin)

Clearly the two flips are independent given that we know we have the fair coin, so we can apply the second corollary to the third law. In fact, we have already done this. Turn back to page 48 in Chapter 3, and you will see p(H and H) worked out under the assumption the coin is fair. For a coin judged to be fair, I think everyone would agree that the probability of heads on one flip is 0·5. So, the probability of two successive heads must be

p(H and H|fair coin) $= 0·5 \times 0·5 = 0·25$

In other words,

$$p(D|H_1) = 0.25$$

Now what is $p(H$ and $H|$biased coin)?

That is hard to answer unless we know the degree of bias. Let us ask the gambler. His reply: 'I once checked on that by flipping the coin a great many times. It came down heads about 60% of the time.' Alternatively, I could measure his degrees of belief about the probability of heads on a single flip by using the standard measuring device introduced in Chapter 2. Suppose the result is that the gambler assigns

$$p(H|\text{biased coin}) = 0.60$$

Again we note that the two flips are independent given that we know we have the biased coin, so

$$p(H \text{ and } H|\text{biased coin}) = 0.6 \times 0.6 = 0.36$$

That gives us

$$p(D|H_2) = 0.36$$

Step 5: Multiply priors by likelihoods.

$$p(H_1)p(D|H_1) = 0.5 \times 0.25 = 0.125$$
$$p(H_2)p(D|H_2) = 0.5 \times 0.36 = 0.18$$

Step 6: Sum the products

$$0.125 + 0.18 = 0.305$$

Step 7: Calculate posteriors

$$p(H_1|D) = \frac{0.125}{0.305} = 0.41$$

$$p(H_2|D) = \frac{0.180}{0.305} = 0.59$$

(Check: $0.41 + 0.59 = 1.00$.)

After observing two heads, the gambler is now 59% sure he holds the biased coin.

Now let us see what the result would have been if revision of opinion had proceeded one datum at a time. The gambler starts with 0·5–0·5 priors, as before, and observes one flip. It is a 'head'. His opinion, posterior to that *one* observation is calculated as follows:

Hypotheses	Priors	Likelihoods	Priors × Likelihoods	Posteriors
Fair	0·5	0·5	0·25	$\frac{0.25}{0.55} = 0.455$
Biased	0·5	0·6	0·3	$\frac{0.3}{0.55} = 0.545$
	1·0	Sum = 0·55		1·0

After observing one 'head' the gambler is 0·545 sure he holds a biased coin. So, he flips again, and another 'head' comes up. When we calculate Bayes' theorem this time, we use the posteriors from the last calculation as the priors for this one.

Hypotheses	Priors	Likelihoods	Priors × Likelihoods	Posteriors
Fair	0·455	0·5	0·2275	$\frac{0·2275}{0·5545} = 0·41$
Biased	0·545	0·6	0·3270	$\frac{0·3270}{0·5545} = 0·59$
	1·000		Sum = 0·5545	1·00

So, you see, we get the same result as before (except for slight differences in the third decimal place caused by error due to rounding off).

This second form of Bayes' theorem is especially useful to the scientist who wishes to carry out experimental work in stages, for posterior opinion after one stage can serve as prior opinion to the next stage. The gambler can decide to keep tossing the coin until he is 0·99 sure if the coin is either biased or not, but stopping periodically to make the necessary calculations to see if his posterior opinion has reached that extreme degree. Similarly, the scientist can design an experiment to enable him to collect data bearing on certain hypotheses which are in question, and as he gathers evidence he can stop from time to time to see if his current posterior opinions, determined by applying Bayes' theorem, are sufficiently extreme to justify stopping the experiment. I shall have more to say about this 'sequential sampling' procedure in Part III.

Now we are ready to calculate the posterior probabilities after ten flips of the coin. The key probabilities are the likelihoods. We need to find

p(H and H and T and H and H and H and H and H and T and H|fair coin)

and

p(H and H and T and H and H and H and H and H and T and H|biased coin)

We can do this by applying the second corollary to the third law, the 'independence rule':

$p(D|H_1) = \frac{1}{2} \times \frac{1}{2} \times \frac{1}{2} \times \frac{1}{2} \times \frac{1}{2} \times \frac{1}{2} \times \frac{1}{2} \times \frac{1}{2} \times \frac{1}{2} \times \frac{1}{2} = (0·5)^{10}$

$p(D|H_2) = 0·6 \times 0·6 \times 0·4 \times 0·6 \times 0·6 \times 0·6 \times 0·6 \times 0·6 \times 0·4 \times 0·6 = (0·6)^8(0·4)^2$

A little deft use of logarithms gives these results (to three significant figures):

$p(D|H_1) = 0·000977$

$p(D|H_2) = 0·00269$

Applying Bayes' theorem (to two significant figures):

Hypotheses	Priors	Likelihoods	Priors × Likelihoods	Posteriors
Fair	0·5	0·000977	0·0004885	$\dfrac{0·0004885}{0·0018335} = 0·27$
Biased	0·5	0·00269	0·001345	$\dfrac{0·001345}{0·0018335} = 0·73$
	1·0		Sum = 0·0018335	1·00

After observing ten flips, eight of which came out 'heads', our gambler is now 73% sure he holds the biased coin.

See if you understand the two ways of applying Bayes' theorem I have presented in this section by trying the next exercise. Please do not skip the exercise for I use the results in the next section. Also the exercise is an abstracted form of a scientific experiment, and some of the lessons learned from the exercise apply to the conduct of scientific inference.

Exercise 4–2

Imagine that you have just been shown two bags that are identical on the outside. One contains 70 blue poker chips and 30 red ones while the other contains 40 blue and 60 red chips. Call them bag B and bag R.

bag B   bag R

One bag is chosen by the toss of a fair coin, but, since you cannot see the contents, you do not know which one it is. Which bag has been chosen? At this point let me assign prior probabilities of 0·5 and 0·5 to the two possibilities.

Next we shake the chosen bag to mix the chips, and open it just enough to reach in and draw out a poker chip. We note its colour, return it to the bag, shake the bag, and draw another chip. This process is repeated until, say, 12 chips have been drawn, 8 of them blue and 4 red.

Before you read any further, turn to Sec. 4.2 and answer the question just under the section heading, 'Revising opinion intuitively'. Then, come back to this exercise.

What are the posterior probabilities that should be assigned to the two bags? (Note that this is an abbreviated version of the more complete question, 'What is the posterior probability that bag B is the chosen bag, and what is the posterior probability that bag R is the chosen bag?')

Answer

We have two hypotheses. Let them be designated as follows:

H_1: bag B is the chosen bag
H_2: bag R is the chosen bag

The data are 8 blues and 4 reds; consider this as one complex event or datum and call it D. We wish to calculate

p(bag B is chosen bag given 8 blues and 4 reds were observed)

and p(bag R is chosen bag given 8 blues and 4 reds were observed),

or, more succinctly,

$p(H_1|D)$ and $p(H_2|D)$.

We use Bayes' theorem. There should be general agreement about the prior probabilities:

$p(H_1) = p(H_2) = 0.5$

The likelihoods can be calculated by applying the independence rule, just as we did for the gambler's coin problem. That rule, the second corollary to the third law, tells us how the probability of a joint event can be calculated if we know the probabilities of the individual events that make up the joint event. It says we multiply the individual probabilities.

First, consider $p(D|H_1)$. What is the probability of getting that particular sequence of 8 blues and 4 reds *given* that they were drawn from bag B? We can calculate that, but first we have to know the probability of a single blue from that bag, and the probability of a single red from bag B. Judging from the composition of the bag, I assume you would assign these probabilities:

p(blue chip|bag B) $= 0.7$
p(red chip|bag B) $= 0.3$

Now you can apply the independence rule:

$p(D|H_1) = (0.7)^8(0.3)^4 = 0.000467$

Repeat this exercise for the other bag and you should get

$p(D|H_2) = (0.4)^8(0.6)^4 = 0.0000849$

Apply Bayes' theorem:

Hypotheses	Priors	Likelihoods	Priors × Likelihoods	Posteriors
Bag B	0.5	0.000467	0.0002335	0.85
Bag R	0.5	0.0000849	0.00004245	0.15
	1.0		Sum = 0.00027595	1.00

We can now be 85 % sure the chosen bag was bag B.

4.2 Revising opinion intuitively

If your prior opinion in Exercise 4–2 is 0.5–0.5, what posterior probabilities do you feel *intuitively* are justified in the light of that sample of 8 blues and 4 reds? Do not calculate, just give your intuitive assessment. Write it here: ....

I asked you to answer that question before you looked at the calculations because it is important to contrast the intuitive revision of opinion with the amount of revision specified by applying Bayes' theorem. Students sometimes ask why the personalist view of probability cannot be applied after an experiment is conducted. Why does the scientist not formulate and express his opinions *after* he has examined his data? Then there is no need to apply Bayes' theorem, and his opinions can be based solely on the data.

My reply is this: The scientist who formulates opinion after conducting an experiment and examining his data runs a much greater risk of holding inconsistent, even internally contradictory, opinions than the scientist who expresses opinion before the experiment and then uses Bayes' theorem to revise those opinions in the light of the data. Of course this argument depends on your accepting consistency of an individual's opinions as a desirable state of affairs in the conduct of scientific inquiry. Let me illustrate what consistency means by engaging in an imaginary dialogue with a scientist who has just completed Exercise 4–2, the bag and poker chip problem.

> **I:** You gave me an intuitive judgement of 0·65 as the probability you assign to the hypothesis that bag **B** is the chosen bag. Weren't you surprised to learn that the probability found by applying Bayes' theorem is 0·85?

Scientist: Yes, but it seems too high. My intuitive judgement feels more reasonable.

> **I:** Most people feel as you do. This sort of experiment has been done hundreds of times with all kinds of people and the general finding is that people don't get as sure as Bayes' theorem says they could.

Scientist: Maybe Bayes' theorem is wrong.

> **I:** Do you accept the third probability law?

Scientist: Of course. That is not controversial.

> **I:** But Bayes' theorem is a logical consequence of the probability laws.

Scientist: You mean if Bayes' theorem is wrong, then something is wrong with the probability laws.

> **I:** Right.

Scientist: O.K., I accept it. Maybe I applied Bayes' theorem incorrectly.

> **I:** Not even a relative frequentist would argue with this application. Your prior opinion was based on the flip of a coin, so we could give your 0·5–0·5 priors a relative frequency interpretation. The probabilities of getting a particular colour of chip from a particular bag, 0·7, 0·3, 0·4, and 0·6, can be given relative frequency interpretations, and you used a probability law, which you accept, to generate $p(D|H_1)$ and $p(D|H_2)$. So all the inputs to Bayes' theorem can be justified.

Scientist: I accept all that, but I still prefer my value of 0·65.

> **I:** Do you accept that
>
> **a** $p(H_1) = p(H_2) = 0.5$
> **b** $p(\text{red}|\text{bag B}) = 0.3$
> **c** $p(\text{blue}|\text{bag B}) = 0.7$
> **d** $p(\text{red}|\text{bag R}) = 0.4$
> **e** $p(\text{blue}|\text{bag R}) = 0.6$
> **f** the 'independence rule' is correct
> **g** Bayes' theorem is correct?

Scientist: Yes.

       I: Then there's an inconsistency in your thinking. The logical conse-
quence of believing those seven items is that $p(H_1|D) = 0.85$. If at
the same time you believe $p(H_1|D) = 0.65$, then you're being
inconsistent.

Scientist: I like to think of my scientific self as striving to be rational, and
inconsistency doesn't seem rational.

       I: It isn't. A clever person can take advantage of this kind of incon-
sistency by setting up a set of wagers which you would accept as fair
but which are bound to lose you money no matter how they turn
out.

Scientist: And I suppose I can avoid this kind of trap by sticking to the probability laws and their consequences.

       I: Right.

Scientist: O.K., I give up my 0.65. I'll accept the value of 0.85, but I don't
feel happy about it!

Well, I suppose if he had felt happy about it he would have given it in
the first place. Then Bayes' theorem and the other probability laws would be
superfluous. If we were all rational, consistent beings, intuitive revision of
opinion would always agree with that prescribed by Bayes' theorem, and the
entire edifice of statistical inference would be unnecessary. In some circumstances intuitive revision of opinion is 'conservative'; it does not change as
much as Bayesian revision. And sometimes people revise their opinions too
radically. A great deal of research on intuitive revision shows that when individual items of data do not tell us very much, we read too much into a collection
of such data, and when individual items do tell us something, in the sense that
they help to distinguish between the hypotheses, then we do not make enough
of several items of data taken together. It is not yet known why we react this
way to strings of experimental data, but it appears that some fundamental
limitations on human ability to process information are involved. Also, it is
possible that our real-world experience, which is mostly with biased samples
of data, leads us to be over-cautious with the less biased samples typical of
scientific experiments. Research on the problem continues (see Peterson and
Beach, 1967; Edwards, 1968; du Charme, 1970; and Slovic and Lichtenstein,
1971).

Another finding of this research is that there are large differences from
one person to the next in the amount of intuitive revision for the same problem.
The range of answers to Exercise 4–2 is quite large. This observation should
come as a disappointment to those people who believe in letting the data speak
for themselves. Apparently the same set of data speak more loudly to some
people than to others—one person's whisper is another person's shout. Add
to this the finding that the whisper from one set of data is sometimes heard
as a shout by most people while the shout from another set of data is heard
as a whisper, and you can see the psychological untenability of letting equivocal
data speak for themselves.

In a phrase, we need Bayesian statistical methods to bring consistency to
informal reasoning.

4.3 How sure is 'sure enough'?

If a scientist continues to collect data and he decides to keep on until his posterior opinions are fairly extreme, when does he stop? If he is considering just two hypotheses does he stop when his posteriors are 0·8–0·2, or 0·9–0·1, or 0·99–0·01, or when? How sure is 'sure enough'?

That question would be easier to answer if this were a book on decision theory. As I said in the first chapter, we would consider the worth of being correct and the costs of being wrong. Let me illustrate by expanding Exercise 4–2.

Suppose you have to guess which bag is the chosen one, but you are allowed to draw from the bag as many times as you wish. How many draws would you take? It is hard to give any guidelines because nothing much is at stake if you are right or wrong. But suppose you were to be paid £10 if you guessed correctly and fined £5 if you guessed the wrong bag. If you cannot afford to lose £5, I imagine you would draw quite a few times; the problem is a little clearer than before. Now, at least, you know you are going to take a great many looks, but, still, you would be hard-pressed to be very definite about the exact number of draws.

Let's add one more qualification. Suppose you are charged 50p per look Now how many draws would you make? Since you stand to win £10 at most, you certainly would not take more than 20 looks, and to prevent the loss of £5 you would take at least one look. So now we know you would take something more than one look but less than 20 looks. By knowing both the *payoff* of a correct or incorrect guess and the *cost* of getting information, we have become clearer about how many looks to take, and that, in turn, dictates how sure we can expect to be.

If I were to develop this example along the lines of decision theory an exact answer could be given to the original question, but I would have to know the *utilities* or subjective values the decision maker would assign to the various costs and payoffs (see Chapter 7 of Raiffa, 1968). A scientist usually has some notion of the cost of his experiment, but he rarely knows the payoffs because the technological, economic, or social consequences of his findings are usually vague and often unknown. And so the scientist faces a dilemma; at what point does he decide he is 'sure enough' to stop experimenting and to publish his findings?

For the most part, social scientists have not squarely faced this issue. Instead, they have relied on fairly arbitrary conventions whose Bayesian equivalent would be (roughly) to publish when you are 95, 99, or 99·9% sure. 'Hard-headed' journal editors often require 99%, while 'soft-headed' ones may allow 95% or less.

Conventions will undoubtedly arise in Bayesian statistics, too, for most scientists still feel unable or unwilling to tackle the 'costs and payoffs' problem, in spite of much talk about social responsibility in science. Hopefully, new technologies, such as those developed by Schlaifer (1969) primarily for the business community, for making decisions where uncertainty, costs and payoffs are all taken into account, will eventually be applied to problems of scientific inference. In this way, perhaps it will be possible to develop conventions that are more rational than the current ones.

In the meantime, you will be facing this problem yourself in your own experimental work. Aside from the obvious advice to take account informally of costs and payoffs, I can offer only a very crude suggestion: be at least 99% sure. This is a fairly conservative criterion which should *not* be taken as a rule. I am suggesting it mainly as a guideline for the newcomer to statistical inference, to be relaxed or tightened according to the situation. Once you have begun to get the feel for research, and have seen the tradeoffs between uncertainty and costs and payoffs in operations, you will be in a better position to make an informed judgement about the criterion.

For now, the main point to remember is that there usually is no clear-cut answer to the question 'How sure is 'sure enough'?' That, like probabilities themselves, is a matter for human judgement.

4.4   Effects of prior opinion

'We were certainly aware that inferences must make use of prior information and that decisions must also take account of utilities, but after some considerable thought and discussion round these points we came to the conclusion, rightly or wrongly, that it was so rarely possible to give sure numerical values to these entities that our line of approach must proceed otherwise.'

That was E. S. Pearson, a non-Bayesian, speaking (in Savage, 1962) about his and J. Neyman's views of statistics in the mid-1920's. Their subsequent contributions to statistical theory form an important school of statistical thinking, all in the relative frequency tradition. They developed statistical methods that allowed inferences to be drawn without regard to prior probabilities but which did require the exercise of careful personal judgement in other matters.

My point is that statisticians of all persuasions agree that human judgement is a necessary ingredient of statistical practice. They disagree on the places where judgement should operate and on the way in which it is incorporated into formal analysis. Bayesians believe that judgement in the form of prior opinion should be included as part of the formal, public procedures, while most non-Bayesians prefer to leave it as part of the informal thinking that leads to the selection of a particular statistical procedure or test.

Since judgement is important in statistical practice, it is necessary to examine the particular role of prior opinion in Bayesian procedures. That is what I do in this section, but bear in mind that more will be said in Part III.

Making prior opinion explicit

Why bother to make prior opinion explicit? Why can it not be left as an implicit part of statistical procedures? Bayesians argue that when prior opinion is not explicitly considered, the resulting inference may be misleading. (An example has recently been given by Pitz, 1968.)

Let me illustrate this by expanding the psychodiagnosis problem of Exercise 4–1. Suppose the rotating spiral is shown to the patient and he reports seeing the after-effect illusion. Since 85% of functionally ill patients see the illusion and only 40% of brain-damaged patients see it, common sense would suggest that the patient is more likely to be functionally ill than brain damaged. The clinician may wish to use this decision rule:

Decision Rule 1: Diagnose functional illness if the patient sees the illusion diagnose brain damage if he does not.

But the clinician has learned to be wary of his common sense so he calls in a statistician, a Bayesian one at that. The statistician examines the hospital's records and then advises the clinician *not* to administer the test but simply to diagnose every patient referred to him as functionally ill.

Decision Rule 2: Diagnose every patient as functionally ill.

The statistician claims that the clinician will be correct more often by following Decision Rule 2 than Decision Rule 1.

This surprising result can be explained by applying Bayes' theorem. The clinician's distrust of his common sense was well-founded, for he was tempted to make a diagnosis on the basis of the likelihoods, $p(I|F)$ and $p(\bar{I}|B)$, instead of using the posterior probabilities. And posterior probabilities depend not only on the likelihoods but also on the prior probabilities. The statistician consulted the records of the hospital to provide a basis for assessing the prior probabilities. He discovered that 90% of the patients at the hospital in the past have been functionally ill, and that only 10% were brain damaged. He used these figures as his prior probabilities.

Prior probabilities: $p(F) = 0 \cdot 9$ and $p(B) = 0 \cdot 1$

The likelihoods are based on the research of Page *et al.*

Likelihoods: $\begin{aligned} p(I|F) &= 0 \cdot 85 \text{ and so } p(\bar{I}|F) = 0 \cdot 15 \\ p(\bar{I}|B) &= 0 \cdot 6 \text{ and so } p(I|B) = 0 \cdot 4 \end{aligned}$

First, let us consider the case where the patient reports seeing the illusion. The steps are shown below.

Computation of Bayes' theorem for the diagnostic problem when the patient reports seeing the illusion.

Hypotheses	Priors	Likelihoods	Priors × Likelihoods	Posteriors
Functional illness	0·9	0·85	0·765	$\dfrac{0 \cdot 765}{0 \cdot 805} = 0 \cdot 95$
Brain damage	0·1	0·4	0·04	$\dfrac{0 \cdot 04}{0 \cdot 805} = 0 \cdot 05$

Sum = 0·805

This calculation shows that when the clinician starts with a prior probability of 0·9 that the patient is functionally ill, the patient seeing the illusion leads to posterior probabilities of 0·95–0·05. The clinician has become more certain that the patient is functionally ill. That result confirms intuition.

Next consider the case where the patient does not report seeing the illusion. Here are the appropriate calculations.

Computation of Bayes' theorem for the diagnostic problem when the patient does not see the illusion.

Hypotheses	Priors	Likelihoods	Priors × Likelihoods	Posteriors
Functional illness	0·9	0·15	0·135	$\dfrac{0\cdot135}{0\cdot195} = 0\cdot692$
Brain damage	0·1	0·6	0·06	$\dfrac{0\cdot06}{0\cdot195} = 0\cdot308$

Sum = 0·195

This time prior probabilities of 0·9–0·1 have changed to posteriors of 0·692–0·308. Notice that the posterior probabilities still favour the diagnosis 'functionally ill' even though the patient did not see the illusion! The clinician will favour the diagnosis of functional illness whether or not the patient sees the illusion.

This example illustrates two points. In the first place, a great deal of information is conveyed by the prior probabilities in the example. Whether or not the patient sees the spiral after-effect illusion tells the clinician something about the patient, but the information conveyed by the test results is far less than that shown in the prior probabilities. In this case the prior probabilities swamp out the information in the test, so that the posterior probabilities are determined more by the priors than by the likelihoods. The extra information given by the test does not change the prior probabilities enough to warrant giving the test.

The second point is that the intuitive approach, which favoured Decision Rule 1, contained an implicit assumption about the prior probabilities. Recall that when the prior probabilities were 0·5–0·5, the posterior probabilities were as follows:

Posterior probabilities if

Hypotheses	Patient sees illusion	Patient does not see illusion
Functional illness	0·68	0·2
Brain damage	0·32	0·8

This time the diagnosis favours functional illness if the patient sees the illusion and brain damage if he does not. When the prior probabilities are 0·5–0·5, the clinician will do better by adopting Decision Rule 1, the rule that initially seemed the more intuitive of the two. The intuitive approach to the problem obviously contained an implicit assumption about the prior probabilities. Adopting the first decision rule is justified only when the prior probabilities are not too extreme. If they are very extreme, so much information is contained in the priors that the modest amount of information yielded by the test is not worth collecting.

This result may make you feel uneasy if you are not very certain about the prior probabilities. In the example here the statistician examined the hospital records to aid him in determining the prior probabilities. But suppose no records were available to you, or the hospital had just opened. The first thing I would do is look up local or national government figures on the frequency of functional illness and brain damage. I would consult local psychiatrists and clinical psychologists to see if the particular locality in which the hospital is situated is likely to get patients in numbers differing from the national rates. Finally, I would use all this information to arrive at an intuitive judgement of the prior probabilities. After the hospital has been operating a few months, I could then look at the records to date and re-evaluate my priors if necessary.

This section began with the criticism that prior probabilities are often not known, and so must be ignored. I hope that this example clearly shows that prior probabilities *cannot* be ignored. A formal approach to this question of 'unknown' prior probabilities starts by establishing certain self-evident principles (axioms) of rationality, and then proves the existence of probabilities. (A good non-technical exposition of this method can be found in Lindley, 1971.) But proving that probabilities exist within some formal system is not the same thing as showing that they are psychologically meaningful, or that they can be assessed. If you prefer anecdotal evidence on this question, I can report that I have not yet met a scientist who did not have some prior information about an experiment he was planning. Some have given me vague prior opinions and others have been certain to the point of assigning zero prior probabilities to hypotheses that seemed to me plausible even if very unlikely. But all have had an opinion. If you prefer experimental evidence, there is a growing body of experiments done by psychologists who have explored the abilities of people to make probability judgements and then to revise these judgements intuitively. I know of not a single subject in these experiments who, when asked to assess a probability, said he could not. Some objected, saying that the probabilities they were giving were meaningless and that they would give entirely different numbers if asked the same question at a later date, but the results of these experiments do not confirm the verbal reports of the subjects. The probabilities they give are not at all random, and show orderly relationships to the variables the experimenter was manipulating in the experiment. Furthermore, when subjects are asked the same questions later on, they give very similar probabilities to their original ones, even though they have forgotten the original judgements. When probabilities are based solely on relative frequency data, then practice in estimating probabilities improves the accuracy of the estimates. When there is no 'objective' standard to serve as the basis for probability assessments, practice in assessing at least improves the consistency of the probabilities, that is, they are more likely to conform to the laws of probability. (In these experiments subjects were not told about the probability laws, nor, if they knew them anyway, were they allowed to check on the consistency of their assessments. The statistician can, of course, make these checks.)

The general conclusion I draw from this research is that for many people assessing probabilities is a difficult task, not because the probabilities are unknown or not there, but simply because people are not used to expressing their uncertainty in this form. Probabilities are the language of uncertainty, probability laws are the grammar of that language. It is my guess that if you had been taught that language and its grammar during your school years, you would have little difficulty now in assessing probabilities for uncertain events or hypotheses. The ability to assess probabilities can be developed, like learning a new language.

If you are interested in reading some of the experiments on probability assessment, you might look at the following. A review of some of the work can be found in Peterson and Beach (1967). Parts of the paper by Edwards (1968) are relevant to the question of assessing prior probabilities. Three experiments by Peterson, Ulehla, Miller, Bourne and Stilson (1965) demonstrate the internal consistency of probability assessments, as does a paper by Beach (1966). One analysis in a paper by Edwards, Phillips, Hays and Goodman (1968) shows that probability assessments made at different times about the same event are very nearly identical. Several papers in the December 1970 issue of *Acta Psychologica* are devoted to questions of assessing probabilities.

Although many of these experiments are concerned with posterior rather than prior probabilities, their results are applicable to assessing prior probabilities. The reason for this is that the only distinction between prior and posterior probabilities is the amount of data on which they are based, and many of the experimental results are valid quite independently of the amount of data presented or available to the subject.

You will recall that in the previous chapter I mentioned the difficulty people have in assessing probabilities for complex events and I suggested that this difficulty may be a source of reluctance to quantifying prior opinion. In this section I have tried to show that whatever the source of this reluctance, the issue of quantifying prior opinion must be faced. Since judgement is an unavoidable part of making an inference, it is better, Bayesians argue, to incorporate prior opinion into the formal mechanisms so that judgement can be publicly displayed rather than left as an implicit part of the process. Attempts to ignore prior opinion, we shall see in Chapter 6, can only be justified by exploiting certain characteristics of prior opinion itself.

Disagreements about prior probabilities

Suppose two scientists hold different prior opinions. What effect will Bayesian revision of opinion have on the difference? As I mentioned early in Chapter 2, the answer is that their posterior opinions will usually be in closer agreement than their priors. Now we can see this process in operation.

Consider again the psychodiagnostic problem. Suppose one clinical psychologist starts with priors of 0·5–0·5, while another psychologist starts with 0·9–0·1. The difference in their prior opinions is $0·9 - 0·5 = 0·4$. Now they test a patient who sees the illusion. Using the calculations made earlier, we see that the first psychologist should revise his opinion to 0·68–0·32, the other to 0·95–0·05. Now the difference is $0·95 - 0·68 = 0·27$. The original difference of 0·4 has been reduced to 0·27, so the two psychologists are now in closer agreement. Note that this does not always happen. You will see an example if you compute the posterior opinions of those two psychologists for the case where the patient *did not* see the illusion.

However, where more than one observation is possible we will find that as more and more data are collected, initially divergent opinion comes more into agreement. You can see this in the next exercise.

Exercise 4–3

Consider again the unscrupulous gambler. Before he gets a chance to see whether the coin he holds is the fair or the biased one, a rival player startles him by grabbing the coin from his hand and announcing to other players that the gambler has been using a biased coin. He says he is not positively sure, but he would be willing to bet on an 0·8–0·2 chance that the coin is unfair. Our gambler still thinks the chances are about equal. What posterior opinions would the men hold after the first five flips? After the second five flips? Assume the sequence of outcomes is as before, H, H, T, H, H, H, H, H, T, H, and that the probability of a single head for the biased coin is 0·6. Compare the two sets of posterior opinions.

Answers

For the first five flips, here are the gambler's probabilities:

Hypotheses	Priors	Likelihoods	Priors × Likelihoods	Posteriors
Fair	0·5	$(0·5)^5$	0·015625	0·38
Biased	0·5	$(0·6)^4(0·4)$	0·02592	0·62

Sum = 0·041545

And here they are for the player:

Hypotheses	Priors	Likelihoods	Priors × Likelihoods	Posteriors
Fair	0·2	$(0·5)^5$	0·00625	0·13
Biased	0·8	$(0·6)^4(0·4)$	0·041472	0·87

Sum = 0·047722

Their initial disagreement was $0·5 - 0·2 = 0·3$. Now it is $0·38 - 0·13 = 0·25$. Five flips resolves their disagreement a little. Now the next five flips.

For the gambler:

Hypotheses	Priors	Likelihoods	Priors × Likelihoods	Posteriors
Fair	0·38	$(0·5)^5$	0·011875	0·27
Biased	0·62	$(0·6)^4(0·4)$	0·032141	0·73

Sum = 0·044016

This is the same result we obtained before. Now for the player:

Hypotheses	Priors	Likelihoods	Priors × Likelihoods	Posteriors
Fair	0·13	$(0·5)^5$	0·004062	0·08
Biased	0·87	$(0·6)^4(0·4)$	0·045101	0·92

Sum = 0·049163

So, after 10 flips the disagreement is $0·27 - 0·08 = 0·19$. Once again their opinions have moved closer. If more data were collected, further revision of their opinions would bring them even closer, until with enough data their posterior opinions would be indistinguishable.

It is this feature of Bayes' theorem that saves Bayesian statistics from being wholly subjective. Initially subjective opinion is brought into contact with data through the operation of Bayes' theorem, and with enough data differing prior opinions are made to converge. This comes about because the prior opinions become less and less relevant to posterior opinion as more and more data are observed. Prior opinion is swamped out by the data, so that posterior opinion is controlled solely by the data. For a Bayesian, this is the only way in which data can 'speak for themselves'.

4.5   Sources of likelihoods

Next we turn our attention to the likelihoods in Bayes' theorem. They are probabilities, and so are given a personal, or subjective, interpretation just as prior probabilities. But there is a difference in practice. A scientist usually designs his experiments so that regardless of which data are actually observed there will be no disagreement over the value of $p(D|H)$. He does this by employing variations on the notion of a simple experiment that was introduced in Chapter 2. He ensures that the experiment is designed so that everyone agrees about the probability to be assigned to each elementary event, in much the same manner that the simple experiment of drawing a ball from an urn yields agreement about the probability of getting a particular colour of ball. Frequently, the scientist takes repeated measurements, so that $p(D|H)$ is based on applications of the probability laws for complex events. You saw instances of this when $p(D|H)$ was computed for several flips of the coin in the gambler's coin example, and again in the bags and poker chip example. In the latter example, the experiment was set up so that there would be agreement about the probabilities to be assigned to drawing a single chip of each colour from a given bag. It was then necessary to apply the probability laws to determine the probability of any particular sequence of draws from a given bag. **It is the public nature of $p(D|H)$ that characterizes all statistical methods.**

Not all experiments allow agreement about $p(D|H)$. That is why it is necessary to think about the statistical analysis of your data when you are designing an experiment. Failure to do this may result in an interesting experiment, but one in which agreement about $p(D|H)$ is difficult or impossible to obtain. Lack of agreement often comes about when the total number of elementary events cannot be precisely specified or when the number of elementary events in the event class is ill defined. One reason why scientists have come to rely in part on laboratory studies to further their science is that observations taken in natural settings often do not allow agreement about the likelihoods, while under controlled laboratory conditions agreement can be reached. However, for the social scientist this method of bringing about agreement on the likelihoods is bought at a cost: behaviour observed in a laboratory experiment may not be representative of behaviour in natural settings. For some studies, this may not matter, for example, many experiments on information processing in humans. Also, an unrepresentative experiment may be the best way to settle some theoretical issue.

The point is that social scientists are sometimes faced with a tradeoff between a well designed, but unrepresentative, experiment that allows agreement about the likelihoods on the one hand, and a representative experiment with no agreement about the likelihoods on the other. You will see in the literature all shades of experiments from one extreme to the other, and there are some ingenious investigators who have managed to capture both extremes in one experiment.

In this book we are concerned only with statistical techniques in which agreement about the likelihoods is possible. There are, however, a number of new Bayesian techniques being developed for situations where $p(D|H)$ is based wholly or in part on human judgement without reference to simple experiments. Applications can be found in business decision making (Schlaifer, 1969; Raiffa, 1968), medical diagnosis (Gustafson, Edwards, Phillips and Slack, 1970), weather forecasting (Murphy and Winkler, 1971), intelligence evaluation (Edwards, Phillips, Hays and Goodman, 1968), and many other areas (Slovic and Lichtenstein, 1971).

4.6 Other forms of Bayes' theorem

Odds-likelihood ratio form of Bayes' theorem

Another form of Bayes' theorem will be used at times in this book when we are considering just two hypotheses. It can be obtained by first writing the theorem in its general form for two hypotheses,

$$p(H_1|D) = \frac{p(H_1)\,p(D|H_1)}{p(D)}$$

$$p(H_2|D) = \frac{p(H_2)\,p(D|H_2)}{p(D)}$$

and then dividing the first expression by the second:

$$\frac{p(H_1|D)}{p(H_2|D)} = \frac{p(H_1)}{p(H_2)} \cdot \frac{p(D|H_1)}{p(D|H_2)}$$

More simply,

$$\Omega'' = \Omega' L$$

The Greek letter omega, Ω, stands for odds, either prior, Ω', or posterior Ω''. (I will frequently make use of a single or double prime to indicate prior or posterior.) Odds, as we saw in Chapter 2, represent a ratio of probabilities, and we will adopt the convention of letting prior odds refer to the ratio of prior probabilities, and posterior odds the ratio of posterior probabilities, both for the two-hypothesis case. The quantity represented by L is the likelihood ratio; it, too, is a ratio of probabilities, but since those probabilities are called likelihoods we naturally call their ratio the likelihood ratio.

Let us be clear about the difference between odds and the likelihood ratio. Odds tell us how much more likely one hypothesis is than the other, either before or after observing data, while the likelihood ratio indicates how much more likely the data are to have occurred given the truth of one hypothesis relative to the other.

In the example of the gambler who is not sure which of his two coins is the biased one, we started with prior probabilities of 0·5–0·5. The prior odds are given by the ratio of these probabilities, 0·5–0·5 or 1. Prior odds of 1 indicate that the two hypotheses are equally likely; the odds are 'even'. After observing one head, we noted that the two likelihoods were

$$p(D|H_1) = 0·6$$
$$p(D|H_2) = 0·5$$

This gives a likelihood ratio of 0·6/0·5 or 1·2. In words this means that heads is 1·2 times more likely to be observed from the biased coin than from the fair coin. Posterior odds are obtained by multiplying the likelihood ratio by the prior odds:

$$\Omega'' = 1 \times 1·2 = 1·2$$

The hypothesis 'biased coin' is 1·2 times more likely than the hypothesis 'fair coin'.

The second flip resulted in a heads, too. The odds prior to the second flip were 1·2, and the likelihood ratio for heads is 1·2. So, the new posterior odds are

$$\Omega'' = 1·2 \times 1·2 = 1·44$$

After two flips, both of which came up heads, we can be 1·44 times as certain that we flipped the biased coin rather than the fair one. The third flip came up tails. The odds prior to the third flip were 1·44, but what is the likelihood ratio for tails? We find this by computing the ratio of likelihoods, where this time D represents tails,

$$\frac{p(D|H_1)}{p(D|H_2)} = \frac{0·4}{0·5} = 0·8$$

Now we can compute the posterior odds:

$$\Omega'' = 1·44 \times 0·8 = 1·152$$

After two heads and a tails we are 1·152 times more certain of the coin being biased than of it being fair.

We could have done this more simply by applying the second corollary to the third law to give the result that the likelihood ratio for N data is equal to the product of the N individual likelihood ratios. Thus, if we have N items of data, then there are N likelihood ratios corresponding to those data. We can label the likelihood ratios in this way: $L_1, L_2, \ldots, L_i, \ldots, L_{N-1}, L_N$. The likelihood ratio for all these data is given by

$$L = L_1 \times L_2 \times \ldots \times L_i \times \ldots \times L_{N-1} \times L_N,$$

or more simply,

$$L = \prod L_i$$

(The capital Greek letter pi is used to indicate 'the product of'.) If this is substituted into the odds-likelihood ratio form of Bayes' theorem, we obtain Bayes' theorem for N independent observations:

$$\Omega'' = \Omega' \prod L_i$$

As applied to the gambler's problem, we note that every time a head comes up we use a likelihood ratio of 1·2 and that every time a tail comes up we use 0·8. For two heads and one tail, the posterior odds are

$$\Omega'' = 1 \times 1·2 \times 1·2 \times 0·8 = 1·152$$

Once you have computed posterior odds, you may wish to translate them into posterior probabilities. Use the probability-odds 'scale' (Fig. 2–6) or the equation in Section 2.3.

$$p(H_1|D) = \frac{1·152}{1+1·152} = 0·535$$

So, $p(H_2|D) = 1 - 0·535 = 0·465$

Exercise 4–4

The police are certain that either Louie 'The Loop' or Shelly 'The Shark' has printed the counterfeit £5 notes that have been turning up in the city. They have heard, though, that Louie has retired, so they think there is only a 0·2 chance that Louie is the current counterfeiter. Then they discover that the silver thread found in genuine notes is printed in light-grey ink on the bogus notes. From past experience, the police estimate that Louie is twice as likely as Shelly to use this method of simulating the silver thread. What is the posterior probability of Louie's guilt?

Answer

Here is an application of Bayes' theorem where human judgement, unaided by considering a simple experiment, is the source of a likelihood ratio. In these cases it is often easier to assess the likelihood ratio rather than the values of $p(D|H)$. Here the police would have found it difficult to assess the probabilities of each suspect using the ink method of simulating the thread, but they could assess how much more likely, in a ratio sense, one was than the other to use this method. This is a fundamental point for applications of Bayes' theorem that rely heavily on unaided human judgement for the likelihoods.

When we are given a likelihood ratio, we must use the odds-likelihood ratio form of Bayes' theorem.

Let H_1 = Louie is guilty
      H_2 = Shelly is guilty

We are told that

$$p(H_1) = 0·2$$

so we can determine

$$p(H_2) = 1 - 0·2 = 0·8$$

Therefore, the prior odds are

$$\Omega' = \frac{0·2}{0·8} = \frac{1}{4} = 0·25$$

The likelihood ratio we want is

$$\frac{p(D|H_1)}{p(D|H_2)}$$

that is, how much more likely is the datum to have been produced by Louie than Shelly (the direction of H_1 to H_2 must be the same in Ω', Ω'', and L). The police estimate that

$$L = 2$$

so the posterior odds are

$$\Omega'' = 0{\cdot}25 \times 2 = 0{\cdot}5$$

Converting that number to a probability gives the posterior probability of Louie's guilt:

$$p(H_1|D) = \frac{0{\cdot}5}{1 + 0{\cdot}5} = \frac{1}{3} = 0{\cdot}33$$

Exercise 4–5

Solve the gambler's problem using the odds-likelihood ratio form of Bayes' theorem. Recall that the sequence of flips resulted in H, H, T, H, H, H, H, H, T, H, and that $p(\text{head}|\text{biased coin}) = 0{\cdot}6$.

Answer

Let $H_1 = $ fair coin
$\phantom{\text{Let }} H_2 = $ biased coin

We wish to find

$$\frac{p(H_1|D)}{p(H_2|D)}$$

where D represents the 8 heads and 2 tails that resulted when the coin was flipped 10 times. For the outcome 'heads',

$$L = \frac{p(\text{heads}|\text{fair})}{p(\text{heads}|\text{biased})} = \frac{0{\cdot}5}{0{\cdot}6}$$

and for the outcome 'tails',

$$L = \frac{p(\text{tails}|\text{fair})}{p(\text{tails}|\text{biased})} = \frac{0{\cdot}5}{0{\cdot}4}$$

Thus, the likelihood ratio for all 10 flips is given by

$$\Pi L_i = \left(\frac{5}{6}\right)^8 \left(\frac{5}{4}\right)^2$$

so the posterior odds (assuming equal priors) are:

$$\Omega'' = 1 \times \left(\frac{5}{6}\right)^8 \left(\frac{5}{4}\right)^2 = \frac{9765625}{26873856}$$

$$= 0{\cdot}363$$

Converting to probabilities:

$$p(H_1|D) = \frac{0{\cdot}363}{1 + 0{\cdot}363} = 0{\cdot}27$$

and so

$$p(H_2|D) = 1 - 0{\cdot}27 = 0{\cdot}73$$

That is the same result we obtained before.

The odds-likelihood ratio form of Bayes' theorem can be summarized briefly in words:

Posterior odds = Prior odds × Likelihood ratio.

Notice that when we start with prior odds of 1, a likelihood ratio greater than one causes the posterior odds to favour H_1, while if the likelihood ratio is less than one, the posterior odds favour H_2. When the likelihood ratio equals one, no revision of opinion occurs. We can say, then, that the size of the likelihood ratio determines the amount of revision of opinion. Data are *informative* if they lead to a very large or very small likelihood ratio, they are *non-informative* if the likelihood ratio is near or equal to one.

Log-odds log-likelihood ratio form of Bayes' theorem*

You can see that the odds-likelihood ratio form of Bayes' theorem is relatively easy to apply, but the computations for very many items of data are tedious, so let us introduce one more simplification. Starting with Bayes' theorem in this form:

$$\Omega'' = \Omega' \prod L_i$$

we take logarithms of both sides:

$$\log \Omega'' = \log(\Omega' \prod L_i)$$
$$= \log \Omega' + \log (\prod L_i)$$

Remember that

$$\prod L_i = L_1 \times L_2 \times \ldots \times L_N$$

so that

$$\log (\prod L_i) = \log L_1 + \log L_2 + \ldots + \log L_N$$

or, more simply,

$$\log \prod L_i = \sum \log L_i$$

Substituting gives the log-odds log-likelihood ratio form of Bayes' theorem:

$$\log \Omega'' = \log \Omega' + \sum \log L_i$$

In words, this form of Bayes' theorem says that the log of posterior odds is obtained by taking the log of prior odds and adding to that for each item of data, the log of the likelihood ratio for each datum. Let us see how this applies to the gambler's problem.

First, consider the log of prior odds. That is the log of 1, which is zero. Next consider the log-likelihood ratio for each of the ten flips. For one flip:

	L	$\log_{10} L$
Heads	5/6	−0·0792
Tails	5/4	0·0969

---

* This section can be omitted. However, the material will be useful in understanding some of the technical points of Chapter 14.

Now we can get the log posterior odds, for ten flips:

$$\log \Omega'' = 0 + 8(-0.0792) + 2(0.0969)$$

$$= -0.4398$$

Taking antilogarithms gives $\Omega'' = 0.363$, the same value as before.

The advantage of this form of Bayes' theorem is that it makes evidence additive. Imagine a vertical stick with decimal markings (any spacing will do) whose middle is zero. That middle position represents the log of odds of 1, so when we are at zero on the stick H_1 is just as likely as H_2. But if we move up, H_1 is favoured, while below 0, H_2 is favoured.

In the gambler's example we start at 0. After the first flip, heads, we move down 0.0792 units, favouring H_2 (biased coin). Now another flip, the outcome is heads, so we move down another 0.0792 units. The third flip is tails so we move *up* 0.0969 units, and so on, for all 10 flips. We will end up 0.4398 units below zero. Each head moved us a fixed distance down, each tails moved us a fixed distance up. That is what is meant by saying evidence is additive under the log-odds log-likelihood ratio form of Bayes' theorem. Perhaps now it will be obvious why the probability-odds scale of Fig. 2–6 has the odds calibrated on a logarithmic scale. I leave it to the reader to determine how the probability-odds scale should be extended below 1 : 1, and how the resulting device can be used for two-hypothesis problems directly without having to look up logarithms.

4.7   Hypothesis testing

I would like to conclude this chapter with some general comments on 'hypothesis testing', a favourite phrase of statisticians, who mean by it that one hypothesis, or more, about some issue has been proposed, data have been collected, and a statistical inference concerning the truth of the hypothesis is carried out. That is the process described in this chapter, and from the Bayesian viewpoint several important generalizations can be drawn.

Specifying the hypotheses

Suppose that after 12 poker chips are drawn from one of the bags in Exercise 4–2, you are told that the original statement of the problem was in error, that the sample of 8 blues and 4 reds could have come from any one of *three*, not two bags. The new bag to be considered contains 50 blue and 50 red chips, so now the possibilities look like this:

bag B   bag ?   bag R

Assuming equal prior probabilities, what are the posterior probabilities?

Here is the solution:

Hypotheses	Priors	Likelihoods	Priors × Likelihoods	Posteriors
Bag B	1/3	0·000467	0·000156	0·58
Bag ?	1/3	0·000244	0·000081	0·31
Bag R	1/3	0·000085	0·000028	0·11
		Sum =	0·000265	1·00

When we solved this problem for just bag B and bag R, we obtained these posterior probabilities:

$$p(\text{Bag B}|\text{D}) = 0·85$$

$$p(\text{Bag R}|\text{D}) = 0·15$$

Including that third bag altered the posteriors even though the data were the same. **The posterior probability of a hypothesis depends not only on that hypothesis and the data but also on the other hypotheses.** That is another way of saying that truth is relative—relative to the other possibilities you are considering. In the two-bag problem, bag B looked like a good bet in the light of the data, but only relative to bag R, for bag B's attractiveness is diminished by introducing a new contender, bag?. A posterior probability is a relative statement, not an absolute one. It does not make sense to talk of *the* probability of a hypothesis being true without considering the alternatives. (There is one important exception to this that will be mentioned shortly.)

You can see, then, that Bayes' theorem can do no more than tell you, in the light of the data, which of the hypotheses you have listed is the most likely. If, as a scientist, you are testing several alternative theories, all of which are absurdly implausible, Bayesian statistics will only help you to identify the least implausible one. If you are really drawing poker chips from a bag whose composition is 90–10, and you only consider 70–30, 50–50, and 40–60 bags in your computations, then, with enough data, Bayes' theorem will eventually give the highest posterior probability to the 70–30 bag, the one nearest the truth. In fact, as large amounts of data are collected the posterior probability of the 70–30 bag will approach one. **It is a general characteristic of Bayesian methods that as the amount of data approaches infinity, the posterior probabilities usually approach zero and one.** This is true whether or not the correct hypothesis is included in the set of hypotheses considered.

Statistics will not help you to invent hypotheses, although the slowness with which the Bayesian posterior probabilities approach zero and one in some particular case may suggest to you that you should look for a different hypothesis. Hypotheses are invented by the scientist, and may be based on theory, on hunches, on flashes of insight, or be suggested by other data. Once you have invented a new hypothesis, you must go back to your data and re-calculate the posterior probabilities for the set of hypotheses that now includes the new one. If the new hypothesis was suggested by the data, then you should go out and collect new data to guard against the possibility that your new hypothesis fits only the original data from which it was derived.

The history of science is filled with examples which, to a Bayesian, appear to be instances in which scientists collected so much data that eventually they came to believe one particular theory because that theory was the most plausible of all those suggested. Then along comes a new scientist with a new theory that is even more plausible, in the light of the data, than the others. A high posterior probability associated with a hypothesis does not guarantee the truth of that hypothesis, it only indicates that the hypothesis is the most likely among those you have considered. Philosophers of science and thinking scientists long ago realized that truth is unattainable, that the best scientists can do in their search for truth is reach agreement with one another. What the layman recognizes as a scientific truth is actually only something about which scientists are in agreement or near agreement. Today's truth may be discarded by the scientists of tomorrow.

When likelihoods are zero or one

Suppose a theory predicts that a certain datum (or collection of data) is sure to be observed, then an experiment is performed and the datum is observed. What can be said about the truth of the theory?

Let us consider the truth of the theory as an hypothesis, H, and let us label the datum, D. To simplify the argument, consider that the only other possible hypothesis is that the theory is not true, $\bar{H}$ ('not H'). Now we wish to find the posterior odds favouring the truth of the theory:

$$\Omega'' = \frac{p(H|D)}{p(\bar{H}|D)}$$

We can find this using Bayes' theorem. Assume that D has been observed:

$$\Omega'' = \frac{p(H)}{(p\bar{H})} \times \frac{p(D|H)}{p(D|\bar{H})}$$

All we know is that if the theory is true, D is sure to be observed, that is,

$$p(D|H) = 1$$

This gives

$$\Omega'' = \frac{p(H)}{p(\bar{H})} \times \frac{1}{p(D|\bar{H})}$$

As long as $p(D|\bar{H})$ is not zero, then the posterior odds are some finite number, so the posterior probability of the theory being correct is less than one. However, you can see that the likelihood ratio must be equal to or greater than 1, since $p(D|\bar{H})$ has to be 1 or less. Thus, the posterior odds will always be at least as big as the prior odds. In other words, if D occurs you will usually become more sure of H, and never less sure. Observing D lends support to the theory, but the degree of support depends entirely on the value of $p(D|\bar{H})$. If $p(D|\bar{H})$ is close to 1, then observing D may lend only marginal support to the theory.

In general, **if a theory predicts that a datum is sure to be observed, and then the datum is observed in an experiment, the only inference we can draw is that the experiment supports the theory, but we cannot say anything about the degree of support until alternative theories are also considered.**

Violations of this principle abound in social science research. An investigator says his theory predicts so-and-so, he performs an experiment and observes so-and-so, and concludes that the experiment supports his theory. If that is all he says, he is not wrong, but the words he uses may well imply that the experiment lent a considerable *degree* of support for the theory, and that is saying too much. Strictly speaking, all one can say in this situation is that if D is observed, one is at least no less sure of the truth of the theory than before the experiment was performed. To claim or imply an increase in the degree of support for the theory is simply not justified without also considering an alternative theory.

Suppose, however, that the datum had *not* been observed. Then what inference is justified? If the probability of observing the datum is 1, given the truth of the theory, then failure of the datum to occur must have probability zero (provided, of course, that the scientist arranges his experiment so it could occur if the theory were false), that is

$$p(\bar{D}|H) = 0$$

Writing Bayes' theorem for the non-occurrence of D:

$$\Omega'' = \frac{p(H)}{p(\bar{H})} \times \frac{0}{p(\bar{D}|\bar{H})} = 0$$

Odds of zero mean that the posterior probability of H is zero, that is,

$$p(\bar{H}|\bar{D}) = 0$$

Thus, failure to observe D when $p(D|H) = 1$ results in complete disproof of the theory! If you look carefully at Bayes' theorem you will see that a posterior probability of zero remains at zero no matter what the nature and number of other hypotheses. For example, if I add a third bag to the two-bag problem of Exercise 4–2 which consists of all red chips, and then I select one of the bags at random and discover that the first chip drawn is blue, I have completely rejected the possibility that I am drawing from the all red bag. And this conclusion is true no matter how many other bags I might wish to consider.

But what of the alternative hypothesis, $\bar{H}$? Since $p(H|\bar{D}) = 0$, it follows that

$$p(\bar{H}|\bar{D}) = 1$$

Has the alternative theory been proved? The answer is no, for the reasons given at the beginning of this section. The alternative theory may be wrong, but relative to H it is a winner. Having rejected H, Bayes' theorem has no other place to put all its posterior probability other than on $\bar{H}$, and it does so irrespective of the truth of $\bar{H}$.

The general lesson to be drawn from this discussion is that **theories can only be disproven with certainty, they can never be proven with certainty.** The history of science is littered with discarded theories, while today's theories are only relatively more true than those that have been put aside. The 'definitive experiment', one which seeks for evermore to establish the truth of some theory, is as elusive as the Holy Grail. A definitive experiment can only reject a theory, so that a theory which is stated in such a way that no data can disprove it, would appear to be unscientific for it can neither be proven nor disproven. This is a view most particularly identified with that philosophical school of thought known as logical positivism.

From a Bayesian viewpoint, the conclusion is not altogether satisfactory. If you believe a theory must be capable of complete disproof, then you are saying that there must exist some datum for which $p(D|H) = 0$. If this is observed, then $p(H|D) = 0$ and the theory is disproven. However, it is entirely possible that there is no such datum. I can envisage, at least theoretically, a theory for which $p(D|H) > 0$ for all possible data. Yet as long as the *likelihood ratios* for various data are not all 1, then the posterior odds will not be 1 and so will favour one hypothesis over the other. Much of social science research proceeds on this basis, rather than by falsification of theories. Both approaches are justified from a Bayesian viewpoint.

4.8 Summary

Bayes' theorem prescribes the amount of revision of opinion that should occur in the light of new information:

$$p(H|D) = \frac{p(H) \times p(D|H)}{p(D)}$$

It is a non-controversial consequence of the third probability law, and is sometimes called the 'theorem of inverse probability'. It can be applied sequentially, the posterior probability from the first stage of experimental work serving as the prior probability for the next stage.

Intuitive revision of opinion is liable to lead to violations of the probability laws, particularly Bayes' theorem, so the procedures of this book can be seen as guides to systematic, consistent revision of opinion.

Without taking a decision-theoretic approach, which would require that we consider the utilities of the outcomes of our decisions and the cost of gathering information, no precise answer can be given to the question of how extreme posterior probabilities should be before reporting experimental results. Requiring a posterior probability of at least 0·99 is a workable, conservative guideline, that should not be taken as a rule.

Prior opinion cannot be avoided in making a statistical inference. Bayesians feel that judgement in the form of prior opinion should be formally incorporated in the statistical procedures, thus making all aspects of the resulting inference 'public'. Non-Bayesians prefer to leave judgement as a part of the informal procedures leading up to a statistical test. Assessing prior probabilities is a matter of experience, and is a skill that can be developed. Disagreements about prior probabilities can be resolved by collecting data and applying Bayes' theorem. With enough data initial disagreement between assessors will become negligible.

Likelihoods, values of $p(D|H)$, are also personal probabilities, but in most statistical applications they are determined by applying the probability laws to judgements about event classes over which there is agreement. New Bayesian techniques are being developed for cases where disagreement over $p(D|H)$ may arise.

A convenient form of Bayes' theorem is the odds-likelihood ratio version:

$$\Omega'' = \Omega' L$$

Posterior odds = prior odds × likelihood ratio

The nearer the likelihood ratio is to 1, the less opinion is revised by the data. The log-odds log-likelihood ratio form of Bayes' theorem is another convenient form, one in which data become additive.

Applying Bayes' theorem does not allow us to discover the 'true' hypothesis; it only tells us which hypothesis is relatively more plausible than the rest. As large amounts of data are collected, one hypothesis is bound to be favoured, even if it is incorrect. When likelihoods are zero or one, it is only possible to disprove a hypothesis. There is no condition in which an hypothesis can be 'proven'.

Problems

4-1 Historians agree that there is about 1 chance in 4 that Jones wrote the 'Q-document,' and 3 chances in 4 that Smith wrote it. In a new analysis of the 10,000-word document, the word 'that' is found to occur 27 times. From the known writings of Smith and Jones, experts assess a probability of 0·0084 that this frequency of 'that' would be observed if Jones were the author, while the probability for Smith would be 0·0004. In light of this new evidence, what now is the probability that Jones is the author? (A similar approach has been used to determine the authorship of some of *The Federalist* papers; see Mosteller and Wallace, 1964.)

4-2 Suppose that the crystals in one brand of breathalyzer have a 0·90 chance of changing colour if the person being tested has high alcohol content in his blood, 0·60 chance if alcohol content is moderate, and 0·10 chance if alcohol content is zero or low. At 11.15 p.m. on a Saturday night, a police officer sees a car weaving in and out of traffic. He stops the car, and the driver sounds and appears intoxicated. The officer figures the chance of high alcohol content in the bloodstream is 0·70, of moderate content about 0·20, and of low content about 0·10. A breathalyzer test is positive—the crystals change colour. What should the police officer's opinions be now? Suppose the crystals hadn't changed colour; what then should the officer's opinions be?

4-3 The California Psychological Inventory is a test that measures 18 aspects of personality. Some of the 18 scores can be combined to yield an index of 'social maturity' that distinguishes delinquents from non-delinquents (see Gough, 1966). In America, about 30% of a sample of 409 delinquents scored above 44 on the social maturity index, while approximately 94% of a sample of 2,483 non-delinquents scored above 44. 'Non-delinquents' consisted of high school students, college and university students, and employed adults; they were all men drawn from the research files of the CPI, selected 'to represent average or above-average levels of social maturity.' 'Delinquents' consisted of institutionalized youths and adult prison inmates. Assume that there is about 1 chance in 5 that a boy of 14 will someday be convicted of an indictable offence. What is the probability that a boy of 14 selected at random in America will someday be convicted if the youth

a scores above 44 on the social maturity index?
b scores at or below 44?

Discuss the problems in applying Bayes' theorem that this example raises.

4-4   Two scientists, Jones and Smith, design an experiment to test two hypotheses, H_1 and H_2. Jones assigns a prior probability of 0.8 to H_1, while Smith thinks that H_2 is twice as likely to be true as H_1. Data are collected and the likelihoods computed. They are $p(D|H_1) = 0.0084$ and $p(D|H_2) = 0.0008$. Show that the posterior opinions of the scientists are closer together than the prior opinions.

4-5   For what range of prior probabilities would you use Decision Rule 1 rather than Decision Rule 2 as regards the psychodiagnosis problem of Exercise 4-1? (*Hint:* Find the priors that would make you indifferent between the two rules.)

4-6   A statistician using Bayes' theorem for a particular problem involving just two mutually exclusive hypotheses and three items of data arrives at posterior odds of 24 to 1; he reports this but neglects to give his prior probabilities. However, he does give his likelihood ratios. They were 8, 1/3, and 18. Consider the hypothesis that was more likely *after* observing the data; what was the statistician's prior probability for this hypothesis?

4-7   The following problem illustrates the care that must be taken in applying Bayes' theorem.

What is the incidence of heroin taking among cannabis takers? Nicholas Wade (in *New Society*, 23 January 1969, 117–118) points out that the figure is difficult to obtain, but that in Britain fairly accurate figures exist on the incidence of cannabis taking among heroin takers, so it might be possible to apply Bayes' theorem to get the inverse probability. He states that the incidence of cannabis taking among heroin takers was around 90 per 100 people, that about 5 people per 100,000 of the population were heroin users, and that between 30 and 60 per 100,000 were cannabis takers. By applying Bayes' theorem he concludes that '. . . between 7·5 and 15 percent, in other words that of those who take cannabis, between 7 to 15 of every 100 are, or will be, takers of heroin'. Criticize and discuss his approach and conclusions.

4-8   An archaeologist in the Yucatan peninsula of Mexico is unsure whether a piece of pottery he has just found belongs to the Mayan period or to the pre-Mayan period. Judging by the site of his dig he feels about 60% sure that the piece is pre-Mayan. Then he notices a small drawing of a sort that shows up twice as often on Mayan as on pre-Mayan pottery. On-the-spot chemical analysis of the piece reveals that its composition is of materials which were more commonly used in the pre-Mayan period. He judges that such materials were found about 4 times more frequently in pre-Mayan than Mayan pottery. What are his posterior probabilities for the two hypotheses?

5 · Functions and their graphs

So far the events and hypotheses we have been talking about are discreet; the coin comes up either heads or tails, the die shows one of six sides, the coin is either biased or fair, the patient is either functionally ill or brain damaged. Guesses about unknown quantities are often formulated in this 'either-or' fashion not so much because the world naturally falls into such convenient categories, but rather because traditional statistics are easiest to apply when only one hypothesis and an alternative are tested. For example, while it is often convenient to think of a coin as either biased or fair, we might instead inquire into the degree of bias of the coin. The degree of bias could be represented by the long-run proportion of heads to total flips, so that a proportion of 0·5 would stand for 'no bias'. Other hypotheses could then be represented by 0·501, 0·502, 0·5000007, 0·62, 0·7, 0·93, or any of the proportions between 0 and 1. One of these numbers must represent the 'true' bias of the coin, and since there are an infinite number of proportions between 0 and 1, there are an infinite number of hypotheses to be considered.

To take another example, suppose we want to know the average I.Q., as measured by some test, of university students in England. If we could administer I.Q. tests to all students we could determine the average I.Q. easily, but such a project is too costly and time-consuming to be practicable, so we must content ourselves with a random sample of students and infer the average I.Q. of *all* students from the average I.Q. of our sample. How this is to be done is the subject of Chapter 11; for now consider what the hypotheses are—all possible values of I.Q. In theory all possible values from zero to infinity could be considered, but in practice the range is limited to, say, 50 to 200. Obviously neither 50 nor 200 is very likely to be the average I.Q. of students in English universities, or anywhere else, for that matter, but those values adequately, if over-cautiously delimit the range of possible values. If I.Q. measurements could be made with infinitesimal precision, then every number between 50 and 200 could represent the 'true' average I.Q. And if each number contains an infinite number of decimal places, then there are an infinite number of possible 'true' I.Q.'s: 93·3568 or 129·4683215 or 167·426733 etc. Even though in practice I.Q. is determined to at most three significant figures, we can still consider that there are an infinite number of possibilities between 50 and 200. The mathematics are easier that way.

That statement may come as a surprise if you were contemplating extending the methods developed in the previous chapter to the case of an infinite number of hypotheses. To an infinite number of hypotheses you would have to assign as many prior probabilities. And that would be only the first step. Fortunately, those mathematics known as 'the integral calculus' can be applied to reduce this Herculean task to manageable proportions. I promised, however, that this book would not introduce mathematics as advanced as the calculus, so from now on I will present only the *results* of applying the calculus to problems involving a theoretically infinite number of hypotheses. You will have to understand only what goes into the problem and the results, not how the results were obtained. For example, in the case of the unknown average I.Q., you will have to know how to characterize the prior probabilities, how to summarize the data, and how the posterior probabilities are determined from applying Bayes' theorem, but you will not actually have to compute it yourself. You will have to do some calculations but they are nothing more than adding, subtracting, multiplying, and dividing.

When many guesses about a quantity are possible and can be as close together as one wants, then the quantity is called *continuous*. From now on this book will consider only continuous hypotheses, for they are by far the most commonly found in social science research. You will often find discrete hypotheses in the literature, but if you look closely you will frequently find that a continuous case has been made artificially discrete. For example, I could have asked the question, 'Is the average I.Q. of university students in English universities above 120 or below 120?' The continuous character of the hypotheses has been made discrete; now only two hypotheses are to be considered, above 120 and below 120. However, the continuous character of the problem is usually preserved right up to the last step and then the discrete hypotheses are derived from the continuous ones to make the results more understandable or more useful.

But before we go on to introduce Bayesian ideas for continuous hypotheses, the mathematical notion of a function must first be introduced. Once you understand what a function is and know how to graph one, then we can go on, in the next chapter, to describing prior probabilities for continuous hypotheses. If you find that you already know the material in this chapter, skim or skip it, and go on to Chapter 6.

The purposes of this chapter are to enable you to understand

> what a function is;
> how functions can be expressed;
> how functions can be used.

In addition, you should be able to

> graph a function from its mathematical expression;
> recognize and interpret linear functions;
> use functions to transform one variable into another.

5.1   Functions

Loosely speaking, a function is a pairing of one thing with another. Consider three names, Atlantic, Mediterranean, and Hudson, and also three descriptions of watery areas, sea, bay and ocean. You have learned the function, that is, the pairing: Atlantic Ocean, Mediterranean Sea, and Hudson Bay. Other combinations are possible, of course, but common usage does not allow us to talk of, say, the Atlantic Bay or the Mediterranean Ocean. This section is a brief introduction to functions.

Variables and constants

A variable is a symbol for a quantity that can take on any of a range of values in a problem. Letters at the end of the alphabet are usually used for variables, like x or y. The variable can stand for anything we like, such as the average I.Q. of students at British universities, or the number of heads in ten flips of a fair coin, or the proportion of students in a class who are blond. If, for a given problem, we know the value of some quantity, we treat it as a constant. **A constant is a quantity that takes on only one value in a problem.** Any of the quantities that were given as examples of variables could be treated as constants if they keep the same value throughout a problem. You have to decide which quantities are to be treated as variables and which as constants by understanding the logic of the problem at hand. There are simply no rules that will help you to decide, except that a few 'universal' constants stay the same from problem to problem. Examples are the speed of light, the charge on an electron, the atomic weight of hydrogen, and other physical constants, $\pi = 3 \cdot 14159 \ldots$, or $e = 2 \cdot 7182 \ldots$. Letters at the beginning of the alphabet are reserved for constants. The distinction between variables and constants is purely arbitrary, except for the well established constants such as those just mentioned. You will only learn through experience when quantities are to be treated as variables and when as constants.

Relations, rules, and laws

When two variables are seen to go together in some way, we say a *relation* exists between them. Brain damage 'goes with' impairment of certain physical functioning, economic growth is partly influenced by the availability of money, delinquency is related to socio-economic status. One of the main concerns of scientists is to find relations between variables. Social scientists in particular spend much of their time just trying to find out which variables are related to which other variables. A new science has to spend a great deal of time discovering which variables are important. The older sciences are more secure in their knowledge of which variables are important and spend a greater proportion of their time formulating the *rules* that govern the relationships. **A rule specifies how variables are related.** Here is a rule: An open body of water is an ocean, a body of water closed by land with perhaps a small opening to an ocean is called a sea, and a partially closed body of water opening on to an ocean is a bay. That rule allows one to connect Atlantic with ocean, Mediterranean with sea and Hudson with bay. The advantage of knowing the rule is that new cases other than the ones investigated can be accommodated. Once the rule relating delinquency and socio-economic status is known, then by measuring the socio-economic status of a community never before studied, the rate of delinquency in that community can be predicted. When the rule can be specified mathematically, the relation is called a *law*. The relationship between force, mass and acceleration is given by the law

$$F = ma$$

Force equals mass times acceleration. Given any two of the quantities, this law allows us to determine the third. As another example, the probability laws discussed in Chapter 3 specify the relationships between the probabilities of individual events and the probabilities of combinations of those events.

Independent and dependent variables

In his search for relations between variables, the scientist often performs experiments in which he systematically changes the value of one variable, the variable that he is controlling, and measures the values of the other variable. The physicist may systematically vary force and mass in an experiment and see what accelerations result. The variables under the control of the experimenter are called *independent variables*; here 'independent' suggests that the value of the variable can be anything within the range of possibilities, the choice is up to the experimenter. The other variable, whose value *depends on* the value of the independent variable and the law relating the two, is called the *dependent variable*. Labelling variables as independent or dependent is simply a convention that is popular among scientists; which variable gets which label is usually dictated by the logic of the experiment.

Functions and their rules

A function is a pairing of exactly one variable with another. More specifically, it is a pairing of just one dependent variable with one independent variable. We can express this abstractly by saying that y is a function of x, or,

$$y = \mathrm{f}(x)$$

Notice that the right side of that equation is *not* read 'f times x' but rather 'function of x', so the whole equation is read 'y equals a function of x'. That is the literal translation. The colloquial expression is 'y is a function of x'. It is important to note that when the value of x is given, the function allows only one value of y to follow. If we consider the name of the body of water to be the independent variable, then the dependent variable can take on only one value; with 'Atlantic', the only permissible element of the pair is 'ocean'. To take another example, if we keep the force constant in an experiment, then acceleration is a function of mass, and for each value of mass there will be one and only one resulting value of acceleration. In some books what I have defined as a function is called a 'single-valued function'. Relations where more than one value of the dependent variable may be associated with one value of the independent variable are called 'multiple-valued functions'. An example of the latter can be seen by taking the type of body of water as the independent variable. Then with 'ocean', for example, we can associate 'Atlantic', 'Pacific', 'Indian', and others. The name of the body of water is a multiple-valued function of the type of body of water, while the type is a single-valued function of name. In this book we will deal only with single-valued functions, so I will call them just 'functions'.

Nothing has so far been said about causality. The reason for this is that relations and functions do not imply anything, necessarily, about causation. A scientist may be able to specify the function relating two variables, but the function itself says nothing about whether or not one variable was caused by the other. **A function is nothing more than a listing of pairs.** It is a list of what goes with what. Even if two things go together perfectly, we cannot necessarily say that one caused the other. My bedside clock always agrees with my wristwatch, but one surely does not cause the other. The statistician can only say that cigarette smoking and cancer are related, he cannot say that one causes the other. The chain of causation can only be established by careful study of the etiology of lung cancer. Remember that statistics is concerned with discovering relations between things, not with the question of causation. An independent variable becomes thought more to be a cause as intervening and surrounding lawful knowledge is obtained.

Sometimes we can save ourselves the trouble of having to list all the pairs in specifying a function for we can rely on a rule that tells us how the pairs can be generated. Such a rule is called a *function rule*. An example is

$$y = 3x^2 - 8$$

If we select a value of x, the value of y can be computed. The rule allows the pairs to be computed rather than listed. Function rules play a very important role in this book for they allow us to get around the problem mentioned earlier of having to make infinitely long lists pairing hypotheses with their prior probabilities. The problem can be solved by specifying a rule that will allow any hypothesis to be paired with a probability. In this way the prior probabilities of hypotheses can be specified with a function rule rather than with an enormously long list. Before we talk of probability functions it is important to understand a few simpler functions. Linear functions will be introduced first.

5.2   Linear functions

A linear function is specified by the function rule

$$y = a + bx$$

How do we arrive at the x–y pairs by using this rule? First, a value for x must be specified—any value will do, but if you are particularly interested in some limited range of values you might start with the lowest value. Next, the rule tells you to multiply that value of x by the constant b. Finally, to that product add the value of a, another constant. You can see that x is the independent variable, a and b are constants, and y is the dependent variable. To obtain a value of y you must multiply x by b and then add a.

Exercise 5–1

Which of the following function rules are linear?

a	$y = 3 + 2x$	e	$y = x/6$
b	$y = 5x$	f	$y = 4 + 2x^2$
c	$y = 2/7 + (7/8)x$	g	$y = \dfrac{\pi x}{2} - 3$
d	$y = -4\cdot3 - 6\cdot2x$	h	$z = \dfrac{x - \mu}{\sigma}$ where μ and σ are constants

Answers

a $y = 3 + 2x$. If we let $3 = a$ and $2 = b$, we can rewrite this equation by substituting the letters for the numbers. The result is $y = a + bx$, the equation for a linear function.

b $y = 5x$. This may be clearer if we add a zero to the right side of the equation, making it $y = 0 + 5x$. Then, let $0 = a$, $5 = b$, substitute, and we get $y = a + bx$, a linear function. Sometimes a may equal zero.

c $y = 2/7 + (7/8)x$. There is no reason why a and b cannot be fractions, so let $2/7 = a$ and $7/8 = b$, and we can see that the equation is linear.

d $y = -4·3 - 6·2x$. a and b can be negative. Let $a = -4·3$ and $b = -6·2$. The equation is linear.

e $y = x/6$. When this is rewritten as $y = 0 + (1/6)x$ you can see that the equation is that of a linear function.

f $y = 4 + 2x^2$. This rule says, 'take x, square it, multiply by 2 and add 4'. In the rule for linear functions there is nothing about squaring x, so that equation is *not* that of a linear function.

g $y = \dfrac{\pi x}{2} - 3$. Let us rewrite this slightly: $y = -3 + \dfrac{\pi}{2}x$.

We can let $-3 = a$, and, since $\pi/2$ is a constant, let $\pi/2 = b$. Then $y = a + bx$, a linear function.

h $z = (x - \mu)/\sigma$. (Do not let the switch from y to z as the dependent variable mislead you, for $z = a + bx$ is just as much a linear function as when y is used.) Let us rearrange the right side of this equation a little so that we can see more clearly whether or not this is a linear function.

$$z = \frac{x - \mu}{\sigma}$$

$$= \frac{x}{\sigma} - \frac{\mu}{\sigma}$$

$$= -\frac{\mu}{\sigma} + \frac{1}{\sigma}x$$

Since μ and σ are both constants, μ/σ must be a constant. Let $-\mu/\sigma = a$. Both 1 and σ are constants, so $1/\sigma$ must be a constant. Let $1/\sigma = b$. Substitute, and we get

$$z = a + bx$$

So this equation is a linear function. You will see this particular linear function again in Chapter 9.

Graphing functions

We have mentioned two ways of specifying functions, listing the pairs or writing the function rule. There is a third way that is frequently convenient, drawing a graph. To do this you must first construct two axes at right angles to one another. The horizontal axis is called the 'x-axis' and is marked off in values of x that lie within the range of interest. The vertical axis is the 'y-axis' and is marked off with values of y. Next you pick some value of x that lies within the range of interest and use the function rule to compute the corresponding value of y. Now imagine that you have drawn a vertical line that intersects the x-axis at the value of x you just chose, and that you have drawn a horizontal line intersecting the y-axis at the value of y you just computed. Place a dot at the point where the two lines intersect one another. That dot represents the x–y pair whose values you just determined. Continue with this procedure for a few more pairs of values and then connect the dots.

Exercise 5–2

Graph the function

$$y = 1 + 2x$$

to cover the range of values of x from 0 to 5.

The first step is to construct the axes of the graph. You know that the x-axis must be marked off in units from 0 to 5. To find out the range of values to be marked off on the y-axis, solve the equation first for $x = 0$ and then for $x = 5$.

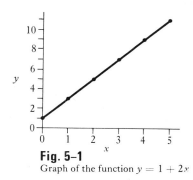

Fig. 5–1
Graph of the function $y = 1 + 2x$

Doing this yields values of y of 1 and 11, respectively, so mark off the y-axis from 1 to 11. This has been done in Fig. 5–1. Now solve the equation for a few more values of x. You might make a table like this one:

x	y
0	1
1	3
2	5
3	7
4	9
5	11

Plot these points and connect them. The result is shown in Fig. 5–1.

Now you can see why $y = a + bx$ is called a *linear* function. **The graph of any linear function is a straight line.** Knowing this makes the job of plotting a linear function relatively easy; you only need to find two points, plot them, and then you can simply connect them with a straight line. The two points you determined when finding the range of the y variable will do very well.

Social scientists occasionally find that two variables they are studying are linearly related. The following exercise illustrates this.

Exercise 5–3

Fitts and Peterson (1964) studied the relationship between the difficulty of a task and the time it takes to complete it. Their subjects had to hold a stylus on a small metal plate placed directly in front of them on a table. When a light came on, the subject was to move the stylus off the home plate and touch a target plate, located some distance from the home plate. The size of the target could be changed. Thus, the task could be made more difficult by either moving the target farther away from the home plate, or by making the target smaller. The independent variable in the experiment was the index of difficulty (ID) obtained, by means of a special equation, from the distance between target and home plate and from the size of the target. There were two dependent variables, reaction time (RT) and movement time (MT). Reaction time is the time that elapses between the light coming on and the subject lifting the stylus off the home plate, while movement time is the time that elapses while the stylus is actually moving from the home plate to the target. The experimenters found that the relationship between the index of difficulty and RT or MT was given by these equations:

$$RT = 0 \cdot 261 + 0 \cdot 0054 \ ID$$
$$MT = -0 \cdot 07 + 0 \cdot 074 \ ID$$

In these equations, time is given in seconds, and the index of difficulty varies from 2 to 8. What do the graphs of these functions look like?

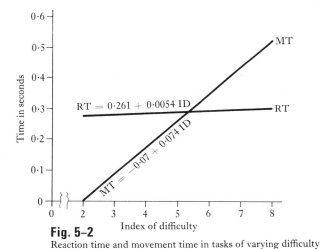

Fig. 5–2
Reaction time and movement time in tasks of varying difficulty
(After Fitts and Peterson, 1964.)

The first step is to find the ranges of the variables. We already know that the x-axis must run from 2 to 8. Let us use the RT and MT equations to find the ranges for the y variables. Here are the results:

ID	RT	MT
2	0·2718	0·078
8	0·3042	0·522

If both plots are made on the same graph, then the y-axis must run from 0·078 to 0·522. First plot the two points for reaction time, then the two for movement time, and then connect the two sets of points with straight lines. The result is shown in Fig. 5–2.

Constants a and b

What meaning, if any, can be given to the constants a and b? First let us look at a. One way to see if a has any easily discerned meaning is to draw several graphs which differ from one another only in the value given to a. For all these graphs, let us assign to b a value of 1. We will plot these functions:

$$y = 0 + x$$
$$y = 1 + x$$
$$y = 2 + x$$
$$y = 3 + x$$

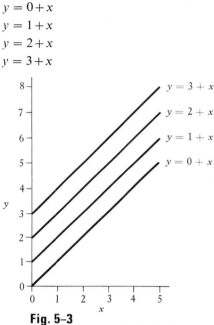

Fig. 5–3
Four linear plots in which only the constant a is different

Figure 5–3 shows these four functions. Notice that the plots are parallel, the only difference between them being the place where they intersect the y-axis. If you look carefully you will see that the value of y at the point of intersection equals the value of y where the graph intersects the y-axis, or, more briefly, a is called the 'y-intercept'. Rather than plot a graph to find the value of the y-intersept it is easier to solve the equation for the case where $x = 0$. If you let $x = 0$ in the equation $y = a + bx$, then

$$y = a + b(0)$$
$$y = a$$

The resulting value of y will equal the value of the constant, a. Often you can determine the value of a simply by inspecting the equation.

To find out what meaning we can attach to the constant b, let us plot the following equations in which a has been kept constant at a value of 1.

$$y = 1 + (1/2)x$$
$$y = 1 + x$$
$$y = 1 + 2x$$
$$y = 1 + 3x$$

Figure 5–4 shows these functions. Since *a* is the same in all the equations, all the graphs pass through the *y*-axis at the same place. The difference in the four plots is in the amount of tilt of the line. The higher the value of *b*, the greater the tilt. The constant *b*, then, reflects the amount of tilt of the plot, so *b* is usually referred to as the 'slope constant', or more briefly, as the 'slope' of the line.

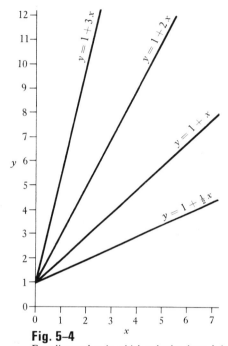

Fig. 5–4
Four linear plots in which only the slope, *b*, is different

We can see, then, that *a* and *b* have meaning: *a* is the *y*-intercept, and *b* is the slope of the line. The point of showing that *a* and *b* have meaning is that in the next chapter, when we meet some rather complicated function rules that allow us to plot probability functions, we shall see that these function rules contain one independent variable, two problem constants and several universal constants. We will be able to understand the rules better if we can attach meaning to the problem constants, and doing this will enable us to use these functions very effectively.

Negative numbers

Before we leave linear functions, it is worth asking what the plots look like when any of *a*, *b*, or *x* are negative. To begin with, let us plot the function. This can be seen in Fig. 5–5. Extending the axes creates four sections of the graph, usually referred to as quadrants I, II, III, and IV. All the previous figures in this chapter have been quadrant I plots. As you would expect, the plot of $y = x$ has a *y*-intercept of 0 and a slope of 1. The line extends down into the third quadrant. You can verify that this is correct: when x equals -1, then y equals -1; when x equals -2, y equals -2, and so forth.

You can probably guess what the plots will look like for negative values of the constants. If a is negative, then the y-intercept will be negative. You can see this in Fig. 5–6 for the line whose equation is

$$y = -3 + x$$

When the slope is negative, the line tilts around so that increasing values of x go with decreasing values of y; we say that the relation between x and y is 'inverse', or y is inversely related to x. An inverse relation is shown in Fig. 5–6 by the line whose equation is

$$y = 2 - \tfrac{1}{2}x$$

Finally, a plot in which both a and b are negative can be seen in Fig. 5–6 as represented by the line whose equation is

$$y = -2 - \tfrac{1}{2}x$$

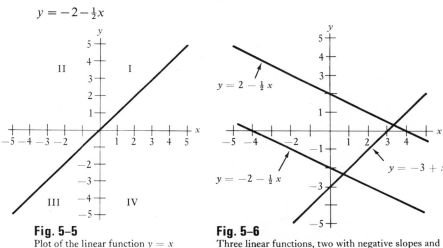

Fig. 5–5
Plot of the linear function $y = x$

Fig. 5–6
Three linear functions, two with negative slopes and two with negative intercepts

Obviously not all functions encountered by a social scientist will be linear. To give you an idea of functional relationships that are not linear, let me introduce you to two functions that you may have encountered already in your studies, power functions and exponential functions.

5.3 Nonlinear functions

Power functions

A power function is given by the rule

$$y = ax^b$$

In words, the rule states that x is raised to some power b and then this result is multiplied by a. An example of the application of the power law is provided by the work of the psychologist S. S. Stevens (1957; 1962; 1966). Stevens believes that the relationship between the magnitude of stimulus intensity and the magnitude of sensation is best described by a power function. He has tested this idea in dozens of experiments and found it to be generally true for many different kinds of stimuli and for different sense modalities. Three possible plots of the power law are shown in Fig. 5–7. Note that when the exponent is 1, a linear function is the result.

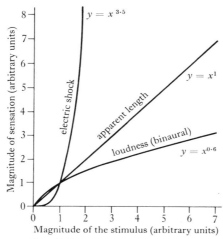

Fig. 5–7

Three plots of the power law for different values of the exponent

Exponential functions

The function rule for an exponential relationship between y and x is given by

$$y = ae^{bx}$$

where a and b are problem constants and e is the universal constant mentioned earlier. An example of an exponential relation can be found in micro-economic theory and in psychological decision theory. As early as 1738 Daniel Bernoulli suggested that the relationship between money and a person's subjective value of that money is not linear but exponential. The basic idea is that the subjective

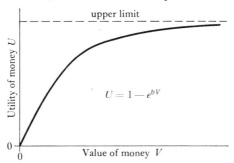

Fig. 5–8

Utility function for money

worth, or utility, of say, one dollar, is less for a millionaire than for a pauper. The more money you have the less you will value one more unit of that money. This kind of relationship is shown in Fig. 5–8 where the function

$$U = 1 - e^{bV}$$

is plotted. The constant b is negative for this plot, U stands for utility and V for objective value.

This curve differs from the power function whose exponent is less than 1 in that this exponential curve levels off and reaches an upper limit only when V reaches infinity. Once you have amassed enough wealth, adding one more unit of money to your hoard increases your utility for the total not a whit, or to be more precise, the increase in utility is infinitesimally small. A good discussion of utility theory is given by Raiffa (1968).

5.4 Transformations

So far we have shown that functions can be used to indicate the relationship between two variables. A number of examples have been given of experimental results expressed in terms of a function, or a function rule. We have seen that scientific laws are expressed in functional form. But in addition to these uses of functions, there is another use that will be important to us in succeeding chapters. Frequent use will be made of functions that enable us to transform one variable into another. Sometimes a variable of interest to us can be manipulated more easily mathematically if it is first transformed into a new variable. You do this when you use logarithms. Rather than multiply several numbers together, it is easier to find the logarithms of the numbers and then add the logarithms. As the last step you change the result back into the original units by taking an antilogarithm. By taking the logarithm of a number you are using a function rule to transform the original number into a new one. You made the transformations to simplify your task of arithmetic.

An example of a linear transformation can be seen by considering the centigrade and Fahrenheit scales of temperature. Letting F stand for degrees of temperature expressed in Fahrenheit, and C for centigrade degrees, this equation will enable you to convert a centigrade reading to Fahrenheit:

$$F = \tfrac{9}{5}C + 32$$

(Here F and C are used as variables, even though they come from the beginning of the alphabet, because of their mnemonic value.) The rule states that the centigrade temperature is to be multiplied by 9/5 and 32 added to the result. You can see that this equation has the form of a linear function, and, indeed, if you plotted it the result would be a straight line.

5.5 Summary

Much of science is concerned with finding the relationship between variables. When a relationship is known it can often be expressed in functional form, as pairs of variables—one value of the dependent variable with one value of the independent variable, as a graph, or as a function rule. One function rule that is useful in statistics is that of a linear function,

$$y = a + bx$$

where y is the dependent variable, x is the independent variable, and a and b are constants. a is the y-intercept and b represents the slope of the line. Another function is the power law

$$y = ax^b$$

where x and y are the independent and dependent variables, respectively, and a and b are constants. A third function is the exponential relation

$$y = ae^{bx}$$

in which x and y are as before, a and b are constants, and e is the universal constant $2 \cdot 7182 \ldots$. In addition to expressing scientifically established laws, functions can be used to transform one variable into another. Sometimes it will be easiest to transform one variable to another, do all the necessary computations with the transformed variable, and then at the last step, transform the results back into the original variable.

Problems

5–1 Which of the following are linear functions?

a $\quad y = 4\sigma$ where σ is a variable

b $\quad z = 1 - e^{Az}$ where e is a constant

c $\quad z = \dfrac{4x}{\pi} - 6 \cdot 3e$ where e is a constant

d $\quad y = 3 + \dfrac{3}{x}$

e $\quad y = \dfrac{2\pi - e}{x}$

f $\quad y = 4 \cdot 2 + 3x + x^2$

5–2 Draw a graph that will enable you to convert any Fahrenheit temperature from -50 to $+250$ into a centigrade reading.

5–3 Draw a graph that will enable you to find the logarithm (to the base 10) of any number from 1 to 100. Use the graph to show that multiplying the following whole numbers is equivalent to adding their logarithms:

a 10 by 10

b 5 by 5

c 1 by 50

5–4 In a number of studies the attraction a person feels toward another has been found to be linearly related to the similarity of attitudes held by the two people. Clore and Baldridge (1968) have published their experimental results on this question in the form of a function rule:

$$y = 6 \cdot 55x + 4 \cdot 46$$

In the equation x represents the proportion of the subject's attitudes that are similar to a stranger's, and y is a measure of the attraction between the people.

a Plot this function.

b In the experiment the subject was first shown the stranger's attitudes about 12 topics and was then asked to rate his liking for the stranger on one 7-point scale, and his desire for the stranger as a partner in an experiment on another 7-point scale. The sum of the two scale ratings was taken as an index of the attraction felt by the subject toward the stranger, and it is this attraction that appears as the y-variable in the equation above. Since the lowest mark one can make on a 7-point scale scores a '1', the minimum attraction score is 2. The maximum is, of course, 14. How would you interpret the y-intercept of this function?

c   What would the function have to look like if attraction and proportion of similar attitudes were inversely related? Not related?

5–5   Draw a graph for each of the following rules of thumb.

a   To determine the outdoor temperature in Fahrenheit, count the number of chirps made by the snowy tree cricket in 15 seconds and add 40 to the number.

b   To find the speed in m.p.h. of a British Rail train, count the number of 'clickety-clacks' made by the wheels in 30 seconds, multiply this number by 15 and divide by 11.

c   To estimate the distance between you and a flash of lightning, count the number of seconds that elapse between the flash and the resulting thunderclap, and divide this number by 5 to obtain the distance in miles.

6 · Distributions of opinion

Now let us return to the problem of assigning probabilities for continuous hypotheses. At the beginning of the last chapter I said that from now on we would be dealing only with continuous hypotheses. Recall that a continuous hypothesis is a very large or infinitely large collection of hypotheses where one hypothesis blurs imperceptibly into the next. Examples are:

average I.Q. of students attending British universities;

proportion of people who will buy a certain product;

difference in amount learned between a group of students given programmed instruction and a group given regular lectures;

proportion of American schools that have swimming pools.

Each of these examples of a continuous hypothesis illustrates uncertainty about some quantity: average I.Q., proportion of people . . ., etc. Let us drop the term 'continuous hypothesis' in favour of the more descriptive 'uncertain quantity'. Remember that the uncertainty exists in the head of the investigator; there is, at any point in time, one and only one average I.Q. of students attending British universities. We do not know that value, so to us it is an uncertain quantity.

This chapter is concerned with the theory and methods of describing opinion about uncertain quantities, with particular emphasis on prior opinion. The basic idea is that opinion about an uncertain quantity can be described by a probability function. We discuss a number of function rules that are frequently used by the Bayesian statistician to describe his opinion. Much of what is said here applies both to prior and to posterior opinions. As I have said before, the only difference between prior and posterior probabilities is the amount of data on which they are based, so you would expect that much of the theory concerning prior opinion would apply equally well to posterior opinion.

Perhaps a reminder of the linkages between this chapter and the previous ones will help to put this chapter in perspective. In Chapter 2 we learned how prior opinion can be expressed in the language of probabilities, and in Chapter 3 we learned the grammar of that language. Chapter 4 was concerned entirely with revising prior opinion in the light of new information, through the operation of Bayes' theorem. Through Chapter 4 we were always talking about discrete events or hypotheses, but now we need to extend the approach to cover the revision of opinion concerning an uncertain quantity. When we talk about an uncertain quantity, we usually wish to spread out our opinion over the range of possible values of the quantity, so we express our uncertainty as a probability distribution. To understand distributions of opinion we first needed to know about functions and their graphs—hence Chapter 5. Now, in this chapter, we get down to the technical details of expressing our opinion about an uncertain quantity in the form of a probability distribution. Although the revision of a distribution in the light of new information is the subject of Part III, a brief preview is given here.

In this chapter you should understand

how prior opinion about an uncertain quantity is expressed as a probability function;

how to express your prior opinion in terms of one of a few standard probability functions;

how probability statements are made on the basis of functions;

when to use a uniform approximation to your prior opinion.

You should also be able to

graph your prior opinions about an uncertain quantity;

describe your prior opinion as a standard probability function;

calculate probabilities based on the probability function.

You will find that this is a fairly demanding chapter, mainly because it contains so much technical detail. It is worth mastering this material now, however, because it will all be needed in Part III.

6.1 Probability distributions

A function showing the relation of probabilities to an uncertain quantity is called a *probability distribution*. There are two major types of probability distributions, but we will save discussion of them until the next section. For now we will call the distributions of prior opinion discussed in this section simply *prior distributions*. An example of a prior distribution is shown in Fig. 6–1. That is my prior distribution about the average age of all university students presently attending English universities. The x-axis shows possible values of the uncertain quantity 'average age'. I consider it so unlikely that the average age is less than 15, or more than 25, that I have not shown values of x outside the interval 15 to 25. Interpretation of the y-axis is a little difficult. Strictly speaking, the y-axis is not probability. You can see why by considering what the probability would be for any specific value of x. What is the probability, for example, that the true average age is *exactly* 21·364921? Virtually zero. The trouble has come by considering x as a continuous variable, for since there are an infinite number of possible values between 15 and 25, the probability of any one of them must be zero. One way to get around this problem is to admit that age would probably be measured at most to the nearest day, so that the x-axis need not be continuous; it could be divided up very finely with 365 days between each year. Then the probability of, say, 21 years and 43 days would have some small, but finite probability.

But this approach is clumsy. The mathematics are far easier if we can treat x as a continuous variable. We know that when we do this the probability of any specific value of x is zero. Meaning can still be given to the graph by interpreting y as not a probability but rather a probability density. The exact meaning of 'probability density' cannot be given without recourse to the calculus, but a rough interpretation would be that the values along the y-axis represent the probability in the vicinity of x. You can see that my prior distribution peaks at 20. This means that I am most certain that the true average age lies in the vicinity of 20. I associate lowest degrees of belief in the vicinities

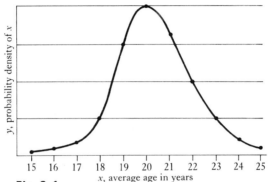

Fig. 6–1
Prior probability distribution of the average age of students attending English universities

of 15 and 25, and so my distribution is lowest at these locations. This graph, then, shows the degrees of belief I would attach to all the hypotheses that lie between 15 and 25. It is a distribution of my prior opinion about the average age of students attending English universities. We will consider next the steps in its construction.

Constructing a prior distribution

In following these steps you should not be too fussy about the details; the purpose of drawing the prior distribution is to see what its general shape is. A rough sketch will do.

a   Determine the range of the x-variable. Include only values of x with noticeable probabilities. In the example of average age, the range 15–25 covers nearly all of the distribution.

b   Draw the x and y axes. Mark off the x-axis in units covering the range of x-values. Make the y-axis about three-fifths the length of the x-axis. This proportion is chosen for purely aesthetic reasons; your graph will be neither too tall and peaked nor too squashed and flat. Do not mark any units on the Y-axis, though you may find it helpful to draw a light horizontal line from the top of the Y-axis, another at the halfway point on the Y-axis, and two more at the one quarter and three quarters points. I have done this in Fig. 6–1.

c Find the value of x which you think is most likely to be the correct one; place a large dot directly above this value on the horizontal line at the top of the graph. In Fig. 6–1 this is the dot at the peak of the graph, above the 20.

d Pick other values of x and place dots above them at heights that represent the probabilities relative to the most likely value of x. For example, I thought that an average age of 19 is about three quarters as likely as 20, so I put a dot above 19 on the horizontal line that is three quarters as high as the top one. I thought 18 is about one quarter as likely as 20, so the dot was placed on the one quarter line. Remember that the horizontal lines do not represent absolute values of probability, they stand for probabilities relative to the most probable.

e Connect the dots with a continuous line.

I suggest now that you draw your own prior distribution for this example. Your distribution will probably be different from mine. If you are presently attending an English university, or have some knowledge of students at English universities, your distribution may be more peaked than mine, for my experience with English universities is limited to just four years at the time of this writing. If you are not British your distribution may be flatter than mine, for you probably have little knowledge of the ages of students at English universities. In general, if you are uncertain about x your distribution should be flatter than that of someone who is more sure than you.

Exercises 6–1 and 6–2

1 Graph your prior distribution of the average number of hours of sleep per day obtained by students in your university during the term.

2 Graph your distribution of the average height of women in your country.

Answers

There is no correct answer that can be given. Your opinion is your opinion. Note, however, in Exercise 6–2 that the uncertain quantity in question is the average height of women. You are *not* being asked to produce a distribution of heights, you are asked to give a distribution of *your opinion* about the *average* height.

Revising prior opinion in the light of data

Having graphed your prior distribution, you would next collect some data. In this example, you would collect a random sample of students attending English universities and find out how old the students are. These data would then be used in the revision of your prior distribution through the application of Bayes' theorem. The result would be a posterior distribution whose peak would probably be shifted relative to the peak of the prior distribution, and the posterior distribution would probably be even more peaked, less broad, than the prior.

An example may help to make the process clearer. The example is an overview of the results of applying a Bayesian analysis to making an inference about an uncertain quantity. For the moment, do not worry about why the analysis is carried out this way, or about how it is done. My purpose is to show the process without the technical details so as to give you a general picture of the subsequent development of this chapter. The example will also serve as an illustration of a small-scale experiment, one that can be (and was) carried out in the classroom.

I asked the students in my statistics class to consider the proportion of students in the class whose fathers are in 'white-collar' occupations. At the time I asked the questions, that proportion was an uncertain quantity, for none of us knew the actual value. To set up a situation analogous to a scientific experiment, I asked each student to write on a 3-in × 5-in card I had passed out, either 'white' or 'blue' according to a set of criteria I had announced about type of occupation, and the cards were collected.

The pack of cards was considered as a 'population' about which I wished to make an inference. Note the special use of the word 'population'. **A population is a collection of elements (often people, in the social sciences) about which I wish to make some inference.** The populations for the four examples mentioned in the first paragraph of this chapter are:

all students attending British universities;

all people who might hear of the product;

all students;

all American schools (here the elements are schools, not people).

One way to make an inference about a population is to observe the whole population; I could then simply note the proportion of 'white' cards. But scientists are rarely in a position to sample everyone in their population simply because the populations are too big. So, instead, they take a sample of the population and use that data to make an inference about the population.

But before drawing a sample I assessed my prior distribution about the uncertain quantity. It is shown in Fig. 6–2 as the 'prior' curve. The curve is fairly flat, indicating my considerable uncertainty about the actual value of the unknown (to me) proportion. The highest density is in the region of 0·6, but it falls off only gradually to either side.

At this point I was ready to collect some data. After mixing the cards, I drew one out, noted the word on the card, returned it to the pack, mixed the cards, drew another and repeated this process until I had drawn out 20 cards, 17 of which had 'white' on them.

The next step was to apply Bayes' theorem. My prior distribution was revised in the light of 17 'whites' out of 20 to give the posterior shown in Fig. 6–2. For now, do not worry about how this was done, just note the result. My new opinion peaks in the vicinity of 0·8, and it is much less flat than the prior. It is more squeezed in, indicating that the range over which my uncertainty extended was now less.

One way to communicate this 'narrowing-in' process is to determine values of x_{low} and $x_{hig.}$ such that most of your opinion falls between those limits. For example, 95% of my prior opinion falls between 0·239 and 0·895, while 95% of my posterior opinion is found between 0·623 and 0·921. This is shown graphically in the lower portion of Fig. 6–2. Research papers more commonly state the posterior range of opinion rather than showing the posterior distribution itself because it is easier and more economical of journal space. Later we will consider how this range is determined once the distribution is known.

At this stage in the experiment an inference can be made: 'I am 95% sure that the true value of the proportion falls between 0·623 and 0·921. That is all there is to it. The statement is the usual end result of a Bayesian analysis for uncertain quantities. It is the continuous-hypothesis counterpart of attaching posterior probabilities to discrete hypotheses.

If you will keep this example in mind, it will help to prevent you from losing the forest for the trees as you travel through the rest of this book.

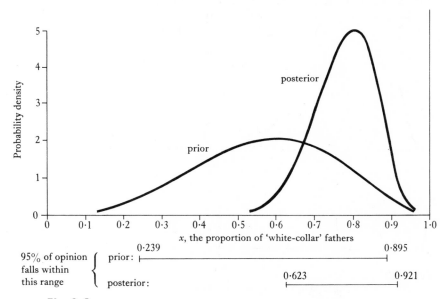

Fig. 6–2
Prior and posterior distributions of opinion concerning the proportion of students whose fathers are in 'white-collar' occupations

Some common distributions

Applying Bayes' theorem to every idiosyncratic prior distribution can be a considerable mathematical chore, so a simpler method is needed. Later we will find that applying Bayes' theorem is comparatively easy if we restrict our prior to a distribution that can be specified by a function rule. Our job will be even easier if we use only certain functions. The distribution shown in Fig. 6–1 is not described by a simple function rule, but the ones in Fig. 6–2 are. Prior opinion in the form of a probability distribution can usually be closely approximated by one of just a few common distributions that are easy to use in Bayes' theorem.

How do we justify using an approximation to our prior distribution? **An approximate prior distribution can be used if the posterior distribution that**

results looks virtually identical to the posterior that would have been obtained had the actual prior distribution been used. There is no point getting involved in complex mathematics with your actual prior distribution, when using an approximation to your prior would simplify the mathematics and still result in virtually the same posterior distribution. This simple idea is what makes Bayesian statistics practical.

Three different kinds of prior distributions will suffice for a great many of the problems you will encounter as social scientists. Each of these distributions can be expressed by a function rule, and a remarkably varied collection of distributions, called a *family*, can be obtained by changing the constants in these rules, just as different straight lines result from changing the *y*-intercept and the slope. By appropriate choice of the function rule and its constants you should find one member of the family that is very close to your prior opinion.

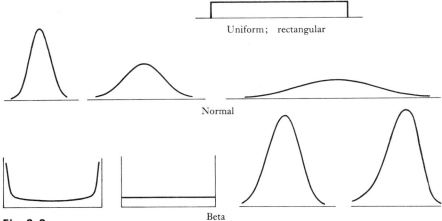

Fig. 6–3
Some of the shapes taken on by three common prior distributions

Further, the distributions that result from using these rules can be easily used in Bayesian calculations. In many instances, you will find that the posterior distribution has the same function rule as the prior, that is, they are both in the same family, and that only the constants have changed. You will not have to calculate Bayes' theorem, you will only have to know how the constants of the prior distribution are changed by the data to give the constants of the posterior distribution. Nothing more than a simple mathematical equation must be known to effect the change. But more of this later. For the time being, it is sufficient to recognize that it will be very convenient to restrict your priors to one of the following kinds of distributions. Others are possible but beyond the scope of this book.

a   *Rectangular or uniform distribution*   If you think all values of *x* are equally likely, then your prior distribution is said to be uniform, or rectangular. The distribution is uniform over all the possible values of *x*.

b   *Normal distribution*   A normal distribution is bell-shaped (though not all bell-shaped distributions are normal). It extends from minus infinity to plus infinity, though by appropriate choice of the constants of the distribution, most of the distribution falls over the desired range of x-values. It is sometimes called a *Gaussian* distribution.

c   *Beta distribution*   This distribution applies when the range of x-values is from 0 to 1, as would be the case when you are interested in making inferences about proportions. By choosing appropriate constants, the distribution can be U-shaped, uniform, bell-shaped, or asymmetrical bell-shaped. It is a very versatile distribution because it can take on so many different shapes. Both the prior and posterior densities in Fig. 6–2 are Beta distributions.

Figure 6–3 shows some of the shapes of these distributions.

6.2   Some distribution theory

After you have sketched your prior distribution you may find that it comes pretty close to one of the three standard distributions. Thus, when someone asks you what your prior distribution is, you do not have to hand him a picture, you can name it. This is, of course, what scientists do when they report their prior distributions in journal reports of their research; they say that their prior is uniform, or normally distributed, or Beta. But the name is not enough for other than uniform priors; you also need to indicate the shape of the distribution. As you can see from Fig. 6–3, if I tell you my prior distribution concerning some proportion is characterized by a Beta distribution, I could mean that my opinion is any of the shapes shown. The method of specifying the exact distribution is different for Beta and normal distributions, but the theory is the same. Like a straight line, these two distributions are completely specified by naming the type of function and by giving two problem constants. Once that is done we can go on to specify values of x_{low} and x_{high} that encompass 95%, or 99%, or any other percentage of our opinion. That is our ultimate goal, so keep this in mind as you read the rest of this section, for now I must introduce the theory that will enable you to make probability statements based on the probability distribution of the uncertain quantity in question.

Credible intervals

The key idea that enables us to determine probabilities of intervals is this: **For a probability density function, the area under the curve equals one.** This applies to any density function, prior or posterior, and is ensured by choosing units on the y-axis so that the area is one. You can see why, in the sub-section on constructing a prior distribution, I advised you not to mark any units on the y-axis. Those units cannot be arbitrarily chosen, for the y-axis must be numbered so as to make the area under the curve equal one. For reasons that will be obvious later, you will never have to determine the scale of the y-axis. You will never have to measure the area, either; that would require the calculus for most of the distributions of concern to us in this book.

This restriction on probability density functions, that the area under the curve must equal one, is nothing more than the continuous equivalent to the probability law for discrete events that says that the probabilities of N mutually exclusive and exhaustive events must add to one. Here, where N equals infinity, the area under the curve must equal one.

A consequence of this limitation on the total area of a probability density function is that **the probability of the true value of x falling between x_{low} and x_{high} is given by the area of the curve between those limits.** This applies for any values of x_{low} and x_{high} you may wish to choose. I can pick any two values, determine the area of the curve between those values, and that area is the probability that the true value of x lies within the interval.

Now suppose instead of choosing the values of x_{low} and x_{high}, I start with any probability, say 0·99, and I then try to find values of x_{low} and x_{high} such that the area between them is 0·99. There would be many such intervals, for there are a good number of ways the density function can be sliced. No matter; we will call any such interval a '*C per cent credible interval*'. **A *C* per cent credible interval is indicated by any two values of x which include *C* per cent of the probability density function between them.**

Exercise 6–3

What are the 95% credible intervals for the prior and posterior distributions shown in Fig. 6–2?

Answer

You can read off the answers below the curves. The two bars represent the length of intervals that cover 95% of the area of each curve. Thus, the 95% credible interval for the prior distribution is 0·239 to 0·895, and for the posterior distribution is 0·623 to 0·921.

I have redrawn just the prior distribution in Fig. 6–4 to show the interval and its relation to the area more clearly.

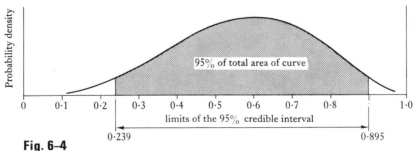

Fig. 6–4
Relation between an area of the probability density function and a credible interval

Of course I could have chosen to locate the 95% of the curve further to the left, or to the right. For example, the interval from 0·271 to 1·00 includes 95% of the curve, so 0·271 to 1·00 is also a 95% credible interval. Why did I choose the interval in Fig. 6–4? Because of all the intervals I *could* have chosen, that one is the shortest. (Note that 0·271 to 1·00, a distance of 0·729, is longer than 0·239 to 0·895, a distance of 0·656). We will adopt the convention of always choosing the shortest interval. You may have noticed that the probability density directly over 0·239 is exactly the same as over 0·895; that is always true of the shortest interval, and therefore densities outside the interval will always be less than densities inside the interval. For this reason, the shortest credible interval is called the '*highest density region*' of the curve. Density of opinion is everywhere higher within the interval rather than outside it, an intuitively appealing property. We will, then, always choose highest-density credible intervals. But how can we do this? We turn to that question next.

Cumulative probability functions

Suppose we were to take a planimeter (a device for measuring area) and measure the area to the left of various values of x in Fig. 6–4. We might start with $x = 0·1$, and measure the tiny area to the left of 0·1. Then we try $x = 0·2$, and measure the area to the left of 0·2, and so forth. In each case, we draw a

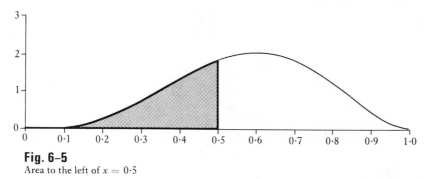

Fig. 6–5
Area to the left of $x = 0·5$

vertical line through the value of x and measure the area of the curve to the left of the line. You can see this in Fig. 6–5 for $x = 0·5$. Now suppose I make a table of my results. This is shown in Table 6–1. (I could have made a finer table by taking measurements at more values of x.) Since the table shows pairings of numbers, it gives us a function.

Table 6–1 Area to the left of x, as a function of x, for the probability density function shown in Fig. 6–4.

x	Area to left of x
0	0
0·1	0·001
0·2	0·017
0·3	0·070
0·4	0·179
0·5	0·344
0·6	0·544
0·7	0·744
0·8	0·901
0·9	0·984
1·0	1·00

A more convenient way of displaying the function is to draw a graph of it. You can see this in Fig. 6–6. Such a curve is called a cumulative probability function. **A graph showing the area of a probability density function to the left of x, as a function of x, is called a cumulative probability function.** The horizontal axis of a cumulative probability distribution shows all the possible values of the uncertain quantity, x, and the vertical axis gives the probabilities that the true value of x is less than the values shown on the horizontal axis. This kind of function is in some ways more useful than probability density functions because the y-axis represents probability itself rather than probability density.

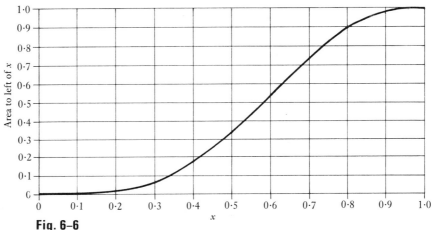

Fig. 6–6
Cumulative probability function for the probability density shown in Fig. 6–5

You may wonder, then, why I did not introduce cumulative probability functions to begin with instead of probability density functions. Why did we not express prior opinion as a cumulative probability function? The answer lies in some research by Winkler (1967). Subjects in his experiment were instructed in several different methods for expressing prior opinions. He found that his subjects not only preferred probability density functions on intuitive grounds, but they were apt to change discrepancies between the two types of functions by changing the cumulative distribution function. They found it more meaningful to assess points on the probability density function than to determine cumulative probabilities. These findings show that people believe probability density functions to be more accurate portrayals of prior opinion than cumulative distribution functions.

What is gained in intuitive appeal is, however, lost in ease of usage. But I think ease of interpretation should win over ease of use, so we will stick with probability density functions as descriptors of prior opinion. This will impose no hardship anyway, for tables have been computed of the cumulative probability distribution for a great many distributions. I used one of these tables rather than a planimeter to find the areas in Table 6–1.

Exercise 6–4

What is the prior probability that the true proportion of 'white-collar' fathers lies:

a   Below 0·8?
b   Below 0·25?
c   Between 0·8 and 0·25?

Answers

a   From Fig. 6–6, we see the area to the left of 0·8 is 0·9, so that is the probability.
b   Again, we read from Fig. 6–6, and obtain a probability of 0·04.
c   What we want is the area *between* 0·25 and 0·8. You can find this by *subtracting* the area to the left of 0·8; 0·9 − 0·04 = 0·86. That is the answer.

This exercise illustrates how, given values of x_{low} and x_{high}, you can find the area between the values; subtract the area to the left of x_{low} from the area to the left of x_{high} (see Fig. 6–7). The resulting area is the probability that the true value of x falls between x_{low} and x_{high}.

Now suppose the problem is turned on its head; instead of starting with x_{low} and x_{high} we start with an area and find low and high values of x. For example, what proportions of 'white-collar' fathers include 90% of the prior

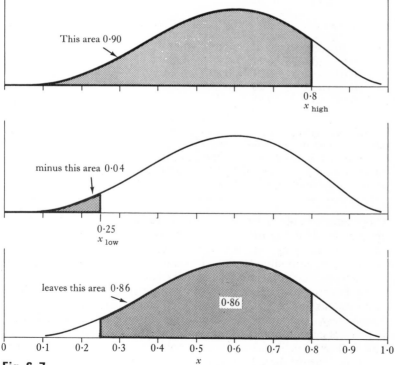

Fig. 6–7
Determining the area in an interval

distribution between them? One answer is obtained by letting $x_{low} = 0$. Then x_{high} is the value of x with 90% of the prior density function to the left. Find this by entering the y-axis of Fig. 6–6 with 0·9, move horizontally to the curve, and read off the value of x, below: $x_{high} = 0·8$. So one acceptable interval is 0 to 0·8. That is one 90% credible interval. Another could be obtained by letting $x_{high} = 1·0$, entering the cumulative curve with $y = 0·1$, and finding that $x_{low} = 0·33$. Still another would result from entering the cumulative probability function with $y = 0·05$ and $y = 0·95$. That would give $x_{low} = 0·27$ and $x_{high} = 0·85$. Many acceptable intervals could be determined by entering the y-axis with values of y whose difference is 0·9.

Exercise 6–5

Construct a list of 95% credible intervals for the prior distribution of the proportion of 'white-collar' fathers (Fig. 6–2). Do this for increments in values of y of 0·01. Find the highest density credible interval.

Answer

We start by entering the cumulative probability function (Fig. 6–6) with $y = 0·95$ and $y = 0$. This gives $x_{high} = 0·85$, and, of course, $x_{low} = 0$. Now we increase the y's by 0·01, and enter the curve with 0·96 and 0·01. Repeating this process gives this table:

95% credible interval

Values of y	x_{low}	x_{high}	Difference
0 and 0·95	0	0·85	0·85
0·01 and 0·96	0·17	0·86	0·69
0·02 and 0·97	0·21	0·87	0·66
0·03 and 0·98	0·23	0·89	0·66
0·04 and 0·99	0·25	0·92	0·67
0·05 and 1·00	0·27	1·00	0·73

By subtracting x_{low} from x_{high} for each pair, the shortest interval (smallest difference) can be determined. With the two-place accuracy possible by reading Fig. 6–6, two intervals are the 'shortest', 0·21 to 0·87 and 0·23 to 0·89, which are as close to the values of 0·239 and 0·895 mentioned earlier as the accuracy of these computations will allow.

This exercise could have been done more accurately by a computer. All the computer needs is the prior density shown in Fig. 6–2 and a program of instructions for carrying out the various computations. These instructions would require the computer to find the cumulative probability function from the prior density function, and then follow roughly the same steps we went through in Exercise 6–5. However, the computer could take much smaller increments and so find x_{low} and x_{high} with greater accuracy.

Fortunately, computers have already performed this task and the results of their labours can be found in tables; some are included in the Appendices to this book. For some density functions you will be able to look up the limits of the credible interval directly, and for others you will have to make a couple of trivial calculations based on tabled values.

Although you will not have to determine a cumulative probability function yourself, you should remember how they are used to find credible intervals, for we will make very frequent use of credible intervals in Part III. An understanding of what they are is vital to using them correctly.

More about credible intervals

Users of Bayesian statistics frequently report their results in the form of credible intervals. Before conducting the experiment on my students, I was 95% sure that the true proportion of 'white-collar' fathers could be found between possible values of 0·239 and 0·895. Those two values are the limits of my (highest-density) prior 95% credible interval. After the experiment, my posterior 95% credible interval was 0·623 to 0·921. The credible interval has become smaller, indicating that I am more certain after the experiment than before.

In this example I reported my 95% credible interval. A more conservative statement, consistent with my advice in Chapter 4, would result by giving my 99% credible interval, or even the 99·9% credible interval. These are shown in Table 6–2. The interval opens up as credibility increases. You want the interval to be reasonably narrow *and* the credibility to be high, so in deciding which credible interval to report you must decide on a tradeoff between narrow limits and high confidence. Eventually, it is possible that scientific journals will establish standards for reporting credible intervals. In the meantime, until you become experienced in using statistics, I suggest you use the 99% credible interval.

Table 6–2 Credible intervals for the posterior probability density function shown in Fig. 6–2

Credible interval	Limits of the interval
95%	0·623 to 0·921
99%	0·561 to 0·946
99·9%	0·488 to 0·967

Finally, let me introduce some helpful notation. In Chapters 2 and 3 when we spoke of the probability of an event E we wrote

$p(E)$

When we find credible intervals we are dealing with a complex event: the true value of x lies between x_{low} and x_{high}. This event can be written

$$x_{low} \leq x \leq x_{high}$$

Literally translated, we read 'x_{high} is greater than or equal to x which is greater than or equal to x_{low}', but more briefly, 'x is between x_{low} and x_{high}'. When we refer to the probability that x is between x_{low} and x_{high} we write

$$p(x_{low} \leq x \leq x_{high})$$

In finding the limits of a 99% credible interval we want to find x_{low} and x_{high} such that

$$p(x_{\text{low}} \leq x \leq x_{\text{high}}) = 0{\cdot}99$$

Thus, in reporting my 99% credible interval for the 'white-collar'-father experiment, I would write in my report that

$$p(0{\cdot}561 \leq x \leq 0{\cdot}946) = 0{\cdot}99$$

That is a brief and economical way to report a credible interval.

Exercise 6–6

Write in mathematical notation the 95% and 99·9% credible intervals listed in Table 6–2.

Answers

For the 95% credible interval:

$$p(0{\cdot}623 \leq x \leq 0{\cdot}921) = 0{\cdot}95$$

For the 99·9% credible interval:

$$p(0{\cdot}488 \leq x \leq 0{\cdot}967) = 0{\cdot}99$$

We have seen in this section that opinion about an uncertain quantity is expressed as a probability density function and that this function is revised in the light of data by Bayes' theorem to give (usually) a more peaked posterior density function. We report our uncertainty in the form of a credible interval, which specifies how sure we are that the true value of the uncertain quantity falls between two limits.

We leave to Part III just how density functions are revised by applying Bayes' Theorem. For now, we take a closer look at rectangular, normal and Beta densities, and discover how credible intervals can be determined once the density function has been specified.

6.3 Three common distributions

It is time to get down to the technical details involved in specifying a prior or posterior distribution. We said earlier that a density function is completely specified by naming it and by stating its problem constants. In this section we see what the problem constants are and how changing them changes the shape of the distribution. We will see that while the problem constants completely specify the distribution, they do not always provide very good descriptions of the densities, so we will consider alternate ways of describing the distributions. Finally, we will see how to determine credible intervals once the distribution is specified. But first, we turn to the difference between specifying a distribution and describing it.

Parameters and statistics

The equation for the prior density in Fig. 6–2 is

$$y = 60x^3(1-x)^2$$

We will see later where this comes from. For now note how it works. You take some value of x (between 0 and 1·0), subtract that from one and square the difference. Then cube the value of x, and multiply that by the previous step. Finally multiply that result by 60. Try it for $x = 0·6$, the value of x under the peak of the curve. You should get $y = 2·0736$.

The equation has only one independent variable, x, though it appears twice, and one dependent variable, y. It appears to have three problem constants, 60, 3, and 2, but actually it has only 2. They are 3 and 2; the 60 is obtained by a part of the general equation which combines the 3 and 2 in a complex way to yield the 60. We will see how this comes about in the section on Beta distributions. For now the important point to note is that there are just two problem constants. If I change those constants a differently shaped curve results.

The problem constants for a probability density function have a special name: *parameters*. **The parameters of a probability density function, along with the function rule, completely specify the function.** By this I mean that if I tell you the function rule, that is, the equation of the function, along with the parameters, you have enough information to make a graph of the function. If I tell you the equation of a straight line,

$$y = a + bx$$

and I tell you that

$$a = 3 \quad \text{and} \quad b = 7$$

then you can plot the line on graph paper.

The only trouble with the parameters of the Beta function is that it is not possible to give them any very intuitively meaningful interpretation. We can for the straight line; a is the y-intercept and b is the slope of the line. So while we *specify* the distribution by giving its parameters, those numbers do not give us a very helpful intuitive *description* of the shape of the curve.

There are two aspects of the shape of a density function that we will usually want to be able to describe: where the middle of the curve is and how spread out it is. A number that locates the middle of the curve is called a measure of central tendency. We will consider three contenders: the mean, the median, and the mode. A number (or pair of numbers) that indicates the spread of the curve is called a measure of dispersion. We have already met one such measure— the credible interval. The bigger the credible interval, the more spread out is the density function. Another measure will also prove valuable; it is called the standard deviation.

These descriptors of a distribution are called *statistics*, and it is often more helpful to report them rather than the parameters.

The *mean* gives us an idea of where the middle of the curve is; specifically, **it is the value of x directly under the centre of gravity of the distribution.** Imagine that the prior distribution in Fig. 6–2 has been cut out of a piece of uniform material of some thickness. Now set the base of the distribution on a knife edge with the knife perpendicular to the base of the distribution. If you move the distribution to one side or the other over the knife edge, eventually you will find some point at which the distribution exactly balances. The value of x just above the knife edge is the mean of the distribution. The situation just described is pictured in Fig. 6–8. This definition of the mean applies to any distribution, but it is not actually the method used to determine the mean of a distribution. I give it here to facilitate intuitive understanding of what a mean means. Practical procedures for determining the mean will be dealt with later.

Another measure of central tendency is called the mode. **The mode of a density function is the value of x with the most probability density.** In other words, it is the value of x under the peak of the distribution. If a density function has two equally high peaks, then there are two modes, and the distribution is called 'bimodal'. (Some definitions of the mode would allow a mode under every peak, whether or not the peaks were of equal height.) Multimodal distributions are rarely encountered as describing prior or posterior opinion. The distribution in Fig. 6–8 is unimodal, and the mode is 0·6.

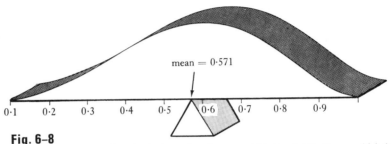

Fig. 6–8
The mean of a density function is that value of x over which the distribution would balance

A third measure of central tendency is the median. **The median of a density function is the value of x below which exactly half the area of the curve is found.** The median cuts the density function in half so that each half has an area of 0·5. The median can be found by entering the cumulative probability function along the y-axis at 0·5. If you do this on Fig. 6–6 you will find that the median of Fig. 6–8 is 0·58.

Notice that while the mean, median and mode for Fig. 6–8 are similar they are not quite equal. This will always be true of asymmetrical distributions. For a symmetrical distribution, one whose right half is a mirror image of its left half, the three measures are identical.

It is not so easy to give an intuitive understanding of the standard deviation. Like an acquired taste, it becomes meaningful with experience in using statistics. I can give a rough interpretation: if you multiply the standard deviation by 6, the result will roughly cover the effective range of the density function. That is probably not very helpful, but let us try it on the prior distribution in Fig. 6–2. The standard deviation for that density function is 0·175. You will notice that most of the density function lies between 0·1 to 1·0, a range of 0·9. If you multiply 0·175 by 6 you get 1·15, a range that more than covers the actual range. Try it for the posterior density. That standard deviation is 0·079. The range is 0·5 to 1·0, or 0·5. Multiply the standard deviation by 6; the result is 0·474. That about covers the range of 0·5. (We will see shortly how to calculate the standard deviation itself.)

As you would expect, the posterior standard deviation, 0·079, is smaller than the prior, 0·175. The smaller the standard deviation, the less spread out the density function. Beyond that statement, not much more can be said about the standard deviation for now. Remember that the standard deviation is not the only measure of the spread of a distribution; the credible interval is also a measure of dispersion.

It will be helpful to introduce some notation. The mean of a density function will always be denoted by m. A single prime on the m denotes the prior mean; a double prime, the posterior mean:

$m' \equiv$ mean of prior density function
$m'' \equiv$ mean of posterior density function

When I want to talk about the mean of a density function without reference to its being a prior or a posterior function, I use the m with no prime. No symbols will be used for the mode or the median; I will use the words.

The standard deviation of a density function will be denoted by s.

$s' \equiv$ standard deviation of prior density function
$s'' \equiv$ standard deviation of posterior density function

From now on symbols will build up at a rapid rate, so if you lose track consult the Index of Symbols at the back of the book.

All of this discussion can be summarized as follows: A density function is completely specified by giving the name of the function rule (for example, Beta or normal) and the parameters. A density function is described by its statistics (for example, mean and standard deviation).

Now we can get down to the business of looking at the function rule for the rectangular, normal, and Beta distributions, and at their parameters and statistics.

Beta distribution

You will often have occasion to make an inference about a proportion or about any number that can take on values only from zero to one. Prior opinion about such numbers is conveniently expressed in the form of a Beta distribution. The reason for the convenience is largely mathematical. If the prior distribution is a Beta and if the data are obtained by making successive, independent observations, on each of which only one of two events can occur (for example, the student's father is either 'white-collar' or 'blue-collar'), then the posterior distribution will also be a Beta. Further, the mathematics that result from applying Bayes' theorem are terribly simple if the conditions just stated are met. And you will see that the conditions are not very restrictive at all. So if you can express your prior opinion as a Beta, then the mathematics involved in finding the posterior will be very easy.

The general equation for a Beta distribution is more complex than the simple equations we met in the previous chapter.

$$y = \frac{(p+q-1)!}{(p-1)!(q-1)!} x^{p-1}(1-x)^{q-1}$$

Here y is the dependent variable (the probability density), x is the independent variable which can take on only values from 0 to 1, and p and q are problem constants, the parameters of the equation, which must be greater than 0. The ! is an odd mathematical symbol meaning 'factorial'; $n!$ is read 'n-factorial'.

$$n! = (n)(n-1)(n-2)(n-3)\ldots(3)(2)(1)$$

for example: 5! means $5 \times 4 \times 3 \times 2 \times 1$.

This equation for the Beta distribution is a general form, like

$$y = a + bx$$

is the general equation for a straight line. If we substitute specific values for a and b, then we get the equation for a particular line. Similarly, if we substitute specific values for p and q in the Beta equation, we get the equation of one particular Beta curve. That was the procedure I followed in arriving at the equation for the prior density in Fig. 6–2. I had decided that my prior opinion was adequately described by a Beta distribution with parameters

$$p = 4$$
$$q = 3$$

(We will see in a moment how I arrived at that decision.)

Substituting those values into the general equation for the Beta distribution gives

$$y = \frac{(4+3-1)!}{(4-1)!(3-1)!} x^{4-1}(1-x)^{3-1}$$

Simplifying:

$$y = \frac{6!}{3!\,2!} x^3(1-x)^2$$

$$= \frac{6 \times 5 \times 4 \times 3 \times 2 \times 1}{3 \times 2 \times 1 \times 2 \times 1} x^3(1-x)^2$$

$$= 60x^3(1-x)^2$$

And that is the result I reported at the beginning of the last section. You may have noticed that there I said the parameters were 3 and 2, while here I said they are 4 and 3. This apparent discrepancy can be resolved by noting the exponents in the general equation. They are $p-1$ and $q-1$. Some writers take $p-1$ and $q-1$ as the parameters, others take p and q. From now on, I will use p and q, but you must always check the usage before you use the Beta distribution.

Exercise 6–7

Find the specific equation and then graph the Beta distribution with parameters:

a $p = 1, q = 1$ (Note that $0! = 1$)
b $p = 2, q = 1$
c $p = 2, q = 2$

Answers

a $y = \dfrac{(1 + 1 - 1)!}{(1 - 1)!(1 - 1)!} \, x^{1-1}(1 - x)^{1-1}$

$ = \dfrac{1!}{0!0!} \, x^0(1 - x)^0$

(Remember that $x^0 = 1$ for any value of x.)

So,

$y = \dfrac{1}{1 \times 1} \, 1 \times 1 = 1$

Thus, $y = 1$ whatever the value of x. This plots as a rectangular distribution (see Fig. 6–9).

b $y = \dfrac{(2 + 1 - 1)!}{(2 - 1)!(1 - 1)!} \, x^{2-1}(1 - x)^{1-1}$

$ = \dfrac{2!}{1!0!} \, x^1(1 - x)^0$

$ = \dfrac{2}{1 \times 1} \, x \times 1$

$ = 2x$

This equation is a linear function with y-intercept 0 and slope 2 (see Fig. 6–9).

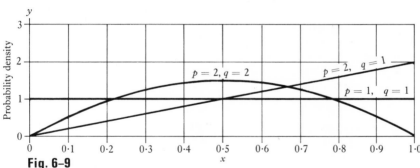

Fig. 6–9
Some Beta distribution

c $y = \dfrac{(2 + 2 - 1)!}{(2 - 1)!(2 - 1)!} \, x^{2-1}(1 - x)^{2-1}$

$ = \dfrac{3!}{1!1!} \, x^1(1 - x)^1$

$ = 6x(1 - x)$

$ = 6(x - x^2)$

This plots as an arc (see Fig. 6–9).

If you will turn to Appendix B you will see a whole gallery of Beta density functions. For convenience, the curves on any one graph all have the same mode. By comparing the curves you should get an idea of what happens to the shape with changes in p and q. (No curves are shown for values of p and q between 0 and 1 because these functions are U-shaped and prior opinion rarely looks like this.)

When p and q are equal (the first page of the gallery) the distributions are symmetrical (right half a mirror image of left half). As p and q become larger, the distribution becomes more peaked.

When p and q are unequal, the distribution is skewed, or non-symmetric. The direction of skew is given by the longer tail of the distribution; if the longer tail is to the right, then the distribution is said to be skewed to the right. Except for the first page, all the Beta distributions in the gallery are skewed to the left. Notice that the skew becomes greater as p and q become more unequal.

Below each graph is a set of lines that show how each curve can be divided into three equal areas. Each curve is associated with one of the lines, indicated by the values of p and q, and the two marks on each line show where the curve should be sliced to make equal areas. For example, the bottom line of the first page of the gallery is associated with the rectangular Beta, and the line shows that the slices should be made at 0·33 and 0·67. Moving up to the next curve, $p = 2$ and $q = 2$, we find that the slices are taken at 0·39 and 0·61. As applied to Bayesian analysis, this means that one third of my opinion falls between possible x-values of 0 to 0·39, another third between 0·39 and 0·61, and the remaining third between 0·61 and 1·0. The implication of holding opinion distributed as Beta with $p = 2$ and $q = 2$ is that if I were to bet on the true, but unknown value of x, I would be indifferent between placing my money on any of the three intervals indicated. They are intervals of equal credibility. These lines are useful in assessing a prior distribution.

No curves are given that have modes less than 0·5. This is because the parameters p and q are symmetrical. Curves whose modes are at 0·4, for example, are the left-to-right mirror image of curves with modes at 0·6; the values of p and q need only to be interchanged to generate curves with modes less than 0·5.

Determining a Beta prior An easy method of assessing your Beta prior is simply to find one that seems reasonable amongst the figures in Appendix B. Here are the steps.

a   Assess the most likely x-value. That is the mode, of course. If the mode is less than 0·5 you can adopt either of these procedures:

  i   Make your inference about the complement of x, that is, about $1 - x$. If you think the proportion of students whose fathers are 'white-collar' is likely to be less than 0·5, then make your inference about the proportion of 'blue-collar' fathers.

  ii   Imagine that the x-axis of the figure is reversed, so the 0 is where the 1 is, and interchange the values of p and q. Then you can make inferences directly about x.

b   Turn to those figures in Appendix B which are characterized by the mode you estimated in Step (a).

c   Choose the distribution which comes closest to your prior opinions. If your prior opinion seems to fall between two distributions, either interpolate* the values of p and q or select the more spread out distribution of the two.

d   Check the appropriate equal-credibility intervals to see that you really think it is equally likely for the true value of x to fall in any one of the three intervals. Another way to think of this is to imagine that you and two other people are each going to place equal bets on the intervals. The other two people get to choose intervals to bet on before you can choose, so you have to take the interval left over. Whoever bets on the interval that turns out to be correct, in the sense that it contains the true value of x, wins the lot. Now, are you happy with last choice of an interval? You should be if you selected a distribution that truly represents your prior opinion. If you are not indifferent among the three intervals you should select another distribution that gives intervals which do seem equally good bets.

e   Record the values of p and q for the curve you chose. Remember to reverse p and q if you have imagined the x-axis to be reversed.

This was the procedure I followed in determining my prior density function shown in Fig. 6–2.

Statistics of the Beta distribution   The parameters p and q can be directly translated into the statistics of the Beta distribution. The mean of a Beta is given by

$$m = \frac{p}{p+q}$$

and the standard deviation is

$$s = \sqrt{\frac{pq}{(p+q)^2(p+q+1)}}$$

The mode of the distribution is

$$\text{mode} = \frac{p-1}{p+q-2}$$

Once you have found the values of p and q you can go on to compute the mean and standard deviation of the distribution. It is not possible to find the median directly from p and q; a table of the cumulative distribution would have to be consulted.

Exercise 6–8

Compute the mean and standard deviation of the prior and posterior Betas of Fig. 6–2. The prior parameters are $p' = 4$ and $q' = 3$; the posterior parameters are $p'' = 21$ and $q'' = 6$. (Note the use of single and double primes to distinguish prior and posterior parameters.)

* Interpolation is explained in Appendix I.

Answers

For the prior,

$$m' = \frac{4}{4+3} = \frac{4}{7} = 0.57$$

$$s' = \sqrt{\frac{4 \times 3}{(4+3)^2(4+3+1)}} = \sqrt{\frac{12}{49 \times 8}}$$

$$= \sqrt{0.030612} = 0.175$$

For the posterior,

$$m'' = \frac{21}{21+6} = \frac{21}{27} = 0.78$$

$$s'' = \sqrt{\frac{21 \times 6}{(21+6)^2(21+6+1)}} = \sqrt{\frac{126}{(27)^2(28)}}$$

$$= \sqrt{0.00617284} = 0.079$$

Recall that those standard deviations were given without explaining their origin in the section 'Parameters and statistics'. Now you can see how they were obtained. First, I looked up my prior in the gallery, noted the values of p and q, and then I used these values in computing the statistics. In a moment we will see how the posterior parameters are obtained.

Credible intervals for the Beta distribution　Finding credible intervals for the Beta density is easy—you just look them up in tables. Tables of highest-density regions can be found in Appendix B. To use them, enter the table with the values of p and q of your distribution, and read off the limits of the desired credible interval. There are two tables, one for 95% credible intervals, the other for 99% credible intervals. Try using the tables to find the posterior credible intervals for the Beta with $p'' = 21$ and $q'' = 6$. Check your results with Table 6–2.

Later in this chapter we will discuss a method for finding credible intervals for Betas whose parameters are larger than those shown in the tables.

Revising opinion for Beta distributions　Revising prior distributions in the light of data is the topic of Part III, but the process is so simple for Beta distributions that a brief introduction here will be instructive.

Suppose that prior opinion about an unknown proportion of events E can be described by a Beta distribution whose parameters are p' and q'. Suppose further that data can be collected in such a way that each observation is independent of the next. Assume that on each observation either an E is observed—call that a 'success', *or* an E is not observed—call that a 'failure'. Take N observations. Let $\bar{s}$ be the number of successes and $\bar{f}$ the number of failures, so $\bar{s} + \bar{f} = N$. Under these conditions the posterior distribution will also be a Beta with parameters p'' and q'' where

$$p'' = p' + \bar{s}$$
$$q'' = q' + \bar{f}$$

That is the result of applying Bayes' theorem.

In the 'white-collar' father example, I started with a Beta prior where

$$p' = 4$$
$$q' = 3$$

Since I was concerned with the proportion of 'white-collar' fathers, it is necessary to define the observation of 'white' as a 'success'. (If I had been making an inference about the proportion of 'blue-collar' fathers, then getting a 'blue' would have been a 'success'.) Twenty independent observations were made, 17 of them 'white', so

$$\bar{s} = 17$$
$$\bar{f} = 3$$

Under these conditions I know that my posterior distribution must also be a Beta, and with parameters

$$p'' = 4+17 = 21$$
$$q'' = 3+3 = 6$$

Knowing the posterior parameters, I can compute the mean and standard deviation of the posterior, and I can look up a credible interval.

So you see it is not necessary to calculate Bayes' theorem for this case. That has already been done, and the result is that you simply add the number of successes to the prior p, and the number of failures to the prior q, to get the posterior parameters.

Exercise 6–9

An investigator wants to determine the proportion of students who have tried hashish in a small college on the west coast of the United States. Before taking a random sample he assesses his prior distribution as Beta with $p' = 8$ and $q' = 4$. In his sample of 50 students he finds 43 who have smoked hashish at least once.

a   Compute the posterior mean and standard deviation.
b   Compare the prior and posterior modes.
c   Compare the posterior and prior 99% credible intervals.

Answers

The parameters of the posterior distribution are:

$$p'' = 8 + 43 = 51$$
$$q'' = 4 + 7 = 11$$

a   The posterior mean is:

$$m'' = \frac{p''}{p'' + q''} = \frac{51}{51 + 11} = \frac{51}{62} = 0\cdot82$$

The posterior standard deviation is:

$$s'' = \sqrt{\frac{51 \times 11}{(51 + 11)^2(51 + 11 + 1)}} = \sqrt{\frac{561}{(62)^2(63)}}$$
$$= \sqrt{0\cdot002317} = 0\cdot048$$

b   prior mode $= \dfrac{p' - 1}{p' + q' - 2} = \dfrac{8 - 1}{8 + 4 - 2} = \dfrac{7}{10} = 0.7$

posterior mode $= \dfrac{51 - 1}{51 + 11 - 2} = \dfrac{50}{60} = 0.83$

The posterior distribution has shifted to the right, nearer 1.0.

c   From the tables in Appendix B:

prior 99% credible interval: $0.326-0.944$
that is, $p(0.326 \leq x \leq 0.944) = 0.99$
posterior 99% credible interval: $0.689-0.931$
that is, $p(0.689 \leq x \leq 0.931) = 0.99$

Thus, the prior range is 0.618 while the posterior range has decreased to 0.242. Even with a sample size of 50, there is still a fair range of uncertainty about the true proportion.

Normal distribution

We will place considerable emphasis on normal distributions in this book, partly because prior opinion can often be expressed in this form, but mainly because statistical methods based on normal distributions have been more completely studied and worked out than for any other distribution.

To a beginner in statistics, the equation of a normal density function looks very formidable indeed:

$$y = \frac{1}{\sqrt{2\pi\sigma^2}} e^{-\frac{1}{2}[(x-\mu)/\sigma]^2}$$

It tells us how we can arrive at y, the probability density, given any value of x. You will never actually have to use this function rule, but it is important to know and understand the various parts of the rule. First, let me define the parts. y is the dependent variable, x is the independent variable. The numbers 1 and 2, and π, are universal constants; you have encountered them before. The letters μ and σ are parameters. So there is nothing in the equation that you have not already seen. It is the way the parts are put together that is new. In words, the function rule says, take the desired value of x, subtract μ and divide the result by σ. Square the resulting quantity and multiply by minus 1/2. Raise e to that power, and multiply the result by 1 over the square root of $2\pi\sigma^2$. The result is y. The only part you would probably have difficulty doing is raising e to the power, but even that is not difficult if you know how to use natural logarithms.

Two examples of normal curves are shown in Fig. 6–10. (For convenience, the y-axis is not shown.) For the left curve the parameters are

$\mu = 125$

$\sigma = 2.5$

while for the right curve they are

$\mu = 130$

$\sigma = 5$

Unlike the Beta distribution, these parameters are easily interpreted; they are the same values as the mean and standard deviation. For a normal distribution

$\mu = m$, the mean

$\sigma = s$, the standard deviation

Remember, too, that for symmetric curves the mean, median and mode are equal, so for a normal density function

$\mu = m = \text{median} = \text{mode}$

Compare the means in Fig. 6–10. One is 5 points above the other, so the peaks of the curves are 5 points apart. Now look at the standard deviations. The right curve is more spread out so it has the larger standard deviation.

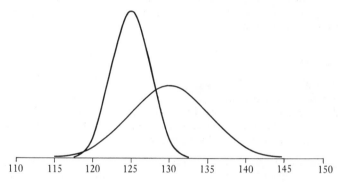

Fig. 6–10
Two normal density functions

These two curves might represent the prior opinion of two professors about to determine the average I.Q. of undergraduate students enrolled in their university. One investigator has taught at the university for many years and feels fairly sure that the average I.Q. is in the vicinity of 125. The other professor is newly appointed to the university, and has not had much previous contact with students. In assessing his prior, he is guided mainly by the reputation of the university as being a high-quality institution attracting top students, but because of his inexperience he is not too sure of his judgement, so he settles for a fairly spread out distribution. Of course the two professors talked to each other before they assessed their priors, and these curves are the final product, after they exchanged information. The new professor feels his colleague's judgement is over influenced by the limited and biased sample of students with whom he comes in contact, while the older professor feels that the newcomer is too dazzled by the institution's reputation. Thus, one mean is lower than the other.

Determining a normal prior   Both professors sketched their prior distribution following the steps outlined at the beginning of this chapter. Their sketches showed curves very slightly skewed to the left, but they were sure that by approximating their priors with normal distributions the slight difference would be of no consequence to the posterior distribution. Then they followed these steps.

a   Assess the most likely x-value. That value is the mean of your prior. (It is also the mode and median, and is the value of the parameter μ.)

b   Find the range of x-values that contains almost all your opinion, that is, almost 100% of your opinion should fall in that range.

c   The range of x-values just found covers 6 standard deviations, so divide the range by 6 to find one standard deviation.

$$s' \simeq \frac{\text{range}}{6}$$

d   Construct three equal-credibility intervals by multiplying the value of s' by 0·43, then adding that product to the mean to get x_{high} and subtracting the product from the mean to get x_{low}. (Justification for this procedure is given in the next section.)

$$x_{\text{low}} = m' - 0 \cdot 43 s'$$

$$x_{\text{high}} = m' + 0 \cdot 43 s'$$

e   Check that you would be just as happy to place a bet on the interval up to x_{low} as on the interval from x_{low} to x_{high} as on the interval above x_{high}. You should think each of those intervals offers an equally fair bet; if you do not, then you must reassess your prior, finding new values of m' or s', or both, until this condition is met.

The newly appointed professor in the example decided that the highest density of his opinion should be in the vicinity of 130, and that nearly all his opinion fell between 115 and 145. That range of 30 implies that

$$s' = \frac{30}{6} = 5$$

Now we turn to the determination of credible intervals.

Credible intervals for the normal distribution   Recall that to find a C per cent credible interval we wish to find values of x_{low} and x_{high} such that

$$p(x_{\text{low}} \leq x \leq x_{\text{high}}) = C/100$$

The general procedure is to consult a table of the cumulative probability function and find values of x_{low} and x_{high} such that C per cent of the area of the curve falls between those x values. Since we are dealing with a symmetric distribution, highest density regions are centred on the mean. Thus, the area above x_{high} will equal the area below x_{low} (see Fig. 6–11). To find the 95% credible interval we could consult a table of the cumulative distribution and read off the value of x with exactly $2\frac{1}{2}\%$ of the distribution below it, and the value of x with exactly $97\frac{1}{2}\%$ of the distribution below it.

The trouble with this procedure is that we would need a great many tables. We could construct a book of cumulative normal tables; each chapter would contain tables for densities with the same mean, and each page in the chapter would be for a different standard deviation. With an infinite number of possible means, and an infinite number of standard deviations, we would have to construct either a very large book, or a coarsely calibrated one.

Fortunately there is a simple alternative procedure. We can apply a linear transformation to any given distribution and end up with a *standard normal distribution* whose mean is 0 with standard deviation of 1. By suitable choice of the constants in the linear equation any normal distribution can be transformed into a standard normal distribution, for which only a single table is necessary.

The transformation is accomplished by expressing each *x*-value as a number of standard deviations above or below the mean. Let me develop this intuitively, then I will express it formally.

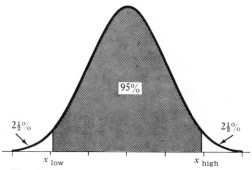

95%

$2\frac{1}{2}\%$ $2\frac{1}{2}\%$

x low x high

Fig. 6–11
The 95% credible interval for the normal distribution

Suppose we take the newly appointed professor's prior distribution, shown by itself in Fig. 6–12(a). First let us subtract the mean, 130, from every value of *x*. That has the effect of moving the curve to the left until its mean is zero. Notice that the standard deviation is unchanged by this transformation [see Fig. 6–12(b)]. The numbers on the *x*-axis now show deviations of *x*-values from the mean. For example, 145 is now expressed as 15 because it is 15 units above 130. The horizontal axis is still measured in the original units, however. To get rid of the units, and to standardize the spread of the distribution, we can divide the deviations by the standard deviation [see Fig. 6–12(c)]. Now the numbers on the horizontal axis show deviations, in units of the standard deviation. The original value of 145 which became 15 after the first transformation is now $15/5 = 3$. The resulting normal distribution is very tall because the area under the curve must remain at 1. Since it is also very squeezed together, I have stretched the *x*-axis, shrunk the *y*-axis, and redrawn the distribution in Fig. 6–13. This is the standard normal distribution, for which

$$\mu = 0 \quad \text{and} \quad \sigma = 1.$$

The numbers on the horizontal axis will be referred to as *z*-values; they are *x*-values that have been transformed by application of this linear equation:

$$z = \frac{x - m}{s}$$

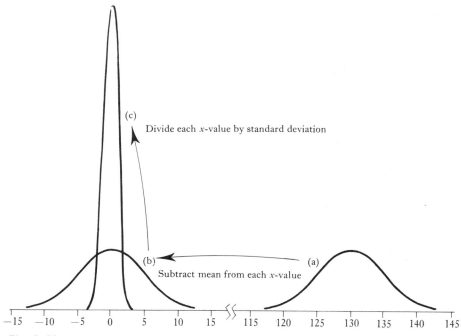

Fig. 6–12
Successive transformations of a normal density function to yield a standard normal distribution

In words, the equation says to subtract the mean, *m*, from the *x*-value, then divide the difference by the standard deviation, *s*. That is what we did in Fig. 6–12.

Now suppose you had done this for the other prior distribution in Fig. 6–10. If you try it you will end up with the standard normal distribution. Generalizing, **every normal distribution, whatever the values of μ and σ, can be**

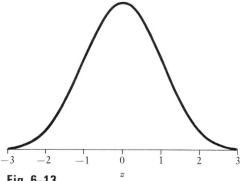

Fig. 6–13
Standard normal distribution

transformed into the standard normal distribution, whose mean is zero and standard deviation is one. Why is this so? Because basically all that is being changed is the x-axis; it is being transformed into a different unit of measurement that is used as a standard. Some analogies may clarify this. Transforming one normal distribution to another is similar to changing yards to metres, or feet to metres, or inches to metres, or any unit of length to metres. Nothing is lost in the transformation, only the units of measurement change. Nothing is lost in changing one normal distribution to another, only the units along the horizontal axis change. Another example is given by temperature. If I decide that a Kelvin scale is the most convenient to use, I can always transform a Fahrenheit or centigrade reading to a Kelvin reading through an appropriate linear function rule. Any temperature scale can be changed to a Kelvin scale through application of the appropriate linear transformation.

Transformations work two ways. Centigrade can be changed to Kelvin, but so can a Kelvin reading be expressed in centigrade. How can a z-value be expressed as an x-value? Since

$$z = \frac{x - m}{s},$$

we can solve this equation for x:

$$sz = x - m$$

$$x = m + sz$$

Now z is the independent variable. You multiply z by the standard deviation and add the mean. Thus, if the professor says his prior is normally distributed with mean of 130 and standard deviation of 5, you can sketch Fig. 6–13 and re-label the horizontal axis: for 0, substitute the mean, 130; when you move out to 1, you are one standard deviation above the mean, or 5 units above 130, so 1 becomes 135; at 2 you are two standard deviations above the mean, at 140; when you are at -1 you are one standard deviation *below* the mean, at 125; etc. **Each z-value of the standard normal distribution indicates the number of standard deviations above or below the mean.** For example, a score of 145 could be described as being '3 standard deviations above the mean'.

Like all normal distributions, the standard normal distribution extends from minus infinity to plus infinity, but the major portion of the curve occurs within a fairly narrow range of z-values; most of the curve falls between -3 and $+3$. In other words, it spans 6 standard deviations. Now you can see why the range of prior opinion in x-values is divided by 6 to obtain the standard deviation. Tabling the cumulative standard normal distribution is quite easy, for only a narrow range of z-values need be included in the table.

Appendix F gives the cumulative probabilities of the standard normal distribution. The second column of the table gives the cumulative probability, but only for *positive* values of z. Cumulative probability up to *negative* values of z can be found by subtracting the tabled value from 1·0; that has been done in the next column. Note that the area to the left of $-z$ is the same as the area to the right of $+z$. The last column gives the area between $-z$ and $+z$.

Exercise 6–10

An investigator assesses his prior distribution concerning some uncertain quantity, x, to be normal with

$$m = 55$$
$$s = 10$$

What is the probability that the true value of x is:

a   less than 65?

b   less than 35?

Answers

The first step in the solution is to change the problem from a statement about x-values to one about z-values. We do this by applying the linear transformation

$$z = \frac{x - m}{s}$$

a   First change 65 to its corresponding z-value:

$$z = \frac{65 - 55}{10} = \frac{10}{10} = 1$$

Now we can re-phrase the problem in terms of the z-value. We want to find

$$p(z \leq 1\cdot0)$$

What is the probability that the true value of z is less than 1? To find this look in the table, Appendix F. Go down the first column until you come to a z-value of $1\cdot0$. Then read off the cumulative probability in column 2. The answer is $0\cdot8413$. So,

$$p(z \leq 1\cdot0) = 0\cdot8413$$

and so

$$p(x \leq 65) = 0\cdot8413$$

b   Find the z-value corresponding to $x = 35$:

$$z = \frac{35 - 55}{10} = \frac{-20}{10} = -2$$

From the symmetry of the normal distribution it should be obvious that

$$p(z \leq -2) = 1 - p(z \leq +2) = p(z \geq +2)$$

From the third column of the table we find that:

$$p(z \leq -2) = 0\cdot0228$$

which is equivalent to saying that

$$p(x \leq 35) = 0\cdot0228$$

Exercise 6–11

For the prior distribution given in Exercise 6–10, what is the probability that the true value of x falls within $2\cdot5$ standard deviations of the mean?

Answer

Look up 2·5 in the table, Appendix F. The value in the last column gives

$$p(-2·5 \leq z \leq +2·5) = 0·9876$$

Verify for yourself that that statement is equivalent to this one:

$$p(30 \leq x \leq 80) = 0·9876$$

Finally, the table can be used to find credible intervals. Here are the steps to find the C per cent credible interval for a normal density function:

a Find the probability $C/100$ in the fourth column of the table in Appendix F.
b Read off the corresponding z-value in the first column.
c Transform the positive z-value into x_{high} and x_{low} using these equations:

$$x_{high} = m + sz$$
$$x_{low} = m - sz$$

Exercise 6–12

Find the posterior 99% credible interval for the prior distribution given in Exercise 6–10.

Answer

From the table in Appendix F we find that

$$p(-2·58 \leq z \leq 2·58) = 0·99$$

Transforming to x values:

$$x_{high} = 55 + 10(2·58) = 55 + 25·8 = 80·8$$
$$x_{low} = 55 - 10(2·58) = 55 - 25·8 = 29·2$$

Thus,

$$p(29·2 \leq x \leq 80·8) = 0·99$$

This last problem shows that it is necessary to go up and down 2·58 standard deviations from the mean to get the 99% credible interval. Reference to the table in Appendix F shows that for the 95% credible interval you would travel 1·96 standard deviations from the mean, while for the 99·9% interval you would go 3·29 standard deviations away. You will use these numbers often, so to save yourself trouble later, you might memorize them now. They are shown graphically in Fig. 6–14.

Exercise 6–13

How many standard deviations from the mean of a normal density function must one go to form three equal credible intervals?

Answer

Three equal intervals will each contain 1/3 of the area. We wish to find z_{low} and z_{high} such that

$$p(z_{low} \leq z \leq z_{high}) = 0·3333$$

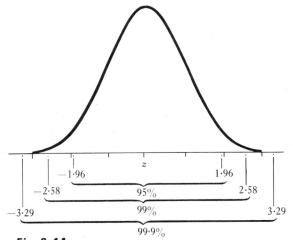

Fig. 6-14
Common credible intervals for the standard normal distribution

Reference to the table in Appendix F gives a z-value of 0.43. Thus, three equal-credibility intervals for any normal distribution can be found by travelling 0.43 standard deviations from the mean, in both directions:

$$x_{low} = m - 0.43s$$
$$x_{high} = m + 0.43s$$

This result justifies step (d) under 'Determining a normal prior'.

Be sure you understand the steps in finding a credible interval for a normal density function; it is an important procedure in Bayesian analysis.

Normal approximation to the Beta

You may have noticed that the very peaked Beta density functions in Appendix B look like normal density functions, especially for curves whose modes are not too far from 0.5. That observation, which is correct, allows us to compute credible intervals for Betas whose parameters are too large to be found in the Beta tables of Appendix B. The general procedure is to compute the mean and standard deviation of the Beta by using the formulae that involve the parameters, then to use the mean and standard deviation to find the credible interval, *assuming that the density is normal*. You follow the procedures for finding a credible interval for a normal density function, using the statistics computed from the Beta parameters.

Exercise 6-14

An investigator's prior concerning some uncertain proportion is Beta with $p' = 4$ and $q' = 3$. He takes 100 observations and observes 62 successes. What is his posterior 99.9% credible interval?

Answer

Under these conditions, his posterior will be Beta with $p'' = 62 + 4 = 66$ and $q'' = 38 + 3 = 41$. This gives a posterior mean of

$$m'' = \frac{66}{66 + 41} = \frac{66}{107} = 0\cdot 62$$

and a posterior standard deviation of

$$s'' = \sqrt{\frac{66 \times 41}{(66 + 41)^2(66 + 41 + 1)}} = \sqrt{\frac{2706}{(107)^2(108)}}$$
$$= \sqrt{0\cdot 002188} = 0\cdot 0468$$

For a normal distribution with that mean and standard deviation, the posterior 99·9% credible interval is given by:

$$x_{\text{low}} = 0\cdot 62 - 3\cdot 29(0\cdot 0468) = 0\cdot 62 - 0\cdot 15 = 0\cdot 47$$
$$x_{\text{high}} = 0\cdot 62 + 3\cdot 29(0\cdot 0468) = 0\cdot 62 + 0\cdot 15 = 0\cdot 77$$

When is it appropriate to use this approximation? The answer depends on how accurately you wish to specify the credible interval and on how close the mode of the Beta density is to 0·5. In general, the approximation holds for values of p and q that are large and not too unequal. However, the larger p and q are, the more unequal they can be for the approximation still to be good. To give you some feeling for the accuracy of the normal approximation, Table 6–3 gives the exact and approximate credible intervals for Beta distributions whose modes are 0·7 (pictured in Appendix B). Notice that the normal

Table 6–3 99% credible intervals, determined exactly and by normal approximations, for various Beta distributions whose modes are 0·7

p, q	Exact interval	Approx. interval
8, 4	0·32–0·94	0·33–1·01
15, 7	0·41–0·89	0·43–0·93
22, 10	0·47–0·87	0·48–0·90
50, 22	0·55–0·82	0·56–0·83

approximation comes closer to the exact results as the curve becomes more peaked. Even so, two-place accuracy would only be assured for values of p and q larger than those in the table. Note that the approximation is conservative: the approximate interval is larger than the exact one. In general, the credible interval will not be far wrong provided that the *smaller* of p or q is 10 or more. When designing an experiment, you should arrange to collect a sample that is big enough to ensure the desired accuracy in the posterior credible interval if you think you will have to use the normal approximation to the Beta.

Rectangular or uniform distribution

Sometimes prior opinion will be so vague that we will feel justified in assigning a uniform prior distribution over a wide range of possible values of the uncertain quantity. This plots as a rectangle (see Fig. 6–3). Practically speaking, it is only necessary to say that your prior is uniform, and we do not bother with statistics and parameters of the distribution. We will always assume that a uniform prior extends well beyond the range of x-values covered by the data.

It is not really correct to say that total ignorance of the value of the uncertain quantity justifies a uniform prior. A uniform prior expresses vagueness, not ignorance. There are logical difficulties with the concept 'ignorance' that make it impossible to quantify. Suppose, for example, that I am ignorant about the value of some proportion. If I assign a uniform prior over x then I am saying that I feel just as sure that the true value of x lies between, say 0·5 and 0·75, as that it lies between 0·75 and 1·0. Now let us look at the implication of that statement for the prior concerning the odds, $x/(1-x)$. The odds corresponding to 0·5, 0·75 and 1·0 are 0·5/0·5 = 1, 0·75/0·25 = 3, and 1·0/0 = ∞. A uniform prior for x implies, then, that I have the same amount of opinion between odds of 1 and 3 as between 3 and ∞. But a uniform prior for the odds would require equal probability between 1 and 3 as between 3 and 5, not 3 and ∞. Thus, if I am ignorant about x, then I must be ignorant about $x/(1-x)$, yet a uniform prior for x implies, logically, a non-uniform prior for $x/(1-x)$. That is why ignorance cannot be quantified.

6.4 Principle of stable estimation

An important application of uniform priors is found in the principle of stable estimation. The purpose of the principle is to justify using a uniform prior even though your actual prior is not uniform. This will happen whenever the data are highly informative relative to the prior. This happens, in the discrete case, whenever the prior odds are near 1 and the likelihood ratio is very far from 1. Then the posterior probabilities are controlled almost exclusively by the likelihood ratio.

The principle of stable estimation allows a Bayesian analysis to proceed using a uniform prior whenever the actual prior is fairly gentle. But what is meant by 'gentle'? With experience, you will frequently be able to tell at a glance. A formal definition of 'gentle' would be too cumbersome and complicated to apply, so let me offer a procedure which is not mathematically rigorous but which will serve well in most situations.

a   Sketch your prior distribution. If you are quite vague about it, a rough sketch will suffice.

b   After collecting data, calculate your posterior distribution on the assumption that your prior is uniform.

c   Find the 99% credible interval. (The 99·9% or 99·99% credible interval would be even better.)

d   Look at your actual prior distribution within this credible interval. Check to see that prior opinion within the interval is almost constant. If it is, then stable estimation applies, and you are justified in using a uniform prior rather than your actual prior (see Fig. 6–15).

A more complete statement of the principle of stable estimation can be found in Edwards, Lindman, and Savage (1963).

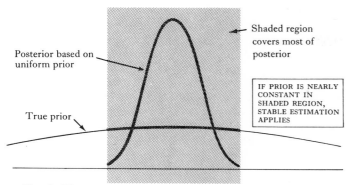

Fig. 6–15
Practical application of the principle of stable estimation

Let us try this out on the 'white-collar' father problem. Recall that the actual prior was Beta with $p' = 4$ and $q' = 3$. Seventeen 'successes' out of 20 were observed, so the posterior was Beta with $p'' = 21$ and $q'' = 6$. Now let us see if we could have used the principle of stable estimation to justify a uniform prior. We follow the steps just outlined:

a   The prior is shown in Fig. 6–2.

b   For a uniform Beta, $p' = 1$ and $q' = 1$. Thus, the posterior would be Beta with $p'' = 18$ and $q'' = 4$.

c   The posterior 99% credible interval is

$$0 \cdot 59 \leq x \leq 0 \cdot 98$$

d   At $x = 0 \cdot 6$, the prior probability density is highest, about 2. At $x = 0 \cdot 98$, the prior density is lowest, less than $0 \cdot 1$. It is clear that 2 is *much* more, in percentage terms, than $0 \cdot 1$, so stable estimation does not apply.

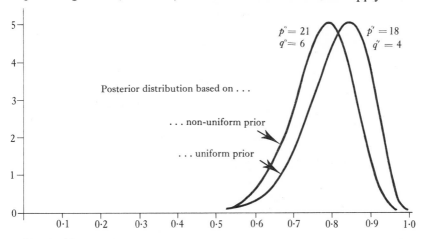

Fig. 6–16
Posterior distributions after 17 successes and 3 failures based on uniform prior, and on prior Beta with $p' = 4 \; q' = 3$

You can see this graphically by comparing the posterior distribution in Fig. 6–2 with the posterior that results from a uniform prior. Both distributions are shown in Fig. 6–16, and it is clear that they are substantially different. Of course you can always check to see if stable estimation applies by computing both posteriors and comparing them, but the steps I have given eliminate the necessity for precisely assessing your actual prior. The advantage of this procedure is that you may be so vague about your prior that you feel uncomfortable about your sketch, yet you do feel fairly certain about the check in Step (d). **By exploiting certain features of very vague prior opinion we are justified in accepting a precise quantification in the form of a uniform distribution.** Thus, the principle of stable estimation provides a possible way of specifying a prior density function even though an individual may feel that his prior opinion is so vague that he is reluctant to quantify it.

Exercise 6–15

An investigator is unsure of the proportion of registered voters in a medium-sized community who would favour fluoridization of the public water supply. In considering his prior opinion he is sure only that the proportion is neither 0 nor 1. A prior in the form of a Beta density with $p' = 2$ and $q' = 2$ could be considered a rather too precise quantification of his vague opinion.

He takes a random sample of 100, discarding 2 registered voters who were never home, and is left with exactly 49 people in favour and 49 people opposing. Is he justified in using stable estimation to determine his posterior density?

Answer

Assume a uniform prior. Then the posterior is a Beta with $p'' = 50$ and $q'' = 50$, and the 99% credible interval is $0.37 \leq x \leq 0.63$. Reference to a prior Beta with $p' = 2$ and $q' = 2$ shows that within the range of 0·37–0·63, the prior distribution changes very slightly (though you can't see it on the graph, the change is from 1·4 to 1·5, an increase of about 7%). This change is not enough to invalidate stable estimation. We would do better to ask the investigator about the change of his opinion within the interval; he is likely to say that he can find no perceptible change.

Another important use of stable estimation is in situations where prior opinion does not conform to any of the standard distributions. Further introspection by the investigator may reveal that while the prior is non-conforming it is still sufficiently vague to justify application of the principle of stable estimation. That saves a lot of messy mathematics.

Heavy emphasis is placed in this book on analyses that start with uniform priors, for it is my experience that prior opinion is often quite vague. This is particularly true for the scientist who is conducting an experiment in a field new to him; the majority of readers of this book will be in that category.

6.5 Summary

Opinion about the true value of an uncertain quantity can be expressed as a probability density function. This shows probability density (along the y-axis) as a function of possible values of the uncertain quantity (along the

x-axis). The first step in a Bayesian analysis is to sketch your prior distribution. Sometimes that sketch can be reasonably approximated by either a normal, Beta, or uniform distribution. Often prior opinion will be sufficiently vague to permit application of the principle of stable estimation; then you are justified in assuming a uniform prior.

Next a sample is collected from a population, and finally Bayes' theorem is applied to determine the posterior distribution. Very often posterior opinion is communicated in the form of a credible interval, leading the investigator to report that he is 'C per cent certain that the true value of the uncertain quantity falls between x_{low} and x_{high}'. The point of a Bayesian analysis is to permit a valid inference to be made, on the basis of the prior and the sample, to the population at large. A generalization is made based on specific, incomplete information.

Bayesian analysis is facilitated by describing prior opinion in a form that enables it to be specified as a mathematical function. By appropriate choice of parameters, a general function can generate an entire family of different curves, and one of these is likely to describe your prior opinion adequately. Using these functions in revising opinion is straightforward; the prior and posterior distributions are in the same family, and the prior parameters are changed by the data to yield the posterior parameters.

When reporting a C per cent credible interval, the shortest one is usually chosen. That will be the interval containing the highest density of opinion, that is, no density outside the interval is larger than any density inside the interval. Credible intervals are computed by reference to cumulative probability functions. It is necessary to consult a table of such a function to determine credible intervals for the normal distribution, a symmetrical distribution, but for the Beta distribution the work of finding the highest density region for these (usually) non-symmetrical functions has already been done by computer and the results tabled.

Statistics of a distribution are often more intuitively meaningful than the parameters. One useful statistic is the mean, the value of x directly under the centre of gravity of the distribution. It is a measure of the central tendency of the distribution. Two other measures of central tendency are the mode, the value of x under the peak of the density function, and the median, the value of x below which exactly half the curve can be found.

Prior opinion about an uncertain quantity that can take on values only from 0 to 1·0, such as a proportion, is often described by a Beta density function, This is a two-parameter distribution that generates a very versatile family of functions. A prior Beta is assessed by finding a curve in the gallery (Appendix B) that appears to describe adequately one's opinion and then checking the three equal-credibility intervals to see that equal amounts of opinion fall in those intervals. If the data consist of independent observations, each of which is either a 'success' or a 'failure', then the posterior distribution is also a Beta with posterior parameters determined by adding the number of successes to the prior parameter p', and by adding the number of failures to the prior parameter q'.

Another useful description of prior opinion about an uncertain quantity is the normal density function. This is a two-parameter distribution whose parameters are equal to the mean and standard deviation of the distribution.

Assessing a normal prior is a matter of determining the mean and standard deviation of the function. The *C* per cent credible interval is found by consulting a table of the standard normal distribution and then applying a linear transformation to convert the tabled *z*-values into the limits of the credible interval. A Beta distribution can be approximated by a normal density function whenever the *smaller* of *p* or *q* is 10 or more.

The rectangular or uniform distribution is often used to describe vague prior opinion. A state of no opinion, or 'ignorance', cannot be quantified; a uniform prior in this case is not satisfactory.

The principle of stable estimation justifies using a uniform prior whenever the actual prior is fairly gentle.

Problems

6–1 For each of the following uncertain quantities, sketch your prior distribution and discuss the possibility that one of the standard distributions (uniform, normal or Beta) can be used to approximate your prior.

a The proportion of all students in your college or university who have a savings account in their name in a bank.

b The average number of calories in all the food eaten yesterday by each student in your college or university.

c The proportion of all students in your college or university who have attended a regularly-scheduled church service this term.

d The number of hours per week the average college or university student in your country spends on all activities directly related to his or her course of study.

e The date of the next major earthquake, comparable to the great earthquakes of 1857 and 1906, along the San Andreas fault in California, assuming that geophysicists do nothing to prevent it. (Some relevant information: The opposite sides of the fault are currently slipping past each other at the rate of 5 centimetres per year. Dr. J. Weertman of the Scott Polar Research Institute has carried out research indicating that a major earthquake will occur when the total slip reaches about 8 metres. At the current rate of slip, that point should be reached 120 years after the slip started. But there is some uncertainty about whether the slip started in 1857 or in 1906.)

6–2 For each of the prior distributions in question 6–1 that you felt could be approximated by a standard distribution, determine

a the parameters of the distribution.

b the mean and standard deviation.

c the 95% and 99% credible intervals.

6–3 The following table gives my cumulative probability distribution for some uncertain quantity, *x*.

x	probability up to *x*
25	0·001
30	0·006
35	0·023
40	0·067
45	0·159
50	0·308
55	0·500

x	probability up to x
60	0·692
65	0·841
70	0·933
75	0·977
80	0·994
85	0·999

a What is the probability that the true value of x

i   is less than 60?
ii is greater than 45?
iii lies between 75 and 35?
iv lies outside the interval 30 to 80?

b For the cumulative function given above, find the highest density region 90% credible interval. (*Hint:* Do it graphically.)

6–4 My prior opinion about the average score of the statistics class on a questionnaire that purports to measure conservatism is normally distributed with a mean of 30 and a standard deviation of 5.

a What is the probability that the average score

i   is less than 25?
ii is greater than 40?
iii falls between 20 and 40?

b Find both my 95% and 99% credible intervals.

6–5 Suppose my prior distribution concerning the proportion of students in my statistics class who received Church of England upbringing is Beta with parameters $p' = 7$ and $q' = 5$. In a sample of 30 students, randomly selected, 15 were or are C of E, and the rest were raised in other denominations or in none.

a Show that the posterior 95% credible interval is smaller than the prior one by computing both, and comparing them.

b Compute the prior and posterior means and standard deviations.

c Note that the posterior standard deviation is smaller than the prior standard deviation. Why is the reduction in uncertainty from prior to posterior usually reported by giving the credible interval of the posterior distribution rather than the standard deviation?

6–6 A psychology student working for the BBC conducted a survey of students enrolled in correspondence colleges who were advised to use particular BBC programmes in their studies. A questionnaire was administered to a carefully-selected sample of students. One question asked, 'Did you watch or listen to any of the programmes?' Of the 342 respondents, 135 replied they had. Consider the population proportion of 'Yes' responses; assume stable estimation applies.

a What is the mode of the Beta posterior distribution?

b What are the parameters of the posterior Beta?

c What are the limits of his posterior 99% credible interval?

6–7 Here is a simple experiment your instructor could arrange to be carried out in class.

The ability to smell freesias appears to have a genetic basis. People either report that the flower is very fragrant or that it has only a faint odour or none at all.

What is the exact proportion of all people who would say that the flower is very fragrant? Consider that proportion to be an uncertain quantity. Assume that your class is a random sample of all people.

a   Sketch your prior distribution.

b   Pass around a bunch of freesias in your class, and note the number of students who say they are very fragrant and the number who say they are not. (Alternatively, if freesias are unobtainable, ask the chemistry department to make up a weak solution of phenyl-thio-carbamide. This chemical either tastes very bitter or is reported to be tasteless or insipid. Students can taste pieces of blotting paper that have been dipped in the solution. The inference should be made about the proportion of people who say that the chemical tastes very bitter.)

c   Determine your posterior distribution, and find the 95% credible interval.

d   Does stable estimation apply to your prior?

Part 2
Dealing with data

7 · Measurement

After assessing his prior opinions, an investigator is ready to collect data. In addition to setting up an experiment and making measurements, he must decide how to attach numbers to the observations he makes and he must understand the meaning of those numbers. Later, he will wish to summarize those numbers as statistics so he can efficiently communicate his results to others. These are the procedures we turn to next in this chapter and in the three chapters to follow. Then in Part III we show how summary statistics are combined with prior information, using Bayes' theorem, of course, to yield posterior opinion.

Back in Chapter 1 I said: If a social scientist carelessly attaches numbers to his observations or to his data, no amount of sophisticated statistical manipulation of those numbers will make them any more meaningful than the original assignment. What comes out of the statistical mill is no better than what goes in.

Now I wish to pick up that point and elaborate it in this chapter, for it is necessary to see how numbers are assigned to data.

When a scientist conducts an experiment he observes *properties*, like the weight of an object, the intelligence of an individual, or the rate of growth of the economy. Often he assigns numbers to the properties; that is the process called *measurement*, and it can be the subject of study itself. Strangely, in the long history of science, logical analysis of the measurement process has only been carried out since the turn of the century. Yet it is important to appreciate certain aspects of measurement theory, for failure to do so can lead the social scientist to claim from his data more than is justified. For example, the weatherman reports that the low temperature last night was 40°F, while the daytime high today was 80°F. Am I justified in saying that today's high temperature was twice that of last night's low? The answer is no, and it is important to see why, but that comes later. First we must look at the steps in carrying out a scientific experiment, then we consider four aspects of the theory of measurement, and finally we present five types of measurement scale.

By the time you have completed this chapter, you should

be acquainted with the processes involved in carrying out a scientific investigation;

understand the distinctions between the four problems encountered in measurement theory: representation, uniqueness, meaningfulness, and scaling;

understand the differences between nominal, ordinal, interval, ratio, and absolute scales of measurement.

7.1 Scientific inquiry

Contrary to the popular opinion of scientists as logical, methodical creatures, following single-mindedly the investigation of some matter, science is often conducted in seemingly haphazard fashion. Data collected today may suggest a new theory to the scientist, leading him to modify his experiment. He may try out a new idea by 'pre-testing' it, a procedure in which he carries out a 'mini-experiment' with inadequate controls, sloppy measurement and insufficient observations. This is when prior opinion is sharpened, measurement techniques perfected, experimental design carefully worked out. It is often a time when the scientist's creative faculties are in full swing, and it may extend

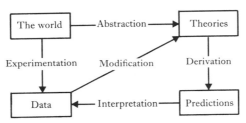

Fig. 7–1
Phases in a scientific investigation

over a few days or several years. Eventually, he carries out a well designed experiment, in which information is collected in a systematic manner, and which will, he hopes, reduce the scientist's prior uncertainty. It is not uncommon for a scientist to have carried out so much pre-testing that he is quite certain of the results of his experiment, and he conducts his experiment mainly to enable him to report his results in a manner acceptable to his profession. Research reported in a journal is an end product that does not reveal very much of the trial-and-error steps that led up to the study. Failure to appreciate this process can easily cause the student in the social sciences to feel quite discouraged when the one-term research project does not work out quite so neatly as the student had hoped.

Behind this activity of the scientist, various phases can be identified. These are shown in Fig. 7–1 (after Coombs, Tversky, and Dawes, 1970). Start in the upper left corner. A scientist observes certain features of the world, characteristics of people or societies, or properties of things, and he *abstracts* certain features, building theories of the relationships among those features. A theory may be expressed in words, in mathematical form, or in any other symbolic system. A particular representation of all or parts of a theory is often called a *model*. For example, the three probability laws and their corollaries can be considered mathematical models of those abstractions called probabilities. In this example, 'the world' consists of people with varying degrees of belief, these degrees of belief are represented as numbers between 0 and 1, and a set of models (laws) is constructed to show how those numbers operate. These models serve as an abstraction of a small portion of the world.

Once we have a theory, or model, we can subject it to certain admissible logical operations in order to *derive* new *predictions*. For example, the probability laws can be manipulated according to the logical rules of mathematics to derive Bayes' Theorem. We can predict how an individual will revise his opinions in the light of new information.

Now go back to the upper left-hand box. The scientist engages in *experimentation* which yields *data*. In our example he may carry out an experiment on revision of opinion, like the bag-and-poker-chip exercise in Chapter 5. The question is, did our subjects revise their opinions in the manner predicted by Bayes' theorem? The answer depends very much on our *interpretation* of the data. If Bayes' theorem predicts that posterior probabilities should be 0·85–0·15 in a particular case, and a subject assesses 0·83–0·17, is that close enough to say that the model predicts reasonably well? If 50 subjects in the experiment give various assessments whose *average* is 0·85–0.15, can we say that Bayes' theorem adequately describes the behaviour of real people? In short, how closely must data match the predictions of a model? How big must the mis-match be to justify rejecting the model?

These are questions for statistics to answer, for we are asking the question, 'What degrees of belief can I, the investigator, assign to the hypothesis that the model is correct, now that I have gathered these data?' In other words, what is $p(H|D)$? Statistics helps us to assess the degree of fit between data and model.

If we discover that the fit is not very good, we may wish to engage in some *modification* of the model. We know from our bag-and-poker-chip experiment that in that situation people do not revise opinions as Bayes' theorem prescribes, so we might wish to build a theory about the discrepancies between subjects' probability assessments and those prescribed by Bayes' theorem. This theory might take into account psychological factors, like past experience in assessing probabilities. Then with our new theory we develop a model which leads to new predictions that can be tested with a new experiment, and so the process continues.

If this were a book on the conduct of scientific investigations, you can see it would have to cover more than statistics, for statistics is mainly concerned only with the *interpretation* process in Fig. 7–1. To be complete, the book would also have to discuss *experimentation*: how experiments are designed and carried out, sometimes called 'methodology', and how measurements are made, which will be discussed briefly in this chapter. A section on logic and deduction would be necessary, for these are both involved in the process of *derivation*. Finally, something should be said about problem solving and the creative process, for *abstraction* and *modification* both involve the creative faculties of the scientist.

Of course, Fig. 7–1 gives an over-simplified view of the conduct of a scientific investigation. Many of the processes are going on all at once and sometimes the directions of the arrows are reversed. Some processes, like experimentation and interpretation, are not really independent but are closely linked. Still, I hope that this discussion serves to illuminate the major steps in a scientific investigation, and, in particular, helps to show where statistics fits in the grand scheme of things.

7.2 Problems in measurement

Perhaps a more accurate description of the process of measurement would be to say that a correspondence is set up between properties of the world and a number system. That way of describing measurement emphasizes the distinction between properties and numbers, and it is important to be clear about this. When I observe the thermometer registering 80°F, I say, 'The temperature now is 80°F', but I do not actually mean that the temperature and the number are the same thing. The number represents, or stands for, temperature, and it may or may not be true that anything I can say about numbers is also true of temperature. The number 80 is certainly twice the number 40, but is the temperature the 80 represents twice the temperature 40 represents?

Recall the distinction made in Chapter 1 between fundamental and derived measurement. In fundamental measurement a property, such as length, is measured in terms of the same property, length. But in derived measurement a property is measured in terms of a different property: temperature is measured by height (of liquid in a tube), voltage by length (of the indicated position from the reference position). In both types of measurement we use numbers to represent properties, but in derived measurement the property represented is not really the property we are interested in, which is the *underlying property*. In what follows we will always be referring to the relationship between characteristics of the numerical system and characteristics of the underlying property. In the temperature example, I am not really interested in the relationship between properties of the numbers on the thermometer and properties of the height of the liquid, but I am concerned about the correspondence between properties of numbers on the thermometer and properties of temperature.

In this section we look at the relationship between numbers and the underlying properties they purport to measure. There are four problems to consider.

a   Representation. We first need to establish that a property we would like to measure can be represented by some numerical system.

b   Uniqueness. We next need to know how free we are in assigning numbers to the property.

c   Scaling. Then we have to construct a scale that will permit us to make measurements.

d   Meaningfulness. Finally, we must know what statements that are true of the numbers we have assigned are also true of the property.

Representation and uniqueness

These are the fundamental problems of measurement theory. We need to show that numbers can be assigned to properties and that relationships between the numbers reflect corresponding relationships about the properties. To show these things formally is not an easy task, and social scientists have mainly ignored the problem. They usually proceed either by investigating only those properties that are 'obviously' measurable, like proportion of people who hold a particular attitude, or time to react in a given situation, or number of correct responses in a problem-solving task, or they assume with little or no formal justification that measurements of a certain type can be made, like I.Q. or the scores on most personality tests.

The formal approach to these problems is beyond the scope of this book, though I can give some indication of the general line of thinking. It is to establish certain self-evident truths, or 'axioms', about relations concerning the property, then to prove formally that a numerical system exists for measuring the relations, and then to show that the characteristics of the property are reflected in the characteristics of the numbers.

Suppose, for example, that I wish to measure intelligence, and I am interested in the relation 'more than'. Am I justified in saying that if person A is more intelligent than person B, and if person B is more intelligent than person C, then it follows that A is more intelligent than C? This kind of relationship is called *transitivity* and it would seem to be satisfied for intelligence. Then it can be formally proven that a numerical representation for 'more intelligent' exists. We call the numerical measurement I.Q., intelligence quotient, to distinguish it from the underlying property, intelligence. Notice that because of errors in measurement, transitivity may not hold with respect to I.Q. How can we say that transitivity is true of intelligence? From our theories of intelligence. We must have a theory about the property we are measuring before we can formally justify our measurement operations.

Now let us turn to the uniqueness problem. So far we have only established that we can assign numbers, I.Q.'s, to persons A, B, and C. If there are no errors in our measurement, and A > B > C reflects the order of their intelligence, then the I.Q. of A must be larger than the I.Q. of B and B's I.Q. must be larger than that of C. Symbolically,

$$I.Q.(A) > I.Q.(B) > I.Q.(C)$$

I could assign any numbers which show that same relationship; here are three possibilities:

$$I.Q.(A) = 110, \quad I.Q.(B) = 100, \quad I.Q.(C) = 90$$
$$I.Q.(A) = 101, \quad I.Q.(B) = 100, \quad I.Q.(C) = 99$$
$$I.A.(A) = 120, \quad I.Q.(B) = 100, \quad I.Q.(C) = 95$$

For all of these, the transitive relation is observed.

But now suppose I ask you to consider the differences in intelligence between the people. Is the difference between A and B's intelligences the same as, less than, or greater than the difference between B and C? In other words, can *differences* in intelligence be ordered, or is it impossible to make any statement about differences in intelligence? Here, again, we must rely on theory to answer the question, but unfortunately theories of intelligence do not give an unequivocal answer to the question. Some theorists would say that within a specified range of I.Q. scores it is possible to order differences in intelligence, others would say it is not. Suppose, for the moment, that we can, and that the difference between A and B is the same as that between B and C. Then, the first two measurement schemes above would be permissible, but the third would not because the equation

$$I.Q.(A) - I.Q.(B) = I.Q.(B) - I.Q.(C)$$

is not satisfied. If on the other hand, the difference between A and B is larger than the difference between B and C, then only the third scheme would be satisfactory. So, this added restriction of preserving the ordering of differences imposes constraints on the numbers I can use to represent intelligence over and above the constraint imposed by transitivity. For this example, we would say that any measurement scale can be used that preserves the ordering of intelligence and the ordering of differences in intelligence.

This is an example of the formal approach to representation and uniqueness. It is, however, not often applied because it is difficult to build theories that enable us to answer questions of uniqueness and representation, and so an empirical approach is more commonly used. This consists of assuming that a particular scale of measurement is appropriate, and then checking to see that predictions made on the basis of scale measurements are useful and not internally inconsistent. We turn to this approach next.

Meaningfulness and scaling

Although there is no limitation on the number of possible scales that could be developed, just five are commonly used and discussed in the social sciences: **nominal, ordinal, interval, ratio,** and **absolute.**

Nominal scales use numbers merely as labels. In the telephone directory each name is associated with a number; the number 'measures' the person in the sense that a label is provided. We could talk of the person whose telephone number is such-and-such, but we would never consider adding, subtracting, multiplying or dividing those numbers for any reason at all. We would not take my telephone number and add it to yours and divide the sum by 2 to find what our 'average' telephone number is. If your telephone number is higher than mine, there is no sense in which you can be said to have 'more' than I. A nominal scale is used only to identify, like the numbers on the football player's jersey. In constructing a nominal scale we are free to use any numbers at all.

Ordinal scales use numbers to represent the orderings of the entities being measured. The winners of a squash contest are rank ordered according to who beat whom; the numbers 1, 2, 3, etc. indicate the relative standing of the winners, so the order of winning is represented by the order of the numbers. But that is all. It certainly is true that

$$2 - 1 = 3 - 2$$

if we think of those numbers just as numbers, but could we say that the difference in ability between the first and second place players is the same as the difference in ability between the second and third place competitors? Not necessarily. The numbers serve only to show the rank ordering of the players. In constructing an ordinal scale we may use any numbers at all provided that ordering is preserved.

Interval scales preserve the rank ordering of differences in the property being measured. Fahrenheit measurement of temperature provides a good example. Suppose I measure the temperatures of three liquids, A, B, and C, and I observe readings of 60°F, 40°F, and 35°F. The difference in temperature between A and B is 20°; between B and C, 5°. A difference of 20 is 4 times as great as a difference of 5; that is a true statement about the numbers, but is it true of the property the numbers represent, temperature? The answer is yes, but we would need to know something about the theory of temperature and heat to see why. Once an interval scale has been established, any linear transformation of that scale will result in another interval scale. If measurement on a Fahrenheit scale is admissible, then it must be just as acceptable to measure on a centigrade scale, for, as we saw in Chapter 5, one scale is a linear transformation of the other.

In constructing an interval scale we are free to make two choices: the zero point of the scale, and the unit of measurement. We can represent the freezing point of water by zero, and then by representing the boiling point with 100, we have fixed the unit of measurement: there are 100 units between freezing and boiling.

Ratio scales allow statements about the ratios of the properties being measured. Length is an example. A board 6 ft long is twice the length of a 3 ft board. The numbers are in a ratio of 2, and the property these numbers represent, length, is also in a ratio of 2. What about temperature? Consider 80°F and 40°F; are the temperatures those numbers represent in a ratio of 2? We can answer the question by observing that the measurements could just as well have been made in centigrade. Had we done that we would have observed 26·7°C and 4·4°C. Those numbers are certainly not in a ratio of 2. Since a proposed statement about the underlying property is true under one scale but not true under another equally valid scale, the statement must not be an admissible one. In general, linear transformations do not preserve ratios of properties being measured; they preserve ratios of differences in the properties. We cannot make statements about the ratios of properties measured on an interval scale. Only when measurement is on a ratio scale can we confidently make statements about ratios of the underlying properties.

In constructing a ratio scale we are free to fix only the unit of measurement. The zero point is determined by theory. Measurement of temperature on the Kelvin scale is an example; there, zero is defined as the point at which molecular motion ceases. Once a ratio scale is established it can be transformed into another, equally valid ratio scale by multiplying the original scale by a constant. That changes only the unit of measurement, which was an arbitrary choice anyway.

Absolute scales admit of no useful transformations at all. Counting is an example. When I measure by counting the number of students out of 20 whose fathers are in 'white-collar' occupations, I am applying an absolute scale of measurement. Transforming the scale would make no sense because the zero-point and unit of measurement are based on convention and long-standing practice.

Determining the level of measurement

Prior to an investigation how does one determine the scale type? Is measurement to take place at a low level, on a nominal scale, where only the identifying characteristics of numbers are used, or is it to take place at a high level, say on a ratio scale, where all the properties of numbers are used? Unless the theory you are testing enables you to provide a formal axiomatic analysis to the representation and uniqueness problems, which is unfortunately all too rare in the social sciences, then you will have to rely on a combination of theory, logic, and empirical observation.

To begin with, it will usually be obvious if the extreme scale types are to be used. Labelling and counting are operations whose application is self-evident in most situations, so it is not hard to justify using nominal and absolute scales. The difficulty comes in deciding between ordinal, interval, and ratio scales.

Theoretical considerations may enable you to establish whether the zero-point on the scale has any meaning. It is clear, for example, that zero I.Q. has no fixed interpretation, because I.Q. is not thought of as an amount of something in any absolute sense. I.Q. is a relative measure that enables people to be scaled relative to each other. On the other hand, absolute zero does make theoretical sense when measuring temperature. If you can find justification for the zero point, ratio-scale measurement is probably appropriate.

Logical argument in establishing the level of measurement relies heavily on the fact that any inference you make based on the scale must remain true for all admissible transformations of the scale. We saw an example of this with temperature. An inference that one liquid is twice the centrigrade temperature of another liquid is true only for measurement on the centigrade scale; since the statement is false on a Fahrenheit scale, we reject the notion that Fahrenheit and centigrade scales are ratio scales. However, ratios of differences of temperature remain the same for all temperature scales; we can say that temperature measured on Fahrenheit or centigrade thermometers is at the level of an interval scale.

Empirical findings can sometimes serve as a guide to the level of measurement. Suppose, for example, that two teams are to be formed from the top four winners of a squash competition. The winners are ranked from 1 to 4, and we wish to determine by empirical test whether those numbers really represent ordinal- or interval-scale measurement. We proceed by matching players 1 and 4 with players 2 and 3; the average rank of each team is then 2·5, and since both teams have the same average rank we infer that the teams are equally matched. We test the notion by having the two teams play several matches. If each team wins about half the time then we might conclude that the original ranks represent more than ordinal information, they also represented roughly equal differences in ability so that the numbers represent interval information. That conclusion would only be true for these players, however, and many more experiments would have to be carried out to establish the general nature of the scale.

Of course this example is not realistic; logical considerations alone would be sufficient to reject the notion of ranks in athletic contests representing interval-scale measurement. The point of the example is to illustrate the logic of the empirical approach: assume a particular level of measurement is correct, make predictions based on that assumption, and if the predictions are not substantiated, reject the original assumption. What if the predictions do work out? Then, following the reasoning in the section in Chapter 4 on hypothesis testing, we are at least no less sure than when we started that the assumption is correct. Several experiments later, confidence in the assumption may be strengthened.

Exercise 7–1

What level of measurement might be appropriate for scaling:

a   Type of mental illness?

b   Gross national product?

c   IQ?

d   Social class?

e   Loudness?

Answers

a   Type of mental illness is a judgement about the category in which a person is placed. If we associate numbers with the category, we have nominal measurement. More commonly, verbal labels are used for the categories, for example, depressive, paranoid, schizophrenic, etc.

b   If gross national product (GNP) is measured in the currency of your country, it is only necessary to count units of that money to arrive at GNP. Although counting is involved, measurement is not on an absolute scale because the unit of measurement, a dollar, pound, etc., is arbitrary. The zero point makes at least some theoretical sense, so measurement takes place on a ratio scale.

c   We have already said that zero I.Q. has no theoretical meaning, so I.Q. cannot be measured on a ratio scale, but the decision between ordinal and interval scales is difficult. No theory helps very much and different investigators using the empirical approach have made different claims. So although I.Q. is useful in making predictions of many sorts, psychologists are not agreed about its measurement status.

d   Social class is at least measurable on a nominal scale. The Registrar General in England publishes an index of social class that gives both a 5-point and 7-point classification on the basis of occupation. It seems fairly evident that distances between social classes are probably not equal, if the concept has meaning, and at least a rough ordering is implied. Again, theory and empirical work have not established the level of measurement. For some purposes it may appear only nominal, for others ordinal.

e   Loudness is an interesting example of a scale that could be interval or ratio depending on how it is arrived at. In one method, called ratio estimation, a subject is asked to assign numbers to tones presented to him. He is instructed to use numbers that represent *ratios* of loudness so that if tone A sounds twice as loud as tone B, the number assigned to A should be twice as big as that given to B. The resulting scale is a ratio scale almost by definition. I say almost, because if the subject cannot do what he is asked, then there is some doubt about the level of measurement of the numbers he gives. Methods that are less demanding of the subject can be employed that yield interval scales. Methods for obtaining numerical measurements in psychology are discussed in more detail in Hays (1967).

7.3   Measurement and statistics

This last exercise was partly meant to illustrate the difficulty in deciding on the level of measurement. As new measurement techniques are developed, new scales appear, in addition to the five mentioned here. This makes it very difficult to give specific guidelines about how measurement theory can aid a scientist in conducting an investigation, and I am not sure it should be done anyway. The scientist involved in his subject is the person to judge the level of measurement; he must decide which of the properties of numbers represent characteristics of the property being measured. As long as he is aware of the general guides to consistency imposed by measurement theory, he is less likely to say such things as '80°F is twice the temperature of 40°F'. At the present state of development of measurement theory, thorough knowledge of the empirical work done in an area as well as appreciation of theory are perhaps the best guides to determining levels of measurement.

What implications does measurement theory have for statistical practice? Some authors have classified statistical methods according to the measurement scale involved. Some statistics books are organized on this principle. Certain procedures, they say, are most appropriate for ordinal data, others for interval data, and so forth. The reasoning behind this classification is that if statistical procedure requires you to perform mathematics on your data beyond the admissible transformations required by the measurement scale, then that procedure should not be used for that kind of measurement scale. For example, if some statistical procedure requires you to compute averages, then that procedure should not be used when ordinal measurement is used because it will be difficult to interpret the result, as we saw with the squash teams.

This argument seems to me to be incorrect for two reasons. In the first place, it is not very practical advice because of the difficulty in determining the level of measurement. In the second place, it fails to recognize that statistical theory is entirely neutral about matters of measurement. The formal statistical apparatus requires only numbers as inputs; nothing is said about what the numbers represent. If the experimenter wishes to use a statistical procedure on ranks that requires averaging the ranks, he may do so, for there is no assumption in the procedure that says it is reserved for interval-scale data or above. If the experimenter, in his good judgement, feels he can meaningfully interpret the result of the statistical procedure, then his use of the procedure is justified. As was said earlier, statistics is concerned with the degree of match or mismatch between predictions and data (Fig. 7–1), while measurement is concerned with the representation of the world by numbers. The provinces of statistics and measurement become linked too closely if one attempts to restrict the use of statistical techniques on the basis of level of measurement. Interpretation of statistical results may be easier if the restrictions are followed, but this is not always true, and sometimes violation of the restrictions still leads to relatively straightforward interpretation. While I agree that it is easier to represent properties of the world with numbers than it is to interpret from statistical results back to the world, I do not think that interpretation is well served by limiting statistical procedures to certain levels of measurement.

Measurement in the social sciences is usually not higher than interval scale. Most of the statistical methods in this book apply to interval-scale measurement, some to nominal and ordinal scales. The book is most lacking in methods for rank-ordered data because appropriate Bayesian methods have not yet been worked out. This is an area where specifying a prior distribution has given statisticians some trouble, but it is hoped that the problem will soon be solved. In the meantime, you will have to learn enough of non-Bayesian methods to be able to use order statistics. Chapter 13 should give you sufficient background to be able to use books about order statistics such as the elementary exposition by Siegel (1956).

7.4 Summary

Conducting a scientific investigation involves the scientist in abstracting a few features of the world and creating a theory about those features. He may find it useful to translate all or part of the theory into a formal model. From the theory, or model, predictions are made, and these predictions are compared to observations made in an experiment.

Statistics, as a subject, is concerned with the degree of match between predictions and observations. Measurement is the process of assigning numbers to observations, while the relationship between characteristics of those numbers and the underlying properties being measured is the realm of measurement theory.

The fundamental problems of measurement theory are representation, establishing that a numerical representation is possible for the characteristics of the property being measured, and uniqueness, showing what limitations exist on the assignment of numbers to the properties. The formal approach to these two problems is to establish axioms concerning characteristics of the property, and then to prove that a numerical representation with certain limitations exists. This also helps to establish the meaningfulness of the scale and often points the way to methods of constructing a measurement scale. The empirical approach is to assume a particular level of measurement and then to see that predictions made on this basis are substantiated by experimental test and do not lead to contradictions.

Five scales of measurement are commonly used. A nominal scale does nothing more than categorize observations. An ordinal scale shows no more than the ordering of observations. An interval scale also preserves the ordering of differences between observations, so that statements about the ratios of differences in properties can be made. A ratio scale allows statements about the ratios of the properties themselves. An absolute scale is wholly determined. Linear transformations of interval scales and multiplicative transformations of ratio scales are permissible, while no transformation of an absolute scale is acceptable.

Determining the level of measurement may be difficult in a particular situation; the decision must be made by the experimenter on the basis of his knowledge of theory and empirical work relevant to the problem at hand. Tying statistical procedures to levels of measurement produces too much constraint on the scientist's judgement. Statistical methods are neutral about questions of level of measurement; the problem of interpreting statistical results is in the hands of the scientist and should be decided on extra-statistical grounds.

Problems

7–1 What scale of measurement is appropriate for measuring time?

7–2 Do measurements made at the level of a ratio scale preserve interval, ordinal, and nominal characteristics? Show why or why not.

7–3 For your major course of study, give examples of nominal-, ordinal-, interval-, and ratio-scale measurement.

7-4 For your major course of study, give an example of a property for which there is no satisfactory numerical measurement procedure. Why is this so?

7-5 Choose some theory that interests you from your major course of study and comment on the four problems of measurement as related to the theory.

8 · Frequency and probability distributions

Up to now we have discussed how prior opinion about some uncertain quantity can be expressed as a probability distribution, and we have considered problems in measuring that uncertain quantity. Always we have in mind some population about which we wish to make an inference after we have obtained a sample from the population. Now it is time to consider how the sample is selected and how we can describe the data we obtain.

By the time you have finished this chapter you should

recognize the importance of translating theoretical propositions into operational terms;

understand the principle of random sampling;

know how to summarize data as a histogram, frequency polygon, or probability distribution;

understand the relationship between theoretical distributions and populations.

8.1 Preliminaries

One day a student in one of my statistics classes who had been struggling with the material for several weeks, cried out in despair, 'Most of us haven't the faintest idea what you're talking about; we've been lost for weeks!' I asked him how he knew that and he replied that he had talked to several of his friends, all of whom agreed they were lost. The opportunity seemed ripe for restoring some perspective to the course, and also for illustrating how a scientific investigation proceeds. I suggested that we put his statement to the test to see if it was true.

Operationalizing

The class discussed how we might see if the student's statement was accurate. The only restriction I imposed was that we treat the class as a population and draw a sample to make an inference. That ruled out a simple show of hands as a means of settling the issue. The discussion went something like this:

'Why don't we just write on a piece of paper whether or not we're lost, draw a sample, and then make an inference about the true proportion of papers with "lost" on them?'

'That's a good idea. Let's do that.'

Sound of many pieces of paper being torn. Someone interrupts: 'Actually, I'm not completely lost. Just a little lost. I was O.K. up to last Friday's lecture. What should I write?'

'I'm having trouble, too. Maybe we should consider what we mean by "lost".'

'I agree. And we ought to decide how long we've been lost. I was following up to a week ago when I became ill, and I've had trouble catching up since then.'

Much discussion followed. Eventually this criterion was suggested: Write 'lost' if you have understood less than about 50% of the material over the past two weeks. Discussion continued.

'That's O.K. if you've been following. But if you haven't, you may not know that you've missed something, so are in no position to judge the 50%.'

Pause. Then someone suggested: 'Let Dr Phillips make up a test covering the work of the past two weeks. If you pass, you aren't lost.'

I said, 'Who's to say what the pass mark is, and how difficult the test should be?'

Another pause. Eventually discussion resumed on the question of the test, and it was finally decided that I should use my experience to construct a test of moderate difficulty and the pass mark would be 50%. I did not actually do it because by then the major point had been made: **Theoretical statements must be translated into operational terms before measurement can proceed.** The general statement about students being lost for weeks was not specific enough to tell us how to take measurements. As a first step in operationalizing, it was agreed to inquire about the proportion of students who were lost, and as a second step the idea of 'lost' was defined as: Failure to pass at the 50% level a moderately difficult test covering the past two weeks work. (The term 'moderately difficult' could have been made more precise.)

At this point we were ready to rephrase the original statement in the form of a prediction. All that remained was to operationalize the phrase, 'most of us . . .'. We finally settled for 'over 75% of us . . .'. So, our operationalized prediction was 'over 75% of the class will fail to pass, at the 50% level, a moderately difficult test covering the past two weeks work'. Quite a difference from the original statement!

Now, you may feel that something has been lost from the original complaint: 'Most of us haven't the faintest idea what you're taking about; we've been lost for weeks!' The connotative meaning has changed from a complaint to a fairly precise prediction. The cost of increased precision is usually a loss in connotative meaning and that is why scientists are sometimes accused of knowing more and more about less and less. Yet, to proceed with a scientific investigation it is necessary to be precise; the tradeoff between richness of meaning and precision is difficult to make, and is often a matter of personal style. Some social scientists opt for a broad picture, and may be criticized by their more precision-minded colleagues for being 'sloppy', and the scientist who is careful to be precise may be accused of studying trivia. Other scientists cleverly design meaningful studies that are quite precise. Still others move from one camp to the other in carrying out a series of investigations. Whose strategy is best? At this youthful stage of development of the social sciences, I prefer to hedge my bet; I will put a little money on each.

Sampling

During one class I asked my students to write 'pass' or 'fail' on a slip of paper depending on whether or not the last quiz had been passed. The slips were collected, I drew out a sample by mixing the papers and pulling one out without looking, noting the word on the slip, returning the paper, mixing, drawing and so forth for 10 draws. I calculated the 95% credible interval on my Beta posterior, checked it against the true proportion obtained by noting all the papers, and—the interval completely missed the true proportion! Bad luck, I thought. After all, there was a 5% chance that the true value would fall outside the interval, so I repeated the process. Again it missed the truth! Twice in a row seemed too unlikely ($0.05 \times 0.05 = 0.0025$, to be exact!).

My suspicions were confirmed when I sorted the papers into two piles, the passes and the fails. Of the few students who had failed, almost all had handed in very small slips of paper. And the pass pile contained some very large pieces. When drawing a sample, my fingers had missed the smaller pieces, even though I had been trying not to be influenced by the size of the paper.

The experience illustrates the importance of considering sampling procedures in carrying out an experiment. The procedures in this book all assume that sampling is random, that is, that each element in the population has an equal chance of being selected. 'Equal chance' has the same meaning as when it is applied to elementary events in a simple experiment (Section 2.1); if you had to place a bet on the occurrence of any one particular elementary event, you would be indifferent about the one on which you actually placed your money. This is a matter for judgement, to be decided by examining all relevant facts concerning the sampling process. Ideally, the scientist arranges his experiment so that the randomness of his sampling procedure is not in question. This is accomplished by the simple experiment introduced in Chapter 2, and it is why I now have my students write 'pass' or 'fail' on identical 3 in × 5 in cards, which are thoroughly mixed in a container.

Unfortunately, the world does not allow random samples to be obtained for most investigations in the social sciences. If you are studying memory processes in people, you just cannot get a random sample of all people in the world. If you are trying to find out the nation's preferences among presidential candidates, a random sample of all people in the country would be too expensive to obtain and would presume that you had a list somewhere of all people with their correct current addresses.

The randomness of a sample is impossible to ensure when the population is ill defined. As an example, consider an experiment in which repeated observations are taken on a single individual. The observations are taken as a sample of all possible responses, past and future, the subject could give. Here the investigator takes a sample of some particular aspect of an individual's behaviour so as to make a generalization about the person. The population consists of past and future responses, so how can the randomness of the sample be guaranteed?

Social scientists have coped with the difficulty in obtaining random samples in a number of different ways. A common response has been to ignore the problem. Many journal articles report statistical inferences without mentioning the characteristics of the population to which the inferences are pertinent. This is, obviously, not a very satisfactory procedure.

Another answer is to note that for *some* studies concerned with *some* topics, any sample can be considered sufficiently representative to be treated as a random sample. For some studies of human memory, there is no theoretical reason to believe that volunteers would respond differently than non-volunteers, that men would behave differently than women, or that college students would give different results than people not in college. This is a reasonable approach provided there is theoretical justification. But too often, investigators have chosen college students as subjects just because they are readily available. Indeed, psychology in particular has been accused of being 'a science of the college sophomore', and many words have been spilled urging investigators to broaden the representativeness of their subject populations.

Perhaps the best approach is to choose as diverse a sample as possible, ensuring that it is at least 'haphazard', and then figure out what population the sample came from. An investigator may select cards at random from the card-file of volunteer subjects maintained at his university, and then construct a description of the population which would make his sample a reasonably random one. If he finds his sample consists entirely of middle-class students, and he thinks his findings might be different for other social classes, that then he defines his population as consisting of middle-class students. Of course, if social class could make a difference, the investigator might make social class an independent variable in his study; he may, for example, select cards at random, assigning students to groups according to their social class, until each social-class grouping has an equal number of subjects.

There are many more ways of ensuring random-appearing samples, such as stratified sampling, but these methods belong more to a book on experimental design than to a book on statistics. For our purposes we will always assume that a sample is random-appearing, that the experimenter knows he is behaving *as if* the sample is random. If he is not willing to admit that, there is no point in using inferential statistics at all.

There is another sense in which randomness helps to ensure that experimental results are representative of the population. Imagine an experiment designed to determine the effects of some new drug on the ability of rats to learn how to run through a maze. First the investigator ensures that *with respect to natural ability to learn mazes* he has a random sample. If he failed to do this, he might end up with a sample of mostly 'maze-dull', or mostly 'maze-bright' rats, and if the drug affects those two groups differentially (improves the maze-dull rats, but not the others, for example), then he could draw the wrong conclusion.

Next, the investigator assigns rats *randomly* to the group to receive the drug and to the group that receives a placebo. If he did not do this, he might unknowingly favour some rats over others in determining who was to get the drug, and thereby bias his results.

Thus, both random sampling, and random assignment to treatments are necessary to ensure that experimental results can be generalized to the population.

In addition to random sampling, two other assumptions are made by all the statistical methods in this book. One is that observations are independent; the other is that the population is stable with respect to the attribute being measured. We discussed independence in Chapter 3; as applied to a sequence of observations, independence is assured if the outcome of any one trial or observation is not influenced by the outcome of previous trials or observations. A stable population is one where the attribute being measured does not change while it is measured. The true value of the uncertain quantity does not change part way through the measuring process.

When we have formulated operational definitions and when we are clear about our sampling procedures, then we are ready to collect some data.

8.2 Frequency distributions

For a simple experiment each elementary event is paired with the event class to which it belongs. In similar fashion, the scientist pairs his measurement with the element sampled from the population. If he is sampling American

Table 8–1 Raw data for three investigations

| Swimming pools | | Social class | | R & D expenditure | |
School	Pool	Name	Class	Company	Amount, $
Birmington	No	Barnett	4	IPE	950,000
Aylesburgh	Yes	Aymen	3	Norwood	20,000
Yeschester	Yes	Sparks	3	Thames	125,000
Elton	Yes	Idleman	5	Hewitt	73,000
Sudbury	No	Sherwin	2	Edgerton	55,000
Trulyville	Yes	Foster	4	Light	370,000
Hampwellaca	No	Otley	2	International	2,300,000
Earlyworm	No	Reaper	3	Gorman	15,000
Orangeburg	Yes	Roydon	4	Heatamatic	210,000
Restange	No	Eaton	4	Tensor	3,000
East Morgantown	No	Vessick	1	Opal	65,000
Middleborough	No	Ingram	3	Farmingham	87,000
Tomlinton	No	Story	5	Newton	450,000
Hurlyburt	Yes	Inkster	3	Elastic	22,000
East Pampton	No	Oglethorpe	4	Westmate	0
		Nabor	3	Ingraham	5,000
		O'Connor	1	Nominal	7,000
		Finch	5	Force	115,000
		O'Malley	3	Overboard	28,000
		Parsons	2	Restman	96,000
		Ivy	4	Maplewood	48,000
		Newcomb	3	Ascention	0
		Isis	3	Timely	79,000
		Oldenburg	2	Interplay	1,000
		Nutter	4	Organic	88,000
				Nested	36,000

high schools and observing whether or not they have a swimming pool, he pairs the name of the school with 'yes' or 'no'. If he is sampling people and determining their social class, he pairs each person's name with his social class. If he is sampling corporations in an area and measuring the amount of money they spent on research and development last fiscal year, he pairs the name of the corporation with an amount of money. In every case he is specifying a function.

It is more economical and more instructive to condense each listing according to the number of elements that fall into similar event classes: the numbers of high schools that do or do not have swimming pools, the numbers of people in each social class, the numbers of corporations whose expenditure on R & D fell within a particular range. In summarizing the data this way we lose the original identification with the elements of the population, so we lose some information, but we gain in being able to grasp at a glance what the data are saying.

A list showing the number of elements falling in each event class is called a *frequency distribution*, while a graphical picture of a frequency distribution is termed a *histogram* or *frequency polygon*. Some hypothetical data for the three cases just mentioned are shown in Table 8–1. Each element is paired with an observation or measurement, so each table is a listing of a function. Next we consider various ways of summarizing these data in more convenient forms.

Ungrouped and grouped frequency distributions

It is difficult to get a very comprehensive picture by examining these *raw data* in this form, so they have been shown as frequency distributions in Table 8–2. Here f stands for frequency.

Table 8–2 Frequency distributions for the raw data in Table 8–1

Swimming pools		Social class		R & D expenditure	
Pool?	f	Class	f	Amount	f
Yes	6	1(upper)	2	200,000$^+$	5
No	9	2	4	175–199	0
	—	3	9	150–174	0
$N = 15$		4	7	125–149	1
		5(lower)	3	100–124	1
			—	75–99	3
		$N = 25$		50–74	4
				25–49	3
				0–24,000	9
					—
				$N = 26$	

The first two distributions were obtained simply by counting the numbers of yeses and noes and the number of 1's, 2's, etc. The third frequency distribution is the result of an intermediate step, where each amount in Table 8–1 was ticked off against the range of values that included it (see Table 8–3).

Notice that for all distributions the event classes are mutually exclusive; none of them overlap. If an expenditure falls in the 50–74,000 category it cannot fall in any other category. Also, the sum of the frequencies must equal the total number of observations.

Table 8–3 Tallies for the R & D data

Class interval	f
200 +	̶H̶H̶
175 −199	
150 − 174	
125 −149	I
100 −124	I
75 −99	III
50 − 74	IIII
25 −49	III
0 − 24	̶H̶H̶ IIII

The first two distributions are called ungrouped *frequency distributions* because no grouping of the data has been carried out. If the social class data were compressed into, say, upper class (1), middle class (2 and 3), and lower class (4 and 5), then the result would have been a *grouped frequency distribution*. The distribution for R & D expenditure is another example. Grouped frequency distributions are necessary whenever the data can fall in any of a great number of categories. Class intervals are chosen so that no observation can fall between adjacent intervals, and so that all intervals, except possibly·the first or last ones, are of equal size. It is common practice to choose between 10 and 20 intervals; that gives a reasonable balance between the amount of detail in the data that is preserved, and condensation of the data to ease interpretation. It is also usual procedure to place the highest values at the top of the list and the lowest ones at the bottom.

Histograms

A frequency distribution gives an even clearer picture of the data when it is shown pictorially, as a histogram. Examples for our three imaginary investigations are shown in Figs 8–1, 8–2, and 8–3. A few comments should be made about Fig. 8–3. The *x*-axis has been marked off with the *midpoints* of the intervals. The midpoint of any interval is the value that falls exactly in the middle of the range of possible values. Marking the interval itself makes the *x*-axis too cluttered and hard to read. Notice that the top interval has been 'cut off' from the *x*-axis to stand alone, and the interval itself, '200+' has been indicated. The break in the *x*-axis reminds the reader that this interval is not equal to the others, that all the data from $200,000 upward are compressed into one bar.

Each profession, and even each journal, seems to have its own standards for drawing histograms. The only general guide I can suggest is to look at your

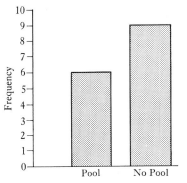

Fig. 8–1

Number of high schools out of 15
that have swimming pools

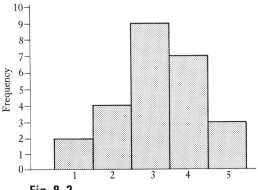

Fig. 8–2

Social class of 25 families

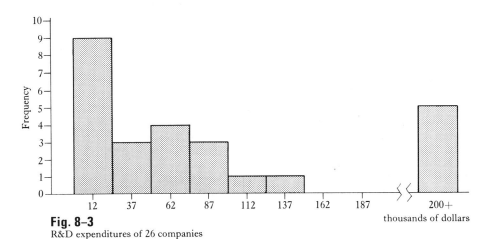

Fig. 8–3

R&D expenditures of 26 companies

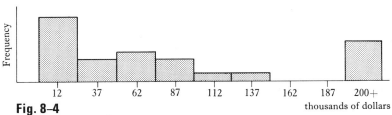

Fig. 8–4

R&D expenditure of 26 companies

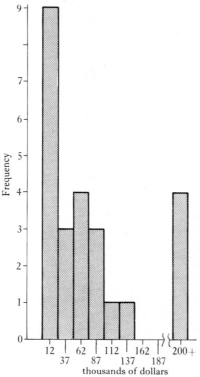

Fig. 8–5
R&D expenditure of 26 companies

completed graph to see that it conveys an unexaggerated picture of the data. Distortions of the *y*-axis can easily create the wrong impression. If one person wishes to show that there are about equal numbers of companies spending a little on R & D as a lot, he can draw the histogram shown in Fig. 8–4. He does not bother to label the *y*-axis, and he neglects to detach the extreme right interval. But if someone else wants to show that most companies are either spending very little or a great deal, he stretches the *y*-axis, as in Fig. 8–5. There are many ways in which graphs of data can mislead. An amusing discussion of the possibilities is given by Huff (1954), who also talks about how the descriptive statistics presented in the next chapter can be 'mendacious truths'.

Exercise 8–1

The scores of 50 subjects on a particular test were obtained. Here are the raw data:

Subject	Score	Subject	Score
1	73	26	71
2	79	27	75
3	72	28	71
4	60	29	63
5	69	30	60
6	70	31	73
7	72	32	76
8	83	33	72
9	66	34	55
10	74	35	70
11	81	36	64
12	53	37	79
13	60	38	80
14	82	39	67
15	75	40	84
16	73	41	82
17	74	42	58
18	60	43	77
19	84	44	61
20	80	45	66
21	65	46	65
22	77	47	69
23	71	48	67
24	73	49	89
25	79	50	65

Draw a histogram of these data.

Answer

The scores range from 53 to 89, or 37 units, including the extreme scores. If a class interval of size 3 is chosen, then the range can be covered in 13 intervals. Construct a frequency distribution:

Class interval	Midpoint	f
88–90	89	I
85–87	86	
82–84	83	卌
79–81	80	卌 I
76–78	77	III
73–75	74	卌 ·III
70–72	71	卌 III
67–69	68	IIII
64–66	65	卌 I
61–63	62	II
58–60	59	卌
55–57	56	I
52–54	53	I

Draw this as a histogram:

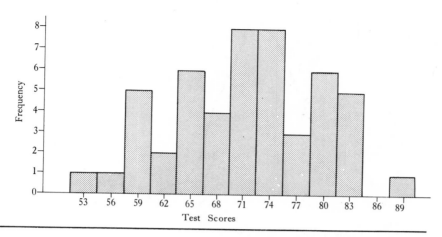

Frequency polygons

When measurements are made in numbers that can represent a continuous variable, it is often more convenient to draw a *frequency polygon* than a histogram. The principle of construction is the same as for a histogram, only the frequencies are connected with straight lines rather than being represented by vertical bars. An example is shown in Fig. 8–6.

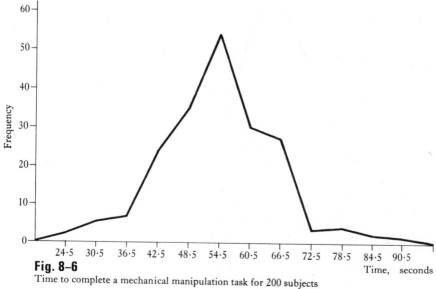

Fig. 8–6

Time to complete a mechanical manipulation task for 200 subjects

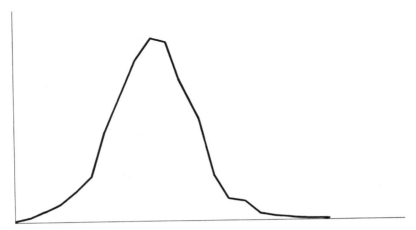

Fig. 8–7
Data as for Fig. 8–6 after 1000 observations

Now imagine that the mechanical manipulation task was given to 1000 subjects, and more class intervals were used in drawing the frequency polygon. Rescaling the *y*-axis to maintain the same proportions as Fig. 8–6 might result in the graph shown in Fig. 8–7. With even more observations, and still more intervals the curve would become smoother and smoother, so that a continuous curve could be faired through the points, as in Fig. 8–8.

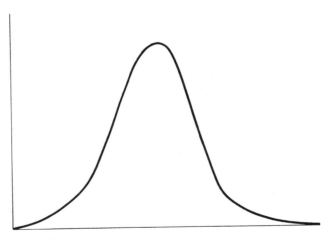

Fig. 8–8
Data as for Fig. 8–6 after a great many observations

Exercise 8–2

Draw a frequency polygon for the data in Exercise 8–1.

Answer

Here is a possibility:

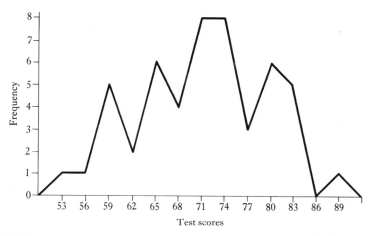

8.3 Probability distributions

We have already met probability functions as applied to prior and posterior opinion; probability density functions pair probability density with values of the unknown quantity, and cumulative probability functions pair cumulative probability with values of the unknown quantity. I could have talked about probabilities assigned to hypotheses or events as probability functions, too. When prior probabilities are assessed for a set of hypotheses, a probability function has been established. The listing in Exercise 3–1 is a probability function; it pairs events with their probabilities:

Event	Probability
man is a policeman	0·3
man is a traffic warden	0·4
man is a bus conductor	0·2
other possibility	0·1

I could draw that as a graph with 4 bars of height 0·3, 0·4, 0·2, and 0·1.

Any probability function is a probability distribution, provided that the events, hypotheses or uncertain quantities are mutually exclusive and exhaustive.

What is the relationship between a probability distribution, which has thus far been used to describe opinion, and a frequency distribution, which has been used to describe data? Imagine that the 25 names in the social class investigation were written on identical cards, the cards were mixed and one was drawn at random. What is the probability of obtaining a person in any particular social class? The frequencies in Table 8–2 can serve as the basis for assigning probabilities to each of the five event classes; divide each frequency by 25:

Class	p
1	0·08
2	0·16
3	0·36
4	0·28
5	0·12
	1·00

The original frequency distribution has become a probability distribution that applies to the outcomes of a simple experiment. In general, any frequency distribution of N observations can serve as a basis for a probability distribution, and when the concept of a simple experiment applies the probabilities are assessed by dividing each frequency by the total N.

8.4   Theoretical distributions and populations

Now we bring together the concepts in the two previous sections to clarify the notion of a 'population'.

Populations

Suppose our concern is the I.Q.'s of all students presently attending American colleges and universities. Imagine that I can accomplish the Herculean task of giving every student in the population an I.Q. test. I could then construct a frequency distribution, which, because there are so many cases, could be smoothed. It might look like this:

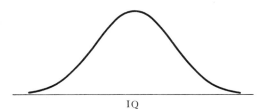

IQ

Imagine, now, the simple experiment of selecting a student at random and measuring the student's I.Q. We are then justified in changing the frequency distribution to a probability distribution. The resulting distribution would look just like the frequency distribution, but now it could be used to describe uncertainty about the possible outcomes of the simple experiment. This probability distribution now provides a complete description of the population, and so is often referred to as the *population distribution*. The collection of individuals whose I.Q.'s were measured is referred to as the *population*. Sociologists often use the term *sampling frame* instead of *population*.

Theoretical distributions

Statistical methods place considerable emphasis on populations whose distributions can be specified by a mathematical function rule. So far we have used functions like the Beta and normal to describe opinion; now we use them to describe populations as well. We can, for example, describe the distribution of I.Q.'s in the general population of people as being normal with a mean of 100 and a standard deviation of 15.

It is important to forestall confusion at this point by introducing a new term and summarizing some old ones. From now on, if I wish to refer to a normal, Beta, or any other probability distribution without reference to its application, the term *theoretical probability distribution* will be used. When a theoretical probability distribution is used to describe prior or posterior opinion, such terms as 'normal prior', or 'Beta posterior', will serve as convenient jargon. When it is necessary to refer to the population distribution, I will say, 'the population is normal .

When a population distribution is known it can serve to generate a theoretical frequency distribution applicable to simple experiments. The frequency expected in each class interval is obtained by multiplying N, the total number of observations in the experiment, by the probability associated with the class interval.

Exercise 8–3

The following theoretical probability distribution characterizes a particular psychological test that has been in use for many years and has been administered to a great many people.

Score interval	p
10–14	0·09
15–19	0·24
20–24	0·34
25–29	0·24
30–34	0·09

An investigator administers the test to 200 people. If the sample is random, what frequency distribution can he expect?

Answer

It is only necessary to multiply each theoretical probability by 200. Here is the result:

Score interval	Expected f
10–14	18
15–19	48
20–24	68
25–29	48
30–34	18

Unknown population

Usually, certain aspects of the population are unknown to us; that is why an investigation is carried out. We may have a rough idea that the population is normal, but we do not know what the mean and standard deviation are, so we set up an experiment to find out. The unknown mean and standard deviation are treated as uncertain quantities about which we wish to make inferences.

Suppose I wish to find the mean of a normal population. I consider the mean as an uncertain quantity, and I find that my prior opinion about it is normal. An experiment is carried out and my posterior distribution is found to be normal. Four distributions are involved:

the normal population;

the normal prior;

the distribution of the data;

the normal posterior.

Each of those distributions can be described by statistics. It is common practice to use the symbols for the parameters in referring to the mean and standard deviation of a normal population, and since the statistics of a normal density function are equal to the parameters, the convention will be followed here. Recall that the mean and standard deviation of the prior and posterior are signified by m and s, with either a single or double prime. Finally, we will refer to the mean and standard deviation of data as M and S; their calculations will be discussed in the next chapter. These symbols are summarized in Table 8–4.

Table 8–4 Symbols used to designate statistics of distributions

Distribution	Mean	Standard deviation
Normal population	μ	σ
Any prior	m'	s'
Any posterior	m''	s''
Any data	M	S

Usually, though not always, lower case Greek letters will be used to designate unknown quantities, lower case Roman letters to designate parameters and statistics of distributions of opinion, and upper case Roman letters to refer to data.

From now on you will have to pay close attention to the symbols being used in order to avoid ambiguity. To see why, consider the values on the horizontal axis of each of the four distributions. For the population, it is the X-scores of all elements in the population; every possible X-score is represented. The unknown mean of these scores is μ, and it is the value of this quantity we wish to infer. Thus, the horizontal axis of the prior shows all possible values of μ. When we think of μ with respect to the population, it has only one value, but since that value is unknown to us we show it as capable of taking on any one of a whole range of values when we represent it on the horizontal axis of the prior or posterior distributions. For short, the horizontal axes of the prior and posterior are labelled 'μ-values'. The horizontal axis of the distribution of data is, like the population, X-values. All of this is shown in Fig. 8–9.

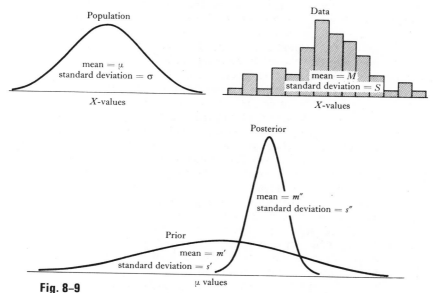

Fig. 8-9

Distributions and their statistics involved in making inferences about the unknown mean
of a normal population

Exercise 8-4

What labels and distributions in Fig. 8-9 would be different if inferences about
the standard deviation of a normal population were being made?

Answer

Neither population nor data distributions would change. However, the horizontal axes of the prior and posterior would read 'σ-values' and the shapes of
the distributions would be different.

The *symbols* for the prior and posterior means and standard deviations would be
unchanged, but their values would be different than before.

Be sure you are clear about Fig. 8-9, and refer back to it whenever
distributions start swimming around in your head.

8.5 Summary

Theoretical statements must be expressed in operational terms before
measurements can be made to test the theories. The investigator often has to
find a balance between a precise operational statement and one that contains
extensive connotative meaning.

Once operational definitions have been made, the scientist can choose a
random sample and take his measurements. Because it is so frequently impossible to obtain a truly random sample, the investigator must at least select a

'haphazard' sample and then describe the characteristics of the population for which the data might be considered a reasonably random sample.

All the inferential procedures in this book assume that the scientist proceeds *as if* his sample is random. They also assume that observations are independent and that the attribute being measured is stable, that is, it does not change while measurement is taking place.

Once measurements have been made the raw data are represented in tabular form as a function that pairs the element of the population being sampled with a measurement. This function can be summarized as an ungrouped or a grouped frequency distribution, which shows the number of elements falling into each event class. Histograms and frequency polygons are graphical representations of frequency distributions. In drawing a graph, one must ensure that it does not present a misleading picture of the data. A frequency distribution based on a great many observations may be smoothed to give a continuous curve. A probability distribution can be obtained from a frequency distribution provided the concept of a simple experiment applies.

When a frequency distribution applies to the entire population, then the probability distribution derived from it is called the population distribution. A population distribution can serve to generate an expected frequency distribution applicable to a simple experiment.

It is important to distinguish between the population distribution, the prior and posterior distributions, and the distribution of data obtained from the sample.

Problems

8–1 Give at least one operational reformulation of each of the following statements (page numbers after each statement refer to sections of McKeachie (1969) in which relevant research is reviewed; you may wish to compare your reformulations with those of investigators who have conducted research on the topics):

a Live lectures are better than televised ones (pp. 100–109).

b Students do better work in classes where the instructor takes a personal interest in students (pp. 197–198).

c Student-centred teaching is more effective than instructor-centred teaching (pp. 65–78).

d Small classes are more effective than large ones for bringing about changes of attitude (pp. 33–36, 160–167).

e Anxiety interferes with good performance on exams (pp. 198–200).

8–2 A student consults the bank statements for his account to find out how many times he was overdrawn in 1971, and for how long each time. He records the number of days overdrawn for each occurrence. They were:

1, 4, 1, 1, 5, 1, 3, 10, 3, 6

a Draw a histogram of these data.

b Construct a frequency polygon for these data.

8–3 Here are the average amounts spent per week on drink and tobacco by 30 students during term time:

£1·50	£0	£1·50	£0·25	£1·00
0·50	0	0·75	0·25	0·25
0	0	0·50	0·50	0·35
2·00	0	0	1·00	0
0	1·00	0·25	0	0
0·25	0·50	0	0	0

a   Construct a grouped frequency distribution.
b   Draw a histogram.
c   Draw a frequency polygon.
d   Which of the three displays that you have drawn conveys the clearest impression of the data?

8–4 Students completed a test of religious knowledge and a test of numerical ability as part of a laboratory project entitled 'Distribution of Human Variables' (the project is discussed in Wakeford, 1968). Here are the frequency distributions for scores on the two tests:

Religious knowledge		Numerical test	
Score	f	Score	f
20	2	54	2
18	1	52	3
16	3	51	1
13	1	48	1
12	4	47	1
11	1	46	6
10	2	45	1
9	2	43	4
8	4	42	5
7	7	40	1
6	7	39	5
5	1	38	2
4	6	37	1
3	5	36	2
2	6	35	2
1	2	33	3
		32	3
		31	3
		30	1
		28	1
		27	1
		26	3
		25	1
		24	2

a   Draw histograms or frequency polygons for these data.
b   How would you describe the general shapes of the two distributions?
c   How might you account for the shapes of the distributions?

8–5 The students mentioned in Problem 2–1 who carried out a postal survey of attitudes to traffic were interested in comparing the percentages of replies in each social class with the percentages of people known to be in each social class. In that way they could check on the possible under- or over-representation of replies from different social classes. The study was carried out late in 1971, too soon for the 1971 Census data to be consulted, so they used the 1966 Census as the source for social class data in the areas they surveyed. Here is the breakdown of people according to social class as given by the 1966 Census:

Social class	Percentage of people
1	7·96
2	8·93
3 non-manual	46·79
3 manual	16·12
4	14·18
5	6·02

a   If the 385 people who responded to the postal survey were representative of the social classes given in the 1966 Census, how many people would you expect in each social class?

b   Compare these expected data with the data actually obtained (Problem 2–1). Is there any evidence that the survey was answered by an unrepresentative sample of people? (This question will be answered more precisely in Chapter 14. See Problem 14–2 at the end of that chapter.)

9 · Computing statistics on data

In the previous chapter we saw how to present data in pictorial form; now it is time to consider descriptions of data that are even more economical than histograms or frequency polygons. These descriptors are called *statistics* and they have the same meaning for data as they do when we use them to describe prior opinion. However, we can calculate statistics for data from the data themselves, while for prior and posterior distributions they are usually either an expression of the scientist's judgement or they are calculated from the parameters.

Statistics summarize data. With just a few statistics we can communicate long lists of data, short-cut involved descriptions, find meaning in a jumble of figures. In addition to describing data, statistics play an important role in making inferences. It is always possible to use raw data in applying Bayes' theorem, but such a procedure is both cumbersome and unnecessary. If we compute the right set of statistics from our data, it is possible to use the statistics rather than the original data as inputs to Bayes' theorem, along with prior probabilities, to arrive at a posterior distribution. In other words, all the information we need from our data to enable us to arrive at a posterior distribution is contained in just a few statistics. We don't need all the information in the raw data, the information summarized by the statistics is sufficient. Those statistics that contain enough information about the data to enable us to compute the posterior distribution are called *sufficient statistics*. Various combinations of the statistics covered in this chapter will serve as sets of sufficient statistics at one time or another, as will be seen in Chapters 11 and 12. Thus, it is necessary to know how to compute statistics on data before inferences can be made.

Calculating statistics for data can be a tedious chore if very many observations are taken. Fortunately various devices are at your disposal to lighten the task. You should at least have access to an electromechanical or electronic calculator. This is a desk-top machine which, in its simplest form, makes easy work of adding and subtracting long columns of figures, and can simplify multiplying and dividing. More complex calculators have memories that enable you to store for future use intermediate steps in your calculations, and they have other mechanisms or circuits that reduce fairly complex operations, like taking a square root, to the push of a button. At their most sophisticated, these calculators have several memories of modest capacity and can be programmed like a computer.

You may have access to an on-line, conversational-mode computer. This facility puts a great many different analyses at the fingertips of the scientist, yet he does not need to know anything about computers or computer programming. The computer 'talks' in English, through a teletype terminal, asking the scientist questions about his data, then asking to be given the data, until it finally has enough information to complete the analysis. The scientist has only to choose from the computer's 'files' the analysis he wants to have carried out, and then to answer the computer's questions. These 'conversational-mode' languages are so simple that you can learn to program the computer in a very short time— a few hours study is more than sufficient—so that you can write programmes for analyses not in the computer's files.

Most readers will have access to a large computer, and a few will know how to program it. Standard statistical programmes are available that can be used without your knowing how to program, though some knowledge of computer programmers' jargon is usually necessary. At this writing, very few Bayesian programmes are available, though one group of authors is preparing an extensive set to accompany their forthcoming book (Pratt, Raiffa, and Schlaifer, 1965), and several can be found in Schlaifer (1971).

These various aids to computing are now so commonly available that this chapter assumes you have access to one. I also assume that you will always be working from the raw data. Detailed methods for carrying out hand calculations, often from grouped frequency distributions, are not presented.

After you have read and studied this chapter you should

> be able to calculate, from raw data, the basic quantities that enter into all statistical calculations;
>
> know how to find the mean, median, and mode of a set of data;
>
> know how to calculate the standard deviation of a set of data;
>
> be able to transform raw data to standard scores;
>
> understand the meaning of these statistics.

9.1 Making calculations

All the statistics in this and subsequent chapters will be introduced in two ways. First, a definition will be given, usually in mathematical form, then a calculating formula will be presented. The calculating formula is derived from the definition of the statistic, and is expressed in a form that facilitates computation on a calculator.

In this chapter, I assume that measurements have been taken on either a whole population or a sample from a population. A numerical *score* is paired with each element of the population, or sample, and we will call these numerical measurements *X-scores*. We wish to compute statistics on X-scores by using the calculating formulae.

Calculating formulae in this chapter will contain these three terms only:

$$\sum X, \quad \sum X^2, \quad N$$

The first, $\sum X$, is the sum of all raw scores in the data, $\sum X^2$ is the sum of the squares of the raw scores, and N is the number of raw scores.

As an example, consider the scores made by five people on some test.

Subject	Scores
1	3
2	1
3	4
4	4
5	2

The term $\sum X$ is obtained by adding the scores; this is shown in the table below. In order to find $\sum X^2$, it is first necessary to square each score, then to add the squares (see the table). Finally, N is determined by counting the number of scores.

Subject	X	X^2
1	3	9
2	1	1
3	4	16
4	4	16
5	2	4

$$\sum X = 14 \quad \sum X^2 = 46 \quad N = 5$$

Sometimes the formulae require you to calculate $(\sum X)^2$. For the example above, this would be $(14)^2 = 196$. Be sure you see the difference between $(\sum X)^2$ and $\sum X^2$:

$(\sum X)^2$: add first, then square;

$\sum X^2$: square first, then add.

With this little bit of mechanics in mind, we can turn now to more important matters.

9.2 Central tendency

When describing a set of data we often wish to know the 'average' so as to locate the centre of the distribution. We wish to get an idea of the 'middle' of the data, to know some X-value that represents the central tendency of the data. In this section methods are shown for determining three such X-values, the mean, median, and mode.

Mode

The *mode* is the X-score that occurs most frequently. For the data above, each score occurs just once except the 4, which occurs twice. The mode, then, is 4. Notice that the mode is itself a *score*, *not* a frequency. You do not necessarily report the frequency with which the mode occurs.

The mode is a useful statistic when the distribution is especially piled up over one X-score. For example, suppose the air mileage travelled in a year by 20 people is as follows:

Person	Mileage	Person	Mileage
A	0	K	0
B	1200	L	0
C	0	M	0
D	0	N	0
E	0	O	4300
F	300	P	0
G	0	Q	0
H	0	R	1750
I	790	S	0
J	0	T	0

A frequency distribution for these data shows that 15 people did not travel by air at all. The most frequently observed measurement is 0, so, mode = 0.

Median

The *median* is the middle *X*-score, after the scores have been arranged in order. For *N* ordered scores, count $(N+1)/2$ places to find the middle score. For example, take these data:

44 54 60 57 43 52 51 47 62

To find the median, arrange the 9 scores in order and then count over to the $(9+1)/2 = $ 5th place to find the median:

5th place

62 60 57 54 (52) 51 47 44 43

median

This procedure is straightforward and will always lead to an observed score when you have an odd number of data. But suppose *N* is an even number; then the median falls between two obtained scores. The usual procedure is to take the average of those two scores, and report this as the median. Here is an example for 10 scores:

$$\frac{10+1}{2} = 5\cdot5\text{th} \quad \text{place}$$

62 60 57 54 (52 51) 47 44 43 41

$$\text{median} = \frac{51+52}{2} = 51\cdot5$$

In this case the median may take on a value that is not possible in practice, but this is acceptable.

The median is often reported when there are one or two 'far-out' *X*-scores, or when the distribution is highly skewed.

Here, for example, are the incomes of the nine residents of a small, rural community, already arranged in order:

```
$325000
    9600
    9200
    8900
    8100 ←– median
    7800
    7700⎫
    7700⎬ ←– mode
    7600
```

The mode, 7700, would not be a very good indication of the central tendency of these data because only two people earn that amount and it is relatively low, but the median, 8100 does describe the group rather better. Note that the median is not influenced by the amount of the wealthy resident's income; it could have been $9600 or a million dollars. That is the sense in which the median is said to be insensitive to extreme values in the data.

Mean

The *mean* is the average of the *X*-scores. It is obtained by adding all the *X*-scores and dividing by *N*, the number of scores. The calculating formula for the mean is

$$M = \frac{\sum X}{N}$$

where *M* stands for 'mean'. For these data:

```
  X
  4
  4
  3
  2
  1
  ──
∑ X = 14
```

the mean is

$$M = \frac{14}{5} = 2{\cdot}8$$

Note that for these data the mode is 4 and the median is 3, once again illustrating the point that values of the mean, median and mode are not necessarily equal.

When many *X*-scores take on the same value, it is often convenient to compute the mean from an ungrouped frequency distribution. Suppose 25 subjects are given one-minute trial periods to learn a list of words. This table shows the frequency distribution of the number of trials each subject took to learn the list so it could be repeated without error twice.

X, number of trials	f
12	1
11	0
10	1
9	2
8	4
7	1
6	5
5	6
4	2
3	1
2	2
	$N = 25$

In words, one person required 12 trials to learn the list, one person took 10 trials, two people needed 9 trials, four people took 8 trials, etc. If we were to compute the mean from the raw data we would first add up one 12, one 10, two 9's, four 8's, etc. A shorter way would be to multiply each score by its corresponding frequency and then sum the products, thus,

$$(12 \times 1) + (11 \times 0) + (10 \times 1) + (9 \times 2) + \ldots + (2 \times 2)$$

Here is the calculation in tabular form:

X	f	Xf
12	1	12
11	0	0
10	1	10
9	2	18
8	4	32
7	1	7
6	5	30
5	6	30
4	2	8
3	1	3
2	2	4
	$N = 25$	$\Sigma X = 154$

The two quantities we need in order to find the mean are the sums of the middle and right columns:

$$M = \frac{154}{25} = 6.16$$

On the average, subjects took 6·16 trials to learn the list of words.

An appreciation of several interesting characteristics of the mean will help you to know when to use it and when not to.

In the first place, the mean uses all the information in the data (excepting the order in which the data occurred); it is sensitive to every item of data. Contrast this with the mode and median. The mode is totally insensitive to all other X-scores, while the median is sensitive only to the ordering of the data.

Examples: For the air-mileage-travelled data, the mode of 0 miles would be the same even if the data for the 5 travellers had been completely different; the mode is insensitive to other values. The incomes of the 8 residents other than the median income of $8100 could have been completely different, as long as 4 were above $8100 and 4 below it; the median preserves only minimal order information, and is insensitive to extreme values in the data.

Sometimes this characteristic of the mean rules it out as a good descriptor of data. Take the income data again.

$$\begin{array}{r} \$325000 \\ 9600 \\ 9200 \\ 8900 \\ 8100 \\ 7800 \\ 7700 \\ 7700 \\ 7600 \\ \hline \end{array}$$

$$\Sigma\, X = 391600$$

The mean (to the nearest dollar) is,

$$M = \frac{391600}{9} = 43511$$

That number certainly does not convey any sense of the central tendency of those data. If someone reported that this community's average income was $43511, the reader might draw the wrong conclusion unless he were told that one person's wealth inflates the average. The median, which is insensitive to extremes, conveys a more accurate picture. Thus, whenever you see data that contain an extreme value or two, the mean may not be a good statistic to describe central tendency.

A second characteristic of the mean, which makes it useful in problems of inference, is that it changes less than the median or mode as different random samples are drawn from the same population. If you take several random samples and compute the mean, median, and mode for each sample, you will find that the mean does not jump around as much as the others do. In other words, the mean is the most stable statistic of the three.

A third characteristic concerns the deviations of each score from the mean. Suppose we have the five scores shown in the first column of Table 9–1. The mean of these five scores is 5. Now consider how much each score deviates from the mean; these deviation scores are also shown in the table. Now compute the sum of the deviations, taking account of the signs. It is zero. In general, no matter what the raw data are, the sum of the deviations of X-scores from the mean of those scores will always be zero. In short, we say that the sum of (signed) deviations from the mean is zero. (I leave it to the interested reader to prove this statement.)

This property of the mean is directly related to its being the centre of gravity of a distribution. Imagine that the scores in Table 9–1 are shown as the histogram of Fig. 9–1. The base of the histogram is a weightless board, and each square is a block of wood, each block being of identical weight. In moving

Table 9–1 Illustration showing that the sum of (signed) deviations from the mean is zero

X-scores	Deviation scores $X - M$
2	-3
2	-3
4	-1
7	$+2$
10	$+5$
$\sum X = 25$	$\sum (X - M) = 0$

$$M = \frac{25}{5} = 5$$

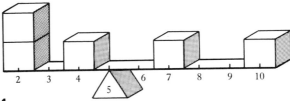

Fig. 9–1
Histogram of the data in Table 9–1, showing that the mean is the balance point of the distribution

the knife-edge fulcrum back and forth, we will find that the balance point is at the mean of the distribution. This is the point at which the deviations to the left of 5 exactly balance the deviations to the right of 5. This same property for continuous distributions was shown in Fig. 6–8.

A fourth property of the mean relates to the squares of the deviations in Table 9–1. If you take each deviation, square it, and then add the squared deviations, the resulting sum will be smaller for deviations taken from the mean than from any other number. In Table 9–2 I have shown the sums of the squared deviations taken from 4 and from 6. You can see that those sums are greater than the sum of the squared deviations taken from the mean. The short-hand

Table 9–2 Illustration showing that the sum of the squared deviations is smaller for deviations taken from the mean than from other numbers

X	$X - M$	$(X - M)^2$	$X - 4$	$(X - 4)^2$	$X - 6$	$(X - 6)^2$
2	-3	9	-2	4	-4	16
2	-3	9	-2	4	-4	16
4	-1	1	0	0	2	4
7	2	4	3	9	1	1
10	5	25	6	36	4	16
		$\sum (X - M)^2 = 48$		$\sum (X - 4)^2 = 53$		$\sum (X - 6)^2 = 53$

way of talking about this property of the mean is to say that the sum of squares about the mean is a minimum.

'Best guesses'

A useful interpretation of these measures of central tendency is obtained by considering what guess you would make about the outcome of a simple experiment performed on the data. Imagine that you have collected the data shown in Tables 9–1 and 9–2, and that you are about to choose one at random. What is your best guess about the score?

The answer depends on what is meant by 'best guess'. Suppose you want to have the highest possible probability of being correct in your guess. Then you would guess a '2', for two elements of the sample have that score, making your chance of being correct $2/5 = 0.40$. If you had guessed a 4, or a 7, or a 10, your chances would have been only $1/5 = 0.2$. **Guessing the mode maximizes your chance of being correct.**

But suppose 'best guess' means that you are to minimize your absolute error. That is, if you are wrong in your guess, the difference between your guess and the truth is to be as near zero as possible. Then you should guess the median, for that is the middle score, and so is as close to *every* score as a single score can get. Any other score may be closer to *some* scores but it will be disproportionately farther from others. **The median minimizes absolute error in the guess.**

On the other hand, if by 'best guess' we wish to minimize *squared* error, then the mean should be given. We have already seen that the squared distances from *every* score are as small as possible to the mean rather than to any other single score, so we say that **the mean minimizes squared errors in the guess.**

For purely descriptive purposes, the median is a very serviceable statistic. It often gives a useful description of sample data, and communicates a reasonable impression of the data. However, the mean is more frequently used in inferential statistics. Not only does it change less from sample to sample than the median or mode, but it has mathematical properties, such as minimizing squared deviations, that make it attractive. Also, it is very often one of the sufficient statistics for an inference. Thus, for most of the inferential procedures described in Part III, the mean will be the favoured statistic for describing the central tendency of data.

Exercise 9–1

Compute the mean, median, and mode for these data:

X	f
7	1
5	4
4	2
2	2
1	1

Answers

For the mean:

X	f	Xf
7	1	7
5	4	20
4	2	8
2	2	4
1	1	1
$N = 10$		$\Sigma X = 40$

$$\text{mean} = M = \frac{\Sigma X}{N} = \frac{40}{10} = 4$$

For the median:

7   5   5   5   (5   4)   4   2   2   1

$$\text{median} = \frac{5 + 4}{2} = 4{\cdot}5$$

For the mode:

$$\text{mode} = 5$$

Exercise 9–2

What would be the most appropriate measure of central tendency to report for the data shown in Table 8–1?

Answers

The information on swimming pools is only nominal-scale data, so it is not possible to compute a mean or median. You could report the mode: 9 high schools out of the 15 sampled do not have swimming pools. But it would be just as appropriate to report that 6 out of 15 do have pools.

For the social-class data, the mode and median coincide at 3. For purely descriptive purposes, the mode and median would be satisfactory for these ordinal data. If you can make sense of the mean and you intend to make inferences based on this sample, then the mean might be appropriate.

The R & D data are fairly skewed and there is one extreme score, the expenditure by International. Here the median conveys the most accurate picture of the data, though you could report the modal class interval, 0–24000.

The last two examples are difficult to answer in the abstract. The circumstances in which you are reporting and the audience you are reporting to should also be taken into account.

9.3 Variability

Reporting only the central tendency of a distribution of data gives us no idea of the spread of the distribution; another statistic is needed for that. We shall be concerned with three contenders: the range, the variance, and the standard deviation.

Range

A rough guide to the spread or variability of a distribution can be given by naming the range of scores. *The range of a set of scores is indicated by noting the low score and the high score.* The range of scores in Tables 9–1 and 9–2 is 2 to 10. If you report that those scores have a mean of 5 and a range of 2 to 10, then you have conveyed more about the data than by giving only the mean.

The range falls down, however, whenever the data include even moderately extreme values. To say that the range of incomes for those 9 inhabitants of the rural community is $7600 to $325000 is perhaps even more misleading than reporting the mean. Another index, less sensitive to extremes is needed. We turn to that next.

Variance

What we really need is an index that will tell us how bad our bet is when we give one of the measures of central tendency as our 'best guess'. If I give the mean, then the *average* of the deviation scores which were discussed in the previous section might be considered as an index of dispersion, for the more spread out the distribution is, the larger the deviation scores. The bigger the deviation scores, the worse the mean is as a best guess.

The trouble with finding an average deviation score is that the sum of the deviations would first have to be found, and we have already seen that this sum is zero. No matter how spread out the distribution, the sum of the deviation scores about the mean will always be zero, and so the average deviation score would be zero.

One way around this difficulty would be to take the sum of the deviation scores without regard to their sign. Then an average could be found. However, a more common approach, one that yields a statistic that has desirable mathematical properties, is to *square* each deviation score and find the sum, as was done in Table 9–2. The average is found by dividing the sum by $N-1$, rather than N, for reasons I will mention in a moment. The resulting average squared deviation is called the *variance*. Its defining formula is:

$$S^2 = \frac{\sum (X-M)^2}{N-1}$$

For the data in Table 9–2, most of the required computations are shown there. The deviation of each score from the mean is shown in the second column, and the squares of these deviations are indicated in the third column. At the bottom of that column can be found the sum of the squared deviations. Thus, for these data, the variance is

$$S^2 = \frac{48}{5-1} = \frac{48}{4} = 12$$

The bigger the variance, the more spread out the distribution. Note that a variance of zero will occur only when all scores are equal, and that a negative variance is impossible.

Now, why take an average by dividing by $N-1$ rather than N? Well, I could have used N and many textbook writers do. However, dividing by $N-1$ makes easier some of the computations required to find parameters of posterior distributions, and it does have theoretical justification. When I calculated the deviations shown in the second column of Table 9–2, I could have stopped after the fourth one, for the next one was determined by knowing the sum of the first four and knowing that the sum of all five has to be zero. In other words, when talking about deviations from the mean, only $N-1$ of these are 'free' to take on any value; once we know the sum of those, the last one is 'fixed' in that it is constrained to take on a value that will make the total sum be zero. We say, then, that there are $N-1$ *degrees of freedom* associated with the variance, so we divide the sum by $N-1$ rather than by N.

Calculating the variance is a bit cumbersome using the defining formula. We can derive this more convenient calculating formula for the variance of a sample:

$$S^2 = \frac{N \sum X^2 - (\sum X)^2}{N(N-1)}$$

Let us apply it to the data in Table 9–2. As I indicated earlier, the calculating formula involves only three quantities: $\sum X$, $\sum X^2$, and N. We first need to find these:

X	X^2
2	4
2	4
4	16
7	49
10	100

$$\sum X = 25 \quad \sum X^2 = 173 \quad N = 5$$

Substituting these values into the formula, being careful to distinguish between $\sum X^2$ and $(\sum X)^2$, gives:

$$S^2 = \frac{5(173) - (25)^2}{5(5-1)}$$

$$= \frac{865 - 625}{20} = \frac{240}{20}$$

$$= 12$$

This method, which works from raw scores, gives the same answer as applying the definitional formula, which works with deviation scores. That is expected, since one formula is derived from the other.

It is worth noting that

$$N \sum X^2 - (\sum X)^2$$

can be carried out in one sequence of operations on a calculator without having to write down the two parts. And on some electromechanical calculators and most electronic calculators, all the steps necessary to find the variance can be carried out without your having to store intermediate steps in memory. Take the trouble to find out how this is done. It is well worth the effort.

Standard deviation

Suppose the data in Table 9–2 are the number of seconds five rats take to run down a simple T-maze. Since the X-scores are expressed in seconds, the deviation scores $(X-M)$ are differences in seconds. Squaring these gives units of seconds squared. That is not a very intuitively meaningful unit, so the square root of the variance is often taken to restore the units to their original form. The square root of the variance is called the *standard deviation*.

$$S = \sqrt{S^2} = \sqrt{\frac{\sum(X-M)^2}{N-1}}$$

The computing formula is

$$S = \sqrt{\frac{N\sum X^2 - (\sum X)^2}{N(N-1)}}$$

The standard deviation is, of course, also an index of the variability or spread of a distribution, but, unlike the variance, it is expressed in the same units as the raw data. On some calculators the square root can be taken by simply pushing the square root button. If this facility is not available to you, then the easiest way to find a square root is to look it up in a table such as that given in Appendix J.

Exercise 9–3

What are the range and the standard deviation of the data in Exercise 9–1?

Answers

The range of scores is from 1 to 7. Here are the calculations for the standard deviation. I have done it two ways, one for deviation scores (defining formula) and one for raw scores (calculating formula). Recall that the mean has already been determined in Exercise 9–1,

$$M = \frac{\sum X}{N} = \frac{40}{10} = 4$$

		For deviation scores			*For raw scores*	
X	f	$X - M$	$(X-M)^2$	$(X-M)^2 f$	X^2	$X^2 f$
7	1	3	9	9	49	49
5	4	1	1	4	25	100
4	2	0	0	0	16	32
2	2	−2	4	8	4	8
1	1	−3	9	9	1	1
$N = 10$			$\sum(X-M)^2 = 30$		$\sum X^2 = 190$	

$$S^2 = \frac{\sum(X-M)^2}{N-1} \qquad S^2 = \frac{N\sum X^2 - (\sum X)^2}{N(N-1)}$$

$$= \frac{30}{9} = 3.33 \qquad = \frac{10(190) - (40)^2}{10(9)}$$

$$= \frac{300}{90} = 3.33$$

$$S = \sqrt{3.33} = 1.83 \qquad S = \sqrt{3.33} = 1.83$$

9.4 Standard scores

An important application of the mean and standard deviation is in converting raw scores into standard scores. We sometimes do this in order to compare seemingly incomparable quantities. For example, suppose you take a series of aptitude tests, and your scores are as follows:

Test	Score
Manual dexterity (MD)	70
Spatial relations (SR)	63
Verbal comprehension (VC)	32
Musical ability (MA)	25

It is certainly true that the *scores* are in the order

MD > SR > VC > MA

but is that a fair statement about the *aptitudes*, even if we assume that the tests are perfect measuring instruments and the scores are error-free?

To answer that question, we observe that each test has been given to hundreds of people in order to establish 'norms', often expressed by giving the mean and standard deviation. These norms enable us to establish how much better or worse an individual's score is than the average. Let us consider first the mean, and the deviation of each of your scores from the mean.

Test	Score	Population mean	Deviation
MD	70	63	7
SR	63	63	0
VC	32	36	−4
MA	25	19	6

Now we can determine your aptitude relative to the average performance of the general population. The deviation scores are in this order:

MD > MA > SR > VC

You scored above the population mean on MD and MA, your performance is average on SR, and below average on VC. Notice that the 70 on MD no longer looks all that much better than the 25 on MA, for we now see that the mean scores on those two tests are high and low, respectively, so that performance *relative to the mean* is above average.

But the deviation scores still do not give us enough information to determine your relative standing on MD and MA. One more piece of information is needed, the standard deviation of the population of test scores. Then each deviation can be divided by the standard deviation, which gives a standard score, indicating how many standard deviations above or below the mean the raw score is.

Test	Score	Population mean	Deviation	Population standard deviation	Standard score
MD	70	63	7	7	1
SR	63	63	0	6	0
VC	32	36	−4	8	−0·5
MA	25	19	6	3	2

Now we see that your score on MD is just one standard deviation above the mean, while your score on MA is two standard deviations beyond the mean. Thus, your score on MA is, relatively speaking, more extreme than your score on MD. We could conclude that while your aptitude is better than average in both categories, you have a higher aptitude for music than for tasks requiring manual dexterity.

The formula for converting a raw score, X, to a standard score, Z, is

$$Z = \frac{X - M}{S}$$

where M and S are the mean and standard deviation of the X-scores. You can see that this linear transformation is the same as the standard-score formula applied to uncertain quantities. It applies to any distribution whatsoever, for it is simply a linear transformation that can be applied to raw data or uncertain quantities whenever it is useful to do so. **A standardized score (or uncertain quantity) shows the relative position of the score in the overall distribution of scores.**

If all raw scores in a distribution are transformed to standard scores, the general shape of the distribution remains the same, but the new mean will be zero and the standard deviation will be one. The frequency with which a particular raw score occurred is just the same when that score is changed to a standard score, and so the general shape of the distribution remains unchanged. The transformation has the effect of shifting the entire distribution along the X-axis, and then stretching or compressing the X-axis. This was shown in Fig. 6–12.

Exercise 9–4

The following table gives the grades a student earned in several mid-term tests, along with the class means and standard deviations.

Test	Score	Class mean	Class standard deviation
English literature	70	58	12
French	65	68	3
Linear algebra	69	60	6
Botany ·	73	75	4

Rank order his performance on the four tests.

Answer

We do not know how well he has done until we see how many standard deviations above or below the mean he is, so first we must calculate his Z-scores for each test, then we determine rank order on the basis of the standard scores.

Test	Z-score	Rank
English literature	$(70-58)/12 = 1$	2
French	$(65-68)/3 = -1$	4
Linear algebra	$(69-60)/6 = 1{\cdot}5$	1
Botany	$(73-75)/4 = -0{\cdot}5$	3

9.5   Summary

Statistics summarize data in a succinct form that enables rapid and efficient communication. Statistics are usually calculated on either an electro-mechanical or electronic calculator, or on a computer, using formulae that facilitate machine calculation. Statistics in this book are first defined and then calculating formulae are given. In this chapter, these formulae involve just three quantities: $\sum X$, the sum of the scores, $\sum X^2$, the sum of the squares of the scores, and N, the number of scores.

The central tendency of a distribution of scores is indicated by the mean, median, or mode. The mode is the X-score that occurs most frequently, the median is the middle score (after all scores have been arranged in order), and the mean, M, is the average score:

$$M = \frac{\sum X}{N}$$

The mode is useful in describing a distribution that has a high peak over one X-score, while the median is often used to describe data that are highly skewed or that contain one or two extreme scores. The mean is most often used in inferential statistics; it fluctuates less from sample to sample than the mode or median. When each X-score is converted to a deviation from the mean, the sum of the deviations for all scores will equal zero. If the deviations are squared and then summed, the sum will be smaller than if the deviations had been taken from any other number.

If one score in a distribution is to be chosen at random, the 'best guess' about its value is the mode if one wishes to maximize the chance of being correct, the median if one wants to minimize absolute error, and the mean if one wants to minimize squared error.

Three statistics that quantify the spread or variability of a distribution are mentioned. The range is given by the highest and lowest score in the distribution. The variance, S^2, is defined as the sum of squared deviations from the mean divided by $N-1$:

$$S^2 = \frac{\sum (X-M)^2}{N-1}$$

The standard deviation, S, is the square root of the variance.

Standard scores, or Z-scores, can be computed from raw data by using this formula:

$$Z = \frac{X-M}{S}$$

These scores show the relative standing of a score in a distribution, and allow a score from one distribution to be compared to a score from another distribution.

Problems

9–1   For the data given in Problem 8–3 at the end of Chapter 8

a   calculate the mean, median, and mode.

b   indicate how one could communicate efficiently an accurate impression of the central tendency of the data.

c   discuss the limitations of statistics in conveying a full impression of the data.

9–2 Compute statistics appropriate for summarizing the data given in problem 8–4. Justify your choice of statistics.

9–3 Ordinal position of birth, or 'birth order', has been found in several studies to be related to certain aspects of personality. Suppose an investigator conducting one of these studies asks each of his subjects to indicate whether they were first-born, second-born, third-born, etc., in their family. He obtains these results for 20 subjects:

1	3	2	1
1	2	1	2
3	1	3	3
1	2	2	1
2	1	4	2

a   What are the mean, median, and mode for these data?
b   Why are the three values different?
c   Find the standard deviation of these data.

9–4 An investigator wishes to know if the ability to solve certain kinds of problems is affected by field dependence–independence, the extent to which an individual making a perceptual judgement is influenced by context. To measure field dependence–independence, he gives 35 subjects a task in which they have to pick out a simple figure hidden in a more complex one. Here are their scores.

26	6	10	12	7
18	25	21	3	17
23	19	19	21	12
0	18	15	13	16
13	19	15	3	15
6	13	26	16	10
15	16	17	8	5

Compute statistics appropriate for summarizing the data. Justify your choice of statistics.

9–5 The table below gives the incomes for three citizens (A, B, C) from their respective countries (X, Y, Z). It also shows the average income in each country, along with the standard deviation of incomes in each country. All income figures are given in the currency of the country. Which citizen is the richest? The poorest? Why?

Citizen	Income	Country	Average income	Standard deviation
A	4000	X	3500	250
B	2000	Y	1500	500
C	10000	Z	10500	1000

9–6 Observe and record the total grocery bill for each person coming through the check-out of a supermarket. Keep observing until you have recorded the data for 40 to 50 people.

a   Draw a histogram or frequency polygon of your data.
b   Compute statistics appropriate for summarizing the data. Justify your choice of statistics.

10 · Correlation and prediction

So far discussion has centred on just one variable, which we have usually referred to as an X-score. The past two chapters have been concerned with describing a set of X-scores either in pictorial form as a frequency distribution, histogram, or frequency polygon, or in terms of statistics, such as the mean and standard deviation. In the next chapter we will see how these descriptors of data are used in making inferences.

But before turning to inference, we must consider ways of describing the association between *two* variables, say, X-scores and Y-scores. Scientists are frequently concerned with questions of what goes with what, of measuring the degree of relatedness between two things. In the early stages of an investigation, a social scientist may wish to know only whether or not two variables are related, and if he finds they are he will next try to learn more about *how* they are related, perhaps eventually determining a function rule that describes the relationship.

It is important to recall at this point one of the major themes of Chapter 7. When I say that we wish to examine the possible association between two variables, I am talking about association predicted by our model of the real world. I am *not* talking about the real world, of which the model is an abstraction. At the practical level, this means that we will be looking for association between two sets of numbers, which we designate X and Y. In this chapter we discuss only the association to be found in the numbers that are our data, while in Chapter 12 we extend the discussion to include inferences about the population itself. But even if we conclude that association in the population of numbers is highly plausible, we still have to make a non-statistical inference about association between the *true properties* represented by the numbers. Methods for doing this were covered in Chapter 7, though I admitted there that the procedures are not entirely satisfactory or complete. Thus, *when I talk about two variables being associated, I am saying something about pairs of numbers, not about the underlying properties.* Some textbook writers remind the reader of this distinction by referring to 'statistical association', but I forgo this in the hope that the distinctions made in Chapter 7 will be borne in mind.

What is meant by saying that two variables are associated? There are at least three interpretations common in statistical usage:

X and Y are correlated;

Y can be predicted from knowledge of X;

X and Y are not statistically independent.

When two variables are correlated, we say that values of X are associated in a non-random way with values of Y. Rather than use that long phrase, I shall say simply that X 'goes with' Y. Different degrees of correlation are possible, implying that the relation 'goes with' is less than perfect. We know, for example, that I.Q. and school grades are related, that higher grades tend to be obtained by the higher-I.Q. children, but the relationship is certainly not a perfect one, for some high-I.Q. children earn low grades, and some children of modest intelligence earn high grades. In this chapter we will see how to compute a coefficient of correlation that indicates the degree to which X 'goes with' Y.

Once we have discovered that X and Y are correlated, it is often useful to find a rule that allows a value of Y to be predicted for some value of X. Such a rule is called a 'regression equation' and we see in this chapter how to compute it.

Perhaps the weakest statement we can make about the association between X and Y is that they are not statistically independent. Basically, questions of independence are problems of inference, so they will not be discussed in this chapter but will be taken up in Chapter 14.

A word of warning about what is *not* meant by association. The statistics presented here do not enable us to say that X *caused* Y. In fact, I know of *no* statistics that specifically quantify causation. It may well be that X causes Y and that is why X and Y appear to be associated, but observing that X and Y are associated and even quantifying the degree of association does not by itself allow us to say anything about causation. Psychologists may observe that children with unusual or odd-sounding first names exhibit more frequent psychiatric disorders than children with more common names, but that does not necessarily mean that odd names are the *cause* of mental disturbance. Perhaps children who are unwanted are more likely to be given odd names by their rejecting parents, and it is the rejection not the name that leads to later disturbance. In general terms, X and Y may appear to be related because they are actually related to a third, unmeasured variable, Z. Causation must be established by extra-statistical argument.

With that brief introduction, let me set out the purposes of this chapter. By the time you have completed study of the chapter, including working through the exercises and the problems at the end, you should

know how and when to compute a Pearson r and Spearman rho correlation coefficient;

be able to determine a linear regression equation for predicting Y from X;

understanding the meaning of a correlation coefficient and of a regression equation.

10.1 Making calculations

In this chapter, I always assume that *pairs* of observations have been made on the elements being measured. For example, suppose that the ages of five people are noted along with their scores on a test of social conformity. We might designate the ages as X-scores, and the social conformity data as Y-scores. The data are recorded like this:

Person	Age X	Social conformity Y
A	40	9
B	20	5
C	50	8
D	60	12
E	30	7

Each statistic introduced in this chapter will be defined with a formula from which a more convenient calculating formula can be derived, as in the last chapter. The calculating formula will contain the familiar terms

$$\sum X \text{ and } \sum X^2$$

and their analogues for the Y-scores,

$$\sum Y \text{ and } \sum Y^2$$

In addition we will need to know the number of *pairs* of scores, N. One more term is required:

$$\sum XY$$

This is the sum of the cross-products of the scores, obtained by first multiplying the X and Y scores together for each element, and then summing the products.

Each of these six terms is worked out below for the example. Be sure you see how they are determined.

X	Y	X^2	Y^2	XY
40	9	1600	81	360
20	5	400	25	100
50	8	2500	64	400
60	12	3600	144	720
30	7	900	49	210

$\sum X = 200$ $\quad \sum Y = 41$ $\quad \sum X^2 = 9000$ $\quad \sum Y^2 = 363$ $\quad \sum XY = 1790$ $\quad N = 5$

Some of the calculations in this chapter require you to find $\sum X \sum Y$. Note that this is not the same as $\sum XY$.

$\sum X \sum Y$ add first, then multiply the sums;
$\sum XY$ multiply first, then add the products.

For the example just given, $\sum X \sum Y = (200)(41) = 8200$.

10.2 Correlation

In this section we see how pairs of measures can be represented graphically, and methods for quantifying the association between the two variables are given. When two measures are made on each element, the data are said to be *bivariate*.

The discussion will be facilitated if we have some data to illustrate the points made. We choose an example in which a moderately high degree of association between two variables is obvious: the height and weight of 50 undergraduate men.

Person	Height, in	Weight, lb	Person	Height, in	Weight, lb
1	71	120	26	76	175
2	71	147	27	72	150
3	70	150	28	67	112
4	65	148	29	68	140
5	74	168	30	72	175
6	70	143	31	72	176
7	72	160	32	71	126
8	67	130	33	69	135
9	72	150	34	67	130
10	72	130	35	67	122
11	66	148	36	67	130
12	67	108	37	66	130
13	69	144	38	67	143
14	68	150	39	72	145
15	64	126	40	71	155
16	66	140	41	75	189
17	71	154	42	64	129
18	74	172	43	69	126
19	71	168	44	72	160
20	64	118	45	70	154
21	74	140	46	70	143
22	71	140	47	70	140
23	67	128	48	67	170
24	74	175	49	71	152
25	69	149	50	75	175

We have taken two measures on each person, height to the nearest inch, and weight to the nearest pound. We know that the taller a person is, the heavier he is, generally speaking. Weight and height tend to be associated, though not perfectly.

Bivariate frequency distributions

How can this association be shown? One approach is to summarize the data in a frequency distribution which shows both a person's weight and height; this is called a bivariate frequency distribution. A convenient representation is obtained by constructing a grid, with intervals of height marked off along the bottom, and intervals of weight marked off along the edge. Each cell in the grid corresponds to a particular combination of height and weight. To make a frequency distribution, locate a person's height along the bottom of the grid; that identifies a vertical column. Then find his weight along the edge; that locates a horizontal row. Now make a mark in the cell that intersects the row and column. This has been done in Fig. 10–1 for all the data. As an example, take person 1. His height is 71 in, so he is located in the fifth column from the

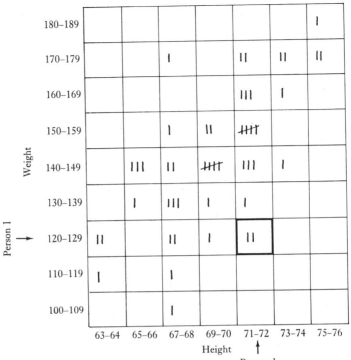

Fig. 10–1

Bivariate frequency distribution for the height–weight data

left, as indicated. His weight is 120 pounds, locating him in the third row from the bottom. Thus, he is one of the two people represented by ticks in the darkened cell.

Bivariate histograms

The frequency distribution of Fig. 10–1 can be turned into a bivariate histogram in the following manner. Imagine that Fig. 10–1 is laid on a table, and then small wooden blocks are stacked up on the grid, the height of the stack on each cell governed by the number of ticks. Thus, the two cells with five ticks will each have five blocks stacked on them, the upper right hand cell with one tick will get just one block, and so forth.

The result is shown in Fig. 10–2. The midpoints of the intervals have been shown along the edges of this diagram. Notice that Figs 10–1 and 10–2 show the expected relationships of height to weight. You do not expect to see many short, heavy people or tall, thin people, so the upper left and lower right cells are vacant. There are not very many short, light people or many tall, heavy people, so the lower left and upper right areas contain few ticks or blocks. Most people are of middling height and weight, so the blocks pile up in the centre of the figure. Finally, the ticks and blocks stretch from lower left to upper right, indicating that increasing height goes with increasing weight.

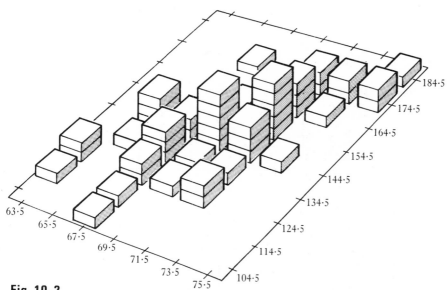

Fig. 10–2
Bivariate histogram for the height–weight data

Marginal distributions

Suppose you want to look only at the distribution of height. You could construct a histogram by referring only to the height data, following the procedures of the previous chapter. What relationship would this univariate distribution show to the bivariate distribution of Fig. 10–2? Imagine that the blocks in Fig. 10–2 were slid straight away from you, and then were restacked along the far edge. For example, the three blocks along the left edge (a single block and a stack of two) would be stacked as a pile of three at the left upper edge. Next to that pile would be a stack of four, formed by combining the single block and the stack of three above the 65·5. The result is called the *marginal distribution of height*, and it is shown in Fig. 10–3.

In like manner, the *marginal distribution of weight* can be obtained from the bivariate distribution by moving the blocks straight to the left. This result is also shown in Fig. 10–3.

It is worth pointing out that while marginal distributions can be obtained from a bivariate distribution, it is not possible to reconstruct a bivariate distribution from the marginals alone. The marginals tell us only how each variable is distributed; the joint or bivariate distribution gives us the extra information of how the variables are associated. Thus, when you collapse a bivariate distribution into its marginals, you lose some information.

Scatterplots

Drawing a bivariate histogram is a tedious job, so a simpler representation called a scatterplot is usually used. Height and weight, as continuous variables, are represented along the *X*- and *Y*-axes, respectively. Each person is shown

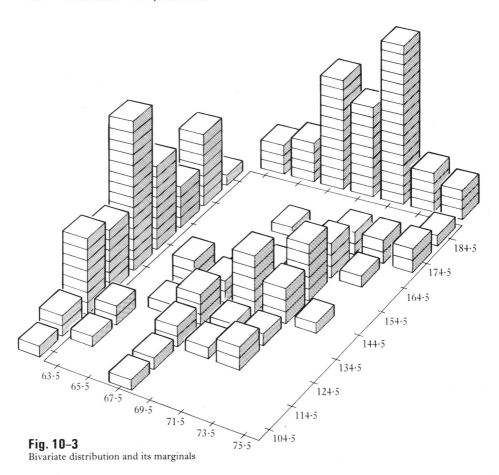

Fig. 10–3
Bivariate distribution and its marginals

by a dot in this X–Y space. A scatterplot for the height weight data is shown in Fig. 10–4. When several dots fall on top of one another, they are shown side by side, for example, three people were 67 in tall and weighed 130 lb, so they are represented as three dots next to each other on the diagram. You might compare Fig. 10–4 with Fig. 10–2 to see which representation conveys a clearer picture of the data.

Correlation coefficient

Drawing a scatterplot should be routine procedure in the early stages of data analysis. Not only does this enable you to get a 'feel' for your data, but, as we will see in the next section, it may prevent you from drawing erroneous conclusions. However, it is not very practical to communicate your results by publishing a scatterplot, particularly if you are investigating several relationships. Nor is it satisfactory to say, 'In my experiment height and weight tended to go together, though not perfectly; I have established that there is some

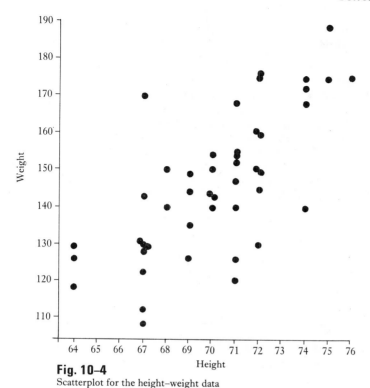

Fig. 10–4

Scatterplot for the height–weight data

relationship between them.' What is needed is a single measure of the degree of association between X and Y.

We have seen in the chapter on functions that two things may be associated in many different ways. The relationship between X and Y may be described as a power function, an exponential function, a linear function and so on. When we talk about measuring the degree of association between X and Y in a correlation problem, we must have some standard in mind, so that we are really measuring the degree to which X and Y are related in a power way, or an exponential way, or a linear way, etc. For example, anxiety shows a U-shaped relation to number of errors in some tasks, as shown in Fig. 10–5. Moderate levels of anxiety yield relatively error-free performance, while errors are greater when anxiety is low or high. Data from an experiment show some scatter, for anxiety is not the sole determinant of number of errors. But we assume that if all those other factors could be held constant in the experiment, then the 'pure' effects of anxiety would cause all the data to lie along the theoretical curve.

Now this may or may not be a reasonable assumption, but the scientist often acts as though it were reasonable not so much because he believes it but rather because it provides a tolerable approximation to the true state of affairs and so simplifies analysis of the data. He proceeds by measuring the degree to which the data conform to a U-shaped function. If he finds a fair degree of relationship, as is implied by Fig. 10–5, he says that number of errors are a

U-shaped function of anxiety. He is well aware that they may not be in a functional relationship at all, and even if they are, he recognizes that the function is probably not single-valued, that more than one value of Y may be associated with a single value of X. But by specifying the degree to which X and Y go together in a U-shaped way, he is communicating a clearer picture of the data than can be seen by looking at the raw data.

The number expressing the degree of relationship may be only a pale reflection of the truth, but, as we shall see in the section on regression, it is a useful reflection, for knowing the state of a person's anxiety gives us a better idea of what his test performance will be. Knowing a person's height gives us a better, though still imperfect, notion of what that person's weight is. Generally speaking, if there is any degree of relationship between X and Y, then knowing a particular value of X reduces our uncertainty about Y. We can predict Y more closely

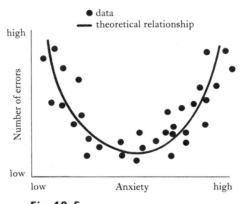

Fig. 10–5
A U-shaped function

by knowing X than if we did not know it. My guess about the weight of a person unseen by me is less likely to be a wild guess if I am told his height.

In developing an index for degree of association, we must, then, assume some function rule. But which is it to be? An eminent statistician once quipped that all relations in science are constant except for a few that are linear. Well, there are not many constants in the social sciences, so most relationships must be linear. What he was saying is not so silly as it first sounds, for a linear relationship is often a tolerable first approximation in social science research. Later, more refined, experimentation may tease out the exact form of a relationship, but in the initial stages of research a linear function rule may provide a useful description.

This chapter focusses on the linear rule, which, you will recall, is given by

$$Y = A + BX$$

(Here I write the rule in capital letters, to conform to the convention of letting capital Roman letters stand for data and their statistics.) Later we will show how the rule can be formulated for scattery data, and we will consider how good the rule is for making accurate predictions. But now we turn to a single index of the degree to which X and Y go together in a linear way.

The *correlation coefficient* (or Pearson product-moment correlation coefficient, as it is sometimes called) is usually designated by r and is defined as

$$r = \frac{\sum Z_X Z_Y}{N-1}$$

To compute r for N pairs of X-Y scores we must first transform each X-score to its Z-score equivalent, and each Y-score to its Z-score equivalent. Recall that we do this by applying the linear transformation

$$Z = \frac{X - M}{S}$$

We take the resulting N pairs of Z_X-Z_Y scores and multiply the scores in each pair together, sum the products, and divide by $N-1$. The resulting r will be between -1 and $+1$, a $+1$ indicating a perfect direct linear relationship between X and Y, a -1 representing a perfect inverse linear relationship (as X increases, Y decreases), and 0 standing for no linear relationship. Intermediate values of r represent varying degrees of linear relationship.

Exercise 10–1

An investigator asks a person to guess the age to the nearest month of five infants.

Here are the results:

Baby	Actual age, months	Guessed age, months
A	3	6
B	12	8
C	17	19
D	22	18
E	30	22

a Draw a scatterplot of these data.
b Compute the correlation coefficient between actual and guessed age.

Answers

Here is the scatterplot:

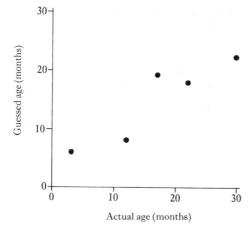

The data are somewhat scattery, though the person generally guesses higher ages for older infants.

To compute Pearson's r, we first convert each score to its Z-score equivalent. To do that we must first find the mean and standard deviation of each column of data. The steps are set out below:

Actual age, X	X^2	Guessed age, Y	Y^2
3	9	6	36
12	144	8	64
17	289	19	361
22	484	18	324
30	900	22	484
$\Sigma X = 84$	$\Sigma X^2 = 1826$	$\Sigma Y = 73$	$\Sigma Y^2 = 1269$

$$M_X = \frac{84}{5} = 16\cdot8 \qquad\qquad M_Y = \frac{73}{5} = 14\cdot6$$

$$S_X = \sqrt{\frac{5(1826) - (84)^2}{5(5-1)}} \qquad S_Y = \sqrt{\frac{5(1269) - (73)^2}{5(5-1)}}$$

$$= \sqrt{\frac{2074}{20}} \qquad\qquad = \sqrt{\frac{1016}{20}}$$

$$= \sqrt{103\cdot7} \qquad\qquad = \sqrt{50\cdot8}$$

$$= 10\cdot2 \qquad\qquad = 7\cdot13$$

Note the use of subscripts on M and S to identify the set of data to which those statistics belong.

Now Z-scores can be obtained by subtracting the appropriate mean from each score and then dividing by the standard deviation. For example, the first X-score, 3, when transformed to a Z-score becomes

$$Z_X = \frac{3 - M_X}{S_X} = \frac{3 - 16\cdot8}{10\cdot2} = -\frac{13\cdot8}{10\cdot2}$$

$$= -1\cdot35$$

The next step is to multiply each pair of Z-scores, and then divide the products by $N - 1$ to give r. Here are the steps.

X	$X - M_X$	Z_X	Y	$Y - M_Y$	Z_Y	$Z_X Z_Y$
3	$-13\cdot8$	$-1\cdot35$	6	$-8\cdot6$	$-1\cdot21$	$1\cdot63$
12	$-4\cdot8$	$-0\cdot47$	8	$-6\cdot6$	$-0\cdot93$	$0\cdot44$
17	$0\cdot2$	$0\cdot02$	19	$4\cdot4$	$0\cdot62$	$0\cdot01$
22	$5\cdot2$	$0\cdot51$	18	$3\cdot4$	$0\cdot48$	$0\cdot24$
30	$13\cdot2$	$1\cdot29$	22	$7\cdot4$	$1\cdot04$	$1\cdot34$
						$\Sigma Z_X Z_Y = 3\cdot66$

$$r = \frac{\Sigma Z_X Z_Y}{N - 1} = \frac{3\cdot66}{4} = 0\cdot92$$

A more convenient formula for Pearson's r, one which facilitates computation on a desk calculator, is this computing formula:

$$r = \frac{N \sum XY - \sum X \sum Y}{\sqrt{N \sum X^2 - (\sum X)^2}\ \sqrt{N \sum Y^2 - (\sum Y)^2}}$$

On the simpler desk calculators you must first find $\sum X$, $\sum Y$, $\sum X^2$, $\sum Y^2$, and $\sum XY$. Then you will find that the entire numerator of the calculating formula can be determined by one sequence of operations without writing down intermediate steps. Also, the term under each square root sign in the denominator can be obtained in one sequence of operations. If your calculator has no square root button, look these up in tables. That leaves one number in the numerator and two in the denominator, a simple chore for the calculator. Particularly on electronic calculators, it is often easiest to compute r^2:

$$r^2 = \frac{\{N \sum XY - \sum X \sum Y\}^2}{\{N \sum X^2 - (\sum X)^2\}\{N \sum Y^2 - (\sum Y)^2\}}$$

Then you only have to look up the square root of the result to get r, if the calculator has no square root button. Be careful not to lose the sign of r in the squaring operation. The sign is determined by the numerator; the denominator is always positive.

Exercise 10–2

Use the calculating formula to find the Pearson r for the data of Exercise 10–1.

Answer

I have set out the calculations in tabular form.

X	X^2	Y	Y^2	XY
3	9	6	36	18
12	144	8	64	96
17	289	19	361	323
22	484	18	324	396
30	900	22	484	660

$\sum X = 84$ $\sum X^2 = 1826$ $\sum Y = 73$ $\sum Y^2 = 1269$ $\sum XY = 1493$ $N = 5$

$$r = \frac{N \sum XY - \sum X \sum Y}{\sqrt{N \sum X^2 - (\sum X)^2}\ \sqrt{N \sum Y^2 - (\sum Y)^2}}$$

$$r = \frac{5(1493) - (84)(73)}{\sqrt{5(1826) - (84)^2}\ \sqrt{5(1269) - (73)^2}}$$

$$= \frac{7465 - 6132}{\sqrt{(9130 - 7056)}\ \sqrt{(6345 - 5329)}}$$

$$= \frac{1333}{\sqrt{2074}\ \sqrt{1016}} = \frac{1333}{(45 \cdot 5)(31 \cdot 8)}$$

$$= 0 \cdot 92, \text{ as before.}$$

Interpreting the correlation coefficient

In this chapter, a correlation coefficient is taken as a statistic that describes sample data, and. as such, it can be computed for any collection of pairs of data. However, when one wishes to make an inference about the *population* correlation coefficient, a topic we take up in Chapter 12, then it is necessary to assume that the joint distribution of X and Y is bivariate normal in form. Although this assumption is irrelevant to the computation of a sample correlation coefficient, one must take it into consideration if inferences are to be made.

Even if attention is to be restricted to samples, correlation coefficients must be used with great care, for they can easily mislead. A few words about what a correlation is and what it is not are in order.

I have already said that a correlation of either -1 or $+1$ indicates a perfect linear relationship, that 0 indicates no relationship, and other values represent varying degrees of linear relationship. In Fig. 10–6 data from six experiments are shown as scatterplots, and the value of r is indicated in the lower right corner.

The scatterplots should give you a rough idea of the connection between amount of scatter and the value of r. Check your understanding by making an intuitive estimate of the correlation of the height–weight data shown in Fig. 10–4. The actual value is given in the summary to this chapter.

Notice that it makes absolutely no difference which of the two sets of measurements is considered as the X-variable and which as the Y-variable. For correlation problems, the distinction between independent and dependent variables is irrelevant. If, in Exercise 10–2, I interchanged the labels on the X and Y columns of data, the value of r would remain unchanged. We say that r is symmetric, that it is an index of the degree to which Y goes with X in a linear way and of the degree to which X goes with Y in a linear way.

However, caution is advised in thinking of r as a 'degree' of relationship. It is neither a ratio nor an interval-scale number. A correlation of 0·6 does not represent twice the degree of association shown by 0·3, and the difference in degree of association between 0·8 and 0·6 may be different than that between 0·5 and 0·3.

The trouble is that there is no absolute meaning we can give to the phrase 'degree of relationship'. Pearson's r is a statistic, a number that can be calculated from pairs of data. It is not a probability, a proportion, or a percentage. It does not have any very precise intuitive meaning. You can look at Fig. 10–6 to get an idea of the relation between amount of scatter and the size of r, and we can describe the relation in these rough terms:

0–0·2 virtually no relationship
0·2–0·4 low to modest relationship
0·4–0·6 moderate relationship
0·6–0·8 substantial relationship
0·8–1·0 high degree of association

But this is only a rough guide, for correlation coefficients must be interpreted in context. A low correlation that is of little use in one context may be very useful in another. A psychological test whose scores show only modest corre-

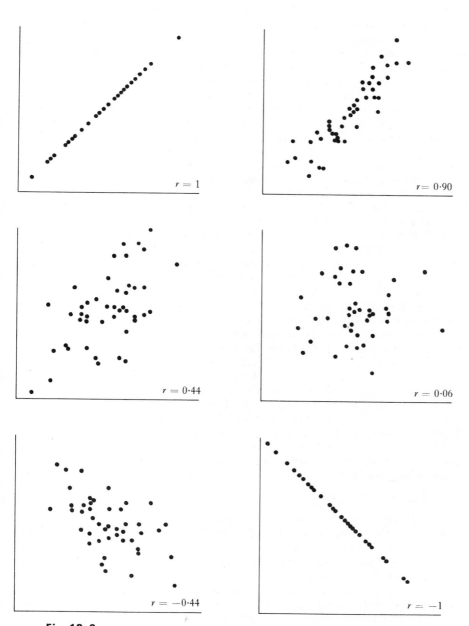

Fig. 10–6
Scatterplots showing varying degrees of correlation

lations with some criterion of performance may be very useful when used along with other tests. Nor does it make sense to talk about *the* correlation between two measures, without specifying the context. What is *the* correlation between I.Q. and success at university? The question is meaningless, though one could inquire about the correlation between I.Q. obtained with a *particular test* given under *specified conditions* to a *clearly defined sample* of students, and some *established criterion* that may measure a particular aspect of success.

In a way, it is unfortunate that established convention takes r as a measure of the degree of association, for more meaning can be ascribed to r^2, sometimes called the *coefficient of determination*. More will be said about r^2 in the section on linear regression, but for now it can be roughly interpreted as an index of the *strength* of association between X and Y. The proportion of variability X and Y have in common in a linear way is given by r^2,* and so $1-r^2$ indicates the proportion of variability *not* shared by X and Y. Thus, a fairly high correlation of 0.7 means that $(0.7)^2$ or only 49% of the variability in one variable is shared by the other; 51% is still 'left over', or 'unaccounted for'.

Remember, too, that r and r^2 refer to a linear relationship between X and Y. It is possible for a high degree of association to exist in the data, but for r to be near zero. This could come about when the relationship is nonlinear, and you can best check for nonlinearity by checking the scatterplot. If you can draw an ellipse around the data such that almost all the points are just contained in the ellipse, then you probably do not have any very serious nonlinearity in your data. Ellipses can be drawn around all the plots in Fig. 10–6, but the points in Fig. 10–5 are best encompassed by a shape like the outline of a curled sausage, not an ellipse. Other statistics, beyond the scope of this book, are available to quantify nonlinear association.

Because the correlation coefficient quantifies the degree of *linear* relationship, any linear transformation of X or Y, or both, will leave the value of r unchanged. For example, consider the scatterplot in Fig. 10–4. Suppose I lop off the zero from all the weights, so the Y-scale then runs from 11 to 19. That amounts to a re-labelling of the scale and does not change the scatterplot at all. Suppose further that I subtract, say, 10 from each number on the 11–19 scale. That gives a new scale whose range is from 1 to 9, and, again the scatterplot is unchanged. These two changes are, of course, nothing more than a linear transformation of the old scale:

$$Y_{new} = -10 + \tfrac{1}{10} Y_{old}$$

Each original value of Y, or Y_{old}, is divided by 10 and then 10 is subtracted to give the new, transformed value of Y. In similar fashion I can transform the X-axis; if 64 is subtracted from each height, the new X-scale will range from 0 to 12. Now, if you go back to the raw data, transforming all heights and weights according to these rules, the new pairs of numbers will all be much smaller than the original pairs, yet you will get exactly the same value of r if you determine it from the new pairs as you would have from the old ones. That is why making linear transformations of the variables is often useful; it lets you deal with smaller numbers, thus easing the work of calculating. Remember that

---

* However, this is not true when the correlation is between related persons. For these genetic correlations r itself, not r^2 gives the proportion of variance held in common. See Jensen (1971).

although the transformations on X and Y may be different from one another, you must use the *same* transformation on *all* the X-values, and the *same* transformation on *all* the Y-values.

As I said earlier, it is always wise to draw a scatterplot of your data. One reason is to check on possible nonlinearities, but another is to see if there are any very extreme points on the plot, for these have the effect of inflating the correlation coefficient. Consider an example shown to me by a master's degree student who had hypothesized that the more a business firm spent on research and development, the more it was likely to receive in royalties. Among other analyses, he computed the correlation coefficient between royalty income and

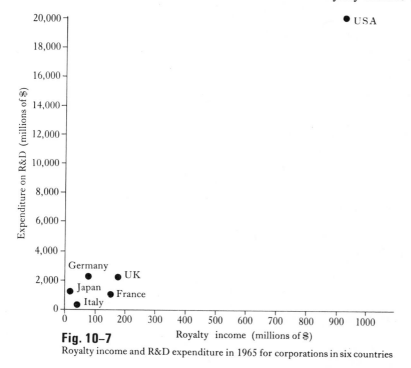

Fig. 10–7 Royalty income (millions of $)

Royalty income and R&D expenditure in 1965 for corporations in six countries

R & D expenditure in 1965 of corporations for six countries and found that $r = 0.987$. This result seemed to confirm his hypothesis, until the scatterplot was examined. It is shown in Fig. 10–7. The data from the USA are so extreme that the correlation coefficient is not a very good statistic to describe the data. Without the single point for the USA, the correlation for the other five countries drops to 0·46. However, further analysis showed that even that figure is misleading, for royalty income and R & D expenditure are related partly through their correlation with gross national product. When this effect is eliminated (by the use of a *partial correlation coefficient*, a topic beyond the scope of this book), the correlation between R & D expenditure and royalty income drops to about 0·2. Thus, what appeared to be a promising relationship at first turned out to be almost no relationship at all. The moral: Correlation coefficients must be used with care.

Spearman's rho

In many circumstances data will be in the form of rankings rather than numerical measurements. When this is the case, the Pearson r could be computed on the ranks. However, an easier method is to apply the formula for the Spearman rho correlation coefficient, applicable when there are no ties in the ranks:

$$r_{rho} = 1 - \frac{6 \sum D^2}{N(N^2 - 1)}$$

Since N is the number of pairs of data, the only new term is $\sum D^2$. This is the sum of the squared differences between the ranks and is found by subtracting one rank of the pair from the other, squaring the difference, repeating this for all pairs of ranks, and then adding the squares of the differences. Spearman's rho is derived from the Pearson r, with ranks used in place of numerical measurements, so you will get the same value for r_{rho} as you would if you computed r for the ranks.

Exercise 10–3

Eight applicants for a job are independently ranked by two personnel officers. A rank of 1 was assigned to the applicant thought to be most suitable, 2 to the next most suitable, etc.

Applicant	Rank assigned by 1st officer	Rank assigned by 2nd officer
A	1	3
B	7	5
C	4	1
D	8	8
E	6	4
F	5	7
G	2	2
H	3	6

Do the personnel officers show much agreement in their rankings?

Answer

It is hard to answer the question just by looking at the pairs of ranks. The Spearman rho correlation coefficient will give a convenient summary of the association between the rankings.

1st ranks	2nd ranks	Difference, D	D^2
1	3	2	4
7	5	2	4
4	1	3	9
8	8	0	0
6	4	2	4
5	7	2	4
2	2	0	0
3	6	3	9

$$\sum D^2 = 34$$

$$r_{rho} = 1 - \frac{6 \sum D^2}{N(N^2 - 1)}$$

$$= 1 - \frac{6(34)}{8(64 - 1)} = 1 - \frac{204}{504}$$

$$= 1 - 0 \cdot 405 = 0 \cdot 595$$

So there is only moderate agreement.

Spearman's rho is sometimes used even when data are in the form of numerical measurements. The measurements are used as a basis for ranking the elements being measured, and then the Spearman rho is computed on the ranks. Imagine, for example, that the 50 people whose heights and weights we have measured are put in order, first according to height. We assign the tallest person a rank of 1, the next tallest a 2, and so forth. Then we order the people according to weight, giving the heaviest a rank of 1, etc. This procedure ensures that each person now has two rankings, one on height and one on weight. We could now find the Spearman rho correlation between the ranks.

The only problem with this procedure is that our measurements were so coarse that some people have the same height. How can ranks be assigned to ties? The usual procedure is to assign the *average* rank to each person in the tie. For example, the 2nd and 3rd person are both 75 in tall. They are both given a rank of 2·5. The 4th, 5th, 6th, and 7th persons are tied at 74 in. Each is assigned a rank of

$$\frac{4+5+6+7}{4} = 5 \cdot 5$$

Unfortunately, the computing formula for Spearman's rho given above only applies when there are no ties in the data. To compute r_{rho} for tied data you must use the Pearson r formula. In this example it obviously would not be worth the trouble; one might as well compute Pearson r on the heights and weights as on the ranks.

So why use Spearman's rho for data on which numerical measurements are made? There are two reasons. First, if you have no ties, not too much data, and no calculator at hand, Spearman's rho can be calculated very quickly to give you a rough idea of whether or not there appears to be any association in the data. Secondly, sometimes numerical measurements contain no more than ordinal information so that computing a Pearson r on the measurements themselves may not yield a very meaningful statistic. In this case the Spearman rho, computed on ranks, may be more satisfactory. Once again, we see that the problem of meaningfulness must be faced when deciding on the appropriate statistic.

10.3 Linear regression

Sometimes one may wish to capitalize on the association found between pairs of measurements and derive a rule for predicting the value of one variable from the other. If we know a person's height, what prediction can we make about the person's weight, and how accurate will the prediction be? In this section we show how a linear prediction rule can be formulated, we see how it is related to the Pearson correlation coefficient, and we present an index that shows how accurate the prediction is.

The goal of *regression analysis* is to find a linear rule for predicting values of Y from values of X. Like all linear functions, the equation for the *regression line* is

$$\tilde{Y} = A_{Y|X} + B_{Y|X} X$$

$A_{Y|X}$ and $B_{Y|X}$ are the familiar Y-intercept and slope of the line, the subscripts denoting that the prediction is *from X to Y* ('Y given X'), the X is the independent variable, often called the *predictor variable* in regression analysis, and $\tilde{Y}$ is the *predicted* value of Y. Notice that the equation does not contain Y itself. The best we can do for scattery data is make a *prediction* of Y, and we want that prediction to be as close to the actual value or values of Y as possible.

In other words, we want to pass a straight line through the data of a scatterplot so that the line allows us to predict Y from X as accurately as possible. Once the equation for the line has been found it can be useful in practical situations where prediction must be carried out. Of course, if the line was determined for a randomly drawn sample, we may wish to know how representative it is of the population regression line; in Chapter 12 we discuss methods for making inferences about the regression line.

Now we turn our attention to finding the equation for the regression line applicable to the sample. But first we must consider what is meant when we say the line allows us to make predictions that are as 'accurate as possible'.

Least squares criterion

Today's newspaper contains advertisements for five houses to rent. The number of bedrooms and weekly rent (in pounds sterling) are as follows:

X No. of bedrooms	Y Weekly rent, £
1	12
2	14
3	30
4	44
5	40

These data are shown in the scatterplot of Fig. 10–8(a).

Suppose one of these houses is chosen at random. Before choosing, you must guess its rent. What is your best guess about its rent? You should, rightly, ask what I mean by 'best guess'. If I reply that I want a guess that minimizes squared error, then you should give the mean of Y, M_Y, which is £28. How wrong is that guess? Well, if the house with one bedroom is the chosen one, then the guess is wrong by $28 - 12 = £16$. The vertical bars in Fig. 10–8(b) show the difference between the guessed value of £28 and each possible true value. If each of those discrepancies is squared and then the average taken, the result is an average squared discrepancy score, an index of how accurate predicting the mean is for these data. If the average is taken by dividing by $N-1$, you will recognize this index as nothing more than the variance of Y, S_Y^2. Taking the square root restores the original units, and gives us a more useful index of how good is the rule 'Predict the mean'. Thus, when we know nothing about X, guessing the mean of Y minimizes squared error, and the standard deviation of Y is an index of how good the guess is; the smaller S_Y is, the better the prediction.

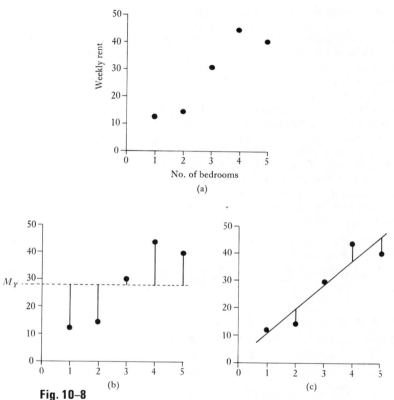

Fig. 10–8
(a) Scatterplot. (b) and (c) Deviations of predictions from actual values under two different prediction rules: (b) Predict the mean of Y, (c) Predict according to the linear regression equation.

But suppose after drawing a house at random I tell you the number of bedrooms. If you know the function, the list of pairings of Y with X, then you can make a perfect prediction. That would be a good procedure for this example, but in general scientists are interested in finding function rules or laws rather than making lists of pairings. The usual procedure is to derive a function rule for a set of experimental data that are representative of the population, then the rule is tested on new data and possibly refined, until finally a rule emerges that can be used on any set of data from the population.

So let us confine our interest to a linear rule for predicting the weekly rent knowing the number of bedrooms. We need to pass a straight line through the data and then use this line to make the predictions. One possibility is shown in Fig. 10–8(c). If you are told, for example, that the selected house has two bedrooms, then your prediction of the weekly rent will be about £20. Once again, the vertical bars represent discrepancies between predicted and true values, only this time the bars are shorter, as would be expected. We say then, that knowing X has reduced our uncertainty about Y.

But where should the regression line be located? There are an infinite number of possibilities, but for some the vertical bars will be longer than for others. The criterion commonly used is to locate the line such that the sum of the squares of the discrepancies is a minimum. If we took the length of each vertical bar, squared it, then added up the squares for all bars, we want the sum to be as small as possible. This is called the *method of least squares*, or the *least squares criterion*. Actually, the line in Fig. 10–8(c) *is* the least squares regression line. If you move it up or down or tilt it in any way you may shorten some of the squared discrepancies, but you will increase others disproportionately.

How accurate are our predictions using this new line? Again, we could find the average of the squared discrepancies, and if we do this by dividing by $N-1$, and then we take the square root, we arrive at a standard deviation reflecting the amount of variability around the regression line. It is an index of the amount of error in our predictions of Y *knowing* X, and is called the standard error of estimate for predicting Y from X; we designate it $S_{Y|X}$. Note the distinction from S_Y:

S_Y standard deviation of Y. An index of error when the prediction rule is always to predict the mean;

$S_{Y|X}$ standard error of estimate. An index of error when the prediction rule is to predict Y from X according to the least-squares regression line.

Another way to look at this is to think of

S_Y^2 as the original variance in Y, and
$S_{Y|X}^2$ as the variance in Y remaining after we know X.

Then we can consider the difference,

$S_Y^2 - S_{Y|X}^2$ as the amount of variance that has been accounted for by the linear regression line.

Thus, the *proportion* of the original variance that has been accounted for by the linear regression line is

$$\frac{S_Y^2 - S_{Y|X}^2}{S_Y^2} = 1 - \frac{S_{Y|X}^2}{S_Y^2}$$

Intuitively, you can see that if the data are pretty scattery, then the linear regression line will not reduce the original variance very much. The data will be so scattered that it will not make much difference whether you just predict the mean of Y every time without reference to the X-scores, or whether you use the linear regression line. But you also know that the strength of linear relationship in the data is given by r^2, so you might conclude that there must be some relationship between r^2 and the proportion of variance accounted for by the linear regression line. There is; they are equal. With a little algebra we could show that

$$r^2 = 1 - \frac{S_{Y|X}^2}{S_Y^2}$$

Rearranging terms gives

$$\frac{S_{Y|X}^2}{S_Y^2} = 1 - r^2$$

Taking square roots of both sides:

$$\frac{S_{Y|X}}{S_Y} = \sqrt{1 - r^2}$$

So, $S_{Y|X} = S_Y\sqrt{1 - r^2}$

This equation tells us that if we take the original standard deviation of Y and multiply by the square root of $1 - r^2$, we get the standard error of estimate. We know that if our linear prediction rule is a good one, $S_{Y|X}$ will be small since it is an index of how good our linear-regression predictions are. You can see from the equation that $S_{Y|X}$ will be small only if $\sqrt{1 - r^2}$ is small, so the closer $\sqrt{1 - r^2}$ is to zero the more perfect our prediction will be.

It is instructive, as a means of getting a better understanding of the Pearson r, to see how big r must be for $\sqrt{1 - r^2}$ to be small.

r	$\sqrt{1 - r^2}$
1·00	0
0·99	0·14
0·95	0·31
0·9	0·44
0·8	0·60
0·7	0·71
0·6	0·80
0·5	0·87
0·4	0·92
0·3	0·95
0·2	0·98
0·1	0·995
0	1·00

The table shows that r must be quite near 1 for $\sqrt{1 - r^2}$ to be near zero. Even with a fairly high correlation of 0·8, we see that $S_{Y|X}$ is 0·6 of the original S_Y. In the area of mental testing, correlations no higher than 0·5 are very common. In these cases, more than 87% of the original standard deviation is still left, so you can see that low correlations imply very little improvement in predictions by the linear regression line.

Exercise 10–4

How good is the linear prediction rule in Fig. 10–8(c)? What is the standard error of estimate for predicting Y from X?

Answer

One way of expressing the 'goodness' of a prediction rule, is to quote the value of the standard error of estimate. But unless we also know S_Y, we do not know if $S_{Y|X}$ is substantially smaller. Perhaps a more useful approach is to quote r^2, for this gives the proportion of the original variance in Y that has been accounted for by the linear rule. Here are the calculations for r^2.

X	Y	X^2	Y^2	XY
1	12	1	144	12
2	14	4	196	28
3	30	9	900	90
4	44	16	1936	176
5	40	25	1600	200

$\Sigma X = 15 \quad \Sigma Y = 140 \quad \Sigma X^2 = 55 \quad \Sigma Y^2 = 4776 \quad \Sigma XY = 506$

$$r^2 = \frac{(N \Sigma XY - \Sigma X \Sigma Y)^2}{\{N \Sigma X^2 - (\Sigma X)^2\}\{N \Sigma Y^2 - (\Sigma Y)^2\}}$$

$$= \frac{\{5(506) - (15)(140)\}^2}{\{5(55) - (15)^2\}\{5(4776) - (140)^2\}}$$

$$= \frac{(430)^2}{(50)(4280)} = \frac{184,900}{214,000} = 0.864$$

Thus, 86·4% of the original variability in Y has been accounted for by the linear relationship to X.

In terms of the original standard deviation, S_Y, we must multiply that by

$$\sqrt{1 - r^2} = \sqrt{1 - 0.864} = \sqrt{0.136} = 0.369$$

to get the standard error of estimate:

$$S_{Y|X} = S_Y\sqrt{1 - r^2} = S_Y(0.369)$$

The original standard deviation of Y is

$$S_Y = \sqrt{\frac{N \Sigma Y^2 - (\Sigma Y)^2}{N(N - 1)}}$$

$$= \sqrt{\frac{5(4776) - (140)^2}{5(4)}} \quad \sqrt{\frac{23,880 - 19,600}{20}}$$

$$= \sqrt{\frac{4280}{20}} = 14.6$$

And so,

$$S_{Y|X} = 14.6(0.369) = 5.4$$

Only a little over one third the original standard deviation is left.

Equation of the regression line

We have already pointed out that the equation for the regression line for predicting Y from X is

$$\tilde{Y} = A_{Y|X} + B_{Y|X} X$$

The values of $A_{Y|X}$ and $B_{Y|X}$ are chosen to meet the least squares criterion, and they can be computed from the raw data. The formulae are expressed in terms of various 'sums of squares', abbreviated 'SS', defined as follows:

Abbreviation	Definition	Computing formula
SS_{XX}	$= \sum (X - M_X)^2$	$= \dfrac{N \sum X^2 - (\sum X)^2}{N}$
SS_{YY}	$= \sum (Y - M_Y)^2$	$= \dfrac{N \sum Y^2 - (\sum Y)^2}{N}$
SS_{XY}	$= \sum (X - M_X)(Y - M_Y)$	$= \dfrac{N \sum XY - \sum X \sum Y}{N}$
$SS_{\tilde{Y}-\text{error}}$	$= \sum (Y - \tilde{Y})^2$	$= \dfrac{(SS_{YY})(SS_{XX}) - (S_{XY})^2}{SS_{XX}}$

Each sum of squares involves the deviation of one quantity from another. The first two are concerned with the deviations of X-scores and Y-scores from their respective means, the third deals with cross products of X and Y deviation scores, and the fourth involves the discrepancies between predicted and true values of Y.

The slope of the regression line for predicting Y from X is

$$B_{Y|X} = \frac{SS_{XY}}{SS_{XX}}$$

Substituting for the two sums of squares gives this computing formula:

$$B_{Y|X} = \frac{N \sum XY - \sum X \sum Y}{N \sum X^2 - (\sum X)^2}$$

The Y-intercept of the regression line is

$$A_{Y|X} = M_Y - B_{Y|X} M_X$$

Thus, you must compute the mean of X, the mean of Y, and the slope of the regression line before you can find $A_{Y|X}$.

When carrying out a regression analysis you will probably wish to know the standard error of estimate. It is given by

$$S_{Y|X} = \sqrt{\frac{SS_{\tilde{Y}\text{-error}}}{N-1}}$$

Finally, once you have determined all these sums of squares, it is an easy matter to compute the Pearson correlation coefficient:

$$r = \frac{SS_{XY}}{\sqrt{SS_{XX} SS_{YY}}}$$

Exercise 10–5

Find the equation of the regression line for predicting weekly rent from number of bedrooms. (The data are given in Exercise 10–4.) Then find $S_{Y|X}$ and r.

Answer

The first step is to find the five fundamental quantities, $\sum X$, $\sum X^2$, $\sum Y$, $\sum Y^2$, and $\sum XY$. We did that in Exercise 10–4.

$$\sum X = 15 \qquad \sum Y = 140$$
$$\sum XY = 506$$
$$\sum X^2 = 55 \qquad \sum Y^2 = 4776$$

Next we find the sums of squares:

$$SS_{XX} = \frac{N \sum X^2 - (\sum X)^2}{N} = \frac{5(55) - (15)^2}{5} = \frac{50}{5} = 10$$

$$SS_{YY} = \frac{N \sum Y^2 - (\sum Y)^2}{N} = \frac{5(4776) - (140)^2}{5} = \frac{4280}{5} = 856$$

$$SS_{XY} = \frac{N \sum XY - \sum X \sum Y}{N} = \frac{5(506) - (15)(140)}{5} = \frac{430}{5} = 86$$

Now we compute the slope:

$$B_{Y|X} = \frac{SS_{XY}}{SS_{XX}} = \frac{86}{10} = 8.6$$

and then the Y-intercept:

$$M_X = \frac{\sum X}{N} = \frac{15}{5} = 3$$

$$M_Y = \frac{\sum Y}{N} = \frac{140}{5} = 28$$

$$A_{Y|X} = M_Y - B_{Y|X} M_X$$
$$= 28 - 8.6(3) = 2.2$$

Thus, the equation for the regression line is

$$\tilde{Y} = 2.2 + 8.6X$$

To find the standard error of estimate, we first find $SS_{\tilde{Y}-\text{error}}$:

$$SS_{\tilde{Y}-\text{error}} = \frac{(SS_{YY})(SS_{XX}) - (S_{XY})^2}{SS_{XX}}$$

$$= \frac{(856)(10) - (86)^2}{10} = \frac{1164}{10} = 116.4$$

This gives:

$$S_{Y|X} = \sqrt{\frac{SS_{\tilde{Y}-\text{error}}}{N-1}} = \sqrt{\frac{116.4}{4}} = \sqrt{29.1} = 5.4$$

Interpreting the regression line

Once we have obtained the equation for the regression line, we are in a position to predict Y from X. If I tell you that a house has three bedrooms, then your prediction of the rent is:

$$\tilde{Y} = 2.2 + 8.6X$$
$$= 2.2 + 8.6(3) = 2.2 + 25.8$$
$$= £28$$

But remember that the equation applies only to the data on which it is based. As long as we treat the regression equation as a descriptive statistic, then we do not have to assume anything about the distributions of X and Y, or about the level of measurement, or about the way the data were obtained. We *will* have to make some assumptions when we come to make inferences about the population regression line, and some assumptions are different from those made when we wish to make inferences about the population correlation coefficient.

It is worth pointing out that we could just as well have taken Y as our independent variable so that we would predict number of bedrooms from knowing the rent. (A word of caution: we do not have this freedom to interchange X and Y if we wish to make inferences about the population regression line; more about this in Chapter 12). The slope of the regression line for predicting X from Y is

$$B_{X|Y} = \frac{SS_{XY}}{SS_{YY}}$$

the X-intercept is

$$A_{X|Y} = M_X - B_{X|Y} M_Y$$

and the standard error of estimate for predicting X from Y is

$$S_{X|Y} = \sqrt{\frac{SS_{\tilde{X}\text{-error}}}{N-1}}$$

where $SS_{\tilde{X}\text{-error}} = \dfrac{(SS_{YY})(SS_{XX}) - (SS_{XY})^2}{SS_{YY}}$

Exercise 10–6

Find the equation of the regression line for predicting number of bedrooms from weekly rent (data in Exercise 10–4). Also find $S_{X|Y}$.

Answers

The slope of the regression line is

$$B_{X|Y} = \frac{SS_{XX}}{SS_{YY}} = \frac{86}{856} = 0 \cdot 100$$

The X-intercept is

$$\begin{aligned} A_{X|Y} &= M_X - B_{X|Y} M_Y = 3 - 0 \cdot 1(28) \\ &= 3 - 2 \cdot 8 = 0 \cdot 2 \end{aligned}$$

So the equation is

$$\tilde{X} = 0 \cdot 2 + 0 \cdot 1 Y$$

Finally, the standard error of estimate is

$$\begin{aligned} S_{X|Y} &= \sqrt{\frac{SS_{\tilde{X}\text{-error}}}{N-1}} = \sqrt{\frac{1164/856}{4}} \\ &= \sqrt{0 \cdot 34} = 0 \cdot 58 \end{aligned}$$

It is interesting to see that the two regression lines, for predicting Y from X, and X from Y, are different (see Fig. 10–9). That is usually the case, so obviously we cannot interpret the regression line as representing *the* linear relationship in the data even if one exists. There may be a true linear functional relationship between X and Y, but it will not generally coincide with either regression line. **The regression equation is a model of our predictions, and is only one way of looking at the true relationship in the data.**

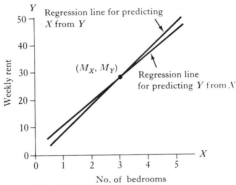

Fig. 10–9
Two regression lines. Note that they intersect at the mean of X and the mean of Y.

It is possible to show that the square root of the product of the two slopes of the regression lines is equal to the correlation coefficient:

$$\sqrt{(B_{Y|X})(B_{X|Y})} = r$$

Suppose one wishes to predict standard scores, not raw scores. What is the regression equation for predicting Z_Y-scores from Z_X-scores? Here it is:

$$\tilde{Z}_Y = rZ_X$$

Or, if we wish to predict in the other direction,

$$\tilde{Z}_X = rZ_Y$$

This formulation has a curious consequence. Suppose I wish to predict a child's I.Q. from one parent's I.Q., and let us suppose that the correlation between the I.Q.'s of parent and child is about 0·5. Now the regression equation for standard scores says that if the parent has an I.Q. two standard deviations above the mean, then our prediction for the child's I.Q. will be

$$\tilde{Z}_Y = rZ_X = (0·5)(2) = 1$$

In other words, while the parent is two standard deviations above the mean, we predict that the child will be just one standard deviation above. You can see that because r is always less than one, the *predicted* Z-score will always lie closer to the mean than the Z-score of the predictor variable. We predict that intelligent parents will sire less intelligent children. This effect has been called the 'regression toward the mean'. It is important to realize that this effect describes our *predictions* and may or may not be true of the underlying relationship. When we agree to model our predictions according to a linear rule, one consequence is that our best guess about Y is that it lies closer to the mean of the Y-scores than X lies to the mean of the X-scores. That is true of our guess, but it may or may not be true of the actual state of affairs. I predict that bright parents will have less bright children, but that does not mean that the children *must* be less bright than their parents.

Regression toward the mean is a consequence of the linear prediction rule employing a least-squares criterion for 'best guess'. As it happens, some biological traits, I.Q. included, do appear to exhibit regression toward the mean. Children of intelligent parents are more frequently than not, less intelligent than their parents. On the other side of the mean, we predict that children of low-I.Q. parents, will be more intelligent than their parents. But one should remember that this regression effect is not always a characteristic of the real world.

10.4 Summary

Two ways of looking at the association between pairs of measures is to compute a correlation coefficient or to determine a regression line. The correlation coefficient quantifies the degree to which two variables, say X and Y, go together in a linear way, while the regression line allows predictions of Y to be made from knowing X. Neither approach says anything about X *causing* Y, or vice versa.

In this chapter, both approaches are treated as descriptive of the data obtained, and calculating formulae are given in terms of $\sum X$, $\sum X^2$, $\sum Y$, $\sum Y^2$, $\sum XY$, and N.

When two measures are taken on each element, the data are said to be bivariate; they can be shown graphically as a frequency distribution, bivariate histogram, or, more usually, as a scatterplot. The distribution of X and Y is referred to as the joint or bivariate distribution, while the distributions of X or of Y by themselves are called marginal distributions.

The Pearson product-moment correlation coefficient, r, quantifies the degree to which X and Y go together in a linear way. It is defined as

$$r = \frac{\sum Z_X Z_Y}{N-1}$$

where Z_X and Z_Y are the standard scores corresponding to the X and Y raw scores. The correlation coefficient can take on values from -1 to $+1$, with $+1$ indicating a perfect direct linear association, 0 representing no association, and -1 standing for a perfect inverse linear relationship. Intermediate values of r represent less than perfect relationship. For example, the correlation coefficient for the height–weight data shown as a scatterplot in Fig. 10–4 is 0·67, indicating a direct but less than perfect relationship. There is no sense in which we can talk about *the* relationship between X and Y, for a correlation coefficient can only be interpreted in the context of a particular situation or experimental setting. The square of the correlation coefficient, r^2, gives an index of the proportion of variance shared by X and Y; it gives the proportion of variance of Y that is accounted for by the regression line for predicting Y

from X. A linear transformation of either X or Y, or both, leaves the value of r unchanged, a fact that can simplify calculations. It is wise to check the data for any extreme values as these can cause correlations that are misleadingly high.

Another index of correlation, one that is derived from the Pearson r and that applies to ranked data, is the Spearman rho. It is useful for ordinal data and for making quick checks of the degree of association when numerical measurements have been made at the interval level or above. However, if ties are present in the data, Pearson's r must be computed.

In regression analysis a linear prediction rule is determined:

$$\tilde{Y} = A_{Y|X} + B_{Y|X} X$$

The more scattery the data, the bigger will be the discrepancy, on the average, between the predicted and true values of Y.

It is usual procedure to find values of $A_{Y|X}$ and $B_{Y|X}$ that minimize the sum of the squares of these discrepancies. This is the least-squares criterion, and it leads to these values:

$$B_{Y|X} = \frac{SS_{XY}}{SS_{XX}} = \frac{N \sum XY - \sum X \sum Y}{N \sum X^2 - (\sum X)^2}$$

$$A_{Y|X} = M_Y - B_{Y|X} M_X$$

The standard error of estimate, $S_{Y|X}$, is an index that is related to how wrong predictions made with the regression line are. It is the standard deviation of the Y-scores once X is known and is related to the original standard deviation of Y and to the correlation coefficient:

$$S_{Y|X} = S_Y \sqrt{1 - r^2}$$

The closer r is to -1 or to $+1$, the smaller $S_{Y|X}$ is, and when $r = 1$, $S_{Y|X} = 0$, for then there is no error in prediction.

One consequence of linear regression is 'regression toward the mean', an observation that predicted scores are always closer to the mean of the Y-scores than the predictors are to the mean of the X-scores. This can be seen in the regression equation for standard scores:

$$\tilde{Z}_Y = r Z_X$$

It is important to remember that when inferences are to be made about the population correlation coefficient or the population regression line, certain assumptions must be met that are not necessary when r and the regression line are treated as descriptive statistics. Also, one cannot say that a regression line represents *the* linear relationship in the data even if one exists. Linear regression is a model of the process of making predictions.

Problems

10–1 Alpert and Haber (1960) have constructed an Achievement Anxiety Test (AAT) that measures the anxiety an individual feels in testing situations. The AAT contains two scales, one for anxiety that facilitates test performance, and one for anxiety that has a debilitating effect on performance. Here are the scores I obtained for 35 men on the two scales of a slightly modified version of the AAT:

Subject	Debilitating anxiety score	Facilitating anxiety score
1	30	21
2	22	19
3	23	27
4	22	26
5	23	24
6	18	32
7	35	20
8	22	30
9	22	26
10	18	23
11	19	25
12	16	31
13	26	26
14	25	24
15	21	29
16	36	20
17	19	31
18	12	34
19	17	21
20	18	28
21	22	28
22	26	19
23	19	27
24	16	36
25	14	23
26	28	28
27	29	25
28	20	29
29	22	21
30	17	27
31	18	27
32	25	27
33	11	31
34	18	23
35	32	25

a Draw a scatterplot of these data.

b Compute the Pearson correlation coefficient between the two sets of scores.

c How would you interpret your result *for these data*?

10–2 Twenty students estimated the amounts they had spent per week on drink and tobacco and also on books, stationery, journals, newspapers, etc. Here are the results:

Student	Amount on drink, etc.	Amount on books, etc.
1	0·50	3·00
2	0·50	0·75
3	0·15	0·50
4	0·75	2·25
5	1·50	2·50
6	0·50	2·00
7	0·15	1·00
8	0·75	1·25
9	0·50	1·50
10	1·00	0·25
11	0·90	0·30
12	0	3·00
13	0·25	0·40
14	0·75	0·50
15	0	3·00
16	2·00	0·50
17	1·50	1·00
18	0·25	1·00
19	2·00	0·50
20	0	0·25

a   Compute the Pearson correlation coefficient for these data.
b   How would you interpret the result?
c   Comment on the suitability of the Pearson r for these data.

10–3 For the data above, find the linear regression line for predicting the amount spent on books, etc., from the amount spent on drink, etc. Is this a very useful equation? Why or why not?

10–4 In 1927 Thurstone presented 266 University of Chicago students with all possible pairs of 19 criminal offences and asked each student to indicate the more serious offence. Applying his theory of comparative judgements, he constructed a scale of relative seriousness of offences based on the paired-comparison data for the whole group of students. In 1966, Coombs repeated the study using 369 University of Michigan students. Scale values for the two studies are as follows:

Offence	Scale values	
	1966	1927
Homicide	100·0	96·4
Rape	86·6	100·0
Kidnapping	79·1	67·1
Arson	64·3	61·7
Assault and battery	63·6	45·0
Abortion	45·62	69·3
Burglary	45·2	46·1
Embezzlement	42·0	50·6
Adultery	41·7	64·2

Offence	Scale values	
	1966	1927
Perjury	39·8	51·2
Larceny	38·8	40·5
Seduction	37·5	69·4
Counterfeiting	37·4	49·9
Forgery	33·5	47·7
Smuggling	30·7	33·6
Libel	30·6	34·3
Receiving stolen goods	17·4	30·5
Bootlegging	13·0	31·5
Vagrancy	0·0	0·0

Note that the least and most serious crimes for each scale have arbitrarily been assigned values of 0 and 100, respectively. This means that changes from 1927 to 1966 are relative, so we cannot tell whether a crime has become more or less serious since 1927. We *can*, however, make statements about the change in position of a crime *relative* to others on the same scale. For example, relative to the other crimes, sex offences are judged to be less serious in 1966 than in 1927. We *cannot* say that sex offences in 1966 were less serious; maybe sex offences were just as serious in 1966 as in 1927, but other crimes became more serious. Of course, if some way could be found to equate two points on one scale with two on the other (as we do in measuring temperature) then we could tell whether a crime has become more or less serious.

a   Compute the Pearson correlation coefficient between the scale values of the offences.

b   How would you interpret the result?

c   Compute the Spearman rho correlation coefficient.

d   Compare the Pearson and Spearman coefficients. How do you account for the difference?

e   Comment on the suitability of these coefficients for these data.

10–5   To find out if prices in Great Britain rose faster than incomes for the five years from 1965 to 1969, an economist noted the percentage growth (using 1955 figures as a base) for average weekly earnings and for retail prices. Here are the data (taken from Sillitoe, 1971):

Year	Per cent increase in	
	Average weekly earnings	Retail prices
1965	181	139
1966	187	143
1967	199	147
1968	213	155
1969	231	164

a   Compute the Pearson *r* correlation between the per cent increases for earnings and for prices.

b   Compute the slope of the linear regression line for predicting price increases from earnings increases. Interpret the meaning of the value in the light of the original question.

Part 3
Inference

11 · Inferences concerning one uncertain quantity

At last we are ready to consider in detail how inferences can be made about uncertain quantities and hypotheses. The four chapters in Part III are all concerned with the technology of making inferences, the main topic of this book. It has taken ten chapters to arrive at this point. In the first three chapters we had to learn the language and grammar of uncertainty before we could talk about inference. Next we saw that to make an inference about an uncertain quantity, one first decides how to measure the attribute or property of interest (Chapter 7), then prior opinion is quantified as a probability distribution (Chapter 6), next a sample is drawn (Chapter 8) and the sufficient statistics calculated (Chapters 9 and 10), and only then is Bayes' theorem applied. We saw in Chapter 4 how Bayes' theorem operates but from now on only the results of applying Bayes' theorem will be given, for its operation on continuous distributions requires mathematics beyond the scope of this book. The end results are, fortunately, easily understood.

At the risk of seeming to be repetitious, let me say again that our inferences will apply to *measurements*, not to *attributes*. For example, anxiety about testing situations is an *attribute* of people. If I use the Alpert-Haber (1960) Achievement Anxiety Test (AAT) to measure test anxiety, then the resulting scores are *measurements*. If the AAT is a good measuring instrument, then the scores should bear a close relationship to test anxiety; differences from one person to the next in test anxiety should be reflected in differences in scores on the AAT. The important point to keep in mind is that inferences are made about AAT scores, not about test anxiety. The best we can do is, say, find the 99% credible interval for the mean of the test scores for the population. But that is not an inference about test anxiety itself. Any inferences I may wish to make about test anxiety require extra-statistical information, such as the reliability and validity of the AAT and the conditions under which the AAT was administered, and other considerations mentioned in Chapter 7.

With that caution in mind we can turn now to the kinds of inferences covered in this chapter. Discussion will centre on uncertain quantities that involve just one variable. Specifically we will talk about inferences concerning medians, means, standard deviations, and proportions. For some procedures we will assume that prior opinion is quite vague, or that the principle of stable estimation applies, and that we know very little about the shape of the population distribution. Other procedures will make more assumptions about the population, and will allow for prior opinion that is not vague.

For all procedures the goal is the same: to arrive at a posterior credible interval for the uncertain quantity in question.

The material presented in this chapter should enable you to

make inferences about population medians, means, standard deviations, or proportions;

know when to use which inferential procedure;

understand the results of similar non-Bayesian analyses.

If you are feeling lost at this point, I suggest you go back and re-read Sec. 6.1 of Chapter 6 to restore some perspective.

11.1 Inferences about medians

In the early stages of an investigation, when you are pretty vague about the distribution of scores in the population, knowing neither its general shape nor its mean and standard deviation, it is often appropriate to make an inference about the median of the population. A very simple procedure for doing this has been provided by Jeffreys (1961). Let me illustrate with an example.

An investigator interested in how people form concepts devises a new experimental task, a series of games that a person plays with a computer. The experimenter hopes that the task is moderately difficult, but he is unsure, for he has tried it out on only a couple of colleagues and one secretary. Any score from 0 to 50 is possible, and he wants to know what the central tendency is for scores that would be obtained by the general population of students at his university. His prior opinion concerning the population median is very vague. He selects 25 volunteer students at random, and has them play the computer games. Their scores are as follows:

8, 17, 26, 20, 27, 24, 41, 24, 21, 26, 31, 29, 31,
16, 21, 22, 27, 30, 42, 44, 31, 50, 29, 26, 34

The Bayesian analysis is based on just two assumptions:

that the prior distribution concerning the population median is uniform;

that the population distribution is symmetrical,

that is, its right and left halves are mirror images. Our investigator feels that both of these are reasonable. He is very vague about the population median and he thinks it unlikely that the distribution is skewed. His very limited pre-testing leads him to believe the latter. Further, a histogram of the data looks like this:

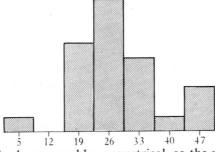

That looks reasonably symmetrical, so the population probably is, too.

Now he rank-orders the data. He carries out this ranking because the posterior distribution will extend over the 25 *ranks* rather than the scores

Rank	Score	Rank	Score	Rank	Score
1	8	9	24	17	30
2	16	10	26	18	31
3	17	11	26	19	31
4	20	12	26	20	31
5	21	13	27	21	34
6	21	14	27	22	41
7	22	15	29	23	42
8	24	16	29	24	44
				25	50

themselves, so that a credible interval will indicate how likely the population median is to fall between any two ranks. For sample sizes of at least 20, the posterior distribution concerning the ranks is approximately normal with

$$\text{posterior mean} = m'' = \frac{N+1}{2}$$

$$\text{posterior standard deviation} = s'' = \frac{\sqrt{N}}{2}$$

Now, what does this tell us? Well, computing say, the 95% credible interval tells us that there is a 95% chance that the population median falls between the scores whose ranks are given by rank_{low} and $\text{rank}_{\text{high}}$. To find those limits we travel up 1·96 standard deviations from the mean, and down that far, too.

$$\text{rank}_{\text{high}} = \frac{N+1}{2} + 1 \cdot 96 \frac{\sqrt{N}}{2} = \frac{26}{2} + 1 \cdot 96 \frac{\sqrt{25}}{2}$$

$$= 13 + 1 \cdot 96(2 \cdot 5) = 13 + 4 \cdot 9$$

$$= 17 \cdot 9$$

$$\text{rank}_{\text{low}} = \frac{N+1}{2} - 1 \cdot 96 \frac{\sqrt{N}}{2} = \frac{26}{2} - 1 \cdot 96 \frac{\sqrt{25}}{2}$$

$$= 13 - 1 \cdot 96(2 \cdot 5) = 13 - 4 \cdot 9$$

$$= 8 \cdot 1$$

Now we know that the 95% credible interval runs from 8·1 to 17·9. In other words, there is a 95% chance that the population median falls between the score whose rank is 8·1 and the score whose rank is 17·9.

But those ranks do not correspond to actual observations, so it is necessary to interpolate* to find the scores that would go with those ranks, if such ranks were possible. What score corresponds to a rank of 8·1? The score for rank 8 is 24, and for rank 9 it is also 24, so 8·1 must have a score of 24. And what about 17·9? Here is the interpolation diagram:

* Interpolation is explained in Appendix I.

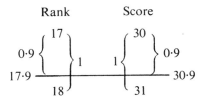

So the score is 30·9. Now we can say that there is a 95% chance that the median falls between a score of 24 and a score of 30·9. More briefly,

$$p(24 \leq \text{median} \leq 30\cdot9) = 0\cdot95$$

(Incidentally, I made up these data by random drawings from a population whose median was 25, so you can see that the inference contained the true value.)

Be sure to remember the assumption that is made: the population distribution is symmetrical. Note also that the posterior distribution is *approximated* by a normal distribution, though the approximation is quite good as long as N is at least 20. Even with samples as small as 10 the approximation gives high and low ranks off by only about 0·2, and in the conservative direction at that. In other words, if your sample size is only 10, the posterior credible interval you compute for a normal distribution will be slightly too large.

What can be done if the population is not symmetrical? One approach is to transform the data so that the transformed variable is symmetrical. This will be discussed in the last section of this chapter.

Exercise 11–1

An investigator administers to a random sample of 16 housewives a questionnaire measuring attitudes toward the church. Here are the scores (the higher the score, the more favourably a person views the church):

18, 19, 13, 23, 18, 11, 18, 15,
17, 18, 21, 11, 17, 9, 6, 22

What is the posterior 99% credible interval for the population median? Assume a uniform prior.

Answer

If the investigator feels that the population distribution is symmetrical, then he proceeds as follows:

a Arrange the scores in order.

Rank	Score	Rank	Score
1	6	9	18
2	9	10	18
3	11	11	18
4	11	12	18
5	13	13	19
6	15	14	21
7	17	15	22
8	17	16	23

b Find the posterior mean and standard deviation.

$$m'' = \frac{N+1}{2} = \frac{16+1}{2} = 8\cdot5$$

$$s'' = \frac{\sqrt{N}}{2} = \frac{4}{2} = 2$$

c Find the limits of the 99% posterior credible interval for the ranks. Remember that 99% of a normal distribution is found between $\pm z = 2\cdot58$.

$$\text{rank}_{\text{low}} = 8\cdot5 - 2\cdot58(2) = 3\cdot34$$
$$\text{rank}_{\text{high}} = 8\cdot5 + 2\cdot58(2) = 13\cdot66$$

d Find, by interpolation, the scores that would correspond to those ranks. First, the low score: Rank 3·34 falls between ranks 3 and 4, but both those ranks have scores of 11, so the 3·34th rank must correspond to a score of 11. Next, the high score:

$$\frac{0\cdot66}{1} \times 2 = 1\cdot32$$
$$19 + 1\cdot32 = 20\cdot32$$

Thus, the credible interval for the median extends from 11 to 20·32, that is,

$$p(11 \le \text{median} \le 20\cdot32) = 0\cdot99$$

We are 99% sure that the population median falls between 11 and 20·32. (Actually, these data were randomly drawn from a symmetrical population whose median was 15.)

11.2 Inferences about means

As the informal aspects of an investigation proceed, the experimenter usually becomes less vague about the population distribution. In this section we present two methods for making inferences about means, both of which assume that the population is normally distributed with respect to the quantity being measured. One of these procedures makes the additional assumption, not too common in the social sciences, that the variance of the population is known. We turn to that first because it illustrates clearly and with minimum fuss how inferences about means can be made for a normal population.

Inferences about the mean of a normal population whose variance is known

In the physical sciences, variability of measurements is often associated only with the measuring instrument. The underlying property is assumed, often for good theoretical reasons, to be stable and unvarying, but the measuring instrument introduces some error because it has limited precision. If the device has been properly calibrated, then the type and extent of error is known. In many instances the slight fluctuations from one reading to the next can be described as being normally distributed with a variance of σ^2 whose value is known. Thus, when some unknown quantity is being measured, the population of possible readings has an unknown mean, whose value we are trying to discover by carrying out the measurements, but with a known variance, σ^2, due to the measuring instrument. In these cases, then, it makes sense to infer the population mean when the population variance is known.

Frankly, I cannot think of any very plausible counterpart in the social sciences. I suppose it is possible to assume that some psychological test that has been given to thousands of people might be administered to a new population in an effort to find the mean for this population, and that there is no theoretical reason to believe that the variance in this new population is any different from the population variance known from the previous work. In this case, perhaps one could say that the population variance is known while the mean is unknown. I will admit the possibility, but say that such instances are fairly rare.

Nevertheless, I want to talk, mainly for instructive purposes, about how inferences are made in this case. All the Bayesian machinery is displayed in elegant form, the mathematical difficulties are minimal, and the distributions are straightforward. If you can follow this case, others will be easier to understand.

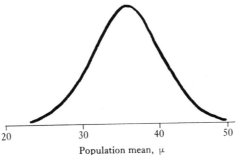

Population mean, μ

Fig. 11–1
Prior distribution for the possible values of the unknown population mean

Let us return to the investigator studying concept formation, who was introduced in the previous section. Suppose that he has carried out enough preliminary work with different populations of people to know that the variability from one population to the next stays the same and, as indexed by the standard deviation, its value is $\sigma = 8$. Only the mean changes from population to population. Also, he has observed that the data are roughly normal, so he feels it is reasonable to assume that the population distribution is normal in shape.

He is about to administer his task to a new group of 20 subjects, randomly selected from some population. He is willing to assume that the population standard deviation is 8, but wishes to infer the value of the mean.

But now he has some prior information concerning the mean of the population. A sketch of his prior distribution can be seen in Fig. 11–1. The shape is roughly normal, the peak is over a value of 36, and most of the curve runs from 24 to 48. Applying the steps in Section 6.8 of Chapter 6 leads him to settle for a prior that is normal with a mean of 36 and a standard deviation of

$$\frac{48-24}{6} = \frac{24}{6} = 4$$

He checks this by forming the equal-credibility interval:

$$\mu_{\text{low}} = 36 - 0 \cdot 43(4) = 34 \cdot 28$$

$$\mu_{\text{high}} = 36 + 0 \cdot 43(4) = 37 \cdot 72$$

'Yes,' he says, 'I would be just as happy to bet that the true value of the mean lies below 34·28, as in the interval from 34·28 to 37·72, as above 37·72.' So, he is satisfied to describe his prior opinion concerning the population mean as normal with

$$m' = 36$$

$$s' = 4$$

If he were to draw a normal distribution with $m' = 36$ and $s' = 4$, it would look like Fig. 11–2. His actual prior is shown there for comparison. With only a very modest amount of data the posterior distribution based on the approximate normal prior would be virtually indistinguishable from the posterior based on the actual prior. With large amounts of data, approximations can be very approximate indeed and yet the posterior will be rarely affected by the discrepancy. And as I said in Chapter 6, the mathematics are much easier if you can use a familiar distribution to approximate your prior.

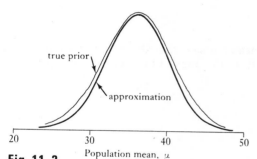

true prior

approximation

20   30   40   50

Fig. 11–2   Population mean, μ

Prior distribution approximated by a normal curve

Having quantified his prior opinion, our investigator selects, at random, a sample of 20 subjects from his population, and has them solve his computer problems. Their scores are as follows:

29, 36, 35, 20, 43, 28, 24, 16, 30, 27
49, 26, 29, 24, 16, 33, 27, 34, 24, 22.

What, in the light of these data, is the posterior 99% credible interval for the population mean? To find the credible interval, we must apply Bayes' theorem to determine the posterior distribution. Actually, I will give only the results of the Bayesian calculation, but I would like to do it in a way that highlights the relative contribution to the posterior of prior and sample information.

For convenience, we will say that the *precision* of information is given by the reciprocal of the variance. As applied to the prior, we know that the prior variance, $(s')^2$, is large if we are vague, so we could say that the precision in the prior is small. If we let h' stand for the prior precision, then

$$\text{precision of prior} = h' = \frac{1}{(s')^2}$$

The smaller the variance, the larger is the precision of the prior.

In similar manner, we define the precision of the population:

$$\text{precision of population} = h = \frac{1}{\sigma^2}$$

Now we can talk about the precision of the prior *relative* to the precision of the population:

$$\frac{\text{precision of prior relative}}{\text{to precision of population}} = n' = \frac{h'}{h}$$

Substituting for h' and h gives

$$n' = \frac{\frac{1}{(s')^2}}{\frac{1}{\sigma^2}} = \frac{\sigma^2}{(s')^2}$$

What does n', the 'prior n', mean? It says that the information in the prior is equivalent to n' observations from the population. For our example,

$$(s')^2 = (4)^2 = 16$$
$$\sigma^2 = (8)^2 = 64$$

Thus, prior n is

$$n' = \frac{64}{16} = 4$$

You can see that the prior assessed by the investigator is fairly vague, for there is as much information in it as there would be in a sample of only four observations from the population.

Bayesian analysis of this case shows that we need to know only two items of information about the sample, the mean and the sample size.

M = sample mean

N = number of observations

By applying Bayes' theorem it can be shown that the posterior distribution is normal with

$$\text{posterior mean} = m'' = m' \left(\frac{n'}{n' + N}\right) + M \left(\frac{N}{n' + N}\right)$$

and

> posterior precision relative
> to precision of population $= n'' = n' + N$

First let us look at the posterior precision relative to the precision of the population. It is found by adding the number of observations to the prior n.

For our example,

$$n' = 4$$

$$N = 20$$

Thus, the posterior n is

$$n'' = 4 + 20 = 24$$

You can see that of these 24 equivalent observations,

$$\frac{4}{24} = \tfrac{1}{6}\text{th are associated with the prior}$$

and

$$\frac{20}{24} = \tfrac{5}{6}\text{ths are associated with the sample}$$

Now turn to the equation for the posterior mean. Notice that the terms in parentheses are these fractions we just found, so that

$$m'' = m'(\tfrac{1}{6}) + M(\tfrac{5}{6})$$

The important result is that these fractions act as weights that determine the relative contribution of the prior and sample means to the posterior mean. Since prior n is small, the prior mean counts for only 1/6 of the posterior mean, while the sample mean is weighted by 5/6. **Here you can see in the mathematics how Bayes' theorem automatically weights the relative contributions of prior and sample information to the posterior.** The weights are determined by the relative precisions of the prior and the population.

To apply the results of the Bayesian analysis to the example, we must first compute the sample mean. Adding the 20 measurements gives $\sum X = 572$, so

$$M = \frac{\sum X}{N} = \frac{572}{20} = 28{\cdot}6$$

The prior mean, you will recall, is equal to 36. Now the posterior mean can be determined:

$$m'' = 36(\tfrac{1}{6}) + 28{\cdot}6(\tfrac{5}{6})$$

$$= 6 + 23{\cdot}8$$

$$= 29{\cdot}8$$

Before we can compute the posterior credible interval, the posterior standard deviation must be found. We find it from posterior n as follows:

> precision of posterior relative
> to that of population $= n'' = \dfrac{h''}{h}$

Like the prior, the posterior precision is the reciprocal of the posterior variance,

$$h'' = \frac{1}{(s'')^2}$$

Recall, too, that the population precision is

$$h = \frac{1}{\sigma^2}$$

Substituting these two expressions in the equation for posterior n gives

$$n'' = \frac{\dfrac{1}{(s'')^2}}{\dfrac{1}{\sigma^2}}$$

which, when solved for the posterior variance, yields

$$(s'')^2 = \frac{\sigma^2}{n''}$$

And so, the posterior standard deviation is

$$s'' = \frac{\sigma}{\sqrt{n''}}$$

Now, for our example,

$$s'' = \frac{8}{\sqrt{24}} = 1\cdot63$$

Finally, the posterior 99 % credible interval can be found:

$$\mu_{\text{low}} = m'' - 2\cdot58s'' = 29\cdot8 - 2\cdot58(1\cdot63)$$
$$= 29\cdot8 - 4\cdot2 = 25\cdot6$$
$$\mu_{\text{high}} = m'' + 2\cdot58s'' = 29\cdot8 + 2\cdot58(1\cdot63)$$
$$= 29\cdot8 + 4\cdot2 = 34\cdot0$$

So, we are 99 % sure that the true value of the population mean extends from 25·6 to 34·0, or, put more succinctly,

$$p(25\cdot6 \le \mu \le 34\cdot0) = 0\cdot99$$

This is the last time the results of a Bayesian analysis will be displayed so clearly in terms of the weighting of prior and posterior information. From now on I will give only the form of the posterior distribution and its relevant statistics. It is important, then, that this case is clearly understood, for it is a good representation of all the analyses to follow.

Intuitive understanding of this example may be helped by showing the prior and posterior distributions (see Fig. 11–3).

You might be interested to know that I generated the data for this example by random sampling from a normal population with

$$\sigma = 8$$

$$\mu = 30$$

That the posterior mean of 29·8 is closer to the truth, 30, than either the prior mean or the sample mean is a happy coincidence. It came about because the prior mean was above the truth and the sample mean below it; their combined effect nearly zeroed in on the true value. But the sample mean could just as well have been greater than 30 as less than 30, and if it had been much greater the posterior mean would have been further from the true value than the sample mean.

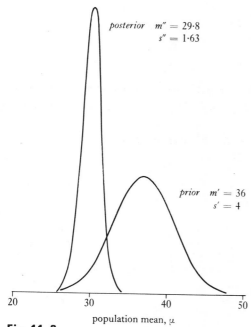

posterior $m'' = 29·8$
$s'' = 1·63$

prior $m' = 36$
$s' = 4$

population mean, μ

Fig. 11–3
Prior distribution concerning the unknown mean of a normal population whose standard deviation is known to be 8, and the posterior distribution, after making 20 observations whose mean is 28·6

Of course, in real problems we never know the true value. But we can make the best of our uncertainty in the light of inconclusive data by using inferential statistical procedures. Even then we must face that the truth may occasionally lie outside our credible interval.

Exercise 11–2

Suppose that the data in Exercise 11–1 were drawn from a normal population with known standard deviation of 5. Find the posterior 99% credible interval for the population mean. Assume that the prior is normal with mean of 18 and standard deviation of 7.

Answer

We are to make an inference concerning the population mean, μ, and our job is to find μ_{low} and μ_{high} such that 99% of our posterior opinion falls between those values. We can do this by first noting that since the prior is normal and the population is normal, the posterior must also be normal. Once we have found the mean and standard deviation of the posterior then we can find μ_{low} and μ_{high}:

$$\mu_{low} = m'' - 2 \cdot 58s''$$
$$\mu_{high} = m'' + 2 \cdot 58s''$$

Here are the steps:

a   Find the prior precision relative to the precision of the population, that is, find prior n:

$$n' = \frac{\text{population variance}}{\text{prior variance}} = \frac{\sigma^2}{(s')^2}$$

$$= \frac{(5)^2}{(7)^2} = \frac{25}{49} = 0 \cdot 51$$

Prior opinion is so vague that it is equivalent to only about half an observation.

b   Find the posterior precision relative to the precision of the population, that is, find posterior n:

$$n'' = n' + N \qquad \text{where } N = \text{number in sample}$$
$$n'' = 0 \cdot 51 + 16 = 16 \cdot 51$$

c   Find the sample mean, M:

$$M = \frac{\Sigma X}{N} = \frac{256}{16} = 16$$

d   Find the posterior mean, m'':

$$m'' = m' \left(\frac{n'}{n' + N} \right) + M \left(\frac{N}{n' + N} \right)$$

$$= 18 \frac{0 \cdot 51}{16 \cdot 51} + 16 \frac{16}{16 \cdot 51}$$

$$= 0 \cdot 56 + 15 \cdot 51$$

$$= 16 \cdot 07$$

You can see that the prior was so vague that even a mere 16 observations almost completely swamped it.

e   Find the posterior standard deviation, s'':

$$s'' = \frac{\sigma}{\sqrt{n''}} = \frac{5}{\sqrt{16 \cdot 51}}$$

$$= 1 \cdot 23$$

f   Find the 99% posterior credible interval:

$$\mu_{low} = 16 \cdot 07 - 2 \cdot 58(1 \cdot 23)$$
$$= 16 \cdot 07 - 3 \cdot 17 = 12 \cdot 90$$
$$\mu_{high} = 16 \cdot 07 + 3 \cdot 17 = 19 \cdot 24$$

So here is the result:

$$p(12\cdot90 \le \mu \le 19\cdot24) = 0\cdot99$$

There is a 99% chance that the population mean lies between 12·90 and 19·24. (In fact, these 16 data are a random sample from a population whose mean is 15.)

Interpreting traditional results

A non-Bayesian statistician presented with the problem of Exercise 11–2 could also have arrived at a statement similar to the Bayesian's posterior credible interval. He would probably call it a 'confidence interval', but his interpretation of it would be different from ours. Confidence intervals are discussed in Chapter 13, but for now it is sufficient to note that our non-Bayesian statistician might say that there is a 99% chance that the confidence interval he has calculated contains the true value of the population mean. He makes a probability statement about the *interval*, not about the population mean.

In this section I want to show that the traditionalist's confidence interval is the same as the Bayesian's credible interval *when the prior is assumed to be uniform*. This point of similarity between traditional and Bayesian approaches holds not only for this case of inferring the mean of a population whose variance is known, but also for other cases. Thus, it allows us to interpret traditional results within a Bayesian framework.

Let us see what happens to the expressions for the posterior mean and posterior n when a uniform prior is adopted. Recall that

$$m'' = m'\left(\frac{n'}{n'+N}\right) + M\left(\frac{N}{n'+N}\right)$$

and $n'' = n' + N$

First, consider n''. The only term affected by the prior is n', and we know that

$$n' = \frac{\sigma^2}{(s')^2}$$

As prior opinion becomes more vague, the prior variance, $(s')^2$, increases, causing n'' to approach zero. Thus, for a uniform prior,

$$n'' = 0 + N$$
$$= N$$

Now look at the consequence for the posterior mean. The weight for the prior mean becomes

$$\frac{n'}{n'+N} = \frac{0}{0+N} = 0$$

and the weight for the sample mean becomes

$$\frac{N}{n'+N} = \frac{N}{0+N} = 1$$

So the expression for the posterior mean now is

$$m'' = m'(0) + M(1)$$
$$= M$$

The posterior mean equals the sample mean. What about the posterior standard deviation?

Recall that

$$s'' = \frac{\sigma}{\sqrt{n''}}$$

But we have just shown that $n'' = N$. And so,

$$s'' = \frac{\sigma}{\sqrt{N}}$$

We have found, then, that when the prior is uniform, the posterior distribution concerning the unknown population mean is normal with

posterior mean $= m'' = M$

posterior standard deviation $= s'' = \dfrac{\sigma}{\sqrt{N}}$

The posterior statistics depend, now, only on the sample mean, sample size, and the population standard deviation. Incidentally, we obtain the same result if the principle of stable estimation applies to the prior. The posterior C per cent credible interval is defined by these limits:

$$\mu_{\text{low}} = m'' - zs'' = M - z\frac{\sigma}{\sqrt{N}}$$

$$\mu_{\text{high}} = m'' + zs'' = M + z\frac{\sigma}{\sqrt{N}}$$

A more compact expression for the limits of the credible interval is this:

$$M \pm z\frac{\sigma}{\sqrt{N}}$$

Remember that z is the standard deviate of the normal distribution; C per cent of the standardized normal distribution is found between $-z$ and $+z$.

Suppose we apply these results to Exercise 11–2. Assuming a uniform prior, the posterior is normal with

$$m'' = 16$$

$$s'' = \frac{5}{\sqrt{16}} = \frac{5}{4} = 1 \cdot 25$$

This gives a posterior 99 % interval whose limits are

$$\mu_{\text{low}} = 16 - 2 \cdot 58(1 \cdot 25) = 16 - 3 \cdot 22 = 12 \cdot 78$$

$$\mu_{\text{high}} = 16 + 3 \cdot 22 = 19 \cdot 22$$

So, $p(12 \cdot 78 \le \mu \le 19 \cdot 22) = 0 \cdot 99$.

This is not very different from the result obtained for the vague prior. The limits of the interval are the same values a traditional statistician would have reported for his confidence interval. If you read that the 99% confidence interval, for this case, extends from 12·78 to 19·22, you can give it a Bayesian interpretation: this is the 99% posterior credible interval that a Bayesian would have computed, assuming a uniform prior.

In the case of inference about the mean of a normal population whose variance is known, a traditional confidence interval for μ can be interpreted as the Bayesian credible interval obtained from assuming a uniform prior over μ.

Some comparisons

We have now used the same set of data under varying conditions and assumptions. It is instructive to compare the posterior credible intervals.

	Inference concerning	*Assumptions*	*Prior*	*Limits of posterior credible interval*	*Size of interval*
a	population median	population symmetrical	uniform	11–20·32	9·32
b	population mean	population normal; σ^2 known	uniform	12·78 –19·22	6·44
c	population mean	population normal; σ^2 known	gentle, not uniform	12·90–19·24	6·34

As we go from (a) to (c), we either assume more or we know more. In either case, more information goes into making the inference. As a result, the posterior distribution is more precise, tighter, less spread out, and so the credible interval is smaller. Whatever your statistical viewpoint, Bayesian or not, it is generally true that the more information you can put into your statistical procedures, the more precise will be the result. For the traditional viewpoints, information goes in informally as assumptions and formally as data. The Bayesian prefers to make some of the informal assumptions formal, expressed as prior opinion, so their contribution can be seen explicitly.

11.3 Inferences about means and standard deviations

It is much more common in the social sciences to be faced with a normal population whose parameters are both unknown. In this case, our prior uncertainty must be expressed for all combinations of possible values of μ with possible values of σ, so our prior probability distribution is a bivariate one. To show it pictorially, we would have to construct a 3-dimensional picture with values of μ along one edge, values of σ along the other edge, and height representing probability density. An example is shown in Fig. 11–4.

There are a number of different ways of assessing these bivariate priors, but I feel that they are as yet too advanced for including them in an introductory textbook. In fact, the only place I know of that discusses the procedures in anything like adequate detail is in the as yet unpublished book of Pratt, Raiffa, and Schlaifer (1965).

Until the technology has developed further, I am afraid we are stuck with making some assumptions that simplify the assessment of prior opinion. The first of these is that uncertainty about μ is unaffected by uncertainty about σ, and vice versa. That enables us to think about μ and σ separately; we do not have to assess bivariate uncertainty, we only have to think about the marginals. In other words, when opinion about μ is independent of opinion about σ, then their prior distributions can be assessed separately. This assumption is not always realized in practice. In some cases, the larger the mean the larger the variance (trees vary in height more than people), but it is often a workable assumption even if not quite true.

The second assumption is that our prior uncertainty is described by uniform distributions, or that stable estimation applies to vague priors. More will be said in a moment about this.

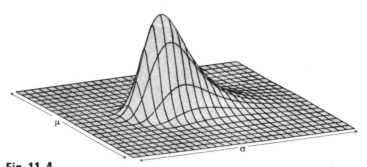

Fig. 11–4

Bivariate prior density function for the unknown mean and standard deviation of a population.
From Schmitt, S.A., *Measuring Uncertainty: An Elementary Introduction to Bayesian Statistics*, Reading, Mass., Addison-Wesley, 1969.

When prior opinion is diffuse or vague, these two restrictions are often quite acceptable. If you do have non-uniform priors, the posterior credible intervals you calculate assuming uniform priors will be larger than if you had used your real priors, so the error introduced by the assumption is at least in the conservative direction.

A major advantage of making these assumptions is that the credible interval statements about μ and σ will be about the same as the confidence intervals a traditional statistician would determine. So, again, we will reach a point of contact with classical methods, enabling us to put a Bayesian interpretation on those results.

Prior distributions

We assume a uniform prior where the unknown population mean is concerned. It is, of course, uniform only over some restricted range, and then it tapers off beyond those limits. But as long as it is uniform in the region of the data, we do not need to be concerned with where opinion droops off. A uniform prior for the mean of the population of housewives referred to in Exercise 11–1 might be as shown in Fig. 11–5. (It does not really matter that the right tail goes out beyond 50, the maximum score on the test.) The solid line indicates that the prior is uniform over the values of interest, while the dashed lines represent prior opinion that falls off gradually beyond the region of interest.

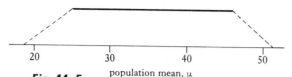

Fig. 11–5

population mean, μ

Uniform prior for the population mean

Prior opinion about the population standard deviation does not fall off gradually in the region near zero, however. We know that the true value of σ cannot be less than zero, so prior opinion drops sharply to zero for possible values of σ less than zero. How can this difficulty be surmounted? The easiest way is to express opinion about the *logarithm* of σ, rather than σ itself. This prior has a number of appealing properties:

a   All prior opinion that was squeezed into the interval of possible values of σ from 0 to 1 is now stretched out over the interval from $-\infty$ to 0 (see Fig. 11–6).

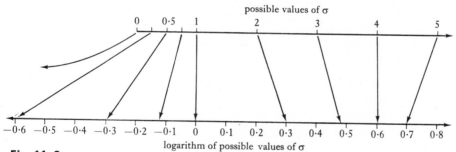

Fig. 11–6

Relationship of a linear scale to a log scale, expressed here for σ and $\log_{10} \sigma$

b   For convenience, re-label the lower scale in Fig. 11–6 so that it shows values of σ, rather than log σ. The log spacing is retained, but the labels are more meaningful. Uniform prior opinion over log σ is, then, as shown in Fig. 11–7. Now you can see more clearly another feature: successive

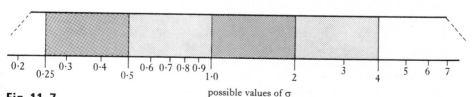

Fig. 11–7

Uniform prior concerning log σ, showing equal credibility intervals doubling of an interval of σ yields equal credibility intervals. I have shown one example. As much opinion falls between 0·25 to 0·5 as between 0·5 to 1·0, as between 1 to 2, as between 2 to 4, etc.

c A uniform prior concerning log σ implies a uniform prior concerning the log of the precision, log h. It is easy to show this. Recall that the precision is defined as

$$h = \frac{1}{\sigma^2}$$

Take logs of both sides:

$$\log h = \log \frac{1}{\sigma^2} = \log 1 - 2 \log \sigma$$

But $\log 1 = 0$, so

$$\log h = -2 \log \sigma$$

In words, log σ has only to be multiplied by a constant, -2, to give log h. Since the uniform prior is simply a constant function of log σ, and since log σ is a linear function of log h, it follows that the prior over log h must be a constant.

In other words, opinion concerning log h is uniform. Vagueness about log σ is logically equivalent to vagueness about log h. I often find my opinion about the spread of the population distribution so vague that I am indifferent between expressing it for σ or for h. Here we see it does not matter.

   In many situations your prior opinion about the population standard deviation will be adequately approximated by a uniform distribution over log σ. When it is, and when opinion about the population mean is uniform, the

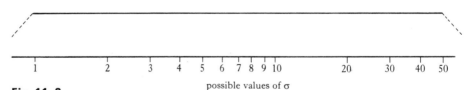

| | | | | | | | | | | | |
|1| |2| |3| |4| 5| 6 7 8 9 10| |20| 30| 40 50|

possible values of σ

Fig. 11–8
Prior that is uniform over log σ

credible intervals we compute from the posterior distributions will be the same as, or similar to, the traditional statistician's confidence intervals. So by choosing uniform priors we again find a point of contact with classical procedures, thus allowing us to understand those results from a Bayesian point of view.

   Back to the housewives problem. My prior opinion concerning the standard deviation of the population is uniform over log σ for values of σ ranging from 1 to 50, and the prior drops off gradually beyond those limits (see Fig. 11–8). That is a pretty vague prior.

Data

Once again we take independent samples at random from the population. This time we will need to compute the mean and standard deviation of the data. Let us use the housewife data again.

X	X^2	X	X^2
6	36	18	324
9	81	18	324
11	121	18	324
11	121	18	324
13	169	19	361
15	225	21	441
17	289	22	484
17	289	23	529

$$\Sigma X = 256 \quad \Sigma X^2 = 4442$$

$$M = \frac{\Sigma X}{N} = \frac{256}{16} = 16$$

$$S = \sqrt{\frac{N \Sigma X^2 - (\Sigma X)^2}{N(N-1)}} = \sqrt{\frac{16(4442)-(256)^2}{16(15)}}$$

$$= \sqrt{\frac{5536}{240}} = 4\cdot8$$

Posterior distribution of μ and σ

When prior opinion is uniform over μ and over log σ, and when a random sample of size N has been obtained from the population, then applying Bayes' theorem shows us that the bivariate posterior distribution for μ and σ is normal–gamma. The distribution shown in Fig. 11–4 is a normal–gamma, so that will give you an idea of what one looks like. Fortunately, you will never have to deal with one directly, for it is really the marginals of the distribution we are interested in. We do not really care about the joint distribution of μ and σ, but we do want to know the posterior distributions of μ and σ separately, and we can find these by looking at the marginals of the joint distribution.

Posterior distribution of μ

Let us consider the posterior distribution of μ first. It is a new distribution, one we have not encountered before, called a Student-t distribution.

It is a symmetrical, bell-shaped curve with tails lifted higher from the horizontal axis than the normal curve. Unlike the normal distribution, the Student-t is a three-parameter distribution, and, unfortunately only one of the parameters admits of an easy intuitive interpretation. I will use the symbol μ_t to stand for that parameter; it has the same value as the mean of the distribution. The next parameter, call it σ_t, is related to but is *not* the same value as the standard deviation of the Student-t. The third parameter is called the *degrees of freedom* and it corresponds roughly to the lift in the tails of the distribution; I will let the mnemonic *df* stand for this parameter, though the Greek lower case 'nu', ν, is frequently used in statistics books and tables.

The mean and standard deviation of the Student-t are easily computed from the parameters.

Mean of Student-$t = m = \mu_t$

Standard deviation of Student-$t = s = \sigma_t \sqrt{\dfrac{df}{df-2}}$

The principle here is exactly the same as for the Beta and normal distributions. Once we know that a distribution is a Student-t, then it is completely specified when we know the values of the parameters μ_t, σ_t, and df. From those parameters we can describe the distribution by computing, say, the mean and standard deviation, m and s.

A word about notation may help to forestall confusion. The symbols m and s are being used here to denote the mean and standard deviation of the Student-t distribution, but it is important to remember that those same symbols were used for the statistics of the Beta distribution and also for the normal distribution. Although the symbols are the same, the formulae for calculating the statistics from the parameters are not, of course, the same. Recall, too, that I use the Greek letters μ and σ to stand for the parameters of a normal distribution. Here the symbols are used again, but with the subscript t so there will be no mistaking that I am referring to a Student-t distribution.

Like the normal distribution, the Student-t can be reduced to standardized form by subtracting all values on the horizontal axis, call them x-values, from the parameter μ_t, and then dividing the result by the parameter σ_t. The result is a t-value, which is the Student-t analogy to the z-value for a normal distribution.

$$t = \frac{x - \mu_t}{\sigma_t}$$

The result of applying this transformation on any Student-t distribution is to reduce it to a standardized Student-t for which $\mu_t = 0$ and $\sigma_t = 1$.

But what about the degrees of freedom? How does that affect the standardized Student-t? Well, unfortunately there are as many standardized Student-t distributions as there are degrees of freedom. A few of them are shown in Fig. 11–9. Notice that the tails are higher for the smaller degrees of freedom. An interesting property of the Student-t distribution is that it becomes more and more like a normal distribution as the degrees of freedom increase, until finally it is normal when $df = \infty$. You can see from Fig. 11–9 that the Student-t approaches the normal rather quickly; by the time the degrees of freedom have reached about 25 or 30, the Student-t becomes very close to a normal distribution. This observation has a very practical consequence that we shall see shortly.

Bayes' theorem tells us, then, that the posterior distribution concerning μ is Student-t, and it also gives us the three parameters of the posterior:

$$\mu_t'' = M$$

$$\sigma_t'' = \frac{S}{\sqrt{N}}$$

$$df'' = N - 1$$

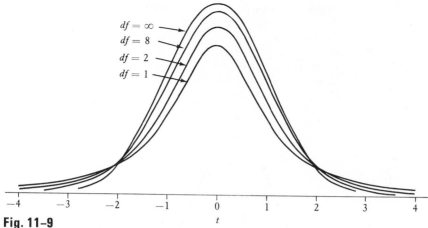

Fig. 11–9
Standardized Student-*t* distribution

In words, the posterior parameter μ_t is given by the sample mean, the posterior parameter σ_t is found by dividing the sample standard deviation by $\sqrt{N}$, and the degrees of freedom are equal to one less than the sample size.

As applied to the data surveying attitudes of housewives toward the church, we now know that the posterior distribution of μ is Student-*t*. Along the *x*-axis we have possible values of μ, and the parameters of the distribution are

$$\mu_t'' = M = 16$$

$$\sigma_t'' = \frac{S}{\sqrt{N}} = \frac{4\cdot8}{\sqrt{16}} = 1\cdot2$$

$$df'' = N-1 = 15$$

What does the posterior look like? It is shown in Fig. 11–10. Our prior uncertainty, which is uniform, has been changed by the data to give the distribution in the figure, a Student-*t* with 15 degrees of freedom. It is not quite normal—the tails are a little too high for a normal—but it is close.

Next we compute the posterior *C* per cent credible interval for μ. We do this by applying a rearranged form of the *t*-value equation:

$$\mu_{\text{low}} = \mu_t'' - t\sigma_t''$$

$$\mu_{\text{high}} = \mu_t'' + t\sigma_t''$$

where *t* is the standard deviate of the Student-*t* distribution; *C* per cent of the standardized curve falls between $-t$ and $+t$. Expressed in terms of the sample statistics, the limits of the credible interval can be found by solving this equation:

$$M \pm t\,\frac{S}{\sqrt{N}}$$

In words, we go up and down *t* sigmas from the mean to find the limits of the credible interval. Now, how do we obtain the appropriate value for *t*?

When we were dealing with a normal distribution we referred to the tables of areas under the normal curve to discover that 99% of the curve fell between $\pm z = 2.58$, 95% between $z = \pm 1.96$, etc. But our job is a little more difficult for the Student-t distribution because the values of t will depend on which standardized curve you are referring to. As you can see from Fig. 11–9, when $df = 1$ the 99% credible interval will be wider than for, say, $df = 8$. The former curve has more area in the tails than the latter, so you must go further out in the tails of the curve for $df = 1$ to cover 99% of the area.

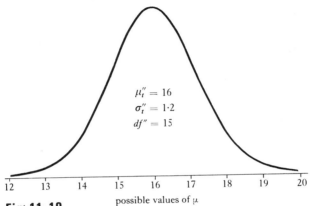

$$\mu_t'' = 16$$
$$\sigma_t'' = 1.2$$
$$df'' = 15$$

possible values of μ

Fig: 11–10
Posterior Student-t distribution concerning the mean of the population of housewives' scores on the attitude survey

We could append a whole page of tables like the normal ones for each Student-t curve; then we would have about 50 pages, one for $df = 1$, one for $df = 2$, and so forth on up to about $df = 50$, when the curve looks so normal that for larger degrees of freedom the normal table could be used. But this is not very practical, so instead it is usual practice to table the values of t for just a few credible intervals, but for many values of df. You will find such a table in Appendix G. To use the table, enter the left column with the degrees of freedom, then move over to the column with the desired credible interval and read off the value of t. Notice that the bottom row, for $df = \infty$, gives values identical to those for a normal distribution, as you would expect.

For the housewife survey, we found that $df = 15$. To find the 99% credible interval we move down the left column to 15, then travel horizontally to the column headed '99' to read off $t = 2.947$. Now we can calculate the credible interval:

$$\mu_{\text{low}} = 16 - 2.947(1.2) = 12.46$$
$$\mu_{\text{high}} = 16 + 2.947(1.2) = 19.54$$

There is a 99% chance that the mean of the population of housewives is between 12·46 and 19·54.

$$p(12.46 \le \mu \le 19.54) = 0.99$$

It is instructive to see where this result fits among the other three inferences we have made on these same data. Turn back to the summary table at the end of the last section, page 247. The result we just obtained fits between the first and second cases, as we would expect. We obtain the biggest interval when we are so uncertain that we can only assume that the population is symmetrical. It becomes smaller when we make the additional assumption that the population is normal (the present case), and it shrinks a little more when we also know the variance of the normal population. The more we know, the smaller the credible interval, given the same data. By now, that should sound like a familiar story.

Exercise 11-3

Suppose that our investigator studying concept formation, having completed his preliminary testing on colleagues, secretaries and willing students, is ready to try the test for a population of middle-class men. He is willing only to assume that the population is normal, and he feels that uniform priors for μ and log σ are reasonable approximations to his fairly vague prior opinion.

He randomly chooses 10 subjects and runs them through the computer tests. Their scores are as follows:

$$35, \quad 41, \quad 28, \quad 22, \quad 13, \quad 31, \quad 38, \quad 40, \quad 31, \quad 22$$

What is his posterior 95% credible interval for the population mean?

Answer

Here are the steps to the solution:

a   Compute the mean and standard deviation of the data.

X	X^2		X	X^2
35	1225		31	961
41	1681		38	1444
28	784		40	1600
22	484		31	961
13	169		22	484

$$\Sigma X = 301 \quad \Sigma X^2 = 9793$$

$$M = \frac{\Sigma X}{N} = \frac{301}{10} = 30 \cdot 1$$

$$S = \sqrt{\frac{N \Sigma X^2 - (\Sigma X)^2}{N(N-1)}} = \sqrt{\frac{10(9793) - (301)^2}{10(9)}}$$

$$= \sqrt{\frac{7329}{90}} = 9 \cdot 02$$

b   The posterior concerning μ is Student-t. Compute its parameters:

$$\mu_t'' = M = 30 \cdot 1$$

$$\sigma_t'' = \frac{S}{\sqrt{N}} = \frac{9 \cdot 02}{\sqrt{10}} = 2 \cdot 85$$

$$df'' = N - 1 = 10 - 1 = 9$$

c   Look up in Appendix G the value of t for a Student-t distribution with 9 degrees of freedom such that 95% of the curve falls between $\pm t$. That value is 2·262.

d   Find the posterior credible interval.

$$\mu_{\text{low}} = \mu''_t - 2\cdot262\ \sigma''_t$$
$$= 30\cdot1 - 2\cdot262(2\cdot85) = 23\cdot7$$
$$\mu_{\text{high}} = \mu''_t + 2\cdot262\ \sigma''_t$$
$$= 30\cdot1 + 2\cdot262(2\cdot85) = 36\cdot5$$

Thus, $p(23\cdot7 \le \mu \le 36\cdot5) = 0\cdot95$

For all the complicated discussion in this section, the mathematics are easy. You just have to know what you are doing!

Some comparisons

It is worth comparing the two cases we have covered for making inferences about the population mean.

Table 11–1   Inferences concerning the mean of a normal population

Assumptions	Prior	Posterior	Posterior credible interval
population normal, σ known	uniform	normal	$M \pm z\dfrac{\sigma}{\sqrt{N}}$
population normal, σ unknown	uniform	Student-t	$M \pm t\dfrac{S}{\sqrt{N}}$

The extra uncertainty introduced when σ is unknown causes the posterior to be Student-t rather than normal, and the posterior credible interval to be computed using the sample, rather than the population, standard deviation. In both cases the posterior mean is given by the sample mean.

Recall that for large samples the posterior degrees of freedom will be so large that the distribution is virtually normal rather than Student-t. When this is the case, you can see from Table 11–1 that we are back to making an inference about a normal population with σ treated as if it were known. In this situation it is approximated by S.

For large samples, inferences concerning μ when σ is unknown can be treated as though σ were known, with the sample standard deviation, S, serving as an estimate for σ.

In other words, the Student-t distribution is only used for small samples.

This is the use that was proposed by W. S. Gosset, writing in 1908 under the pseudonym 'Student', a statistician who worked in an English brewery, and whose nom de plume now identifies this distribution.

Posterior distribution of σ

The posterior distribution of σ is another newcomer to our collection of distributions. It is called the inverted gamma-2 distribution, a rather fancy name which perhaps disguises the ease of its use here. I shall refer to it by the abbreviation IG2.

The IG2 distribution has just two parameters. One of these corresponds to the mode of the distribution, while the other is called the degrees of freedom. In Fig. 11–11 you can see several IG2 distributions, all with the same mode of 1. Notice that the distribution covers only positive values of x, a feature that is particularly suitable for describing opinion about σ since we know that σ cannot be less than zero.

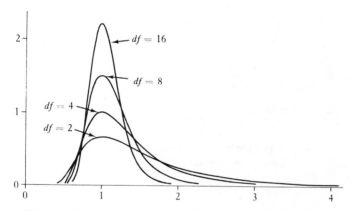

Fig. 11–11
Some inverted-gamma 2 distributions

How are values of the posterior parameters determined? Once again, when prior uncertainty about μ and $\log \sigma$ is uniform and when N independent observations are randomly selected from the population, then Bayes' theorem tells us that the posterior distribution of σ itself (*not* $\log \sigma$) is IG2 with

$$\text{posterior mode} = \text{mode}'' = S \sqrt{\frac{N-1}{N}}$$

and posterior degrees of freedom $= df'' = N - 1$

Now let us apply this to our uncertainty concerning the population of housewives and their scores on the attitude questionnaire. Recall that the standard deviation of the sample of 16 was $S = 4\cdot8$. Then, our posterior distribution concerning σ is IG2 with

$$\text{mode}'' = S \sqrt{\frac{N-1}{N}} = 4\cdot8 \sqrt{\frac{15}{16}} = 4\cdot65$$

$$df'' = N - 1 = 16 - 1 = 15$$

I have shown this posterior distribution in Fig. 11–12.

Posterior credible intervals are obtained by a very simple procedure. Since IG2 is not symmetrical, highest density regions have been determined and tabled. In Appendix E you will find highest density regions corresponding to 95, 99, and 99·9% credible intervals. However, these are for IG2 distributions whose modes are 1.

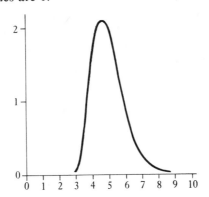

Fig. 11–12
Posterior IG2 concerning σ for the survey of housewives

Curves with modes other than 1 are simply multiplicative transformations of IG2 with mode = 1. Thus, to get the credible interval for an IG2 distribution whose mode is other than 1, you simply multiply the tabled values by the mode of your posterior distribution:

σ_{low} = tabled low limit × posterior mode

σ_{high} = tabled high limit × posterior mode

As applied to our example, if we wish to find the 99% credible interval, we move down the left column to $df = 15$, then over to the column headed 99, and read off the values 0·66 and 1·774. Those are the limits of the IG2 distribution with 15 degrees of freedom and whose mode is 1. To get the credible interval for σ we multiply those limits by 4·65:

σ_{low} = 0·66 × 4·65 = 3·07

σ_{high} = 1·774 × 4·65 = 8·25

So, we are 99% sure that the true value of σ lies between 3·07 and 8·25, that is,

$$p(3·07 \leq \sigma \leq 8·25) = 0·99$$

(I generated those data from a normal population whose standard deviation was 5, and the inference neatly brackets that value.)

Exercise 11–4

Return to the problem in Exercise 11–3. Compute the posterior 95% credible interval for the standard deviation of the population. Assume that the prior of log σ is uniform.

Answer

a Compute the sample standard deviation. That was done in Exercise 11–3. There we calculated $S = 9\cdot02$.

b Compute the parameters of the posterior IG2 distribution.

$$\text{mode}'' = S\sqrt{\frac{N-1}{N}} = 9\cdot02\sqrt{\frac{9}{10}}$$

$$= 8\cdot56$$

$$df'' = N - 1 = 10 - 1 = 9$$

c Look up the limits of the 95% credible interval for the IG2 distribution whose mode is 1 in Appendix E. For $df = 9$, we get $0\cdot661$ and $1\cdot771$.

d Compute the credible interval for σ:

$$\sigma_{\text{low}} = \text{tabled low limit} \times \text{mode}''$$

$$= 0\cdot661 \times 8\cdot56 = 5\cdot66$$

$$\sigma_{\text{high}} = \text{tabled high limit} \times \text{mode}''$$

$$= 1\cdot771 \times 8\cdot56 = 15\cdot2$$

Thus, $p(5\cdot66 \le \sigma \le 15\cdot2) = 0\cdot95$

As for inferences concerning μ, the mathematics are simple; it is the logic that counts.

Interpreting traditional results

You will on occasion come across a statement something like this in the social science literature: 'The confidence interval for the population mean is $6\cdot2$ to $18\cdot9$'. What sense can we make of this from a Bayesian point of view?

Let us assume that the statement is made in the context of inference about the mean of a normal population whose mean and variance are unknown. We have seen that the credible interval for the mean is, in the last steps of the analysis calculated from this equation, assuming uniform priors:

$$M \pm t \frac{S}{\sqrt{N}}$$

This version is exactly the same equation, using exactly the same t-distribution, that would be used in a traditional analysis to determine the confidence interval; only the route to the equation is entirely different.

Remember, though, that this point of contact between the two approaches holds only when the Bayesian assumes uniform priors over μ and $\log \sigma$. We are led to this generalization:

In the case of inference about the mean of a normal population whose mean and variance are unknown, a traditional confidence interval can be interpreted as the Bayesian credible interval obtained from assuming uniform priors over μ and $\log \sigma$.

A similar parallel holds for inference concerning the unknown population variance. Some Bayesian writers present methods for making inferences about the population variance, others, myself included, do it for the population standard deviation. I took this approach because it seems a little more intuitively appealing to deal directly with the standard deviation rather than the variance, but it has the drawback that the posterior credible interval is slightly different from the traditional confidence interval.

We have seen that when making an inference about σ, the posterior is distributed as inverted gamma-2. If we were to make our inference about σ^2 rather than σ, then the posterior would be in the form of a distribution that we have not yet encountered: chi-squared, a close relative of IG2. The identical chi-squared distribution forms the basis for the traditionalist's confidence interval, though he usually determines the limits of the interval by lopping off equal areas from the two tails; for example, he removes $2\frac{1}{2}\%$ of the area in each tail to find the 95% confidence interval. The chi-squared distribution, like IG2, is not symmetrical, so a Bayesian making an interval estimate of σ^2 will find the highest density region. Consequently, even if both traditionalist and Bayesian are concerned with σ^2, and both use the same chi-squared distribution, they will come up with slightly different intervals. This is simply a matter of different conventions. A traditionalist *could* find a highest density region, and some do, but the vast majority of social scientists do not.

A Bayesian making an inference about σ rather than σ^2 will refer to the IG2 distribution. It is usually true that the highest density regions for the distribution of one variable, here σ, are not the same as for a transformation of that variable, say σ^2 or $\log \sigma^2$. Consequently, if you make your inference about σ^2, which involves you with the chi-squared distribution, even if you take the square root of the limits to give an interval concerning σ, you will not get the same limits as for an inference concerning σ which uses the IG2 distribution.

Table 11–2 Comparison of three approaches to finding an interval estimation for σ or σ^2 in Exercise 11–4.

Approach	Distribution	Type of interval	95% interval for σ^2	Interval for σ
Traditional	Chi-squared	equal area in tails	38·5–271	6·2–16·5
Bayesian	Chi-squared	highest density	36·5–248	6·04–15·7
Bayesian	IG2	highest density	—	5·66–15·2

Take Exercise 11–4 as an example. First I computed the 95% confidence interval for σ^2 using the traditional approach. Then I found the 95% posterior credible interval for σ^2 from a Bayesian viewpoint, assuming a uniform prior for $\log \sigma$. Next, I took the square roots of the limits of those two intervals to give intervals concerning σ. These results are shown in Table 11–2, along with the interval for σ found in Exercise 11–4.

The results are not identical, so we cannot draw an exact parallel between usual traditional practice and Bayesian inference. However, there is enough similarity in the approaches to enable us to put an approximate Bayesian interpretation on traditional results.

In the case of inference about the standard deviation of a normal population whose mean and variance are unknown, the square roots of the limits of a traditional confidence interval about σ^2 will give an interval concerning σ that is closely similar to the Bayesian credible interval obtained from assuming uniform priors over μ and $\log \sigma$.

Exercise 11–5

The author of an article in a social science journal reports that his 99 % confidence intervals for the mean and variance of a normal population are as follows:

for μ: 27·8–35·9
for σ^2: 5·62–139·2

How would a Bayesian interpret these results?

Answers

First, we have to ensure that the author has not done a Bayesian analysis. Some Bayesians use the words 'confidence interval' rather than 'credible interval'. If there is no reference to prior distributions, you can be quite sure that the approach is traditional.

Suppose the author has computed traditional confidence intervals. Take the square roots of the limits for the variance interval. This gives

for σ: 2·37–11·8

Now we can say that a Bayesian would have obtained exactly the same interval for μ, and a similar interval for σ, if he had started with uniform priors concerning μ and $\log \sigma$. In other words, for the Bayesian whose prior opinion was sufficiently vague to justify stable estimation,

$$p(27{\cdot}8 \le \mu \le 35{\cdot}9) = 0{\cdot}99$$
and
$$p(2{\cdot}37 \le \sigma \le 11{\cdot}8) \simeq 0{\cdot}99$$

(Remember that ' $\simeq$ ' means 'approximately equal to'.)

11.4 Inferences about proportions

This topic was covered in Chapter 6 under the sections concerned with the Beta distribution. There we saw that the Beta distribution conveniently expresses opinion about some uncertain proportion. I will use the Greek lower case 'pi', π, to represent the unknown proportion; you should have no difficulty in distinguishing when π stands for an unknown proportion and when it refers to the well-known constant, $3 \cdot 1415 \ldots$.

A review

To make an inference about the value of π, we first express prior opinion in the form of a Beta distribution.

$\left.\begin{array}{l} p' \\ q' \end{array}\right\}$ parameters of the prior Beta

Next we make N independent observation on each of which either a 'success' or 'failure' is noted.

$\bar{s}$ = number of successes

$\bar{f}$ = number of failures

$\bar{s} + \bar{f} = N$

(The definition of a 'success' must accord with the expression of the uncertain quantity. For example, if one wishes to infer the proportion of working-class families in an area, then in the random sample each working-class family counts as a 'success' and all other classes of families count as 'failures'.)

Applying Bayes' theorem to the Beta prior in the light of these data gives a posterior that is also Beta.

$\left.\begin{array}{c} p'' \\ q'' \end{array}\right\}$ parameters of the posterior Beta

Furthermore, Bayes' theorem tells us that the values of the posterior parameters can be found by adding the numbers of successes and failures to the prior parameters.

$p'' = p' + \bar{s}$

$q'' = q' + \bar{f}$

The statistics of the Beta distribution are given on page 127 of Chapter 6.

Finding the posterior C per cent credible interval is simply a matter of entering the Beta tables, Appendix B, with values of p'' and q'' and with C, and then reading off the limits of the credible interval. If the values of p'' and q'' are bigger than those tabled, it is necessary to use the normal approximation to the Beta (see page 138 of Chapter 6).

Interpreting traditional results

If you run across a confidence interval for π in the literature you will not be far wrong if you interpret it as a Bayesian credible interval obtained with a uniform prior. Confidence intervals are usually computed only when the sample size is fairly large because only then can methods be applied that make use of the normal distribution. For small samples the procedures are more complex and seldom covered in statistics textbooks written for the social sciences. So you are not likely to find in the literature confidence interval statements regarding π when samples are small.

In the case of inference about an unknown population proportion, π, a traditional confidence interval is closely similar to a Bayesian credible interval obtained by assuming a uniform prior over π.

In other words, if in your reading you come across a confidence interval statement concerning some proportion, it is pretty safe to interpret it as if it were a Bayesian credible interval calculated on the assumption that the prior is uniform.

It is worth pointing out that the Bayesian procedures given here which lead you to look up a credible interval in the table of Appendix B are applicable for any size of sample whatsoever.

11.5 Transformations*

The methods in this chapter for making inferences about medians or means all carry with them certain assumptions about the form of the population: the distribution is either symmetrical or normal. But what can we do if the condition is not met, or, as is more commonly the case, we are uncertain as to whether the assumption holds? Sometimes neither our past experience nor our theories give us any information about the form of the population. What do we do then?

The answer is to look at the data, for they are a random sampling from the population, so their distribution gives us some notion of how the population looks. Having drawn a histogram or frequency distribution of the data, we can proceed in one of four ways, depending on the shape of the data distribution.

a   If the data appear to be roughly normally distributed, you can use any of the procedures that assume the population is normal.

b   If the data appear roughly symmetrical but definitely not normal (for example, bimodal data) then make your inference about the median.

c   If the data look pretty spikey and scattery, so you are not at all sure if they came from a normal population, you can probably proceed as if the population is normal.

d   If the data are clearly not normally distributed (for example, obviously skewed), then try using a mathematical transformation to change the data into a *new* set of numbers that *do* appear to be distributed in normal form. Then carry out the Bayesian analysis on these new numbers, and transform the resulting credible interval back into the original units.

I would like, now, to expand on these last two points.

When populations **might** be normal

When the frequency distribution of your data does not clearly rule out the possibility that the population may be normal, there are two points you should consider.

In the first place, most of the procedures in this book are what the statistician calls 'robust'. He means that the resulting inference, in our case a credible interval, is fairly insensitive to violations of the assumptions. For example, in making an inference about the mean of a population, the posterior credible interval we compute under the assumption that the population is normal is almost identical to the one we would get if the population were, say, somewhat skewed, and we used Bayesian methods appropriate to a skewed population. Of course, if the skew is very great the results *would* be different, but the point is that the assumption of normality can withstand a fair amount of violation before we have to use other methods. This statement is particularly applicable to making inferences about means. The procedure for making an inference about the standard deviation is not as robust, and requires that the normality assumption be at least reasonable. There are statistical procedures that enable tests of normality to be made, and one is mentioned in Chapter 14 (chi-squared tests). But the test is seldom made because if the data distribution does not

*This section is a diversion from the main development and could be omitted.

clearly lead you to reject the possibility of normality, then the presumed departure from normality is probably well within the limits of robustness.

In the second place, most people's intuition about the representativeness of random samples is faulty in a conservative direction. So what may appear to you as non-normal may, in fact, be a random sample from a normal population.

As an illustration, suppose I select a random sample of size 40 from a normal population. A perfectly representative distribution is shown in Fig. 11–13.

But, of course, one never gets such a distribution; purely by chance some measurements are over-represented while others are under-represented. Look at the histograms in Fig. 11–14. Which ones do you think were the result of random sampling from a normal population, and which do you think came from a non-normal population?

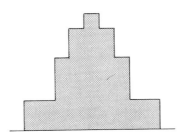

Fig. 11–13
Normal distribution of 40 observations

The answer is that they all came from a normal population. And they are not a special selection of samples, they are the first six that I drew, shown in the order that I drew them. Furthermore, the horizontal axes of all the histograms are directly comparable so you can see the shifts in the peaks of the distributions from one sample to the next. In particular, the modes of (b), (d) and (f) are quite different. The little arrow at the bottom of each column of histograms shows the class interval in which the population mean falls.

If your conclusion is that nothing appears so non-random as a random sample, then your sentiments echo exactly the findings of numerous investigations into how people perceive randomness. For our purposes the moral is simple: do not be too eager to discard the possibility that a population is normal simply because a random sample does not look very normal.

Thus, because our judgement about normality is likely to be conservative when it is based on random samples, and because the procedures in this book are robust, you will probably be on safe ground if you use the methods that assume normality even if you are not too sure.

Of course no population is probably ever exactly normal, and we usually never do find out the precise form of the population. We assume normality as a convenient approximation that enables us to use simple methods for making inferences. Fortunately, our statistical procedures are not very sensitive to that assumption.

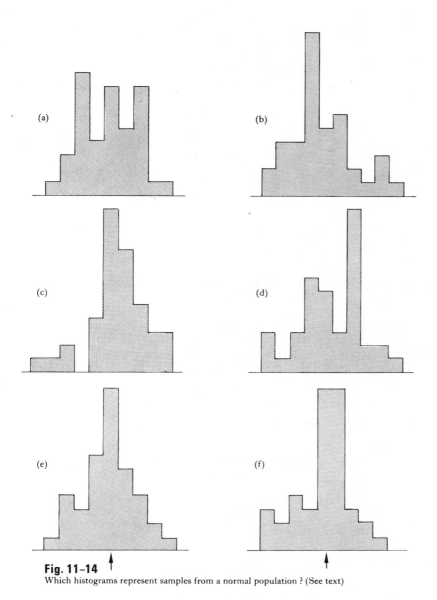

Fig. 11–14
Which histograms represent samples from a normal population ? (See text)

When populations are not normal

Not by any stretch of the imagination could we assume that the data shown in the left-hand histogram of Fig. 11–15 came from a normal population. Fairly drastic measures are needed for such highly skewed distributions, and one possibility is to effect a mathematical transformation of the scores so that a histogram of the transformed scores will appear reasonably normal. Here I have shown the effects of a logarithmic transformation: a histogram of the logs of the original scores looks reasonably normal in shape. I could then go on to find a posterior credible interval, using the usual Bayesian machinery, but since the interval would concern the logs of the original scores, I would have to take the antilogarithm* of the limits of the interval to get them back to the original units.

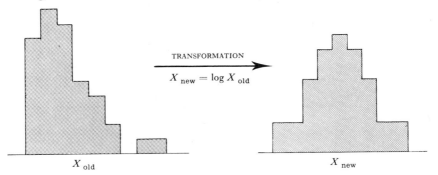

Fig. 11–15
Logarithmic transformation on highly skewed data often yields a distribution that is approximately normal

Now let us see how the log transformation works. Imagine that an investigator has measured the need–achievement of 11 subjects who were randomly selected from a larger group. He wishes to make an inference about the average level of need–achievement in the larger group. The eleven scores are as follows:

10, 6·84, 5·37, 4·43, 3·72, 3·16, 2·68, 2·26, 1·86, 1·46, 1

It will be convenient to represent these scores along a horizontal scale:

A histogram of these 11 scores is shown in Fig. 11–16. Obviously the distribution

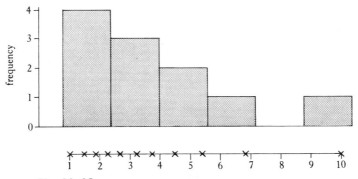

Fig. 11–16
Histogram of the need–achievement scores

* logarithms and antilogarithms are covered in Appendix H.

is most unlikely to have arisen from a normal population. However let us try a logarithmic transformation on the scores. You can look them up in the table in Appendix H. Here is what you will get:

X	$Log_{10} X$
10·00	1·000
6·84	0·835
5·37	0·730
4·43	0·646
3·72	0·571
3·16	0·500
2·68	0·428
2·26	0·354
1·86	0·270
1·46	0·164
1·00	0

You can see in Fig. 11–17 how the log transformation works. Values of X are shown along the horizontal axis, while the curve is a plot of $Y = \log X$. Thus, the Y-axis gives values of $\log X$. Notice that when $X = 1$, $Y = 0$; recall that the log of 1 is 0.

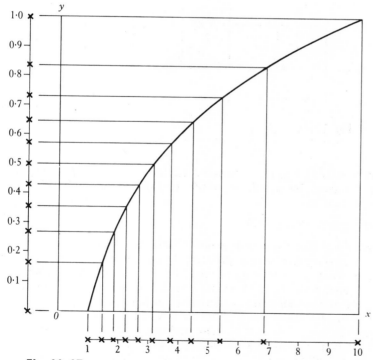

Fig. 11–17
Logarithmic transformation applied to the need achievement data

As an example, take the X-score of 3·16. Move vertically up from an X-value of 3·16 until you meet the curve, then move horizontally to the left. The Y-value is 0·5, that is, the $\log_{10}$ of 3·16 is 0·5.

Now look at the spacing of the Y-values. Here is the vertical scale, tipped horizontally.

The skew is gone, as you can see in the histogram of Fig. 11–18. Now it is appropriate to assume that the population of $\log_{10} X$ is normal, so I proceed using the new values. Assuming that the population variance is unknown, my calculations yield a posterior 99% credible interval of 0·2162 to 0·7838. But that is for $\log X$, not X, so to get a credible interval for X, I take antilogarithms.

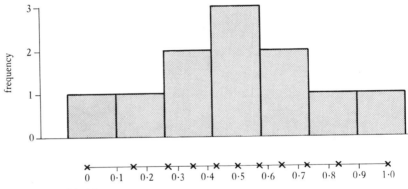

Fig. 11–18
Histogram of the transformed need–achievement data

I enter the Y axis of Fig. 11–17 with 0·2162 and 0·7838 and read off the corresponding X-values. Better still, I use the log table in Appendix H. This gives 1·65 to 6·08, that is,

$$p(1·65 \le \mu \le 6·08) = 0·99$$

Using a log transformation is not as easy as is implied by this example, however. A particularly vexing problem when the data do not swamp the prior is expressing prior opinion in terms of the units of the new scale rather than the original scale. In the example above, I assumed a uniform prior with respect to $\log \mu$, convenient mathematically but hard to justify intuitively. Also a linear transformation of the original data is often necessary so that the logs will range from 0 to 1. Because of these technical difficulties, you should probably seek the help of a statistician when you come across an obviously skewed distribution. Sometimes, of course, you can just switch to a different dependent variable, and it might turn out to be normally distributed. Then you discard the old, skewed one, and work with the new one.

11.6 Summary

Four basic methods of making inferences about a single uncertain quantity have been covered in this chapter:

a   inferences about a population median when the population is assumed to be symmetrical;

b   inferences about the mean of a normal population with known variance;

c   inferences about the mean and standard deviation of a normal population with unknown mean and variance;

d   inferences about a proportion.

Each of these procedures is outlined at the end of this summary.

All of these procedures yield a posterior credible interval, which if the prior is uniform, is identical, or similar to the confidence interval that would be calculated under a traditional approach.

The inferences are generally robust with respect to the assumptions, though it may be necessary to apply a transformation to very skewed data to make their distribution normal.

Inferences concerning the population median

a   *Want to infer:* the median of a population;

b   *Experiment:* a random sample of N observations from the population, on each of which a numerical measurement, X, is made;

c   *Assumptions:* population is symmetrical;

d   *Data:* Rank-order the N scores;

e   *Prior distribution:* uniform over possible values of the median;

f   *Posterior distribution concerning the ranks:*

approximately normal with

$$m'' = \frac{N+1}{2}$$

$$s'' = \frac{\sqrt{N}}{2}$$

g   *C per cent credible interval concerning the ranks:*

$$m'' - zs'' \leq \text{rank of population median} \leq m'' + zs''$$

where z is the standard deviate corresponding to the C per cent credible interval for the normal distribution; z is found by entering the normal table with $C/100$ and reading off z.

To get the credible interval for the median itself, find the scores in the data corresponding to the ranks of the credible interval just computed, interpolating if necessary.

Inferences concerning the population mean

a *Want to infer:* μ, the mean of a population;

b *Experiment:* a random sample of N observations from the population, on each of which a numerical measurement, X, is made;

c *Assumptions:* **i** population is normal; **ii** variance of population, σ^2, is known;

d *Data:* Calculate . . .

$$M = \frac{\sum X}{N}$$

e *Prior distribution:* normal over μ, with prior mean $= m'$, prior standard deviation $= s'$;

f *Posterior distribution:* normal over μ, with

for non-uniform prior

$$m'' = m' \left(\frac{n'}{n'+N}\right) + M \left(\frac{N}{n'+N}\right)$$

$$s'' = \frac{\sigma}{\sqrt{n''}}$$

where $n' = \dfrac{\sigma^2}{(s')^2}$ and $n'' = n' + N$

for uniform prior

$$m'' = M$$

$$s'' = \frac{\sigma}{\sqrt{N}}$$

g *C per cent credible interval:*

$$m'' - zs'' \le \mu \le m'' + zs''$$

where z is the standard deviate corresponding to the C per cent credible interval for the normal distribution; z is found by entering the normal tables with $C/100$ and reading off z.

Inferences concerning the population mean and standard deviation

a *Want to infer:* μ, the mean of a normal population; σ, the standard deviation of a normal population.

b *Experiment:* a random sample of N observations from the population, on each of which a numerical measurement, X, is made;

c *Assumptions:* population is normal;

d *Data:* Calculate . . .

$$M = \frac{\sum X}{N} \qquad S = \sqrt{\frac{N \sum X^2 - (\sum X)^2}{N(N-1)}}$$

e *Prior distributions:* **i** uniform over μ and $\log \sigma$; **ii** both prior distributions independent of one another.

f   *Posterior distributions:*

Concerning μ: Student-t with parameters

$$\mu_t'' = M \qquad \sigma_t'' = \frac{S}{\sqrt{N}} \qquad df'' = N - 1$$

Concerning σ: Inverted-Gamma 2 with

$$\text{mode}'' = S \sqrt{\frac{N-1}{N}} \qquad df'' = N - 1$$

g   *C per cent credible intervals:*

Concerning μ:

$$\mu_t'' - t\sigma_t'' \le \mu \le \mu_t'' + t\sigma_t''$$

where t is the standard deviate corresponding to the C per cent credible interval for the Student-t distribution; t is found by entering the Student-t table with $df = N - 1$ and with C.

Concerning σ:

$$\text{IG2}_{\text{low}} \times S \sqrt{\frac{N-1}{N}} \le \sigma \le \text{IG2}_{\text{high}} \times S \sqrt{\frac{N-1}{N}}$$

where IG2_{low} and IG2_{high} are the tabled limits of the credible interval for IG2 whose mode is 1. The tabled limits are found by entering IG2 table with $df = N - 1$, and with C.

Inferences concerning the population proportion

a   *Want to infer:* π, the population proportion;

b   *Experiment:* a random sample of N observations, on each of which either a success or a failure is noted;

c   *Assumptions:* π does not change during experiment;

d   *Data:* number of successes, $\bar{s}$, and number of failures, $\bar{f}$, where

$$\bar{s} + \bar{f} = N$$

e   *Prior distribution:* Beta over possible values of π, with parameters p' and q';

f   *Posterior distribution:* Beta with parameters p'' and q'', where

$$p'' = p' + \bar{s}$$
$$q'' = q' + \bar{f}$$

g   *C per cent credible interval:* find from Beta table directly by entering the table with values of p'' and q'' and with C.

Problems

Questions 11–1 to 11–3 concern this experiment:

An investigator wishes to find out how much time per week students at English universities spend on activities directly relevant to their courses (including lectures, seminars, tutorials, and laboratory work). He asks a random sample of 20 students to keep diaries of how they used their time each day during a week in the middle of the autumn term. After collecting the diaries, he codes the records for various activities, and finds, for each student, the number of hours in the week devoted to activities directly relevant to the course. He computes the mean to be 38·8 hours and the standard deviation to be 8·6 hours.

11–1 Suppose that this investigation was one of a series he had been conducting over a period of years. Each year histograms of the data appeared roughly normal in shape, and while the mean number of hours spent on activities directly relevant to the course has fluctuated over the years, the standard deviation of the samples has remained fairly constant, hovering from year to year around 10. This past information enables the investigator to assume that the population is approximately normal with a standard deviation of 10. He describes his prior opinion concerning this year's population mean as normal with a mean of 40 and a standard deviation of 2.

a What is his posterior 95% credible interval for the population mean?

b Comment on the relative contribution to the posterior of his prior opinion and of the data.

11–2 Suppose his prior had been uniform.

a What, then, would his 95% credible interval for the mean be?

b Compare this interval with the one computed in (1); why is it different?

11–3 Suppose that these data are the first set the investigator has collected; he is willing to assume only that the population is normal, and is vague about the values of the population mean and standard deviation. He feels that stable estimation applies to his prior opinions.

a What are his posterior 95% credible intervals concerning the population mean and standard deviation?

b Compare your answer concerning the mean with (1) and (2).

11–4 My wife and I enjoy playing 'Score-Four', a sort of three-dimensional noughts-and-crosses (tic-tac-toe) in which four balls of the same colour must be played in a horizontal, vertical or diagonal line for a 'win' to be scored. Out of the last 98 games, I have won 45 and she has won 53. What inference could be made concerning our relative skills at this game?

11–5 A survey carried out in England, Scotland and Wales on Tuesday, April 18, 1972, by the Opinion Research Centre (reported in *The Times*, Wednesday, April 19, 1972) showed that 69% of those interviewed felt that a secret ballot should be held to find out if members of the railway union would accept the increased offer of 12% made on Sunday evening. The sample of 561 people was drawn from the electoral register and was selected to ensure that it was representative of the electorate by sex, age, region, and socio-economic grouping. How accurate is the sample result?

11–6 (Refers to Problem 8–4) If the population of numerical test scores is assumed to be symmetrical but not necessarily normal, what inference can be made about the central tendency of the population, given the data in the problem?

11–7 (Refers to Problem 9–4) What inferences could be made about the mean and standard deviation of the population of scores on the field dependence–independence task?

11–8 Theory A predicts that people will be unable to discriminate between two particular perceptual stimuli, while Theory B predicts that they can. Only two responses are possible, X and Y. Failure to discriminate would lead to an equal chance for either response to be given, while the Y response would tend to be made if people could discriminate the stimuli. Thirty subjects are tested; 21 subjects give the Y response, and the remaining 9 give the X response. Explain what a Bayesian might do with these data, what statistical inference(s) he might make, and what he would say about the relative plausibility of the two theories.

11–9 A student wishes to find out the average number of times sociology books in the reserve-book collection of his university's library were checked out on overnight loan during the autumn term. During the Christmas vacation he selects 20 books at random by drawing from the sociology section of the reserve-book card-catalogue. He then locates the book and counts the number of times it was stamped with a due-date from the autumn term. Here are his results:

30, 32, 37, 22, 2, 37, 29, 33, 25, 24,
34, 12, 33, 35, 33, 38, 22, 26, 16, 35

a Draw a histogram of these data to see if they are approximately normal.

b What is the 95% posterior credible interval for the mean number of times sociology books are checked out? Compare the credible interval computed without transforming the data with the one found from the transformed data.

11–10 Find an example from social science journals of each of the inference methods discussed in this chapter and give a Bayesian interpretation for each one.

12 · Inferences concerning two uncertain quantities

Now it is time to consider inferences about two variables. This is the type of inference most commonly found in the social sciences literature, because experimental work frequently is focussed on such questions as 'Is this different than that?', 'Are these two related in some way?', or 'How can this variable be predicted from knowing that one?'.

Take a specific example. Suppose a theory predicts that the speed of learning a new skill depends in part on the time lag between performing the task and receiving knowledge of results. The sooner a person is given knowledge of results, the more quickly he learns. To study this, a psychologist randomly assigns subjects to two groups, and subjects in both groups are given several trials in which to learn a simple task, like keeping a pointer on an erratically-moving spot. Subjects in one group, the control group, are only told at the end of each trial the number of seconds they kept the pointer on the spot. The other group, the experimental group, receives this information throughout the trial, so each subject in this group can check on his score as it accumulates. By comparing the mean performance of the subjects in the two groups, the experimenter can get some notion of the effectiveness of feedback given during the learning of the task.

That general concern reduces to this statistical problem: What is the difference between the population means of the two groups? Suppose the experiment reveals a slight difference. Is it then correct to infer that since the sample means are different that the population means must also be different? Not necessarily, for the differences between the samples could have arisen purely by chance. Then again, the difference might reflect a real difference in the populations. How can we decide?

Our approach to this question should by now be familiar. We make an inference, using the Bayesian machinery, concerning the difference between the *population* means, and we express this inference as a posterior credible interval. We will end up stating that there is, say, a 99% chance that the true difference lies between a particular low value and a particular high value. If that interval happens to include a difference of 0, then we cannot rule out the possibility that there is no difference between the effectiveness of the two kinds of knowledge of results.

This chapter progresses fairly fast, for I am counting on your recognizing the basic operation of Bayes' theorem in all these methods. It is only the little details that make these methods appear different. As in the previous chapter, I have given detailed summaries of the methods at the end of the chapter. Comparing the summaries should help to highlight the similarities.

This chapter should enable you to

understand and carry out inferences concerning two uncertain quantities;

know when these methods are appropriate and when they are not;

be able to interpret corresponding traditional analyses from a Bayesian viewpoint.

12.1 Differences between means

In this section I first introduce a simple method for making inferences about the difference between two population means that applies whenever the two posterior distributions (one for each population) are normal. Then I go on to discuss methods that apply to non-normal posteriors, and in the process we pick up a new distribution to add to our already extensive collection, the Behrens distribution.

General method for independent normal posteriors or priors

Suppose that our uncertainty about some uncertain quantity is normally distributed with mean m_1 and variance s_1^2. Suppose, too, that our opinion about a second uncertain quantity is normal with mean m_2 and variance s_2^2. Often we are interested in the difference between the uncertain quantities, call it δ (Greek lower-case delta), and it is a useful fact that in this case the distribution of δ is also normal with mean given by $m_1 - m_2$ and variance equal to $s_1^2 + s_2^2$. You subtract the two means and add the two variances to get the mean and variance of the new distribution. There is only one assumption to watch out for: the two original distributions must be independent.

This principle is often useful in Bayesian analysis. If you have measures on random samples drawn from two independent populations and you are interested in finding out how much greater the population mean of one group is than the population mean of the other, then if your posterior distributions concerning each sample mean are normal, you can apply this principle to get the posterior distribution concerning the difference between the population means. You can see how this works in the next example.

Exercise 12–1

A psychologist studying thought disorders in schizophrenic patients devises a special testing procedure which yields, among other measures, a single number that represents the degree to which concepts used to describe people are interconnected in the patient's thinking. High values of the index indicate high interconnectedness, or low discrimination between concepts, while low values suggest that an individual uses concepts that are seen as distinct and fairly unconnected.

In developing his test he administers it to patients with clear-cut histories of schizophrenia, and also to normal individuals with no evidence or history of mental illness. He expects to find a difference between the means of the two groups. Failure to find much of a difference would suggest that his test is no good, or that current theories of schizophrenia need revision.

He is initially very unsure of the population mean and variance of each group, but because he administers the test to a large number of people, his posterior distributions concerning the means have so many degrees of freedom that normal approximations to the actual Student-t distributions apply.

Suppose, then, that his posterior opinions about the population mean score of schizophrenics is normal with mean of 27 and standard deviation of 2·6, while the mean of the normal posterior for normal people is 19 with standard deviation of 3·2. What is the posterior 99% credible interval for the difference between the population means?

Answer

First, some terminology. Let's refer to the population of schizophrenics as population 1, the normals as population 2. We wish to find the difference between the means of the populations, $\mu_1 - \mu_2$. For short, let $\delta = \mu_1 - \mu_2$. Our goal is to find a posterior 99% credible interval for δ.

We know that the two posterior distributions concerning μ_1 and μ_2 are normal with

$$m_1'' = 27 \qquad m_2'' = 19$$
$$s_1'' = 2\cdot6 \qquad s_2'' = 3\cdot2$$

These distributions are shown in Fig. 12–1.

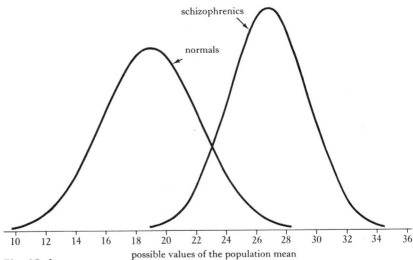

schizophrenics

normals

| 10 | 12 | 14 | 16 | 18 | 20 | 22 | 24 | 26 | 28 | 30 | 32 | 34 | 36 |

possible values of the population mean

Fig. 12–1

Posterior distributions for the population means of normal and schizophrenic groups on a particular test

The posteriors look fairly separate, though there is some overlap. It is in this region of overlap where at least some posterior opinion favours the possibility of the mean of the normal group being higher than that of the schizophrenics.

We can get a better idea of how serious this overlap is by finding the distribution of δ. This distribution is itself normal with mean equal to $m_1'' - m_2''$ and variance given by $(s_1'')^2 + (s_2'')^2$. This means that the posterior concerning δ is normal with

$$m'' = m_1'' - m_2'' = 27 - 19 = 8$$

and $\quad s'' = \sqrt{(s_1'')^2 + (s_2'')^2} = \sqrt{(2\cdot6)^2 + (3\cdot2)^2} = \sqrt{17} = 4\cdot123$

This posterior is shown in Fig. 12–2. The curve indicates that some posterior opinion falls over negative values of δ, suggesting that the mean of the *normal* group might be higher. We can see this in the credible interval:

$$8 - 2\cdot58(4\cdot12) \le \delta \le 8 + 2\cdot58(4\cdot12)$$
$$-2\cdot64 \le \delta \le 18\cdot64$$

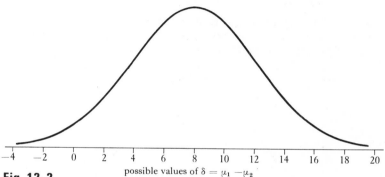

Fig. 12–2

possible values of $\delta = \mu_1 - \mu_2$

Posterior distribution for the difference between the population means whose posterior distributions are shown in Fig. 12–1

Some values in the interval are negative. Even the shorter 95% interval includes some negative values:

$$8 - 1\cdot96(4\cdot12) \le \delta \le 8 + 1\cdot96(4\cdot12)$$
$$-0\cdot08 \le \delta \le 16\cdot08$$

Thus, we conclude, there is some possibility that the mean performance of the normal group is higher than that of the schizophrenics.

You can see from this example that the overlap of two posterior distributions must be no more than slight in order for the distribution of their differences to fall well away from 0.

Testing hypotheses

Although this topic will be discussed fully in Chapter 14, it is worth a brief introduction at this point while the previous exercise is still in mind. The question we now consider is how to assign probabilities to these two hypotheses:

H_1: schizophrenic population mean is greater than mean of normals

H_2: mean of normals is greater than schizophrenic population mean or, put more succinctly,

$$H_1: \mu_1 > \mu_2$$
$$H_2: \mu_2 > \mu_1$$

We can rule out the possibility that the means are equal, $\mu_1 = \mu_2$, because that is equivalent to finding the probability of δ, an uncertain quantity, being equal to a specific value, 0. Recall that when we deal with continuous uncertain quantities we usually talk about probabilities of *intervals* of values, for the probability of any specific value must be 0. Thus, the probability of $\delta = 0$ is 0.

We could also phrase our two hypotheses in terms of δ.

$$H_1: \mu_1 > \mu_2, \quad \text{that is, } \delta \text{ is positive}$$
$$H_2: \mu_2 > \mu_1, \quad \text{that is, } \delta \text{ is negative}$$

Then it should be obvious from Fig. 12–2 that the probability of H_1 is given by the area of the posterior to the right of 0, while the probability of H_2 is represented by the area to the left of 0 (see Fig. 12–3).

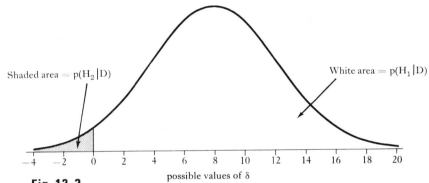

Fig. 12–3
How posterior probabilities of hypotheses are found from the posterior distribution of δ

To find the area to the left of $\delta = 0$, we follow the usual procedure for normal distributions: find the z-value corresponding to $\delta = 0$, then look up the area to the left of z in the cumulative normal tables. The z-value for this posterior is

$$z = \frac{\delta - m''}{s''} = \frac{0 - 8}{4 \cdot 123} = -1 \cdot 94$$

From the normal tables, the area to the left of $z = 1 \cdot 94$ is $0 \cdot 9738$, so the area to the left of $z = -1 \cdot 94$ must be $1 - 0 \cdot 9738 = 0 \cdot 0262$. We conclude, then, that

$$p(H_1|D) = p(\mu_1 > \mu_2) = 0 \cdot 974$$

and

$$p(H_2|D) = p(\mu_2 > \mu_1) = 0 \cdot 026$$

In words, there is a 97·4% chance that the group mean of the schizophrenics is greater than that of the normals.

This is just one example of how probabilities of hypotheses can be obtained from the posterior distribution concerning some uncertain quantity. The procedure is valid as long as the hypotheses are formulated in terms of intervals of the uncertain quantity. There is no very satisfactory parallel in traditional statistics, for the relative frequency notion of probability usually rules out the assigning of probabilities to intervals of an uncertain quantity.

When population variances are equal, though unknown

If we are making inferences about the means of two populations whose variances are unknown, then, as we saw in the previous chapter, the posterior distributions are Student-t. If we have only a modest amount of data, then the degrees of freedom associated with each posterior are too small to allow the Student-t to be approximated by the normal. To find the posterior distribution of the difference between the population means we cannot, then, use the general method just given, for it applies only to posteriors that are normal. In this section and the next, methods will be presented for dealing with the difference between Student-t posteriors. This section assumes that the unknown variances of the two populations can be assumed equal; the next section does not make that assumption.

Sometimes our past experience or our theories that we are putting to the test give us reason to believe that while the means of two populations may be different, their variances will be roughly the same. This will be true, for example, whenever the treatment we administer to an experimental group affects only the mean performance of the group, but has no appreciable influence on the variability of performance in the group. Then we would expect experimental and control groups to have different means, but similar variances.

When the posterior distributions for each of two independent population means are Student-t, then the posterior distribution concerning the difference between the means is itself Student-t, assuming the population variances are equal though unknown.

All that remains, now, is to specify the parameters. Some familiar terminology will be used. Let the two populations be designated 1 and 2. Their means are μ_1 and μ_2 and their variances σ_1^2 and σ_2^2. Assume that the populations are normal and that the variances are equal, $\sigma_1^2 = \sigma_2^2 = \sigma^2$. We have drawn random and independent samples from the two populations, of size N_1 and N_2. Numerical measurements were made on the samples; designate these as X_1 and X_2.

Now we are ready to make some calculations on our data. First the means of the two samples:

$$M_1 = \frac{\sum X_1}{N_1} \quad \text{and} \quad M_2 = \frac{\sum X_2}{N_2}$$

There is nothing new there. Now, instead of calculating the standard deviations, compute the sums of squares:

$$SS_{XX_1} = \sum (X_1 - M_1)^2 = \frac{N_1 \sum X_1^2 - (\sum X_1)^2}{N_1}$$

$$SS_{XX_2} = \sum (X_2 - M_2)^2 = \frac{N_2 \sum X_2^2 - (\sum X_2)^2}{N_2}$$

Remember that if you *do* want to calculate the standard deviations, it is a short step from the sums of squares:

$$S_1 = \sqrt{\frac{SS_{XX_1}}{N_1 - 1}} \quad \text{and} \quad S_2 = \sqrt{\frac{SS_{XX_2}}{N_2 - 1}}$$

Sometimes we will find it more convenient to work with the sums of squares, other times with the standard deviations or variances.

Now we are ready to specify the parameters of the posterior distribution concerning δ, where δ equals the difference between the population means, $\mu_1 - \mu_2$. It is a Student-t with these parameters:

$$\mu_t'' = M_1 - M_2$$

$$\sigma_t'' = \sqrt{\left(\frac{SS_{XX_1} + SS_{XX_2}}{N_1 + N_2 - 2}\right)\left(\frac{N_1 + N_2}{N_1 N_2}\right)}$$

posterior degrees of freedom $= df'' = N_1 + N_2 - 2$

Once you know the parameters you can find any posterior credible interval by travelling up and down t sigmas from the mean. In general, the C per cent credible interval is

$$\mu_t'' - t\sigma_t'' \leq \delta \leq \mu_t'' + t\sigma_t''$$

where t is the standard deviate corresponding to the C per cent credible interval for the Student-t distribution. Remember when finding t from the Student-t table to enter the table with $N_1 + N_2 - 2$ degrees of freedom.

Exercise 12–2

A scientist studying the effects of RNA on short-term memory in old people administers a drug containing RNA to a sample of 20 men and women over the age of 70. To ensure that any effects on memory he may observe are due to the drug and not, say, to the special attention given to his subjects, he administers a placebo drug to another sample of 20 people, the control group. These 20 people are chosen at random from the same population as the experimental group, but with the restriction that IQ's in the control group must *match* those in the experimental group. In this way, the scientist ensures that differences in short-term memory are not associated with differences in intelligence. Only the scientist knows whether a subject received the drug or the placebo.

Each subject is tested a specified time after receiving the drug or placebo; the time lapse gives the drug time to be absorbed. An assistant who does not know whether the subject received the drug or the placebo carries out the tests. One test gives the subject's 'digit-span', the maximum number of digits a person can repeat back without error immediately after hearing them. Here are the results for the two groups.

Control:

5	4	5	3
4	5	5	6
6	5	4	6
6	5	4	6
6	5	5	7

Experimental:

7	8	6	7
7	7	6	7
7	6	7	8
6	6	6	6
7	9	5	6

What is the posterior 99% credible interval for the difference between the means of these groups?

Answer

Now that the experimental group has been 'treated', we say that it represents a new population, even though all subjects in the experiment originally came from the same population. We are interested in the difference δ between the mean μ_1 of the population of 'treated' patients and the mean μ_2 of the population of 'untreated' patients. The scientist has no reason to believe that RNA will increase the variability of digit-span in the experimental group, so he assumes that the unknown variances of the two populations are equal. He also assumes the populations are normal; histograms of his data give him no reason to disbelieve this. He is ready, now, to make the calculations in the following steps.

a Compute the mean and sum of squares for each group. First he finds $\sum X$ and $\sum X^2$ for each group:

	$\sum X$	$\sum X^2$
Experimental	134	914
Control	102	538

Then the means:

$$M_1 = \frac{\sum X_1}{N_1} = \frac{134}{20} = 6\cdot7$$

$$M_2 = \frac{\sum X_2}{N_2} = \frac{102}{20} = 5\cdot1$$

And next the sums of squares:

$$SS_{XX_1} = \frac{N_1 \sum X_1^2 - (\sum X_1)^2}{N_1} = \frac{20(914) - (134)^2}{20} = \frac{324}{20} = 16\cdot2$$

$$SS_{XX_2} = \frac{N_2 \sum X_2^2 - (\sum X_2)^2}{N_2} = \frac{20(538) - (102)^2}{20} = \frac{356}{20} = 17\cdot8$$

b If the scientist assumes uniform priors over μ_1, μ_2, and log σ, then the posterior distribution concerning δ is Student-t with parameters

$$u_t'' = M_1 - M_2 = 6\cdot7 - 5\cdot1 = 1\cdot6$$

$$\begin{aligned}\sigma_t'' &= \sqrt{\left(\frac{SS_{XX_1} + SS_{XX_2}}{N_1 + N_2 - 2}\right)\left(\frac{N_1 + N_2}{N_1 N_2}\right)} \\ &= \sqrt{\left(\frac{16\cdot2 + 17\cdot8}{20 + 20 - 2}\right)\left(\frac{20 + 20}{20 \times 20}\right)} \\ &= \sqrt{\left(\frac{34}{38}\right)\left(\frac{40}{400}\right)} = \sqrt{0\cdot0895} = 0\cdot299\end{aligned}$$

and $df'' = N_1 + N_2 - 2 = 38$

c Compute the posterior 99% credible interval:

$$\mu_t'' - t\sigma_t'' \leq \delta \leq \mu_t'' + t\sigma_t''$$

Reference to the Student-t table for 38 degrees of freedom gives $t = 2\cdot71$ (by interpolation). Now we have all the ingredients for computing the credible interval.

$$1\cdot6 - 2\cdot71(0\cdot299) \leq \delta \leq 1\cdot6 + 2\cdot71(0\cdot299)$$
$$1\cdot6 - 0\cdot81 \leq \delta \leq 1\cdot6 + 0\cdot81$$
$$0\cdot79 \leq \delta \leq 2\cdot41$$

You might be interested to know that I generated these data from two normal populations with means of 5 and 7, so the true difference is 2. The credible interval contains that value.

This method is quite robust with respect to the assumptions of normality of the populations, and less so concerning the equal-variance assumption, especially if the samples are of different size. If there is any doubt about the variances being equal try to arrange for your samples to be of the same size.

You will, on rare occasions, find in the social science literature, a confidence interval for the difference between population means. How should you interpret it? Well, it will be exactly the same as a Bayesian credible interval calculated under the assumption of uniform priors over μ_1, μ_2, and $\log \sigma$. However, be sure that the equal-variance assumption is made. If it is not, then the traditional confidence interval will *not* be the same as the Bayesian credible interval, as we shall see in the next section.

This exercise introduced two new concepts: *blind trials* and *matching*. It is often important for the subject not to know whether he received a genuine treatment. This controls for effects that might be connected with, for example, the subject's conscious or unconscious desire to please the experimenter, for it is hoped that the effect would work equally for both groups and so cancel out when the difference between groups is examined. As an extra precaution, the person doing the testing is kept in ignorance of the type of treatment each person received, so he cannot unconsciously influence the results. When both the subject and tester are not informed of the type of treatment, the experiment is said to be *double blind*.

Matching is introduced to cut down on variance due to uncontrolled effects. It is another way to exercise control in an experiment. If you think that differences between groups might be caused by factors other than the treatment, then you try to equalize the factors in the two groups, so their differences cancel. Ideally, random selection of control and experimental groups would cause these uncontrolled factors to cancel out, but especially in small samples there is no guarantee that will happen. You can cut down on uncontrolled sources of variability, and so make more efficient use of small samples, by matching groups on variables that you think might make a difference. Methods for doing this are discussed in books and articles on experimental design, and will not be pursued further here.

It is important to recognize that blind trials and matching are aspects of the design of experiments, and are not required by our statistical machinery. You will find many inferences made about the difference between population means where neither blind trials nor matching are employed. There is no requirement for the sample sizes to be equal, either, although they were for this experiment because of the matching. It *is* necessary for the samples to be independent, though. Cases where they are not, and the procedures to be followed then, are discussed in the section after the next one.

When population variances are unknown and possibly unequal

If we suspect that the population variances may be unequal, then the difference between our two Student-*t* posteriors concerning the population means is no longer a Student-*t*, it is a Behrens distribution. This distribution, like the normal and Student-*t*, is bell-shaped and symmetrical, but it is much more complex. It is a five parameter distribution and even in its standardized form it still needs three parameters to be specified to complete its description. This makes tabling an almost impossible task. However, we need to use the Behrens distribution only for small samples, so extensive tables are not necessary.

The experimental situation is identical to the last section. There are only two differences up to the posterior distribution. First, in addition to the means, it will be convenient to compute the variances of the two samples.

$$S_1^2 = \frac{N_1 \sum X_1^2 - (\sum X_1)^2}{N_1(N_1 - 1)}$$

$$S_2^2 = \frac{N_2 \sum X_2^2 - (\sum X_2)^2}{N_2(N_2 - 1)}$$

Secondly, we assume uniform priors over μ_1 and μ_2, as before, but also over $\log \sigma_1$ and $\log \sigma_2$. All four of these prior distributions must be independent of one another.

Under these conditions, the posterior distribution concerning δ, the difference between the means, is given by a Behrens distribution with these parameters:

$$\mu_d'' = M_1 - M_2$$

$$\sigma_d'' = \sqrt{\frac{S_1^2}{N_1} + \frac{S_2^2}{N_2}}$$

posterior degrees of freedom$_1 = df_1'' = N_1 - 1$

posterior degrees of freedom$_2 = df_2'' = N_2 - 1$

$$\text{posterior angle} = \omega'', \text{ where } \tan \omega'' = \sqrt{\frac{S_2^2/N_2}{S_1^2/N_1}}$$

(Once you have found tan ω'', you can look up ω'' in Table L.)

Just as z identifies the independent variable along the horizontal axis of the standardized normal distribution, and t serves the same function for the Student-*t* distribution, so d is used to signify the independent variable of the Behrens distribution. A rather coarse table of d is given in Appendix A. You enter it with df_1, df_2 and ω for the credible interval of interest, and then read off the value of d. Then you compute a credible interval in the usual way:

$$\mu_d'' - d\sigma_d'' \le \delta \le \mu_d'' + d\sigma_d''$$

Exercise 12–3

Students in my statistics class filled out a special abbreviated version of a questionnaire that measures what might be called 'ideological conservatism' (see Wilson and Patterson, 1968, for the full questionnaire). Possible scores could range from 0 to 24, a high score denoting greater conservatism. I decided to take a random sample of 7 men and 9 women (the samples are of unequal size purely for illustrative purposes), and these are their scores on the test:

Men		Women	
2	8	4	12
0	10	1	13
8	8	12	10
8		13	3
		12	

What is the posterior 99% credible interval for the difference between the means?

Answer

If we assume uniform prior distributions over the means and logs of the standard deviations of the two populations, that the priors are independent, and that the populations are normal, then we proceed as follows:

a Let μ_1 = mean score of population of men, and μ_2 = mean score of population of women. We wish to find a credible interval for δ, the difference between the means, $\delta = \mu_1 - \mu_2$.

b Find the means and variances of the two samples. First we find N, $\sum X$ and $\sum X^2$ for each sample.

$$\sum X_1 = 44 \qquad \sum X_2 = 80$$
$$\sum X_1^2 = 360 \qquad \sum X_2^2 = 896$$
$$N_1 = 7 \qquad N_2 = 9$$

The means are:

$$M_1 = \frac{\sum X_1}{N_1} = \frac{44}{7} = 6\cdot29 \qquad M_2 = \frac{\sum X_2}{N_2} = \frac{80}{9} = 8\cdot89$$

The variances are:

$$S_1^2 = \frac{N_1 \sum X_1^2 - (\sum X_1)^2}{N_1(N_1 - 1)} \qquad S_2^2 = \frac{N_2 \sum X_2^2 - (\sum X_2)^2}{N_2(N_2 - 1)}$$

$$= \frac{7(360) - (44)^2}{7(7 - 1)} \qquad = \frac{9(896) - (80)^2}{9(9 - 1)}$$

$$= \frac{584}{42} = 13\cdot905 \qquad = \frac{1664}{72} = 23\cdot111$$

c Find the parameters of the posterior Behrens distributions.

$$\mu_d'' = M_1 - M_2 = 6\cdot29 - 8\cdot89 = -2\cdot60$$

$$\sigma_d'' = \sqrt{\frac{S_1^2}{N_1} + \frac{S_2^2}{N_2}} = \sqrt{\frac{13\cdot905}{7} + \frac{23\cdot111}{9}}$$

$$= \sqrt{1\cdot9864 + 2\cdot5679} = \sqrt{4\cdot5543} = 2\cdot13$$

$$df_1'' = N_1 - 1 = 7 - 1 = 6$$
$$df_2'' = N_2 - 1 = 9 - 1 = 8$$
$$\tan \omega'' = \sqrt{\frac{S_2^2/N_2}{S_1^2/N_1}} = \sqrt{\frac{2\cdot5679}{1\cdot9864}} = 1\cdot14$$

Go to Table L, look up $1\cdot14$ in the tan column, and read off the nearest angle. This gives

$$\omega'' = 49°$$

d Look up d for the 99 % credible interval in Table A. Enter the table with $df_1 = 6$ and with $df_2 = 8$. The exact value of d for $\omega = 49°$ is not tabled, but we can interpolate between $\omega = 45°$ and $\omega = 60°$.

From the interpolation diagram we get $d = 3\cdot398$.

e Compute the credible interval.

$$\mu_d'' - d\sigma_d'' \le \delta \le \mu_d'' + d\sigma_d''$$
$$- 2\cdot60 - 3\cdot398(2\cdot13) \le \delta \le - 2\cdot60 + 3\cdot398(2\cdot13)$$
$$- 9\cdot84 \le \delta \le 4\cdot64$$

Now we can be 99% sure that the true difference between the population means lies between $- 9\cdot83$ and $4\cdot63$, the positive values signifying that the men's mean is greater. From this credible interval we might conclude that, on the average, men and women's scores are not very different.

The Behrens Table is fairly coarse, so interpolation is almost always necessary. But this is a tedious job for a table of triple entry, so let me suggest an alternative. Round df_1 and df_2 *down* to 6, 8, 12, or 24, whichever is nearest, and enter the table with those rounded-down values. (For df less than 6, consult Table VII, of Fisher and Yates, 1963.) Then, if ω'' is *not* equal to any of the values along the top of the table, round ω'' either up *or* down to one of those values, whichever direction of rounding gives the *larger* tabled value of d. The value of d that results from these procedures will be slightly larger than the correct one, so the credible interval will be a little on the conservative side.

When both samples are at least as big as 25, then the Student-t distribution provides a fair approximation to the Behrens, so you can use the procedures of the previous section. Of course, if the samples are large, the normal approximation will be very satisfactory, for the Behrens distribution tends to normality as the degrees of freedom increase.

You will almost never find in the social science literature a confidence interval for the differences between two means of independent populations when the variances are not assumed equal. There are several reasons for this. In the first place, this case is not even discussed in many social science statistics textbooks, so some investigators just assume that the variances are equal.

Secondly, when it is discussed, writers usually note that there is controversy in the traditional literature as to what distribution is appropriate, so some scientists avoid the procedures altogether and rely on methods (often called non-parametric statistics) that make few or no assumptions about the form of the population distribution. Thirdly, a convention has grown up among social scientists that places heavy emphasis only on finding out whether the population means differ by an amount greater than could be expected by chance, not on what the difference actually is. As a consequence, you are more likely to read 'the means are significantly different' rather than be given a confidence interval. As you will see in Chapter 14, I think the emphasis is in the wrong direction. More attention should, in my opinion, be paid to inferences concerning the true values of the differences, and less to decisions about whether an observed difference is just a chance variation hiding a true difference of zero.

Finally, I should point out that the Bayesian credible interval you find with the methods of this section will be the same as the confidence interval calculated by those non-Bayesians who subscribe to Fisher's work on the Behrens distribution. But there are few statisticians who agree with the Behrens–Fisher result. The Bayesian viewpoint does, however, support the end result of Fisher's work, though not his argument since it is in the relative frequency tradition. Thus, if you do run across a traditional confidence interval, it is likely *not* derived from the Behrens–Fisher distribution, so it cannot be given an exact Bayesian interpretation. This is one point where Bayesian and traditional methods disagree.

When populations are not independent

So far, the methods of this Chapter have assumed that the populations are independent. As long as we are comparing two different groups that assumption will usually be valid. But suppose we have 'before' and 'after' measures on the same person. Can these two measures be taken as independent? The answer is no, if you think that the scores will be correlated. The treatment may, for example, cause most people's scores to improve, so the relative standing of one person to the next may remain fairly stable. Thus, if a person scores low before treatment, his after-treatment scores is also likely to be low relative to the other scores. We would expect, then, to see a correlation between the 'before' and 'after' scores, so the inference methods that assume independence could not be used.

To handle this situation, it is necessary to define a new variable, D, which stands for the difference between the 'before', or X_1, and 'after', or X_2, scores.

$D = $ after score $-$ before score

$D = X_2 - X_1$

We can then use the methods of the previous chapter to make an inference about μ, the mean of the population of difference scores.

***

Exercise 12–4

A statistics instructor wishes to find out how effective 'A First Program in Mathematics', the programmed textbook mentioned in Chapter 1, is for students taking his course. He has recommended the book to his students, but does not require them to read it. At the beginning of term he administers a mathematics test to all his students, and a month later administers an equivalent test which is not compulsory and which asks if the student has completed the program. Fifteen students replied that they had. Here are their before and after scores.

Student	Before score	After score
A	36	71
B	59	74
C	49	73
D	55	72
E	45	66
F	27	72
G	52	75
H	38	72
I	66	78
J	49	71
K	34	64
L	50	67
M	35	68
N	46	70
O	52	73

Suppose the instructor assumes that those 15 people are reasonably representative of a population of potential students who will take his course and will conscientiously use the programmed textbook. What is the 95% credible interval for the amount of improvement the population would show on the test scores?

Answer

We start by defining a new variable, D, the difference between the test scores. Our interest is in μ, the mean of the *population* of difference scores, and we are particularly concerned to find the 95% credible interval for μ. Assume that prior knowledge about the mean and variance of the population difference scores is vague, so the priors can be taken as uniform over μ and $\log \sigma$, and assume that the population is normal. Now we proceed using the methods for making an inference about the mean of a normal population whose variance is unknown.

Find the difference score, D, for each person. Then find the mean and standard deviation of the difference scores.

Person	$D = X_2 - X_1$	D^2
A	35	1225
B	15	225
C	24	576
D	17	289
E	21	441
F	45	2025
G	23	529
H	34	1156
I	12	144
J	22	484
K	30	900
L	17	289
M	33	1089
N	24	576
O	21	441
	$\Sigma D = \overline{373}$	$\Sigma D^2 = \overline{10389}$

$$M = \frac{\Sigma D}{N} = 24 \cdot 87$$

$$S = \sqrt{\frac{N \Sigma D^2 - (\Sigma D)^2}{N(N-1)}} = \sqrt{79 \cdot 552} = 8 \cdot 92$$

b   The posterior concerning μ is Student-t. Compute its parameters.

$$\mu_t'' = M = 24 \cdot 87$$

$$\sigma_t'' = \frac{S}{\sqrt{N}} = \frac{8 \cdot 92}{\sqrt{15}} = 2 \cdot 30$$

$$df'' = N - 1 = 14$$

c   Look up in Appendix G the value of t for a Student-t distribution with 14 degrees of freedom such that 95% of the curve falls between $\pm t$. That value is 2·145.

d   Find the posterior credible interval.

$$\mu_t'' - t\sigma_t'' \le \mu \le \mu_t'' + t\sigma_t''$$

$$24 \cdot 87 - 2 \cdot 145(2 \cdot 30) \le \mu \le 24 \cdot 87 + 2 \cdot 145(2 \cdot 30)$$

$$19 \cdot 94 \le \mu \le 29 \cdot 80$$

The instructor can safely conclude that students who voluntarily use the book will show a substantial improvement in their scores on the maths test. To find out whether this improvement lasted, and whether it affected performance in the statistics class, he would have to engage in further research.

12.2 Ratios of variances

Interest is sometimes centred not on the means of two populations but on their variances. To what extent is the variability in this group different from the variability in that group? We could talk about the difference between the variances of the two groups, but the mathematics are easier if we enquire about the *ratio* of the variances. Equal variances will yield a ratio of 1, while ratios greater or less than one come about when the variances are unequal. The goal of this section is to present a method for finding the posterior distribution concerning the ratio of two variances, so that we can find a credible interval for the ratio.

We start by defining some terms, all of them familiar. We have two populations whose means are μ_2 and μ_2, and whose variances are σ_1^2 and σ_2^2. A random sample is taken from each population in such a way that the samples are independent. From population 1 we take N_1 observations on each of which a numerical measurement, X_1, is made. Also, N_2 observations are made from population 2, and a numerical measurement, X_2, is taken for each observation. This is the same procedure as in the last section.

Now we calculate the variances of the samples.

$$S_1^2 = \frac{SS_{XX_1}}{N_1 - 1} = \frac{N_1 \Sigma X_1^2 - (\Sigma X_1)^2}{N_1(N_1 - 1)}$$

$$S_2^2 = \frac{SS_{XX_2}}{N_2 - 1} = \frac{N_2 \Sigma X_2^2 - (\Sigma X_2)^2}{N_2(N_2 - 1)}$$

Then we find their ratio, S_1^2/S_2^2. What does this sample ratio tell us about the population ratio? The posterior distribution of σ_1^2/σ_2^2 gives us the answer. If we assume that the populations are normal, and our prior knowledge is vague so that we assess uniform and independent priors over μ_1, μ_2, $\log \sigma_1$, and $\log \sigma_2$, then the posterior is given by a distribution new to our arsenal, the F-distribution. This is a skewed distribution that, like the IG2, extends from 0 to $+\infty$. However, it is not σ_1^2/σ_2^2 that is distributed as F, but rather, for mathematical convenience, a simple transformation of σ_1^2/σ_2^2 If we take the reciprocal of σ_1^2/σ_2^2 and then multiply by S_1^2/S_2^2, the ratio of the sample variances, then we get

$$\frac{S_1^2/S_2^2}{\sigma_1^2/\sigma_2^2}$$

and it is *this* quantity that has a posterior F-distribution. The parameters are

$$df_1'' = N_1 - 1$$
$$df_2'' = N_2 - 1$$

It is important to get the order of the parameters correct, for if you interchange them, you end up with a different F-distribution. We will help to forestall confusion by referring to the F-distribution as the $F(df_1, df_2)$-distribution. As I have just said, $F(df_1, df_2)$ is different from $F(df_2, df_1)$.

A little algebra is necessary to establish the credible interval for σ_1^2/σ_2^2. First, we know that the limits on

$$\frac{S_1^2/S_2^2}{\sigma_1^2/\sigma_2^2}$$

go from $F_{\text{low}}(df_1'', df_2'')$ to $F_{\text{high}}(df_1'', df_2'')$. We can state that algebraically in this familiar form:

$$F_{\text{low}}(df_1'', df_2'') \leq \frac{S_1^2/S_2^2}{\sigma_1^2/\sigma_2^2} \leq F_{\text{high}}(df_1'', df_2'')$$

It will be convenient to express the interval in two equations:

$$F_{\text{low}}(df_1'', df_2'') \leq \frac{S_1^2/S_2^2}{\sigma_1^2/\sigma_2^2}$$

$$F_{\text{high}}(df_1'', df_2'') \geq \frac{S_1^2/S_2^2}{\sigma_1^2/\sigma_2^2}$$

Rearranging terms in both equations gives:

$$\sigma_1^2/\sigma_2^2 \leq \frac{S_1^2/S_2^2}{F_{\text{low}}(df_1'', df_2'')}$$

$$\sigma_1^2/\sigma_2^2 \geq \frac{S_1^2/S_2^2}{F_{\text{high}}(df_1'', df_2'')}$$

Since we now have σ_1^2/σ_2^2 on the left side of both those equations, we can write the credible interval for σ_1^2/σ_2^2:

$$\frac{S_1^2/S_2^2}{F_{high}(df_1'', df_2'')} \leq \frac{\sigma_1^2}{\sigma_2^2} \leq \frac{S_1^2/S_2^2}{F_{low}(df_1'', df_2'')}$$

Do not be alarmed that F_{high} appears in the expression for the lower limit and F_{low} for the higher limit. This is a straightforward consequence of the algebraic steps needed to get the credible interval concerning σ_1^2/σ_2^2 from the credible interval for $(S_1^2/S_2^2)/(\sigma_1^2/\sigma_2^2)$.

If that is not confusing enough, I have to say that only tables for F_{high} exist, so a special procedure is needed to find F_{low} from the F_{high} tables. What you have to do is interchange the degrees of freedom, look up the corresponding value in the table and then take its reciprocal to get F_{low}. In symbols,

$$F_{low}(df_1, df_2) = \frac{1}{F_{high}(df_2, df_1)}$$

Substituting that expression into our equation for the credible interval gives:

$$\frac{S_1^2/S_2^2}{F_{high}(df_1'', df_2'')} \leq \frac{\sigma_1^2}{\sigma_2^2} \leq F_{high}(df_2'', df_1'')(S_1^2/S_2^2)$$

For each credible interval there is a separate table of values for F_{high}, and they are given in Appendix D. After you have chosen the desired table, you enter with df_1'' and df_2'' degrees of freedom, and the tabled value gives $F_{high}(df_1'', df_2'')$. Now interchange the degrees of freedom, enter the table with the switched values, and the value you read off will be $F_{high}(df_2'', df_1'')$.

It all sounds rather confusing, but the application is terribly simple, as will be obvious from this example.

Exercise 12–5

The investigator in Exercise 12–3 wishes to examine the degree to which the population variances of men's and women's scores are different. How might he do this?

Answer

One approach would be to find the posterior credible interval for the ratio of population variances. If he assumes uniform priors over μ_1, μ_2, $\log \sigma_1$, and $\log \sigma_2$, that the priors are independent, and that the populations are normal, he should follow these steps:

a   Let σ_1^2 = variance of population of men's scores, and σ_2^2 = variance of population of women's scores. We wish to find a credible interval for σ_1^2/σ_2^2, the ratio of the variances.

b   Find the variances of the two samples. We did that in step 2 of Exercise 12–3. There we found that

$$S_1^2 = 13 \cdot 905 \quad \text{and} \quad S_2^2 = 23 \cdot 111$$

c   Find the parameters of the posterior F-distribution.

$$df_1'' = N_1 - 1 = 7 - 1 = 6$$
$$df_2'' = N_2 - 1 = 9 - 1 = 8$$

d Look up $F(df_2'' \, df_2'')$, that is to say, $F(6, 8)$, in Appendix D. Let us do it for the 95% credible interval. From the table, $F(6, 8) = 4\cdot65$. Now interchange the degrees of freedom, and enter the table again. You should get $F(8, 6) = 5\cdot60$.

e Compute the 95% credible interval.

$$\frac{S_1^2 S_2^2}{F(df_1'', df_2'')} \le \frac{\sigma_1^2}{\sigma_2^2} \le F(df_2'', df_1'')(S_1^2/S_2^2)$$

$$\frac{13\cdot905/23\cdot111}{4\cdot65} \le \frac{\sigma_1^2}{\sigma_2^2} \le 5\cdot60(13\cdot905/23\cdot111)$$

$$0\cdot129 \le \frac{\sigma_1^2}{\sigma_2^2} \le 3\cdot37$$

Since the interval includes values that are less than 1 as well as greater than 1, these data do not give us any reason to believe that there is much of a difference between the population variances, even though the sample variances are different.

There is one final note. The values of $F(df_1, df_2)$ in the table of Appendix D do not, unfortunately, give the limits of the highest density region. The table gives values of $F_{\text{high}}(df_1, df_2)$ above which falls half the area outside the credible interval. Thus, if you are concerned with a 95% credible interval, then $2\frac{1}{2}\%$ of the area under the curve lies above the tabled value. Tables of limits for the highest density region have not yet been calculated.

12.3 Inferences concerning correlations

We turn now to procedures for making inferences concerning a correlation coefficient. First we look at a method appropriate for the Pearson-r correlation when data consist of numerical measurements, and then we turn to a procedure that is sometimes useful for ranked data.

Procedure for numerical measurements

The experimental situation is that we have randomly selected N elements from the population, and made two numerical measurements, X and Y, on each element. The Pearson correlation coefficient, r, between the measurements is computed, and now that we know the sample correlation, we wish to know what inference is valid about the *population* correlation coefficient, which we will call ρ (Greek lower case rho, not to be confused with Spearman's rho, r_{rho}).

Let us look first at the assumptions that go into the Bayesian procedures for computing the posterior distribution. First, we assume that the population is bivariate normal. This is a distribution with five parameters, each of which has a straightforward interpretation:

μ_X the mean of the population of X-scores;

σ_X the standard deviation of the population of X-scores;

μ_Y the mean of the population of Y-scores;

σ_Y the standard deviation of the population of Y-scores;

ρ the correlation coefficient between the population of X–Y scores.

Two bivariate-normal distributions are shown in Fig. 12–4, one for $\rho = 0.75$, and one for $\rho = 0.9$.

The marginal distributions of the bivariate-normal distribution are each normally distributed themselves. As you might expect the means and standard deviations of the marginals are, for the X-scores, μ_X and σ_X, and for the Y-scores, μ_Y and σ_Y. This fact gives us a means of determining whether the population is bivariate normal. If we think it is reasonable to consider the X and Y scores separately as being each normally distributed, then it is safe to conclude that the distribution of X and Y taken together is bivariate normal. Of course, it is important to remember that we are talking about the degree of *linear* correlation between X and Y. That, too, is an assumption of this method.

$$\sigma_X = \sigma_Y$$
$$\rho = 0.75$$

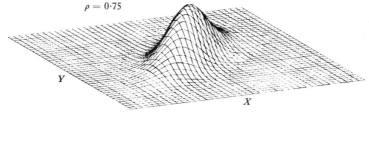

Y X

$$\sigma_X = \sigma_Y$$
$$\rho = 0.9$$

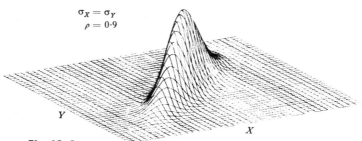

Y X

Fig. 12–4
Two bivariate-normal density functions.
From Schmitt, S.A., *Measuring Uncertainty: An Elementary Introduction to Bayesian Statistics*, Reading, Mass., Addison-Wesley, 1969.

Returning, now, to the remaining assumptions, we take our prior uncertainty to be vague, so that it can be considered uniform over μ_X, μ_Y, $\log \sigma_X$, and $\log \sigma_Y$. Your prior distribution concerning ρ is likely to be vague; as long as you are willing to assign at least a little opinion to all possible values from -1 to $+1$, then the results of this section will apply. We assume that you have observed enough data that your prior opinion about ρ is swamped. As usual, we consider those five prior distributions to be independent of each other.

Now consider the data. We have N pairs of measurements, so we calculate the Pearson-r. Recall the defining and computing formulae:

$$r = \frac{SS_{XY}}{\sqrt{SS_{XX}SS_{YY}}} = \frac{N \sum XY - \sum X \sum Y}{\sqrt{N \sum X^2 - (\sum X)^2}\sqrt{N \sum Y^2 - (\sum Y)^2}}$$

The posterior distribution of ρ is, sadly, highly skewed, and is not in any of the forms we have considered so far. However, Fisher has provided a transformation which changes ρ into a new variable ζ (Greek lower case zeta), and Bayesian analysis shows that the distribution over ζ is approximately normal. The transformation is

$$\zeta = \tfrac{1}{2} \ln \frac{1+\rho}{1-\rho}$$

where 'ln' refers to the natural logarithm, that is, logarithm to the base e.

The posterior distribution concerning ζ is approximately normal (the approximation is better the more data you have), with

$$m'' = \text{the Fisher-} z \text{ transformation of } r$$

$$s'' = \sqrt{\frac{1}{N}}$$

To find the Fisher-z transformation of r you do not need to use the formula given above, for a table has been prepared. It is in Appendix K. You look up r in the left column and read off the Fisher-z in the right column.

Credible intervals are found in the usual way for a normal posterior. The credible interval for ζ is

$$m'' - zs'' \leq \zeta \leq m'' + zs''$$

where z is the standard deviate corresponding to the C per cent credible interval for the normal distribution. (Do not confuse this z with the Fisher-z transformation of r.) This procedure gives you ζ_{low} and ζ_{high}. To get the posterior credible interval concerning r, you simply look up ζ_{low} and ζ_{high} in the z-column of the Fisher-z table, and read off the corresponding values of r to give r_{low} and r_{high}.

As you will see from the following exercise, it is very easy to apply these procedures.

Exercise 12–6

In Fig. 10–6, scatterplots are shown for varying degrees of correlation. Consider the plot for which $r = 0.44$. If we assume that the plot represents a random sample from a population, what inference can be made about the population correlation coefficient? Recall that $N = 40$.

Answers

We really should know the context of the experiment in order to assess the prior distributions, but let us assume they are all independent and uniform over μ_X, μ_Y, $\log \sigma_X$, and $\log \sigma_Y$, and that the prior over ρ is nowhere 0. Also, assume the population is bivariate normal. Now follow these steps.

a   Normally, we would first have to compute the correlation coefficient. But here that has already been done: $r = 0.44$.

b   Find the Fisher-z transformation of r. From Appendix K we find that Fisher-$z = 0.47$.

c   Find the statistics of the posterior concerning ζ.

$$m'' = \text{Fisher-}z \text{ transformation of } r = 0{\cdot}47$$

$$s'' = \sqrt{\frac{1}{N}} = \sqrt{\frac{1}{40}} = 0{\cdot}158$$

d   Compute, say, the 99% credible interval for ζ:

$$m'' - zs'' \leq \zeta \leq m'' + zs''$$

$$0{\cdot}47 - 2{\cdot}58(0{\cdot}158) \leq \zeta \leq 0{\cdot}47 + 2{\cdot}58(0{\cdot}158)$$

$$0{\cdot}062 \leq \zeta \leq 0{\cdot}878$$

e   Convert that interval to one concerning r by working the transformation backwards. Look up $0{\cdot}062$ and $0{\cdot}878$ in the z-column of the Fisher-z table and read off the corresponding values of r. I get $r_{low} = 0{\cdot}06$ and $r_{high} = 0{\cdot}70$. The 99% credible interval concerning r is, then,

$$0{\cdot}06 \leq r \leq 0{\cdot}70$$

Notice how wide the limits are. That comes as a surprise to most people. On the basis of our sample of 40, we are 99% sure that the population correlation is between $0{\cdot}06$ and $0{\cdot}70$.

This exercise shows that you have to collect a fair amount of data before you can be very sure about the value of the population correlation. Thus, there is not much point in presenting inference procedures for small samples.

It is possible, though unlikely, that you will come across a confidence interval for a correlation coefficient in your reading. If you do, it can be interpreted as a Bayesian credible interval that was calculated under the assumptions of this section.

Procedure for ranked data

Unfortunately, Bayesian methods have not been worked out for Spearman's-rho correlation, so there is no way we can make an inference about population values. For the time being, Bayesians will have to be content to treat Spearman's-rho as a descriptive statistic.

However, there is a procedure that can be followed for ranked data. It can be applied whenever you think that the ranks could reasonably represent an underlying variable which is normally distributed. When this is the case, you transform the ranks into normal scores, compute the Pearson-r between the pairs of scores and use the inference method just discussed.

Transforming ranks to normal scores is done by using the table in Appendix M. The heading of each column gives the number, N, of observations, while the scores themselves are listed in the column. Notice that the scores refer to the standardized normal distribution, so that only positive values are tabled. That takes care of half the ranks; the other half receive the same scores only with negative signs attached. Thus, the top rank receives the biggest score in the column, while the bottom rank is also assigned the biggest score but with a minus sign in front. The exercise should make this clear.

Exercise 12–7

In a study of creativity, two artists rank-order nine paintings according to the degree of originality shown in each painting. Here are their rankings:

Painting	Judge 1	Judge 2
A	8	6
B	2	1
C	1	4
D	6	5
E	7	9
F	3	8
G	4	2
H	9	7
I	5	3

If those nine paintings can be considered a random sampling from some specified population, what inference can be made about the correlation between the judges' rankings for the whole population?

Answer

This time the judges' rankings are a sample of the rankings they might give if they were presented with the whole population of paintings. We might enquire about the 99 % credible interval concerning the population correlation coefficient. To make an inference we first convert the ranks to normal scores. It seems reasonable to represent the ranks with scores that are normally distributed if we assume that 'originality', however defined, is normally distributed: most people in the specified population show average originality in their paintings, a few are not at all original, and a few are very original.

Ranks are easily transformed to scores by referring to Appendix M. Find the column headed with 9, the sample size. Read off the positive scores corresponding to ranks 1–4, assign the middle or 5th rank a score of 0, and then give ranks 6–10 scores that are negative and the mirror image of the first four scores.

Rank	Score
1	1·485
2	0·932
3	0·572
4	0·275
5	0·000
6	−0·275
7	−0·572
8	−0·932
9	−1·485

Now assign those scores to the judges' rankings:

Painting	Judge 1	Judge 2
A	− 0·932	− 0·275
B	0·932	1·485
C	1·485	0·275
D	− 0·275	0
E	− 0·572	− 1·485
F	0·572	− 0·932
G	0·275	0·932
H	− 1·485	− 0·572
I	0	0·572

Next, compute the Pearson-r between the two sets of normal scores (see the simplified formula, below.) My calculations give $r = 0.50$. Now we can use the procedure in the previous section to make an inference about ρ. First, the posterior distribution concerning ζ is approximately normal with statistics

$$m'' = \text{Fisher-}z \text{ transformation of } 0.50 = 0.55$$

$$s'' = \sqrt{\frac{1}{N}} = \sqrt{\frac{1}{9}} = \frac{1}{3} = 0.333$$

(For small N, the normal approximation is not at all bad when r is around 0.5.) That gives a 99% credible interval for ζ of

$$0.55 - 2.58(0.333) \leq \zeta \leq 0.55 + 2.58(0.333)$$
$$-0.31 \leq \zeta \leq 1.41$$

Transforming back to correlations gives

$$-0.31 \leq \rho \leq 0.89$$

That is quite a wide interval, but with only nine pairs of observations you cannot expect a narrow one.

It is very easy to calculate the Pearson-r for this case because of the symmetry of normal scores. You can see that the sum of the normal scores is, necessarily, zero; that is, $\sum X = \sum Y = 0$. In addition, since the X-scores are the same as the Y-scores, $\sum X^2 = \sum Y^2$. With a little algebra, you can verify that these facts about the normal scores simplify the expression for r to this:

$$r = \frac{\sum XY}{\sum X^2}$$

You will find the value of $\sum X^2$ at the bottom of each column in the table of Appendix M, so that leaves you with having to calculate only the sum of the cross-products, $\sum XY$. For the exercise above, the sum of the cross-products of the normal scores is

$$\sum XY = 3.471$$

From the table,

$$\sum X^2 = 6.953$$

and so the Pearson correlation coefficient is

$$r = \frac{3.471}{6.953} = 0.50$$

Returning now to the inferential procedure of this section, we are left with the problem of interpreting the result. Normally, the Pearson-r is interpreted as reflecting the degree of linear relationship between X and Y, but in this case, where X and Y are scores *based* on ranks, we cannot talk about a linear relationship between ranks. To be on the safe side, we should say only that a relationship between the normal scores reflects *monotonicity* in the relationship between the underlying properties. By a *monotone increasing* relationship we mean no more than that increases in one variable are always associated with increases in the other variable. A *monotone decreasing* relationship means that increases in one variable always go with decreases in the other. A linear relationship is monotone; so is an exponential or power relationship. But a U-shaped function is not, for as X increases, Y first decreases then increases. You cannot have both in a monotone relationship.

The other problem of interpretation lies in the justification for representing ranks by normal scores. Is the underlying property, measured only crudely by the ranks, really normally distributed? Only rarely will theory give a clear answer, so justification must be based on a combination of past experience, experimental evidence, and hunch.

In sum, caution is advised in making very much of the posterior credible interval calculated by the methods of this section. The posterior credible interval should be interpreted as giving a rough idea of the possible tendency toward monotonicity between the underlying properties and of the direction of the monotone relationship. If the interval contains only moderate to high positive values, we can be pretty sure that the relationship is monotone increasing while moderate to high negative values indicate a monotone decreasing relationship. If small values and zero are found in the interval, then either there is no relationship or it is not monotone. Even if there is a relationship, you will need a fair amount of data for the posterior credible interval to show that fact.

12.4 Inferences concerning linear regression

Next we consider how to make inferences that involve the linear regression equation. Remember that the equation for predicting Y from X is

$$\tilde{Y} = A_{Y|X} + B_{Y|X} X$$

where $\tilde{Y}$ is the predicted value of Y, and X is the predictor variable. The regression coefficients, $A_{Y|X}$ and $B_{Y|X}$, determine the exact location of a straight line through the data which minimizes the squared deviations between predicted and actual values of Y.

Inferences about the regression coefficients and the standard error of estimate

The regression coefficients are calculated from data, and insofar as the data are a representative sample from a population, one might wish to make inferences about the population values of the regression coefficients. We can imagine that there must be a regression line for predicting Y from X applicable to the population itself, and that errors in the predictions made from this line are indexed by the population standard error of estimate. Let us designate the population regression coefficients as $\alpha_{Y|X}$ and $\beta_{Y|X}$, following our convention of letting lower case Greek letters stand for uncertain quantities. (Incidentally, the regression coefficient $\beta_{Y|X}$ is often called a 'beta-weight'; it has no relationship to the Beta-distribution.) And, let us use $\sigma_{Y|X}$ to refer to the population standard error of estimate for $\tilde{Y}$. In this section methods are given for making inferences about $\alpha_{Y|X}$, $\beta_{Y|X}$, and $\sigma_{Y|X}$.

Sometimes you will wish to know not only what value of Y is predicted from a specific value of X, but also what your posterior uncertainty is about that prediction. We shall see in this section how to develop a posterior credible interval for $\tilde{Y}$, given that you know a particular value of X. And we shall also consider the posterior credible interval for the true value of Y, given some value of X.

The experimental situation might be either of these:

a   The experimenter controls the values of X and measures obtained values of Y. For example, an experimenter studying the effects of group size on riskiness of group behaviour randomly assigns 100 subjects to groups of different size. He creates four groups of size 3, four of size 4, four of size 5, four of size 6, and four of size 7.

No. of groups	4	4	4	4	4	
No. of subjects in the group	3	4	5	6	7	
Total no. of subjects	12	16	20	24	28	100

He presents each group with problems involving risky choices, and measures the level of risk in the solutions given by the group. Thus, each of the 20 groups has associated with it two numerical measurements:

> X: number of subjects in group

> Y: level of risk

Notice that the population consists not of people but of varying sized groups, so $N = 20$. Random assignment of subjects to groups helps to ensure that the groups are a random sample from the population of groups. By creating more than one group of a fixed size, any biases introduced into the groups by chance will tend to cancel each other out.

b   The experimenter samples from the population at random, and takes two numerical measurements, X and Y, on each element of the sample. An example: the experimenter administers a short questionnaire that measures a person's anxiety about testing situations to 100 randomly selected students in a university. He also notes each student's average grade in the end of year examinations. Thus, there are two measurements for each of the 100 students:

> X: score on test-anxiety questionnaire

> Y: average examination grade

In both of these experimental situations the experimenter wishes to make inferences about the regression coefficients of the linear equation for predicting Y from X. Once he has the regression equation, he may wish to make inferences about the uncertainty in any particular prediction.

Now consider the data. We calculate these statistics of the sample:

a $M_X = \dfrac{\sum X}{N}$ (mean of X)

b $M_Y = \dfrac{\sum Y}{N}$ (mean of Y)

c $\quad SS_{XX} = \sum (X - M_X)^2 = \dfrac{N \sum X^2 - (\sum X)^2}{N}$

d $\quad SS_{YY} = \sum (Y - M_Y)^2 = \dfrac{N \sum Y^2 - (\sum Y)^2}{N}$

e $\quad SS_{XY} = \sum (X - M_X)(Y - M_Y) = \dfrac{N \sum XY - \sum X \sum Y}{N}$

f $\quad SS_{\tilde{Y}\text{-error}} = \sum (Y - \tilde{Y})^2 = \dfrac{(SS_{YY})(SS_{\bar{X}X}) - (SS_{XY})^2}{SS_{XX}}$

g $\quad B_{Y|X} = \dfrac{SS_{XY}}{SS_{XX}}$ (slope of regression line)

h $\quad A_{Y|X} = M_Y - B_{Y|X} M_X$ (Y-intercept of regression line)

i $\quad S_{Y|X} = \sqrt{\dfrac{SS_{\tilde{Y}\text{-error}}}{N-1}}$ (standard error of estimate)

You might also like to calculate the Pearson correlation coefficient.

j $\quad r = \dfrac{SS_{XY}}{\sqrt{SS_{XX} SS_{YY}}}$ (correlation coefficient)

Next, we look at the assumptions. First, we assume that the population distribution of Y conditional on X is normal, and that this is true for any value of X. Second, we assume that the standard deviations of these conditional distributions are all equal to one another, that is, $\sigma_{Y|X}$ is the same for all values of X, a condition referred to as homoscedasticity. I have tried to show the conditional distribution of Y at a few selected values of X in Fig. 12–5. The distributions are all normal, and they all have equal standard deviations.

As to the prior distributions, we assume they are uniform over $\alpha_{Y|X}$, $\beta_{Y|X}$, and log $\sigma_{Y|X}$, and that the three distributions are independent of one another.

With these provisos in mind, we turn to the posterior distributions that result from applying Bayes' Theorem:

a $\quad$ The posterior distribution of $\alpha_{Y|X}$ is Student-t with parameters

$\mu_t'' = A_{Y|X}$

$\sigma_t'' = \sqrt{\left(\dfrac{SS_{\tilde{Y}\text{-error}}}{N-2}\right)\left(\dfrac{\sum X^2}{N(SS_{XX})}\right)}$

$df'' = N - 2$

b $\quad$ The posterior distribution of $\beta_{Y|X}$ is Student-t with parameters

$\mu_t'' = B_{Y|X}$

$\sigma_t'' = \sqrt{\left(\dfrac{SS_{\tilde{Y}\text{-error}}}{N-2}\right)\left(\dfrac{1}{SS_{XX}}\right)}$

$df'' = N - 2$

c   The posterior distribution of $\sigma_{Y|X}$ is Inverted Gamma-2 with

mode$'' = S_{Y|X}$

$df'' = N - 2$

For $\alpha_{Y|X}$ and $\beta_{Y|X}$ we form credible intervals in the usual way for the Student-t distribution:

$$\mu_t'' - t\sigma_t'' \leq \left\{ \begin{array}{c} \alpha_{Y|X} \\ \text{or} \\ \beta_{Y|X} \end{array} \right\} \leq \mu_t'' + t\sigma_t''$$

These credible intervals agree exactly with the traditionalists' confidence intervals.

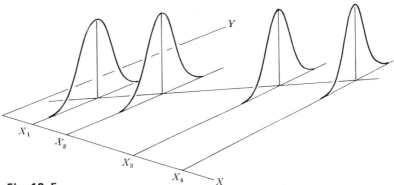

Fig. 12–5

Distribution of Y conditional on X, for a few selected values of X

For $\sigma_{Y|X}$, we follow the usual procedure for computing credible intervals for the IG2 distribution:

$$\text{IG2}_{\text{low}} \times \text{mode}'' \leq \sigma_{Y|X} \leq \text{IG2}_{\text{high}} \times \text{mode}''$$

This credible interval agrees approximately with the traditional confidence interval. Lack of precise agreement was discussed in the previous chapter.

Exercise 12–8

From my statistics class of first year students, I randomly selected three students from among the 18 year olds, three from the 19 year olds, three from the 20 year olds and three from the 21 year olds. A special shortened version of the Wilson and Patterson (1968) conservatism questionnaire was administered to these twelve students. Here are their scores:

Age	Score
18	12, 3, 13
19	2, 10, 8
20	12, 0, 7
21	2, 6, 3

The higher the score, the greater the conservatism. Find the posterior 95% credible interval for the parameters of the population linear regression line for predicting conservatism score from age and for the population standard error of estimate.

Answers

Before we rush to calculate the coefficients of the regression equation, we should check the assumptions that must be met if we are to make meaningful inferences about the population regression coefficients.

First, is the population distribution of Y conditional on X normal for all X? As applied to this problem, we ask if the distribution of conservatism scores *within* each age grouping is roughly normal. I suspect that the population distribution is slightly skewed to the right because my students, who are studying social sciences, are a fairly non-conservative group, so tend to have low scores, with a few high ones contributing to the skew. But normality is not seriously violated, so this is a workable assumption.

Second, does homoscedasticity hold? In simple terms, is the population standard deviation within an age group the same for all groups? Well, by one line of reasoning the standard deviation would seem to me to be smaller for the older ages, but then another argument occurred to me that gives the opposite result. Neither argument seems compelling, and I am left believing that homoscedasticity is at least tenable.

My prior opinions are very vague, so uniform and independent priors concerning $\alpha_{Y|X}$, $\beta_{Y|X}$, and $\sigma_{Y|X}$ are acceptable.

Now we turn to the data, making the necessary calculations.

X	Y	X^2	Y^2	XY
18	12	324	144	216
18	3	324	9	54
18	13	324	169	234
19	2	361	4	38
19	10	361	100	190
19	8	361	64	152
20	12	400	144	240
20	0	400	0	0
20	7	400	49	140
21	2	441	4	42
21	6	441	36	126
21	3	441	9	63

$$\Sigma X = 234 \quad \Sigma Y = 78 \quad \Sigma X^2 = 4578 \quad \Sigma Y^2 = 732 \quad \Sigma XY = 1495$$

a $\quad M_X = \dfrac{\Sigma X}{N} = \dfrac{234}{12} = 19.5$

b $\quad M_Y = \dfrac{\Sigma Y}{N} = \dfrac{78}{12} = 6.5$

c $\quad SS_{XX} = \dfrac{N \Sigma X^2 - (\Sigma X)^2}{N} = \dfrac{12(4578) - (234)^2}{12} = \dfrac{180}{12} = 15$

d $\quad SS_{YY} = \dfrac{N \Sigma Y^2 - (\Sigma Y)^2}{N} = \dfrac{12(732) - (78)^2}{12} = \dfrac{2700}{12} = 225$

e $\qquad SS_{XY} = \dfrac{N \sum XY - \sum X \sum Y}{N} = \dfrac{12(1495) - (234)(78)}{12}$

$\qquad\qquad = -\dfrac{312}{12} = -26$

f $\qquad SS_{\hat{Y}\text{-error}} = \dfrac{SS_{YY} SS_{XX} - SS_{XY}}{SS_{XX}} = \dfrac{(225)(15) - (-26)^2}{15}$

$\qquad\qquad = \dfrac{2699}{15} = 179 \cdot 93$

g $\qquad B_{Y|X} = \dfrac{SS_{XY}}{SS_{XX}} = \dfrac{-26}{15} = -1 \cdot 73$

Note that the slope is negative. *For this sample,* older first year students are less conservative.

h $\qquad A_{Y|X} = M_Y - B_{Y|X} M_X = 6 \cdot 5 - (-1 \cdot 73)(19 \cdot 5)$

$\qquad\qquad = 6 \cdot 5 + 33 \cdot 74 = 40 \cdot 24$

i $\qquad S_{Y|X} = \sqrt{\dfrac{SS_{\hat{Y}\text{-error}}}{N - 1}} = \sqrt{\dfrac{179 \cdot 93}{12 - 1}} = \sqrt{16 \cdot 357} = 4 \cdot 04$

j $\qquad$ And, just for information, here is the correlation coefficient.

$\qquad r = \dfrac{SS_{XY}}{\sqrt{SS_{XX} SS_{YY}}} = \dfrac{-26}{\sqrt{(15)(225)}} = \dfrac{-26}{\sqrt{3375}} = -0 \cdot 45$

This is a modest, inverse relationship.

Next, the posterior distributions. For $a_{Y|X}$, it is Student-t with these parameters:

$\qquad \mu_t'' = A_{Y|X} = 40 \cdot 24$

$\qquad \sigma_t'' = \sqrt{\left(\dfrac{SS_{\hat{Y}\text{-error}}}{N - 2} \right)\left(\dfrac{\sum X^2}{N(SS_{XX})} \right)} = \sqrt{\left(\dfrac{179 \cdot 93}{12 - 2} \right)\left(\dfrac{4578}{12(15)} \right)}$

$\qquad\qquad = \sqrt{457 \cdot 62} = 21 \cdot 4$

$\qquad df'' = N - 2 = 12 - 2 = 10$

And for $\beta_{X|Y}$, the posterior is also Student-t:

$\qquad \mu_t'' = B_{Y|X} = -1 \cdot 73$

$\qquad \sigma_t'' = \sqrt{\left(\dfrac{SS_{\hat{Y}\text{-error}}}{N - 2} \right)\left(\dfrac{1}{SS_{XX}} \right)} = \sqrt{\left(\dfrac{179 \cdot 93}{12 - 2} \right)\left(\dfrac{1}{15} \right)}$

$\qquad\qquad = \sqrt{1 \cdot 20} = 1 \cdot 10$

$\qquad df'' = N - 2 = 12 - 2 = 10$

Finally, for the standard error of estimate, $\sigma_{Y|X}$, the posterior is IG2 with

$\qquad \text{mode}'' = S_{Y|X} = 4 \cdot 04$

$\qquad df'' = N - 2 = 12 - 2 = 10$

From these posterior distributions we can compute the 95% credible intervals. Both Student-t posteriors have 10 degrees of freedom; from the Student-t table we read off $t = 2 \cdot 228$ for the 95% credible interval. The credible interval for $a_{Y|X}$ is:

$\qquad 40 \cdot 24 - 2 \cdot 228(21 \cdot 4) \le a_{Y|X} \le 40 \cdot 24 + 2 \cdot 228(21 \cdot 4)$

$\qquad\qquad -7 \cdot 44 \le a_{Y|X} \le 87 \cdot 92$

The credible interval for $\beta_{Y|X}$ is:

$$-1\cdot73 - 2\cdot228(1\cdot09) \le \beta_{Y|X} \le -1\cdot73 + 2\cdot228(1\cdot09)$$
$$-4\cdot16 \le \beta_{Y|X} \le 0\cdot70$$

And the credible interval for $\sigma_{Y|X}$ is:

$$0\cdot674(4\cdot04) \le \sigma_{Y|X} \le 1\cdot708(4\cdot04)$$
$$2\cdot72 \le \sigma_{Y|X} \le 6\cdot9$$

The values of $IG2_{low}$ and $IG2_{high}$, $0\cdot674$ and $1\cdot708$, were obtained from the IG2 table for 10 degrees of freedom under the 95 column.

Having gone through the mechanics of that exercise, we should not overlook the meaning of the results. In the first place, it does not make much sense to find the limits for $\alpha_{Y|X}$, because that coefficient is not really very interesting. It gives us the value of Y when $X = 0$, and who wants to know the conservatism score for a new-born babe who has just joined the university's first-year class of social science students? We must remember that the linear regression equation was determined for a range of X-values that extends from only 18 to 21. To predict outside that range is risky business, for the regression line may be linear *only* over the range investigated.

In the second place, note that the posterior credible interval for $\alpha_{Y|X}$ is very large. As we will see in the next section, this is because we are finding an interval that corresponds to a value of X lying a fair distance outside the range covered in the problem. In general, the further the value of X from M_X, the wider will be the credible interval for $\tilde{Y}$.

Third, notice that the slope of the regression line for the *sample* is negative; the older students are less conservative. Now this finding contrasts with the results obtained by Wilson and Patterson in their original work. They found that conservatism *increases* with age. It increases slowly between 15 and 25, then more rapidly from 25 to 55, then slows down again. While a linear function will not do over the whole range, it is a reasonable approximation over the 18–21 range. Over that range, Wilson and Patterson show a slight positive slope to the curve. If you will note the posterior credible interval for the *population* slope, you will see that it includes some positive values. Thus, while the sample result disagrees with the original investigation, our *inference* does not. We have to give some posterior opinion to the possibility that the slope is really positive, in agreement with the results of Wilson and Patterson.

Finally note that the non-Bayesian statistician would have calculated confidence intervals that are exactly the same as our credible intervals for $\alpha_{Y|X}$ and $\beta_{Y|X}$, and approximately the same as our interval for $\sigma_{Y|X}$.

Posterior credible intervals for actual and predicted Y

When an investigator is interested in predicting Y for a given value of X, he of course recognizes that his prediction contains error to the extent that the sample regression line does not coincide with the population regression line. If the sample and population regression coefficients are not equal, the prediction is in error. One way of showing the effect of this error on the prediction is to establish a posterior credible interval for the predicted value of Y. Let us designate the value of X we are interested in X_0; the value of Y we would predict from knowing X_0 we will call $\tilde{Y}_0$. We get $\tilde{Y}_0$ by substituting X_0 in the sample regression equation.

Under the assumptions and priors of the previous section, the posterior distribution for $\tilde{Y}_0$ is Student-t with these parameters:

$$\mu_t'' = \tilde{Y}_0 = A_{Y|X} + \beta_{Y|X} X_0$$

$$\sigma_t'' = \sqrt{\frac{SS_{\tilde{Y}\text{-error}}}{N-2} \left[\frac{1}{N} + \frac{(X_0 - M_X)^2}{SS_{XX}}\right]}$$

$$df'' = N - 2$$

The posterior credible interval is formed in the usual way for Student-t distributions.

Be sure to notice the extreme right term in the posterior standard deviation. It is $(X_0 - M_X)^2$. If that term is large, then σ_t'' will be large, and so the credible interval will be wide. And $(X_0 - M_X)^2$ will be larger the further X_0 is from M_X. In other words, predictions made for values of X that are far from the mean of X will result in a wide range of uncertainty in the posterior credible interval for the predicted value of Y. That is one reason why economists are wary of making predictions very far into the future, and why social scientists in general should be cautious in making predictions outside the range of their data. As I have said, another reason is that a linear relationship may not hold for values of X not covered by the experiment.

The posterior distribution concerning $\alpha_{Y|X}$ is a special case of this procedure in which $X_0 = 0$. Two influences were at work to make the posterior credible interval for $\alpha_{Y|X}$ so large: the distance of $X_0 = 0$ from the mean of X, and the small sample. It is generally true that for small samples the interval will be very wide.

It is also possible to establish a posterior credible interval for the true value of Y, instead of the predicted value. In this case our uncertainty stems not only from lack of knowledge concerning the precise location of the population regression line, but also from the scatter of the data around the line. Thus, error in predicting Y along with the uncertainty embodied in the standard error of estimate contribute to our uncertainty concerning the precise value of Y for a given value of X.

As before, let the value of X be designated X_0, and the corresponding true value of Y be Y_0. Under the assumptions and priors of the previous section, the posterior distribution for Y_0 is Student-t with these parameters:

$$\mu_t'' = \tilde{Y}_0 = A_{Y|X} + \beta_{Y|X} X_0$$

$$\sigma_t'' = \sqrt{\frac{SS_{\tilde{Y}\text{-error}}}{N-2} \left[1 + \frac{1}{N} + \frac{(X_0 - M_X)^2}{SS_{XX}}\right]}$$

$$df'' = N - 2$$

The posterior credible is, as usual,

$$\mu_t'' - t\sigma_t'' \leq Y_0 \leq \mu_t'' + t\sigma_t''$$

This credible interval is wider than the one for $\tilde{Y}_0$, as you can verify by comparing the posterior sigmas. This one contains an extra term, 1, in the multiplier of $SS_{\tilde{Y}\text{-error}}/(N-2)$.

Exercise 12–9

Find the posterior 95% credible intervals concerning $\tilde{Y}_0$ and Y_0 for $X_0 = 22$, with reference to Exercise 12–8.

Answers

First, for predicted Y, the parameters of the posterior Student-t are:

$$\mu''_t = \tilde{Y}_0 = A_{Y|X} + B_{Y|X} X_0 = 40.24 + (-1.73)(22)$$
$$= 40.24 - 38.06 = 2.18$$

$$\sigma''_t = \sqrt{\frac{179.93}{12-2}\left[\frac{1}{12} + \frac{(22-19.5)^2}{15}\right]}$$
$$= \sqrt{(17.993)(0.5)} = \sqrt{8.996} = 3.00$$

$$df'' = 12 - 2 = 10$$

The posterior 95% credible interval for $\tilde{Y}_0$ is:

$$2.18 - 2.228(3.00) \le \tilde{Y}_0 \le 2.18 + 2.228(3.00)$$
$$-4.50 \le \tilde{Y}_0 \le 8.864$$

Now consider the actual Y. The parameters of the posterior Student-t are:

$$\mu''_t = \tilde{Y}_0 = 2.18, \text{ as above.}$$

$$\sigma''_t = \sqrt{\frac{179.93}{12-2}\left[1 + \frac{1}{12} + \frac{(22-19.5)^2}{15}\right]}$$
$$= \sqrt{(17.993)(1.5)} = \sqrt{26.990} = 5.2$$

$$df'' = 12 - 2 = 10$$

So, the posterior 95% credible interval for Y_0 is:

$$2.18 - 2.228(5.2) \le Y_0 \le 2.18 + 2.228(5.2)$$
$$-9.41 \le Y_0 \le 13.77$$

Of course, in both cases we get negative values in the interval because we assumed that the population of scores was normal, which includes negative scores, and because the sample size is so small that the posterior distribution is quite spread out. However, for large samples the posterior standard deviation would be sufficiently small to preclude any appreciable amount of posterior opinion on negative values. The methods of this section are particularly sensitive to the assumptions of normal distributions for given values of X, and of equal variances (homoscedasticity). A non-Bayesian statistician would have obtained confidence intervals for $\tilde{Y}_0$ and Y_0 in exact agreement with ours.

12.5 Inferences about differences between proportions

When a scientist wishes to make an inference about the difference between two population proportions, say π_1 and π_2, he has several options open to him, depending on how large his samples are.

If the samples are large, then his posterior distributions, which are in fact Betas, can be approximated by normal distributions, as we saw in Chapter 6. Then the problem of finding a posterior credible interval for $\pi_1 - \pi_2$

becomes one of finding the difference between two normal distributions, a procedure that was covered at the beginning of this chapter. All you have to do to apply those procedures is find the parameters of the two posterior Betas, then calculate the means and standard deviations from the parameters using the formulae on page 127 of Chapter 6, and apply the methods at the beginning of this chapter by assuming the Betas to be approximately normal.

With modest amounts of data it is convenient to make inferences about the difference of the logarithms of odds. The odds corresponding to a proportion π are given by $\Omega = \pi/(1-\pi)$. Let the log of the odds be designated $L\Omega$. Thus,

$$L\Omega_1 = \log \frac{\pi_1}{1-\pi_1} \quad \text{and} \quad L\Omega_2 = \log \frac{\pi_2}{1-\pi_2}$$

Inferences will be made about $L\Omega_1 - L\Omega_2$:

$$L\Omega_1 - L\Omega_2 = \log \frac{\pi_1}{1-\pi_1} - \log \frac{\pi_2}{1-\pi_2}$$

which is the same thing as

$$L\Omega_1 - L\Omega_2 = \log \left(\frac{\pi_1}{1-\pi_1} \right) \Big/ \left(\frac{\pi_2}{1-\pi_2} \right) = \log \frac{\pi_1(1-\pi_2)}{\pi_2(1-\pi_1)}$$

The reason for changing to log odds is that the posterior concerning $L\Omega$ is approximately normal, and the approximation is much better for modest N than assuming that the posterior concerning π is normal.

Applying the procedures for the difference between two normal distributions gives a posterior distribution concerning $L\Omega_1 - L\Omega_2$ as approximately normal with

$$m'' = \log \frac{\bar{s}_1}{\bar{f}_1} - \log \frac{\bar{s}_2}{\bar{f}_2} = \log \frac{\bar{s}_1 \bar{f}_2}{\bar{s}_2 \bar{f}_1}$$

$$s'' = \sqrt{\frac{1}{\bar{s}_1} + \frac{1}{\bar{f}_1} + \frac{1}{\bar{s}_2} + \frac{1}{\bar{f}_2}}$$

where $\bar{s}_1$ and $\bar{f}_1$ are the numbers of success and failures in the sample from the first population, and $\bar{s}_2$ and $\bar{f}_2$ are the successes and failures from population 2. The credible interval is formed in the usual way for normal distributions. Once you have the limits you can take the antilogarithms to get the ratio of odds themselves, but unfortunately that is as far as you can go. There just is not enough information in the ratio of odds to recover the odds making up the ratio, let alone recover the difference in proportions. That is one difficulty with this approach, though for many applications the ratio of odds will provide sufficient information.

Another procedure is to use the BETADIF computer program, one of several programs written for Bayesian analysis by Robert Schlaifer (1971). The program can be implemented in conversational language, so that no familiarity with computers or computer programming is necessary. The program asks you for parameters B and C for each distribution. (Schlaifer's B is simply our posterior parameter p'', while his C is our $p''+q''$.) The program then figures out for you the posterior distribution of the difference.

A fourth method is to use the chi-squared approximation introduced in Chapter 14. That is the most popular approach.

12.6 Summary

This chapter has covered several methods for making inferences concerning two quantities. A general method for making inferences concerning the difference between two uncertain quantities was presented first. In this case, when opinion concerning one uncertain quantity is normal with mean m_1 and variance s_1^2, and opinion about another, independent uncertain quantity is also normal with mean m_2 and variance s_2^2, then opinion about the difference between the uncertain quantities is normal with mean $m_1 - m_2$ and variance $s_1^2 + s_2^2$. The chapter ended with an application of this method: finding the posterior distribution of the difference between two population proportions when sample sizes are large and the samples are independent. When the samples are not large, it is necessary to make inferences about the ratio of the logarithms of the odds corresponding to the proportions, or to use the BETADIF computer program prepared by Schlaifer (1971) or to use the Chi-squared approximation presented in Chapter 14.

The other methods of making inferences are summarized as follows:

Inferences concerning the difference between two population means (variances assumed equal, though unknown)

a   *Want to infer:* $\delta = \mu_1 - \mu_2$, the difference between the means of two normal populations;

b   *Experiment:* A random sample from each of the two populations; the samples independent. N_1 observations from population 1, on each of which a numerical measurement, X_1, is made; N_2 observations from population 2, on each of which a numerical measurement, Y_2, is made;

c   *Assumptions:* **i** $\sigma_1 = \sigma_2 = \sigma$, that is, the standard deviations of the populations are equal, though unknown   **ii** The populations are each normal.

d   *Data:* Calculate . . .

$$M_1 = \frac{\sum X_1}{N_1} \qquad SS_{XX_1} = \sum (X_1 - M_1)^2 = \frac{N_1 \sum X_1^2 - (\sum X_1)^2}{N_1}$$

$$M_2 = \frac{\sum X_2}{N_2} \qquad SS_{XX_2} = \sum (X_2 - M_2)^2 = \frac{N_2 \sum X_2^2 - (\sum X_2)^2}{N_2}$$

e   *Prior distributions:* **i** Uniform over μ_1, μ_2, $\log \sigma$.   **ii** All three prior distributions are independent of one another.

f   *Posterior distribution concerning δ:* Student-t with parameters

$$\mu_t'' = M_1 - M_2$$

$$\sigma_t'' = \sqrt{\left(\frac{SS_{XX_1} + SS_{XX_2}}{N_1 + N_2 - 2}\right)\left(\frac{N_1 + N_2}{N_1 N_2}\right)}$$

$$df'' = N_1 + N_2 - 2$$

g   *C per cent credible interval:*

$$\mu_t'' - t\sigma_t'' \le \delta \le \mu_t'' + t\sigma_t''$$

where t is the standard deviate corresponding to the C per cent credible interval for the Student-t distribution. t is found by entering the Student-t table with $df = N_1 + N_2 - 2$ and with C.

Inferences concerning the difference between two population means (variances unknown and not assumed equal)

a   *Want to infer:* $\delta = \mu_1 - \mu_2$, the difference between the means of two normal populations;

b   *Experiment:* A random sample from each of the two populations; the samples independent. N_1 observations from population 1, on each of which a numerical measurement, X_1, is made; N_2 observations from population 2, on each of which a numerical measurement, X_2, is made;

c   *Assumptions:* The populations are each normal. (Variances are unknown and may be different.)

d   *Data:* Calculate . . .

$$M_1 = \frac{\sum X_1}{N_1} \qquad S_1^2 = \frac{N_1 \sum X_1^2 - (\sum X_1)^2}{N_1(N_1 - 1)}$$

$$M_2 = \frac{\sum X_2}{N_2} \qquad S_2^2 = \frac{N_2 \sum X_2^2 - (\sum X_2)^2}{N_2(N_2 - 1)}$$

e   *Prior distributions:* **i** Uniform over μ_1, μ_2, $\log \sigma_1$, $\log \sigma_2$.   **ii** All four prior distributions are independent of one another.

f   *Posterior distribution concerning δ:* Behrens with parameters

$$\mu_d'' = M_1 - M_2$$

$$\sigma_d'' = \sqrt{\frac{S_1^2}{N_1} + \frac{S_2^2}{N_2}}$$

$$df_1'' = N_1 - 1$$

$$df_2'' = N_2 - 1$$

$$\omega'', \quad \text{where } \tan \omega'' = \sqrt{\frac{S_2^2/N_2}{S_1^2/N_1}}$$

g   *C per cent credible interval:*

$$\mu_d'' - d\sigma_d'' \le \delta \le \mu_d'' + d\sigma_d''$$

where d is the standard deviate corresponding to the C per cent credible interval for the Behrens distribution. d is found by entering the Behrens table with $df_1 = N_1 - 1$, $df_2 = N_2 - 1$, ω, and with C. To avoid interpolation, round df_1 and df_2 *down* to 6, 8, 12, or 24, whichever is nearest; then, if ω is not equal to either 0°, 15°, 30°, 45°, 60°, 75°, or 90°, round it *either* up or down to one of these values, whichever rounding gives the *larger* tabled value of d.

Inferences concerning the ratio of two variances

a   *Want to infer:* σ_1^2/σ_2^2, the ratio of variances of two normal populations;

b   *Experiment:* A random sample from each of the two populations; the samples independent. N_1 observations from population 1, on each of which a numerical measurement, X_1, is made; N_2 observations from population 2, on each of which a numerical measurement, X_2, is made;

c   *Assumptions:* Populations are each normal;

d   *Data:* Calculate . . .

$$S_1^2 = \frac{SS_{XX_1}}{N_1 - 1} = \frac{N_1 \sum X_1^2 - (\sum X_1)^2}{N_1(N_1 - 1)}$$

$$S_2^2 = \frac{SS_{XX_2}}{N_2 - 1} = \frac{N_2 \sum X_2^2 - (\sum X_2)^2}{N_2(N_2 - 1)}$$

e   *Prior distributions:* **i** Uniform over μ_1, μ_2, $\log \sigma_1$, $\log \sigma_2$. **ii** All four prior distributions are independent of one another.

f   *Posterior distribution regarding* $(S_1^2/S_2^2)/(\sigma_1^2/\sigma_2^2)$: F with parameters

$df_1'' = N_1 - 1$

$df_2'' = N_2 - 1$

g   *C per cent credible interval:*

$$\frac{S_1^2/S_2^2}{F(df_1'', df_2'')} \leq \frac{\sigma_1^2}{\sigma_2^2} \leq F(df_2'', df_1'')(S_1^2/S_2^2)$$

where $F(df_1'', df_2'')$ is found by entering the appropriate F table with df_1'' and df_2'' degrees of freedom. $F(df_2'', df_1'')$ is found by interchanging the values of df_1'' and df_2'' and entering the appropriate F table with the interchanged values. The value of C determines which table is appropriate: there is a separate table for each value of C: 90, 95, and 99.

Inferences concerning the population correlation coefficient

a   *Want to infer:* ρ, the population correlation coefficient between two variables (not to be confused with Spearman's rho, r_{rho}).

b   *Experiment:* A sample of N observations from the population, on each of which two numerical measurements, X and Y, are made;

c   *Assumption:* Population is bivariate normal;

d   *Data:* Calculate r, Pearson's coefficient of correlation:

$$r = \frac{SS_{XY}}{\sqrt{SS_{XX} SS_{YY}}} = \frac{N \sum XY - \sum X \sum Y}{\sqrt{N \sum X^2 - (\sum X)^2}\sqrt{N \sum Y^2 - (\sum Y)^2}}$$

Then find Fisher-z transformation of r by looking up r in Fisher-z table and reading off corresponding value of z.

e   *Prior distributions:* **i** Uniform over μ_X, μ_Y, $\log \sigma_X$, $\log \sigma_Y$. **ii** All four prior distributions are independent of one another and of the prior distribution of ρ. **iii** Prior distribution of ρ is gentle and is nowhere 0.

f   *Posterior distribution concerning ζ (the Fisher-z transformation of ρ):*
Approximately normal (as $N \to \infty$) with

$m'' = $ the Fisher-z transformation of r

$$s'' = \sqrt{\frac{1}{N}}$$

g   *C per cent credible interval for ρ:*

i   First find the credible interval for ζ:

$$m'' - zs'' \leq \zeta \leq m'' + zs''$$

where z is the standard deviate corresponding to the C per cent credible interval for the normal distribution. z is found by entering the normal table with $C/100$ and reading off z.

ii   Enter the z column of the Fisher-z tables with the two limits of the credible interval for ζ just calculated. The corresponding numbers in the r column are the values of ρ_{low} and ρ_{high}.

In addition, a procedure for ranked data was given.

Inferences concerning the linear regression coefficients

a   *Want to infer:* **i** $\alpha_{Y|X}$ and $\beta_{Y|X}$, the Y-intercept and slope of the population linear regression line for predicting Y from X; **ii** $\sigma_{Y|X}$, the standard error of estimate for $\tilde{Y}$, the predicted Y-scores.

b   *Experiment:* A sample of N elements from the population; a pair of numerical measurements, X and Y, is available for each element;

c   *Assumptions:* **i** Population distribution of Y conditional on X is normal, for all values of X; **ii** $\sigma_{Y|X}$ is same for all values of X.

d   *Data:* Calculate . . .

i $$M_X = \frac{\sum X}{N}$$

ii $$M_Y = \frac{\sum Y}{N}$$

iii $$SS_{XX} = \sum (X - M_X)^2 = \frac{N \sum X^2 - (\sum X)^2}{N}$$

iv $$SS_{YY} = \sum (Y - M_Y)^2 = \frac{N \sum Y^2 - (\sum Y)^2}{N}$$

v $$SS_{XY} = \sum (X - M_X)(Y - M_Y) = \frac{N \sum XY - \sum X \sum Y}{N}$$

vi $$SS_{\tilde{Y}\text{-error}} = \sum (Y - \tilde{Y})^2 = \frac{(SS_{YY})(SS_{XX}) - (SS_{XY})^2}{SS_{XX}}$$

vii Slope of the regression line for the sample data:

$$B_{Y|X} = \frac{SS_{XY}}{SS_{XX}}$$

viii Y-intercept of the regression line for the sample data:

$$A_{Y|X} = M_Y - B_{Y|X} M_X$$

ix Standard error of estimate for the sample:

$$S_{Y|X} = \sqrt{\frac{SS_{\hat{Y}\text{-error}}}{N-1}}$$

x (optional) Sample correlation coefficient

$$r = \frac{SS_{XY}}{\sqrt{SS_{XX} SS_{YY}}}$$

e *Prior distributions:* **i** Uniform over $\alpha_{Y|X}$, $\beta_{Y|X}$ and $\log \sigma_{Y|X}$; **ii** All three prior distributions independent of each other.

f *Posterior distributions:*

i Concerning $\alpha_{Y|X}$: Student-t with parameters

$$\mu_t'' = A_{Y|X} \qquad \sigma_t'' = \sqrt{\left(\frac{SS_{\hat{Y}\text{-error}}}{N-2}\right)\left(\frac{\sum X^2}{N(SS_{XX})}\right)} \qquad df'' = N-2$$

ii Concerning $\beta_{Y|X}$: Student-t with parameters

$$\mu_t'' = B_{Y|X} \qquad \sigma_t'' = \sqrt{\left(\frac{SS_{\hat{Y}\text{-error}}}{N-2}\right)\left(\frac{1}{SS_{XX}}\right)} \qquad df'' = N-2$$

iii Concerning $\sigma_{Y|X}$: Inverted Gamma-2 with

$$\text{mode}'' = S_{Y|X} \qquad df'' = N-2$$

g *C per cent credible intervals:*

i For $\alpha_{Y|X}$ and $\beta_{Y|X}$: The general form is . . .

$$\mu_t'' - t\sigma_t'' \leq \begin{Bmatrix} \alpha_{Y|X} \\ \beta_{Y|X} \end{Bmatrix} \leq \mu_t'' + t\sigma_t''$$

where t is the standard deviate corresponding to the C per cent credible interval for the Student-t distribution. t is found by entering the Student-t table with $df = N-2$ and with C.

ii For $\sigma_{Y|X}$:

$$IG2_{\text{low}} \times \text{mode}'' \leq \sigma_{Y|X} \leq IG2_{\text{high}} \times \text{mode}''$$

where $IG2_{\text{low}}$ and $IG2_{\text{high}}$ are the tabled limits of the credible interval for the IG2 whose mode is 1. The tabled limits are found by entering the IG2 table with $df = N-2$ and with C.

In addition, procedures for making inferences about the predicted value of Y and about the true value of Y were given.

Problems

12–1 (Refers to Problem 2–5) To what extent do the two standard devices for measuring probability give different results?

12–2 Group A was given traditional classroom instruction throughout the year, while Group B received a mixture of classroom instruction and computer-based instruction. Both groups were given a final examination at the end of the year. There were 26 students in each group.

Scores on final examination

	Mean	Standard deviation
Group A	65	5
Group B	75	3

Is computer-assisted instruction superior to traditional classroom instruction? Assume normal populations.

12–3 Alpert and Haber (1960) examined the extent to which anxiety helps or hinders a student on a final examination. They devised a questionnaire that measures facilitating anxiety and debilitating anxiety. For a sample of 283 students they found that facilitating anxiety correlated 0·26 with the final examination grade for the introductory psychology course, and debilitating anxiety scores correlated $-0·28$ with the final exam grade. What are the 95% credible intervals for the population correlations?

12–4 A scientist wants to find out if brain-damaged children score lower on Test X than normal children. The population mean for normal children is 50 and the standard deviation is 10. For brain-damaged children the population mean is unknown, but the standard deviation is known to be the same as for normal children. The investigator's prior opinion about the population mean for the brain-damaged children is normal with a mean of 30 and a standard deviation of 12. He selects a random sample of 20 brain-damaged children; the mean test score turns out to be 35 with a standard deviation of 8.

a What is the posterior mean?

b How would you answer the scientist's original question?

12–5 A random sample of 10 men and 10 women were given a test of intolerance of ambiguity. The average score for men was 51·0; for women, 44·0. For the men $SS_{xx} = 360$; for the women $SS_{xx} = 450$. On the basis of these data what conclusion would you draw about the difference in average performance of men and women on this test?

12–6 An investigator wishes to discover whether the presence of other people influences the speed with which an individual will offer help to someone in distress. He decides to conduct a series of studies to see whether the speed is different when the person in distress and the person offering help are the same sex or different sex. His first study uses women in both roles. The scientist designs an experiment in which a 'personal emergency' arises, and the time for the subject to offer help is recorded. In Condition A no other person other than the subject knows of the emergency, while in Condition B the subject knows she is only one of several people who have just learned about the emergency. He finds that 25 out of 35 subjects in Condition A offer help, while 30 out of 45 offer help in Condition B. Here are the response times (in seconds) for subjects who offered help.

Condition A					Condition B					
96	40	96	96	80	88	97	97	84	108	75
72	78	82	84	74	104	134	126	108	44	136
86	72	100	68	42	94	103	86	66	112	136
76	78	84	88	92	99	90	60	58	124	70
88	72	66	100	92	107	49	92	97	102	100

a   Is there any difference in the variability of response times between the two conditions?

b   Is there any difference in the mean response times of the two groups?

c   Does the presence of other people influence whether or not a person decides to offer help?

d   What conclusions and possible suggestions for further work would you offer on the basis of these data and your inferences?

12–7 (Refers to Problem 10–3) Find the posterior 99% credible intervals for the population regression coefficients and for the standard error of estimate. In light of your answers, how useful, now, do you think the regression equation is?

12–8 (Refers to Problem 10–3) Suppose a student told you he spends about £1·75 per week on drink and tobacco. If we assume that he is a member of the population from which the sample of 20 was selected, what inference could you make about

a   the predicted amount of money spent on books, etc.?

b   the actual amount of money spent on books, etc.?

12–9 (Refers to Problem 10–5) What inference could you make about the actual per cent increase in retail prices (over the 1955 figures) for 1970?

12–10 Murdoch and Smith (1969) examined the relationship between order of birth and affiliation. In a sample of student men, they found that men who were only children or born first tended to marry earlier than men who were later born children. Here are the means and standard deviations of marriage-age for both birth orders.

	N	Mean	Standard deviation
First borns	73	22·8	2·13
Later borns	67	23·6	3·02

What conclusions about birth order and affiliation would you draw on the basis of these data?

12–11 Moskos and Bell (1964) report in a study on the attitudes of a sample of West Indian leaders towards democracy that 5 out of 21 revolutionary radicals and 9 out of 22 counter-revolutionary reactionaries condoned overthrow of the government. Could one conclude that West Indian reactionary leaders are more likely than radical leaders to condone overthrow?

12–12 Find at least three examples in the social science journals of the different kinds of inferences discussed in this chapter and give a Bayesian interpretation for each.

13 · Traditional methods

This chapter deals with inferential methods that derive from a relative frequency interpretation of probability, and which do not make use of Bayes' theorem. I cover only those procedures most commonly encountered in the social science literature, but it is important to recognize that some traditional methods cannot be interpreted with the Bayesian machinery developed so far. Thus, while you are reading this chapter do not worry if you cannot see how a Bayesian might interpret the analysis. That will come in the next chapter.

On reading this chapter, you should

understand the concept of a sampling distribution;

be acquainted with the central roles played by sampling distributions and estimation in the making of non-Bayesian inferences;

understand what a non-Bayesian means by a confidence interval;

be aware of the procedures followed by a non-Bayesian in testing hypotheses.

The chapter explains only enough of the traditional logic to enable you to understand simple analyses you may read in the social science literature. For the most part, it does not give enough information for you to carry out traditional analyses, so no exercises are included.

13.1 Sampling

It will be helpful to keep in mind a specific problem as we discuss traditional approaches to statistical inference. Let us resurrect Exercise 12–4, the one in which a statistics instructor wished to find out how effective programmed instruction in mathematics was for students in his class. As it turned out, he was not interested only in the 15 students who completed the program, for he wanted to make an inference that would apply to the population of potential students who *might* take his course and use the programmed material. In other words, he is making a general enquiry about the effectiveness of the programmed instruction, and assumes that his 15 students are a representative sample of that population.

He administered equivalent forms of a mathematics test before and after the programmed instruction was completed, and took the difference in those scores for each person. The mean and standard deviation of those difference scores were

$$M = 24 \cdot 87$$
$$S = 8 \cdot 92$$

Now, on the basis of those statistics for a sample of size 15, what inferences about the population *mean* can be made without resort to Bayes' theorem?

Sampling distributions

To answer that question the relative frequentist has to develop a mechanism different from Bayes' theorem, a mechanism that will allow him to make inferences about the population. The device used is quite ingenious, and its development is an important landmark in the history of statistics. It is called a *sampling distribution*, and it is the result of repeated sampling from the population. To get a feeling for what a sampling distribution is, imagine, for the example above, the population of difference scores. In other words, imagine all those potential students and their difference scores. Now suppose a sample of size 15 is selected, and the mean difference score is computed. We record the mean. Next another sample is drawn; its mean will probably be a little different than the mean of the first sample; we note it, too. We keep drawing samples of size 15, always computing the mean of each sample and recording it. Of course, because the sampling is random, we will not get the same value for the mean every time.

After we have done this a huge number of times, we have a very long list of means. There might be a few extreme means on the list, but not very many, for most means would tend to cluster around some central value, with fewer and fewer means taking values away from that central value. To see this we could construct a histogram of those means. The histogram will be fairly jagged if we have only 30 or 40 means on our list, but you can imagine that as more and more samples are taken, smaller and smaller class intervals can be chosen until eventually the histogram looks like a smooth distribution. We would then have a theoretical sampling distribution of means, and it is this distribution that is meant when reference is made to *the* sampling distribution of means. Figure 13–1 shows this process of sampling from a population, computing the sample means, and then constructing a distribution of these means. Normally we would not know what the population distribution looks like; if we did, there would be no need to draw samples and make inferences. But for the moment, I want to show the population so that I can compare it to the sampling distribution. Once those points of similarity have been noted, we can then return to the more realistic situation in which the population distribution is unknown.

First, note that the peaks of the distributions occur in the same place over the X-axis, at $X = 24$. The mean of the sampling distribution equals the mean of the population. Recall that we let μ stand for the parameter equal to the population mean; let us designate the parameter equal to the mean of the sampling distribution of means by μ_M. From the figure we see that

$$\mu = \mu_M = 24$$

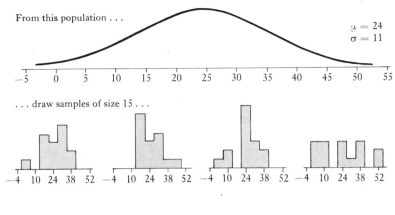

From this population . . .

$\mu = 24$
$\sigma = 11$

. . . draw samples of size 15 . . .

. . . then compute the sample means . . .

24·7   25·2   22·9   23·7

. . . and draw the distribution of these means

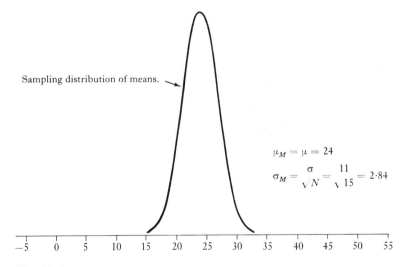

Sampling distribution of means.

$\mu_M = \mu = 24$

$\sigma_M = \dfrac{\sigma}{\sqrt{N}} = \dfrac{11}{\sqrt{15}} = 2 \cdot 84$

Fig. 13–1
Relationship between a population and the sampling distribution of means

Second, the variance of the sampling distribution is very much smaller than the variance of the population. We expect that, for the population shows the variability of the *X-scores*, while the sampling distribution gives the variability of the *means* of samples of fixed size. We do not expect nearly as much variability from one mean to the next as we do from one score to the next.

Suppose, however, that the samples had each been smaller, 5, say, instead of 15. And suppose several samples of size 5 had been drawn. Would you not expect the means of those samples to differ more from each other than the means of the larger samples differed from each other? If samples of size 2 had been selected, their means would have been even more different from one another.

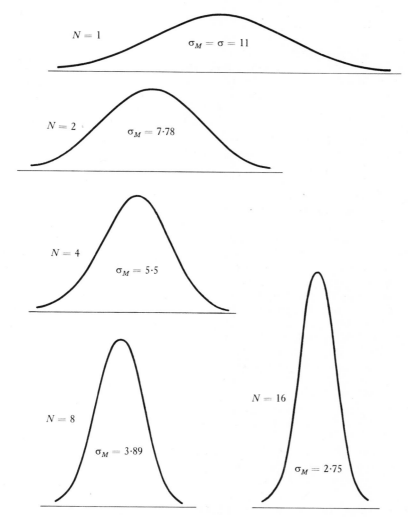

Fig. 13–2
Some sampling distributions for samples from a normal population with $\sigma = 11$

At the extreme, we could have chosen samples of size 1; the 'mean' of such a sample is equal to the X-score itself, so the distribution of means when the sample size is 1 is just the population distribution itself. In other words, the larger the sample size, the smaller is the variance of the sampling distribution of means. You can see this relationship in Fig. 13–2.

We see, then, that while the mean of the sampling distribution equals the mean of the population, it is not true that the standard deviations of those two distributions are equal. But we can find the standard deviation of the sampling distribution of means, σ_M, from the population standard deviation, σ:

$$\sigma_M = \frac{\sigma}{\sqrt{N}}$$

where N is the size of each sample. In words, the standard deviation of the sampling distribution is found by dividing the population standard deviation by the square root of the sample size. This equation confirms intuition about the sampling distribution of means; the distribution of sample means will be more spread out for smaller sample sizes, and for population distributions with larger standard deviations. Using this equation we can compute the standard deviation of the sampling distribution shown in the lower portion of Fig. 13–1. The population has a standard deviation of 11, so

$$\sigma_M = \frac{\sigma}{\sqrt{N}} = \frac{11}{\sqrt{15}} = 2 \cdot 84$$

We have seen, then, that **if we know the parameters of the population, we can find the parameters of the sampling distribution of means.** We must add one qualification. Although the sampling distribution shown in Fig. 13–1 is normal, one must not conclude that *all* sampling distributions are normal. The sampling distribution of means will be normal whenever the population is normal, *or*, if the population is *not* normal, when large samples have been drawn. It may seem surprising that the sampling distribution of means could be normal when the population is not, but the *central limit theorem* says that the distribution of sample means *is* approximately normal and that the approximation gets better the larger the size of each sample. This is an important result for traditional statistics, for it allows inferences to be made even though the shape of the population distribution is not known.

Confidence intervals

Armed with the information of the last section, let us return to the problem of the statistics instructor who wishes to make an inference about the mean of the population of difference scores. For the moment assume that he knows the population is normal with standard deviation equal to 11. He does not known the population mean, but he has taken a sample which, you will recall, has a mean of 24·87. What inference can he make about the population mean?

The goal of this section is to explain how an inference can be made in the form of an interval of values that has a certain probability of containing the true mean. Such an interval is called a *confidence interval*. A 95% confidence interval, for example, is a range of values that are 95% sure to include the true mean.

Our route to the confidence interval is via the sampling distribution. We know that the sampling distribution must be normal, and, since we know the population standard deviation, we can find the standard deviation of the sampling distribution of means; it was calculated above: $\sigma_M = 2 \cdot 84$. The only thing we do not know is where the sampling distribution is located along the horizontal axis. We do know that our sample mean, 24·87, falls within the sampling distribution of means. If only we knew exactly where it falls, then we could locate the mean of the sampling distribution, and our problem would be solved, for we know that the mean of the sampling distribution equals the mean of the population. But we do not know whether the sample mean falls in the left tail, or the right tail, or near the middle of the sampling distribution, so we will not be able to pinpoint the mean of the sampling distribution precisely. We do know that the sample mean falls somewhere within a normal distribution whose standard deviation is 2·84, and we know that most values of a normal distribution fall within ± 3 standard deviations of the mean. So unless the sample mean is a freak result, we can be quite sure that the mean of the sampling distribution is not more than 3 standard deviations away.

Now let us give those intuitive ideas more precise form. Suppose our investigator wishes to find the 95% confidence interval for the population mean. He first considers the possibility that the sample mean is located, say, in the *left* tail of the sampling distribution, at a point that leaves 2·5% of the area of the distribution to the left of 24·87. Where, then, must the mean be located? We know that for the standard normal distribution, a Z-score of $-1·96$ leaves 2·5% of the distribution to the left. Our investigator reasons that 24·87 must be 1·96 standard deviations below the mean. Thus, if he adds 1·96 standard deviations to 24·87, the result will be one estimate of the mean of the sampling distribution:

high estimate of $\mu_M = 24·87 + 1·96(2·84) = 30·4$

The statistics instructor reasons further that the sample result could have been located in the *right* tail of the sampling distribution of means. He then asks where the sampling distribution would be located if that were the case. Allowing a 2·5% chance for getting a sample mean of 24·87 *or more*, he figures that the mean of the sampling distribution would then have to fall 1·96 standard deviations *below* 24·87, that is, at

low estimate of $\mu_M = 24·87 - 1·96(2·84) = 19·3$

He concludes, then, that there must be a 95% chance that the interval from 19·3 to 30·4 contains the mean of the sampling distribution. The steps in this development are shown graphically in Fig. 13–3. Since we know that the mean of the sampling distribution of means equals the mean of the population, the limits just calculated serve to define a confidence interval for the population mean. The investigator can now state that there is a 95% chance that the interval from 19·3 to 30·4 contains the true value of the population mean.

The logic is a little involved, so go back over the argument if you did not understand it the first time. The basic idea is to figure out where the sampling distribution would be located if (a) the obtained sample mean is an unlikely result from the left tail of the sampling distribution, then, (b) the sample mean is an unlikely result from the right tail of the distribution. The sampling distribution can be located because you know its standard deviation and you know it is normal. Thus you know there is only a 2·5% chance for the mean of the sampling distribution to be greater than a value that is 1·96 standard deviations above the mean of 24·87. Similarly, you know there is only a 2·5% chance for the mean of the sampling distribution to be less than a value that is 1·96 standard deviations below 24·87. And so you conclude that there is a 95% chance for the interval so calculated to include the true value of the population mean.

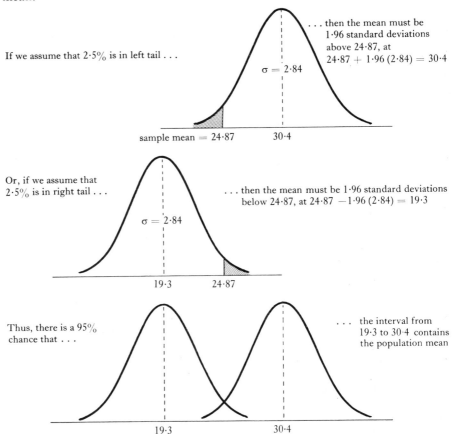

If we assume that 2·5% is in left tail . . .

. . . then the mean must be 1·96 standard deviations above 24·87, at 24·87 + 1·96 (2·84) = 30·4

σ = 2·84

sample mean = 24·87   30·4

Or, if we assume that 2·5% is in right tail . . .

. . . then the mean must be 1·96 standard deviations below 24·87, at 24·87 − 1·96 (2·84) = 19·3

σ = 2·84

19·3   24·87

Thus, there is a 95% chance that . . .

. . . the interval from 19·3 to 30·4 contains the population mean

19·3   30·4

Fig. 13–3
Deriving a confidence interval by considering possible locations of the distribution of sample means

Notice that the probability in that statement is made about the interval, not about the population mean. Adherents of a relative frequency view of probability do not make probability statements about population parameters; either the true value is 24·87 or it is not. There is no probability about it. The sampling distribution is obtained by repeated sampling of the population, so statements derived from the sampling distribution are entirely consistent with the relative frequency view of probability. Thus, we can make probability statements about the interval, which was obtained by considering the location of the sampling distribution. We say that there is a 95% chance *that the interval* contains the true value of the population mean. The probability concerns the interval, not the population mean.

A Bayesian faced with the data of this problem would find the posterior distribution of the population mean, assuming a normal population whose standard deviation is known and equal to 11. If he also assumed a uniform prior over the population mean and the logarithm of the population standard deviation, then the posterior would be normal with

$$\text{posterior mean} = m'' = M = 24{\cdot}87$$

$$\text{posterior standard deviation} = s'' = \frac{\sigma}{\sqrt{N}} = 2{\cdot}84$$

Notice that under the assumption of uniform priors the posterior distribution has the same shape and parameters as the sampling distribution. That is why Bayesian and traditional methods often arrive at the same results. The calculation for the confidence interval is exactly the same as the calculation for the credible interval.

Another, more common term for the standard deviation of the sampling distribution, is the *standard error*. When we are making inferences about the population mean, then the standard deviation of the distribution of sample means is called the *standard error of the mean*.

13.2 Estimation

The argument in the previous section assumed that the population variance is known. 'How can a confidence interval be found,' you might ask, 'when the population standard deviation is *not* known?' The answer seems simple enough: since we do not know the population variance, σ^2, we estimate it from the sample variance, S^2. Thus, the equation for the standard error of the mean, σ_M, would then be

$$\text{estimated } \sigma_M = \sqrt{\frac{\text{estimated } \sigma^2}{N}}$$

As we shall see shortly, the 'best' estimate of σ^2 is given by the sample variance, S^2, provided that the sample variance is defined as in Chapter 9. Consequently, our 'best' estimate of the standard error of estimate for the population mean is

$$\text{estimated } \sigma_M = \frac{S}{\sqrt{N}}$$

That is what we do when we have a single sample, and wish to find a confidence interval for the mean. But there is a complication: when the standard deviation of the population is not known and has to be estimated from a sample, then the confidence interval must be calculated with reference to a Student-t distribution rather than the normal distribution of sample means. We turn next to the reason for this.

Sampling distributions of test statistics

When we do not know the population standard deviation, we have to develop a sampling distribution that takes into account that lack of knowledge. To see how this can be done, let us return to the situation in which we take repeated samples from the population in order to find the sampling distribution.

This time, instead of just calculating the mean of each sample, we also compute the standard deviation. We then divide each sample standard deviation by the square root of N; that gives us an estimate of σ_M for each sample, according to the formula a few lines back. Thus, for each sample we have the mean, M, and an estimate of σ_M, which I will call est σ_M.

For each sample we next compute a t-value:

$$t = \frac{M - \mu}{\text{est } \sigma_M} = \frac{M - \mu}{S/\sqrt{N}}$$

For this hypothetical process we know the mean, μ, of the population, so we only have to subtract μ from each sample mean and then divide by est σ_M to get the t-value for each sample. That gives us a t-value for each sample. We call the t-value a *test statistic*.

Let us draw a histogram of those t-values. If we have enough of them the histogram approaches a smooth distribution, and it probably comes as no surprise that the distribution is a Student-t, provided that the population itself is normal. Thus, the sampling distribution of the test statistic t is a Student-t, and it happens to have $N-1$ degrees of freedom. As you might expect, the mean of the distribution of t is 0, for at this point $M = \mu$, so that $M - \mu = 0$.

Now let us return to the problem at hand: finding a confidence interval for the population mean, μ, when we do not know the standard deviation of the population. Recall that our statistics instructor obtained a sample of size 15 whose mean and standard deviation were

$$M = 24 \cdot 87$$

$$S = 8 \cdot 92$$

If we want a 95% confidence interval, we look up the t-values that include between them 95% of the area of the Student-t distribution that has $15 - 1 = 14$ degrees of freedom. The Student-t table gives a value of $2 \cdot 145$. Ninety-five per cent of the curve falls between $-2 \cdot 145$ and $+2 \cdot 145$; that is, $2 \cdot 5\%$ falls to the left of $-2 \cdot 145$ and $2 \cdot 5\%$ to the right of $+2 \cdot 145$. If we assume for the moment that the sample result fell in the left tail so that only $2 \cdot 5\%$ of the area is to the left, then the t-value corresponding to the sample result is $-2 \cdot 145$. Knowing this, we can solve the equation for computing t-values to give us the values of the mean of the population. Recall that

$$t = \frac{M - \mu}{\text{est } \sigma_M}$$

Solving for μ gives

$$\mu = M - t(\text{est } \sigma_M)$$

For our example we know M and t, and we can compute est σ_M from the sample standard deviation:

$$\text{est } \sigma_M = \frac{S}{\sqrt{N}} = \frac{8 \cdot 92}{\sqrt{15}} = 2 \cdot 3$$

Now we solve for the population mean:

$$\mu = M - t(\text{est } \sigma_M)$$
$$= 24\cdot87 - (-2\cdot145)(2\cdot3)$$
$$= 29\cdot8$$

In other words, if the population has a mean of 29·8, then the *t*-statistic for our sample would have been found 2·145 standard deviations below the zero mean of the sampling distribution of the test statistic. We just worked that logic backwards to find the population mean.

We can do it again to find the other limit for the confidence interval. This time we assume that the sample result fell in the right tail of the sampling distribution of the *t*-statistic. Under this condition we expect to find 2·5% of the sampling distribution to the right of a *t*-value of +2·145. Again, we solve for the population mean that would locate the sample at this spot on the sampling distribution:

$$\mu = M - t(\text{est } \sigma_M)$$
$$= 24\cdot87 - (2\cdot145)(2\cdot3)$$
$$= 19\cdot94$$

Now that we have both limits of the confidence interval, we can say that there is a 95% chance that the interval from 19·94 to 29·8 contains the true value of μ. You can see that the logic used in finding the limits of the confidence interval is basically the same as for the case in which the population standard deviation is known. The only difference is in the nature of the sampling distributions. When σ is known, the sampling distribution concerns the statistic M itself, but when σ is not known the sampling distribution is for the test statistic t.

You may have noticed that the confidence interval computed for σ unknown is actually shorter than the interval calculated for σ known. Normally, you would expect that having to estimate σ from the sample standard deviation would result in a longer interval than if σ is known. That usually is the case; if you were to take a number of samples of size 15 and compute the confidence intervals first assuming that σ is known and then assuming σ is not known, you would find that the latter procedure would more often give the larger intervals. You can see that this would have to be true by considering the case where the sample variance turns out to be equal to the population variance. Then est σ_M equals σ_M, but because the tails of the *t*-distribution are lifted higher than the tails of the normal distribution, it is necessary to travel 2·145 standard deviations from the sample mean rather than 1·96 standard deviations, so the confidence interval will be larger. The interval was shorter in the example given here because the sample standard deviation turned out to be *less* than the population standard deviation. The interval would have been larger, as expected, if the sample S has been just a little less than σ, or equal to σ, or more than σ.

Other sampling distributions

Two methods have now been shown for finding a confidence interval for the unknown population mean of a normal population. In one case the population standard deviation was known, in the other it was not. It is possible to apply the arguments given here to inferences about any population parameter of interest; the standard deviation of a population, the difference between two population means, the ratio of two population variances, etc. In every case it is first necessary to know the test statistic of interest and also the form of the sampling distribution of the test statistic. Because test statistics and sampling distributions of the test statistics usually have the same names, for example, the t-statistic has a Student-t distribution, only the form of the sampling distribution along with the standard error are usually given. Recall that the standard error is the standard deviation of the sampling distribution. Thus, for inferences about a population mean when the variance is unknown, a traditional statistics book would say that the sampling distribution is a Student-t and that the standard error of estimate is

$$\text{est } \sigma_M = \frac{S}{\sqrt{N}}$$

Approximations, holding only for large samples, are often given when the population is not normal. Special procedures and tables are sometimes provided for use with small samples.

The main point to remember is that the standard error in a traditional analysis will often be equal to the standard deviation of the posterior distribution in a Bayesian analysis that has been conducted with uniform priors. For example, let us compare traditional and Bayesian procedures for the case of inference about the mean of a normal population whose variance is unknown. The traditionalist will find limits of a confidence interval by solving this equation:

$$\mu = M \pm t(\text{est } \sigma_M)$$

But we know that

$$\text{est } \sigma_M = \frac{S}{\sqrt{N}}$$

Substituting this expression into the equation for the confidence interval gives

$$\mu = M \pm t \frac{S}{\sqrt{N}}$$

The value of t is found by reference to the Student-t distribution with $N-1$ degrees of freedom.

The Bayesian notes that, if his priors are uniform, his posterior distribution concerning μ is Student-t with $N-1$ degrees of freedom, and that the posterior credible interval is found by solving this equation:

$$\mu = \mu_t'' \pm t\sigma_t''$$

But we know that the posterior parameters μ_t'' and σ_t'' are given by

$$\mu_t'' = M$$

$$\sigma_t'' = \frac{S}{\sqrt{N}}$$

Substituting these values into the expression for μ gives:

$$\mu = M \pm t \frac{S}{\sqrt{N}}$$

So, you see, the results are the same. As I have said before, only the route is different. Do not forget that the interpretation of the interval is different. The Bayesian says there is a 95% change that μ is between 19·94 and 29·8, while the traditionalist says there is a 95% chance that the interval from 19·94 to 29·8 contains the true value of μ.

Properties of estimators

At the beginning of this section I said that the 'best' estimate of σ^2, the population variance, was S^2, the sample variance. We turn now to consider what 'best' means. This is an important question not only for estimating standard errors, but also for making point rather than interval estimates for population parameters. Sometimes the investigator does not want a confidence interval, he just wants a 'best' guess. The Bayesian in this position can give the posterior mean, or any other measure of central tendency if the posterior is not symmetrical. He chooses whichever measure is appropriate in the circumstance, just as he reports whichever measure of central tendency in his data conveys the most accurate impression of his data.

The traditional statistician takes a different view. He asks that his statistic, to be a good estimator of a population parameter, should be *unbiased, consistent,* and *sufficient,* and that the method of estimation should be *efficient.* An estimator may not satisfy *all* these properties, but it should satisfy some. Let us consider each of these properties in turn.

If we use some sample statistic as an estimator of a population parameter, the estimator is considered *unbiased* if the sample statistic is, on the average, neither larger nor smaller than the population parameter. Another way of saying this is that the mean of the sampling distribution is equal to the true value. As an example, suppose we wish to make an inference about the mean of a normal population. If we were to draw many samples of size N, and we note the mean of each sample, we would find that in the long run the mean of those sample means exactly equals the population mean. The sample mean is an unbiased estimate of the population mean. If we were trying to make an inference about the population proportion, it is also true that the sample proportion is an unbiased estimate of the population proportion. Furthermore, the sample variance, as it has been defined in this book, is an unbiased estimate of the population variance. It is worth noting that some statistics books define the sample variance with N rather than $N-1$ in the denominator, thus:

$$S^2 = \frac{\sum (X - M)^2}{N}$$

But that statistic is not an unbiased estimator of the population variance. It would be if the numerator were divided by $N-1$ rather than N, and that is one reason why some non-Bayesian statistics textbooks define the sample variance as I have done in this book.

A statistic is *consistent* if it tends to the true value as N gets large. If we are making an inference about a population mean, then we would hope that the mean of a large sample is closer to the true value of μ than the mean of a small sample. That is true for sample means, so we consider the sample mean a consistent estimator of μ. The sample mean, the sample variance, the sample proportion and all the other sample statistics we have discussed in this book are consistent estimators.

We have already met the concept of *sufficiency* in Chapter 9. There we said that a statistic is sufficient if it contains all of the information in the data that is needed to make an inference. For Bayesian inference, sufficient statistics are those summaries of the data that still allow us to obtain the posterior distribution, given the prior. For example, when making an inference about the mean of a normal population whose variance is known, we only need to know the sample mean and the sample size in order to find the posterior distribution. Thus, M and N are sufficient for the posterior distribution of μ.

To take another example, suppose you are interested in making an inference about the population proportion. You need to know the number of successes, $\bar{s}$, and the number of failures, $\bar{f}$, in the sample so that you can calculate the parameters of the posterior. We say that $\bar{s}$ and $\bar{f}$ are together the sufficient statistics, because only their values are needed to find the posterior distribution. If you were presented with the data themselves, you would have some extra information: the order of the successes and failures. But as we saw in the bag-and-poker-chip example of Chapter 4, the order in which the successes and failures occur is irrelevant to the posterior probabilities. The same principle applies to making inferences about a population proportion; you get the same posterior distribution whatever the order of successes and failures. Thus, the original data tell us the number of successes, the number of failures, and the order in which they occurred, but to find the posterior distribution concerning the population proportion, we do not need all that information. Only the values of $\bar{s}$ and $\bar{f}$ are required, so they are the sufficient statistics. Notice that the *ratio* of successes to total number of trials, $\bar{s}/(\bar{s}+\bar{f})$, is *not* a sufficient statistic. It is not enough to report the *proportion* of successes, for that statistic does not contain enough information to allow calculation of the posterior distribution. For example, if the proportion of successes is given as 0·8, one does not know if 8 successes out of 10 were observed, or 24 out of 30, or 400 out of 500, etc., yet each of those hypothetical experiments would give successively more peaked posterior distributions.

Many statisticians, whatever their persuasion, have urged scientists to report the sufficient statistics of their investigation, along with whatever inferences are made. This allows the reader to come to his own conclusions; a Bayesian reader, for example, could then apply his own opinions to the data of the experiment to see how his posterior opinion may differ from that of the experimenter. But the reader cannot do this unless the sufficient statistics are reported. Unfortunately, this advice has fallen on deaf ears in the social sciences. All too often the sufficient statistics are not given and only a statement that the results are unlikely to be due to chance is indicated, leaving the critical reader with insufficient information to form his own opinion.

Perhaps adopting a Bayesian point of view will add weight to the desirability of reporting sufficient statistics. You will, surely, want your reader to be able to find his own posterior distribution, given your data. If you adopt a uniform prior, it is only necessary to give the parameters of the posterior distribution. Alternatively, or if your prior is not uniform, you can report the statistics of your data that you needed to find your posterior distribution. You will find them in the 'Compute . . .' sections of the summaries to Chapters 11 and 12. Remember to give the sample size, too, for that is needed to compute the degrees of freedom.

This discussion about sufficiency has been given a Bayesian interpretation in the past few paragraphs, so you might ask what a non-Bayesian view is. Well, it is the same: a sufficient statistic is one that contains all the information necessary to make an inference about a population parameter. It is just that since Bayesians and non-Bayesians go about making inferences differently, their applications of the principle sometimes differ.

The last characteristic of an estimator is that it should be relatively *efficient*. We mean by this that the standard error associated with the statistic should be small relative to the standard errors of other statistics. In that way, the most efficient statistic will yield the shortest confidence interval, relative to other statistics that might have been used as estimators. For example, we might have used the sample median rather than the sample mean as an estimator of the mean of a normal population, since the mean and median of a normal population are equal. If we were to consider only the bias of the statistic, we would not have any basis for choosing between the sample mean or sample median, for both are unbiased estimators. But there is a choice if we also consider their efficiency. For sample sizes greater than 2 the sampling distribution of means is less spread out than the sampling distribution of medians. In other words, the standard error associated with the mean is smaller than the standard error associated with the median. That makes the mean relatively more efficient than the median as an estimator. You saw the parallel to this characteristic in Chapter 11; when making an inference about the median of a normal population we found that the posterior credible interval was longer than when we made an inference about the population mean.

For many statistical problems, the sample mean fulfills all these criteria. But this is not always true, and then the scientist using traditional statistics must use his judgement about which criteria are most important for the inference in question, and choose accordingly the sample statistic to use as an estimator. The Bayesian is unconcerned with these characteristics of estimators because his estimation procedures derive from the posterior distribution. He can report the form and parameters of the posterior distribution as a complete description of his posterior opinion, or he can give summary statistics of his posterior, for example, the posterior mean and standard deviation, a posterior credible interval, etc.

13.3 Testing hypotheses

The theory of hypothesis testing looms large in the literature of traditional statistics. It is also a complicated topic, one that cannot be covered adequately in one section of one chapter of a predominantly Bayesian textbook. Instead, I have elected to discuss the *practice* of testing hypotheses, the procedures one encounters most frequently in the social science literature. Statistical practice exemplified in the social science journals is usually considerably simpler than statistical theory, particularly insofar as certain arbitrary conventions have become a substitute for careful judgement and thought.

In practice, social scientists frequently proceed as follows. First, they establish some statistical hypothesis, and they collect data to see if the hypothesis is false. Next, they calculate the probability of the observed data or more extreme data given the truth of the hypothesis. If that probability is small, then the hypothesis is considered unlikely to be true. These steps can be put in the form of a syllogism applied after the scientist has observed the data, D.

If H is true, then it is unlikely that D or more extreme data would be observed.

D was observed.

Therefore it is unlikely that H is true.

If, on the other hand, the scientist's calculation gives a probability that is fairly high, then the hypothesis is not rejected. He does not necessarily accept the hypothesis; he can choose to suspend judgement.

As an example, suppose we attempt to find out if a coin is biased. Let us assume that the coin is not biased; our statistical hypothesis is that the long-run proportion of heads is 0·5. We toss the coin 100 times, and it comes up heads 83 times. Now 83 heads *or more* out of 100 is very unlikely if the coin is fair, so we reject the notion that the coin is unbiased.

A Bayesian objects to this procedure for three reasons.

1 It does not take account of prior probabilities. If the coin was just received in mint condition from a bank, then my prior opinion so strongly favours the hypothesis 'fair coin' that even 83 heads out of 100 is not enough evidence to lead me to reject the hypothesis. But if the coin is known to belong to a gambler of dubious reputation, then I am willing to reject the hypothesis on the strength of the evidence. Inferences depend in part on prior probabilities.

2 No alternative hypothesis is considered. Suppose we are reliably informed that the coin, if it is biased, favours tails, not heads. Then 83 heads or more out of 100, while unlikely for a fair coin, is even more unlikely for a coin with a tails bias. So if 'fair coin' and 'tails-bias coin' are the only two hypotheses possible, then the data favour the fair coin. Recall the point made in section 4.7 of Chapter 4: The posterior probability of a hypothesis depends not only on that hypothesis and the data but also on the other hypotheses.

3 The inference depends on data not observed. When calculating the probability of 83 heads or more out of 100, one must find not only the probability of the sequence of 83 heads and 17 tails that was observed, but also the probability of every other possible sequence of 83 heads and 17 tails, even though they did not occur, *and* the probability of every other sequence of more than 83 heads that did not happen. To compute $p(D|H)$ in Bayes' theorem, one is required to consider only data that were observed, so data that were not observed are irrelevant for Bayesian inference. That seems an intuitively appealing principle: why should an inference be influenced by data that were not observed?

Traditional procedures employing the above syllogism are often called significance tests or tests of null hypotheses. We turn to them next.

Null hypotheses and significance tests

Let us return to the statistics instructor's problem. Recall that he wants to make an inference about the mean of the population of difference scores, and that the sample mean is 24·87. For now, we again assume that the population standard deviation is known to be 11. Suppose that the instructor has some reason to suspect that the population mean is 35; he wishes to test this hypothesis. He designates that hypothesis as H_0. Symbolically,

$$H_0: \mu = 35$$

The subscript 0 is intended only to serve as a reminder that the hypothesis in question is the 'null' hypothesis; that some specific hypothesis is being examined. In this case, the hypothesis is that the mean of the difference scores is exactly 35, a specific value.

Traditional procedure recognizes that inferences about a null hypothesis could be misleading if an alternative hypothesis is not specified. It is common practice to specify an inexact alternative hypothesis, usually of this form:

$$H_1: \mu \neq 35$$

In words, the population mean is *not* equal to 35; some value other than 35 is true. **It should be assumed when making inferences about null hypotheses that if data are obtained which are unlikely given the truth of the null hypothesis, then the data are relatively likely under the truth of the alternative hypothesis.** The null hypothesis and the alternative should be specified so that this is true. Unfortunately, one can find, without any difficulty, violations of this assumption in statistical analyses in the social science literature. Frequently the alternative hypothesis is ignored and the syllogism discussed in the previous section is applied only to the null hypothesis.

To make the inference about the null hypothesis we begin by assuming H_0 is true, that is, that the population mean really is 35. We observe that the sample mean is 24·87, so next we wish to find out how likely that result or one more extreme is if the null hypothesis is true. The sampling distribution of means enables us to answer that question. We know that the mean of the sampling distribution must be at 35, if the null hypothesis is true, and we know that since the population standard deviation is 11, the sampling distribution must have a standard deviation of $11/\sqrt{15} = 2\cdot84$. That is the standard error of the mean. Figure 13–4 shows the sampling distribution of means, if the null hypothesis is true.

Now we are in a position to make a statement about the likelihood of the data given the truth of the null hypothesis. You can see from Fig. 13–4 that a sample mean of 24·87 falls way out in the left tail of the sampling distribution. Such an observation is quite unlikely if the population mean is really 35, so we might reject the null hypothesis.

We need to make that procedure a little more precise. An easy way is to establish regions of the sampling distribution which will be termed 'rejection regions'; if a sample result falls in these regions, we deem the sample or one more extreme so unlikely to have occurred given the truth of the null hypothesis that we agree to reject the null hypothesis. By traditional convention, these regions usually encompass either 5% of the sample results, or 1%. Take the

5% region as an example. One approach is to establish two-tailed rejection regions, with 2·5% in the left tail and 2·5% in the right tail. You know that when this is done for a normal distribution, the remaining 95% falls within $\pm 1·96$ standard deviations from the mean. This is shown in Fig. 13–5.

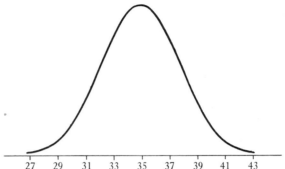

Fig. 13–4

Sampling distribution of means for samples of size 15, given that the population mean is 35

In other words, if a sample result falls farther than 1·96 standard deviations from the mean of the sampling distribution, then we reject the null hypothesis. For the statistics instructor's problem, the borderline for the lower rejection region is $35 - 1·96(2·84) = 29·43$, and the upper region is $35 + 1·96(2·84) = 40·57$. Notice that the sample mean of 24·87 falls in the left-tail rejection region.

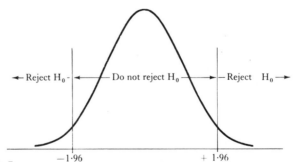

Fig. 13–5

Regions of the sampling distribution for which a sample result would lead to rejection of the null hypothesis.

We say, then, that the null hypothesis is rejected at the 5% level of significance. This result would probably be reported in the following manner: 'The sample mean is significantly different ($p < 0·05$) from 35'. The little bit in parentheses indicates the significance level.

A word of warning is needed at this point. Obtaining a significant result has nothing whatsoever to do with finding an important result. The word 'significant' is used in a very special sense, and means only that a result is most likely *not* attributable to chance. A result that is small or trivial may be declared statistically significant, but that only means that the small, trivial result is not due to chance. The magnitude or importance of the result is not given by the significance level.

If an investigator finds his result is significant at the 5% level, he usually goes on to discover if it is significant at the 1% level. In this case, the rejection regions of Fig. 13–2 are pushed farther out into the tails so that they extend, for the normal distribution, from −2·58 to +2·58. For our example, the lower limit would be found at 35−2·58(2·84) = 27·67. The sample mean falls below that limit, so the null hypothesis could be rejected at the 1% level. We say that the sample mean is significantly different ($p < 0.01$) from 35.

Many social scientists have adopted the practice of finding the limit of the rejection region at which the result would be *just* significant. For our example, the limit would have to be moved farther to the left. How far? It is only necessary to convert the sample mean to a Z-value, then find the area of the curve to the left of that value. In other words, we want to know how many standard deviations the sample mean is below the mean of the sampling distribution of means. We get that by subtracting 35 from 24·87 and dividing the result by the standard error of the mean:

$$\frac{M - \mu_M}{\sigma_M} = \frac{24 \cdot 87 - 35}{2 \cdot 84} = -3 \cdot 57$$

From the normal table we see that only 0·0002 of the curve falls beyond a Z-value of 3·57. We expect that amount in each of the tails, so the total area in the tails is 0·0004. We say, then, that the sample mean is significantly different from 35 at the 0·04% level. Alternatively, we might declare the result significant and add the little parenthetical expression. We could indicate the level at which the result is just significant: ($p < 0.0004$); or round off the result to the nearest 5 or 10: ($p < 0.0005$); or, as is frequently done, simply report the smallest of 0·05, 0·01, or 0·001: ($p < 0.001$).

These results would most likely be reported as follows:

The sample mean is significantly different from 35
(CR = 3·57; $p < 0.001$).

The abbreviation 'CR' stands for 'Critical Ratio' and refers to the test statistic given above when the sampling distribution is normal. It tells us how far, in standard deviation units, the sample mean is from the hypothesized value. As can be seen from the formula, the CR is computed by finding the difference between the sample mean and the hypothesized value of the population mean, and dividing the difference by the standard error of the mean. This procedure is often called a 'Critical Ratio test'.

For those cases in which the sampling distribution is a Student-t, a non-Bayesian will carry out a 't-test'. He computes the t-statistic by subtracting the hypothesized value of the population parameter from the sample value and then divides by the standard error of the statistic. The smallest rejection region, 0·05, 0·01, or 0·001, at which the result is significant (if it is at all) is reported. As an example, suppose the statistics instructor does not know the population standard deviation. Then he must compute the t-value

$$t = \frac{M - \mu}{S/\sqrt{N}} = \frac{24 \cdot 87 - 35}{8 \cdot 92/\sqrt{15}} = -4 \cdot 398$$

For 14 degrees of freedom, a *t*-value of only 4·14 (see Appendix G) is required for significance at the 0·001 level, so the instructor might report his results as follows:

The sample mean is significantly different from 35
($t = 4.398$; $p < 0.001$).

The decision to put a rejection region in each tail was dictated by the prior desire to know only whether a sample result was different from 35. If the investigator was interested only in the possibility that the sample mean was, say, *less* than 35, he would put all of the rejection region in the *left* tail. That is an example of a one-tailed hypothesis test. Such tests are used by traditionalists when, before collecting any data, a directional hypothesis is of interest.

Because significance testing is so simple, it has become the most frequently-used non-Bayesian method in the social sciences. The investigator has only to compute the test statistic, then look up the appropriate table to see if the test statistic is larger than the tabled value. If it is, then he rejects the null hypothesis. The procedure is so simple that it can be communicated in cookbook form and applied with little thought about the underlying rationale. One consequence is that some social scientists behave as though they believe the significance level indicates how likely the null hypothesis is to be true. To reject a null hypothesis at the 0·01 level of significance does *not* mean that there is a 1% chance or less of the null hypothesis being true, nor does it imply that the alternative hypothesis has a 99% chance of being true. There is no way in which a relative frequency definition of probability can allow for probability statements to be made about hypotheses. Unfortunately, as Bakan (1966) has pointed out so well, this confusion is rife amongst social scientists.

Some common null hypotheses

In the literature you are likely to run across a number of very abbreviated statements that indicate rejection of the null hypothesis. In this section I mention a few of them so that you will know what the researcher is talking about.

One of the simplest types of inference is the one we have already covered; testing whether a population mean is a specific value. This type of inference can easily be extended to medians or variances of populations in addition to means. Always the question of interest is whether a sample value is significantly different (that is, unlikely to be due to chance) from some specific value. Inferences about a population proportion can also be made in this way.

Another type of inference concerns the difference between two population means. Here the null hypothesis is often assumed to be that there is no difference, that is,

$$H_0: \mu_1 - \mu_2 = 0$$

If an investigator concludes that 'the two groups are significantly different' he probably means that he can rule out chance as causing the sample means to differ. Of course, two groups could be different because their variances are unequal, but if this kind of inference is being made, explicit reference is made to the variances. The investigator might report, 'The variances of the two groups are significantly different ($p < 0.01$)'. In either case, if the sample result fell within the 'do not reject' region of the sampling distribution, then the investigator would simply say, 'There was no significant difference between . . .'.

Another common type of inference concerns the Pearson correlation coefficient. The scientist may report a 'significant correlation of 0.67 ($p < 0.05$)'. He means that the null hypothesis of zero correlation was rejected at the 5% level of significance. Unless specified otherwise, you can assume that the test was two-tailed.

Interest sometimes focusses on the slope of the regression line in a regression problem. If a 'significant Beta-weight' is reported, the author means that the sample value of $B_{Y|X}$ is significantly different than zero. In other words, the slope of the population regression line is unlikely to be zero, indicating some degree of relationship between X and Y.

Many other examples could be given, but you should by now have the feel for the very abbreviated kinds of reports you will read in the social science literature. Generally, when the null hypothesis is not specifically spelled out, you can probably assume that 'no difference' or 'zero correlation' or 'no association' is meant. This usage is so common that the null hypothesis is sometimes thought *always* to mean that.

A Bayesian critique of null-hypothesis testing

Let me give very briefly the Bayesian objections to these procedures. In the first place, the Bayesian argues, the null hypothesis is rarely of much interest. To ask whether the population mean is exactly 35 is not very meaningful, for, *a priori*, we are sure that the mean is not *precisely* 35. There are probably not two population means in the world whose difference is exactly zero. And some correlation, however small, can be found between any two variables.

Closely related to this objection, is the obvious point that the null hypothesis is only one of many possible values of the uncertain quantity, and if our prior distribution over that uncertain quantity includes the null hypothesis, then only an infinitely small amount of prior opinion can be assigned to the null hypothesis. The continuous nature of an uncertain quantity assures this. In this sense, the prior probability of the null hypothesis is zero, so that even after data are observed, it will still be zero. Strictly speaking, we do not make probability statements about specific values of uncertain quantities, only *intervals* of uncertain quantities. The null hypothesis is a specific value of an uncertain quantity, so we would not normally make probability statements about it. The Bayesian argues that inferences should be made about *all* possible values of an uncertain quantity, not just one specific value of the uncertain quantity. I have yet to meet an example in the social sciences of a null hypothesis test that could not be expressed as an inference about an uncertain quantity. That sort of inference tells us much more than a null-hypothesis test, for it gives a posterior credible interval and so indicates *how* much of an effect there is, *how* different the population means are, *how* large the population correlation might be.

A third objection is that by continuing to collect data, one can always reject the null hypothesis, even if it is true, at any level of significance desired. At some point in collecting data chance deviation from the truth will be large enough and the standard error small enough that a significant result will be obtained.

A fourth problem is that null-hypothesis testing may lead to erroneous inferences. The general conclusion of such Bayesians as Good (1950, 1965) and

Edwards, Lindman and Savage (1963), is that a significance level of 0·05 or even 0·01 does not necessarily indicate heavy weight against the null hypothesis. Pitz (1968) showed, for an example concerning inference about a population proportion, that rejection of the null hypothesis at the 0·05 level implied a posterior probability of at *least* 0·16 *for* the null hypothesis.

A fifth difficulty has been formulated by Lindley (1957) as a statistical paradox. He points out that it is possible for a random sample to lead a traditionalist to reject the null hypothesis at, say, the 0·05 level, while a Bayesian would assign a posterior probability to the null hypothesis of as much as 0·95. His analysis shows that for those random samples yielding a highly significant rejection of the null hypothesis, then the larger the size of the sample the closer to one is the posterior probability assigned to the null hypothesis. One consequence is that a sample can always be found that strengthens the Bayesian's belief in the null hypothesis while leading the traditionalist to reject it.

Many of these and other inherent difficulties with traditional statistical methods are well known to statisticians of all persuasions. Various prescriptions for coping with these difficulties have been offered, such as the necessity for considering not only the significance level but also statistical 'power' when designing an experiment. (*Power* refers to the probability of correctly rejecting the null hypothesis.) But in practice power is rarely considered explicitly, judging by the rarity of its mention in journal articles. Instead scientists usually apply intuitive and judgemental 'adjustments' when interpreting significance and null-hypothesis tests. But, as Bakan (1966) has pointed out so well, these 'adjustments' have led to a number of misinterpretations that are now widely believed, such as interpreting the level of significance as if it were the probability to be associated with the truth of the null hypothesis. Furthermore, Tversky and Kahneman (1971) have found the judgement and intuition of professional psychologists to be seriously in error when they were asked to make research decisions after being given the results of statistical tests from previous experiments. Thus, it appears that in many cases the 'adjustments' just do not work very well.

One way out of these difficulties is to adopt a Bayesian approach. Whenever possible, inferences should be made about uncertain quantities, for these inferences are quite straightforward and less likely to lead to misinterpretation. Instead of reporting a traditional significance level, like $p < 0.05$, one should report the more informative posterior credible interval: $p(19.94 \leq \mu \leq 29.8) = 0.95$. On occasion, interest will legitimately be centred on null hypotheses, on interval hypotheses, or on tests of independence. The Bayesian approach to them is covered in the next and concluding chapter.

13.4 Summary

Traditional methods of making inferences do not normally use Bayes' theorem; instead, inferences are based on the sampling distribution of a statistic. A sampling distribution is a hypothetical distribution, one that would result if repeated samples of size N were drawn from a population, the statistic of interest calculated for each sample, and then a distribution of those sample statistics were drawn.

The sampling distribution might be used in three ways: to find a confidence interval for a population parameter, to make an estimate of the specific value of some population parameter, or to test some hypothesis of interest.

A confidence interval for a population parameter is found by assuming that the sample statistic obtained in an experiment is an unlikely result found in one of the tails of the sampling distribution, and then locating the mean of the sampling distribution as so many standard deviations from the sample result. For example, in finding the 95% confidence interval concerning the population mean, one assumes that the mean of the sampling distribution is either 1·96 standard deviations *above* the sample mean, or 1·96 standard deviations *below* the sample mean, or anywhere in between. Those extreme values of the mean of the sampling distribution form the limits of the 95% confidence interval for the population mean. This procedure is justified because the mean of the sampling distribution of means is equal to the population mean. A non-Bayesian states that there is a 95% chance that the confidence interval contains the true value of the population mean. A Bayesian would say there is a 95% chance that the population mean falls between the obtained limits. One is a probability statement about the interval, the other about the population parameter. Sometimes sampling distributions are given for test statistics, which are transformations of the data that involve population parameters.

In making an inference in the form of a point estimate about some population parameter, the non-Bayesian tries to select a sample statistic that will provide an unbiased, consistent, sufficient, and efficient estimator of the population parameter. Of particular importance to Bayesians and non-Bayesians alike, sufficient statistics are those statistics computed from the data that contain enough information to enable an inference to be made. Sufficient statistics should always be included in communicating the results of an investigation so that the reader can form his own inference.

Sometimes an investigator wishes to test some hypothesis, often called the *null hypothesis*, against an alternative hypothesis. The non-Bayesian observes data in an experiment, and if he finds that the data are quite unlikely to have been obtained given the truth of the null hypothesis, then he rejects the null hypothesis. This procedure is carried out with reference to the sampling distribution; the sampling distribution can be worked out given the truth of the null hypothesis, and regions of rejection can be established. These regions are usually in the tails of the sampling distribution, for it is assumed that if a sample result falls there, then the data were more likely to have been obtained given the truth of the alternative hypothesis. Finally, if the data for an experiment are found to fall in a rejection region, then the null hypothesis is rejected.

A Bayesian objects to testing null hypotheses by these procedures because they fail to take explicit account of prior probabilities, alternative hypotheses are easily ignored, the resulting inference depends on data not observed, they lay undue emphasis on null hypotheses that are not really of much interest, they are concerned with one specific value of an uncertain quantity and so must have virtually zero prior probability, and they tend to be too ready to reject the null hypothesis. The exercise of wisdom in applying and interpreting traditional significance tests is frequently based on an unsatisfactory collection of statistical lore and on misinformed intuition. Good sense has not been able to patch up the logical shortcomings of traditional methods; it has often made matters worse.

Problems

13–1 Carry out significance tests for any of the problems given at the ends of Chapters 11 and 12.

13–2 Find examples of non-Bayesian tests in the literature of your major subject, and try to interpret them from a Bayesian point of view.

14 · Testing hypotheses

So far our inferences about uncertain quantities have been expressed in terms of credible intervals. Now it is time to consider some other ways of making inferences, all within a Bayesian framework. The general theme underlying this chapter is that meaningful inferences can sometimes be made about hypotheses themselves, rather than about uncertain quantities. We will consider three ways of doing this:

by making inferences about hypotheses that concern intervals of an uncertain quantity (tests of interval hypotheses);

by noting whether some hypothesis of interest falls outside the posterior credible interval of some uncertain quantity (significance tests);

by testing a specific null hypothesis against a diffuse alternative (null-hypothesis tests).

On completion of this chapter you should know how to carry out each kind of test. You should also be well aware of the limitations and possible misinterpretations of significance tests and null-hypothesis tests.

The topic of the next section was covered briefly in Chapter 12. Here it is discussed in more detail.

14.1 Tests of interval hypotheses

One is sometimes interested in whether an uncertain quantity is more or less than a fixed value. For example, we know that 100 denotes an average I.Q. If we are conducting an experiment on a sample of people drawn from a special population, we might need to know if the population has a mean I.Q. greater than 100. We set up two hypotheses:

H_1: population mean greater than 100
H_2: population mean less than 100

Of course, we do not need to consider the hypothesis that it is *exactly* 100; recall that when we are dealing with an uncertain quantity we make probability statements only about intervals, because the probability of any precise value is zero.

We wish to find the probabilities we should attach to those hypotheses, that is,

$$p(H_1|D) = p(\mu > 100)$$
$$p(H_2|D) = p(\mu < 100)$$

The methods explained in Chapter 6 and discussed briefly in Chapter 12 will solve the problem. We simply find the areas of the posterior distribution that lie to the right of 100 and to the left of 100; those areas give the probabilities of H_1 and H_2.

Exercise 14–1

A scientist wishes to discover which of two theories of visual perception is more plausible. Theory A predicts that a certain measurement, or index, computed from hundreds of observations of an individual's choice behaviour will be greater than 1, while theory B predicts that the number will be less than 1. The scientist makes observations on 20 people and computes the measure for each person. Because of measurement error, some indices are below 1 and others are above. However, the scientist knows from previous experience what the measurement error is, so he treats his problem as one of inferring the mean of a normal population whose variance is known.

He carries out a Bayesian analysis which gives his posterior distribution concerning μ as normal with

$$m'' = 1\cdot2$$
$$s'' = 0\cdot125$$

What probability should he associate with the hypothesis that the population mean is greater than 1?

Answer

The solution is obvious when you look at the posterior distribution. Here it is:

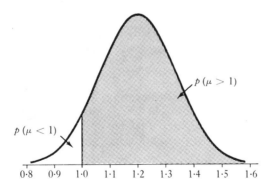

The probability of μ being greater than 1 is given by the shaded area. To find the area, we first find the z-value equivalent to an x-value of $1\cdot0$.

$$z = \frac{1\cdot0 - 1\cdot2}{0\cdot125} = \frac{-0\cdot2}{0\cdot125} = -1\cdot6$$

Next we consult the cumulative probability table for the normal distribution (Appendix F) to see how much area occurs to the right of $z = -1\cdot6$. That is the same as asking how much area occurs to the *left* of $z = +1\cdot6$. I get $0\cdot9452$. Thus,

$$p(\mu > 1) = 0\cdot9452$$

There is a $94\cdot52\%$ chance that the population mean is greater than 1. Whether or not you attach that same probability to the truth of Theory A is an extra-statistical matter!

Of course, you cannot use cumulative normal tables for problems in which the posterior distribution is Student-*t* (unless *N* is very large) or IG2. Then you need cumulative tables for those distributions. You will find cumulative Student-*t* tables in Appendix G. Be sure you get the right one; each column is for a separate curve—note the degrees of freedom at the top of the column.

Exercise 14–2

A posterior distribution concerning the population mean is Student-*t* with

$$\mu''_t = 86\cdot5$$
$$\sigma''_t = 2\cdot5$$
$$df'' = 14$$

What is the probability that the true value of the mean is less than 90?

Answer

First, the *t*-value corresponding to 90:

$$t = \frac{90 - 86\cdot5}{2\cdot5} = \frac{3\cdot5}{2\cdot5} = 1\cdot4$$

Next, consult the cumulative Student-*t* function for 14 degrees of freedom. For a *t*-value of $1\cdot4$ note that $0\cdot90836$ of the curve lies to the left. So,

$$p(\mu < 90) = 0\cdot90836$$

You will rarely, if ever, be interested in finding the probability that the true value of σ is above or below some specific value, so I have not felt it worthwhile to compute and append the fairly extensive tables of the cumulative IG2 distribution.

Of course, the methods in this section apply as well to any of the uncertain quantities discussed in Chapters 11 and 12. For example, to find the probability that the true value of a median is either above or below a certain value, you first find the rank that corresponds to that value (interpolating if necessary), and then find the areas of the posterior distribution that lie above and below that rank. Since the posterior is a normal distribution, the procedure is straightforward. Similarly, to find how probable it is that the mean of a normal population (with known variance) is above or below a particular value, you find the areas of the normal posterior that lie above and below that value.

To find the probability that an unknown proportion is above or below a certain value, you need cumulative tables for the Beta distribution. They take up a whole book in themselves because there are so many different Beta distributions. You will find the cumulative function tabulated in *Tables of the Incomplete Beta-Function*, by K. Pearson, Biometrika, London, 1934. The tables cover values of p and q up to 50, but only for values of p greater than q. If you wish to find the cumulative probability up to some value π^* when q is greater than p, you should interchange the values of p and q, find the table corresponding to those values, then enter the table with $1 - \pi^*$, and subtract the tabled cumulative probability from 1. This procedure works because the density function for $q > p$ is the mirror image of the one for $p > q$ (see Fig. 14–1).

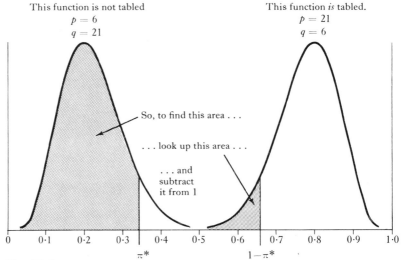

Fig. 14–1

How to find cumulative probabilities for Beta functions in which q is greater than p

In making an inference about whether the difference between two population means is greater or less than some particular value (often, 0), you find the areas of the posterior distribution that are above and below the value of interest. If the population variances are assumed equal, then we know that the posterior is a Student-t, and cumulative tables are in Appendix G. But if you cannot make that assumption, then the posterior is a Behrens distribution, a distribution with so many parameters that cumulative tables have not been calculated. You should, in this situation, try to collect sufficient amounts of data to enable your posterior to be approximated with a Student-t or a normal distribution. Alternatively, you might carry out a Bayesian significance test, as discussed in the next section.

A similar difficulty is encountered if you wish to know how probable it is that the ratio of two population variances is above (or below) a certain number (often, 1). Cumulative tables of the F-distribution do not exist, so your inferences must take the form of a credible interval. A Bayesian significance test is also possible.

Sometimes an investigator is interested in whether a population correlation coefficient is greater or less than a particular value (often, 0). He can find the probabilities by noting the areas under the normal posterior to the right and to the left of the Fisher-z transformation of that value.

Exercise 14–3

An investigator finds a Pearson correlation of 0·42 between two measures for a random sample of size 25. What are the posterior odds favouring a population correlation that is positive rather than negative?

Answer

To find the odds we must first find the areas of the posterior distribution to the right and to the left of the Fisher-z transformation of $\rho = 0$. Here are the steps.

1   Find the Fisher-z transformation of $r = 0·42$. From Table K, it is $z = 0·45$.

2   Find the parameters of the posterior distribution. They are

$$m'' = 0·45$$

$$s'' = \frac{1}{\sqrt{N}} = \frac{1}{\sqrt{25}} = 0·2$$

3   Find the Fisher-z transformation of $\rho = 0$. From Table K, it is 0.

4   At this point we have a normal distribution whose mean is 0·45 and whose standard deviation is 0·2. We want to find the areas of the curve to either side of 0. We can do this by referring to the cumulative normal distribution, but first we need to know the z-value corresponding to 0.

$$z = \frac{0 - m''}{s''} = \frac{0 - 0·45}{0·2} = -2·25$$

5   From Appendix F, we see that 0·9878 of the area of the curve is found to the right of a z-value of $-2·25$, leaving 0·0122 to the left. Thus, there is a 98·78% chance that the population correlation is positive.

6   The posterior odds favouring a positive correlation are, then,

$$\Omega'' = \frac{p}{1 - p} = \frac{0·9878}{0·0122} = 81$$

Thus, the odds are 81 to 1 in favour of a positive correlation.

14.2 Significance tests

I write this section with some reluctance because the procedure to be explained here does not allow the assigning of a probability to the hypothesis of interest, and because the test is easily misinterpreted.

The key idea is quite simple. Once a null hypothesis has been defined, the Bayesian has only to see whether that hypothesis lies outside or inside the C per cent credible interval. If the null hypothesis lies outside the interval, then the null hypothesis is said to be rejected at the $(100 - C)$ per cent level of significance. For example, suppose we are interested in the hypothesis that the mean of a population is exactly 100, and we have found the posterior 99% credible interval for μ to be 104 to 119. The null hypothesis of 100 lies outside the interval, so we reject the null hypothesis at the 1% level of significance.

Exercise 14–4

Carry out a Bayesian significance test of the null hypothesis that there is no difference between the means of the population of men's and women's scores for Exercise 12–3.

Answer

Recall that the difference between the population means is designated by δ, where $\delta = \mu_1 - \mu_2$. The null hypothesis, H_0, is defined as follows:

H_0: $\delta = 0$

In Exercise 12–3 we found that the posterior 99% credible interval for δ is:

$$-9.84 \leq \delta \leq 4.64$$

Since 0 is contained in that interval, we cannot reject the null hypothesis at the 1% level of significance.

This approach is particularly useful when interval hypotheses cannot be tested because tables of the cumulative posterior do not exist, or are not readily available, and when the methods of the next section do not apply. If the prior is uniform, then this test gives the same result as a traditional significance test. Thus, a non-Bayesian significance test can be interpreted, in most cases, as identical or similar to a Bayesian significance test carried out with a uniform prior.

My reservations about Bayesian significance tests are similar to those about non-Bayesian significance tests. The significance level does not give the posterior probability to be associated with the null hypothesis; strictly speaking, the posterior probability of the null hypothesis is zero, for it is a point hypothesis, one particular value of the uncertain quantity. The argument is sometimes made that the null hypothesis is not really a point hypothesis at all, it is instead a very narrow interval. The null hypothesis should not be defined as a difference of zero in the above exercise, it should be thought of as a difference of *near* zero or zero. But, the Bayesian argues, if you think of the null hypothesis as a narrow region, then it is a simple matter to find the probability of the parameter lying within that interval; you just calculate the area of the posterior distribution over that interval. Thus, the testing of a narrow null hypothesis is a straightforward application of principles discussed before.

On the whole, I think Bayesian significance tests of sharp null hypotheses are not fully sustained by Bayesian logic, and so should be avoided where possible. If one is really interested in a point null hypothesis, then the procedures of the next section make a little more sense from a Bayesian point of view, and so should be preferred to significance tests.

14.3 Null-hypothesis tests

Usually one wishes to know how much of an effect something has, so that interest focusses on the actual value of some uncertain quantity. We have seen, from a Bayesian point of view, that an inference about the uncertain quantity can be expressed as a posterior distribution, as a posterior credible interval, or as interval hypotheses. And we have expressed some doubt about the meaningfulness of Bayesian significance tests, which on the surface seem to be straightforward tests of null hypotheses. We have seen that they have at least two troubles: the probability, prior and posterior, associated with the null hypothesis is zero, and the alternative hypothesis is not explicitly taken into consideration.

The methods of this section avoid both those difficulties. Some of the methods have other troubles, usually difficulties in defining an alternative distribution or in assigning prior probabilities. But at least the limitations are out in the open to a greater degree than for significance tests.

A great deal of work on testing sharp null hypotheses against diffuse alternatives has been carried out by Jeffreys (1961). His book contains tests to cover all the experimental situations described in this book. However, his methods are not accepted by all Bayesians, so it is probably premature to give

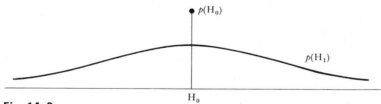

Fig. 14–2
Some prior opinion concentrated on a specific (null) hypothesis with the remainder spread out over a diffuse alternative hypothesis

extensive coverage of them in an introductory textbook. Considering that the first edition of his book appeared in 1939, and that the first thoroughgoing Bayesian textbook appeared in 1959 (Schlaifer, 1959), it would appear that Jeffreys was and is well in advance of Bayesian practice.

Most of the methods of this section apply whenever the investigator has in mind some specific hypothesis, which we will again call a null hypothesis, to which he is willing to assign some prior probability. His remaining prior probability is spread out over the possible values that go to make up the diffuse alternative hypothesis. In other words, some of his prior probability is spread out over possible values of an uncertain quantity, while the rest of his prior opinion appears as a blob over one specific value of the uncertain quantity. I have shown this in Fig. 14–2.

Testing a specific proportion

Suppose that in making an inference about a proportion as an uncertain quantity, you believe before doing the experiment that there is some chance that the population proportion, π, might be some specific value, call it π^*. The rest of your prior opinion you are willing to spread out uniformly over all the other possible values of π. Your prior opinion is uniform over the interval from 0 to 1, with a lump of it sitting on π^* (see Fig. 14–3).

Thus, we have two hypotheses, a null and an alternative, defined as follows:

$$H_0: \pi = \pi^*$$

$$H_1: \pi \neq \pi^*$$

Our prior probabilities are, as usual, designated as $p(H_0)$ and $p(H_1)$. If half your opinion is assigned to π^*, then,

$$p(H_0) = 0\cdot5$$

$$p(H_1) = 0\cdot5$$

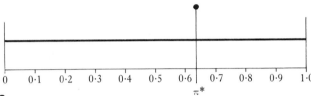

Fig. 14–3

A lump of prior opinion on π^*, with the remainder spread out uniformly over values of the population proportion from 0 to 1

An experiment is conducted in which $\bar{s}$ successes are observed, and $\bar{f}$ failures. In order to find the posterior probabilities in the light of these data, we need to know the likelihoods. It will be convenient to work with the likelihood ratio, L:

$$L = \frac{p(D|H_0)}{p(D|H_1)} = \frac{p(\bar{s}, \bar{f}|\text{null})}{p(\bar{s}, \bar{f}|\text{alternative})}$$

For this problem, it turns out that the likelihood ratio is equal to the Y-value of a Beta distribution whose parameters are $p = \bar{s}+1$ and $q = \bar{f}+1$, at $X = \pi^*$. Recall that the equation for the Beta distribution is

$$Y = \frac{(p+q-1)!}{(p-1)!(q-1)!} X^{p-1}(1-X)^{q-1}$$

If we substitute π^* for X, $\bar{s}+1$ for p, and $\bar{f}+1$ for q, then we get an expression for the likelihood ratio:

$$L = \frac{(\bar{s}+\bar{f}+1)!}{\bar{s}!\bar{f}!} (\pi^*)^{\bar{s}}(1-\pi^*)^{\bar{f}}$$

To get the posterior odds, remember that it is necessary to multiply the likelihood ratio by the prior odds.

Exercise 14–5

Let us resurrect our gambler discussed in Chapters 1 and 4. Recall that he has either a fair coin or a biased one. In Chapter 4 we had to specify the degree of bias in order to apply Bayes' theorem, but now we do not. Our two hypotheses are:

H_0: coin is fair, that is, $\pi^* = 0.5$
H_1: coin is biased, that is, $\pi^* \neq 0.5$

We assign half our prior opinion to H_0 and we spread out the other half uniformly over the possible values of π^* from 0 to 1. The coin is flipped and 8 heads out of 10 flips are observed. What are the posterior probabilities?

Answer

First we evaluate the likelihood ratio.

$$L = \frac{(8 + 2 + 1)!}{8!\,2!}\,(0.5)^8(0.5)^2 = \frac{11!}{8!\,2!}\,(0.5)^{10}$$

$$= \frac{11 \times 10 \times 9 \times 8 \times 7 \times 6 \times 5 \times 4 \times 3 \times 2}{(8 \times 7 \times 6 \times 5 \times 4 \times 3 \times 2)(2)}\,(0.5)^{10}$$

$$= 11 \times 5 \times 9\,\frac{1}{1024} = \frac{495}{1024} = 0.483$$

Multiplying by prior odds of 1 gives the posterior odds:

$$\Omega'' = 0.483$$

Converting the odds to probabilities gives:

$$p(H_0|D) = \frac{\Omega''}{1 - \Omega''} = \frac{0.483}{1.483} = 0.326$$

Thus, on the strength of this evidence, and considering a uniform prior over the diffuse alternative hypothesis, there is a 32.6% chance that the coin is fair.

Computing the likelihood ratio for sizeable values of $\bar{s}$ and $\bar{f}$ can be a chore, so it is best to use logarithms. Logs of the factorials are already worked out and tabled in Appendix H. As an example, here is the log of the likelihood ratio for the example above:

$$\log L = \log 11! - \log 8! - \log 2! + 10 \log 0.5$$
$$= 7.6012 - 4.6055 - 0.3010 + 10(-0.3010) = -0.3153$$

Taking the antilog of that value gives $L = 0.484$, which is close enough.

This procedure, or some variation of it, is occasionally useful when numerical measurements have been made from a population of unknown distribution. Since the population cannot be assumed normal or even symmetrical, the methods of Chapters 11 and 12 do not apply. But if the investigator is willing to lose some information from his data, he can carry out a *Bayesian sign test*. Here is an example.

Exercise 14–6

In Exercise 12–4 a statistics instructor obtained scores on a mathematics test before and after students had completed programmed learning in mathematics. There we enquired about the population mean of the difference in scores. To do this we assumed the population was normal. If we do not make that assumption, we can look at the proportion of times the after score was greater than the before score. If the instruction has no effect, we would expect that proportion to be around 0·5, for only chance would dictate which score was larger. The two hypotheses we wish to consider are

$H_0: \pi = 0\cdot5$

$H_1: \pi \neq 0\cdot5$

What inference can we make about those hypotheses?

Answer

Suppose that the statistics instructor thinks it is about three times as likely that the instruction will cause some change of score as that it will not. The prior odds are, then,

$$\Omega' = \frac{p(H_0|D)}{p(H_1|D)} = \frac{1}{3}$$

Looking at the before and after scores (on page 287 of Chapter 12), we see that all 15 of the after scores are larger, so $\bar{s} = 15$ and $\bar{f} = 0$. Now the likelihood ratio:

$$L = \frac{16!}{15!\,0!}(0\cdot5)^{15}(0\cdot5)^0 = 16(0\cdot5)^{15} = \frac{16}{32768} = 0\cdot000488$$

The posterior odds are

$$\Omega'' = \tfrac{1}{3}(0\cdot000489) = 0\cdot000163$$

These odds imply a probability of

$$p(H_0|D) = \frac{0\cdot000163}{1\cdot000163} = 0\cdot000163$$

In words, that is overwhelming evidence for the effectiveness of the programmed instruction, as should have been obvious from inspection of the data.

The only assumption that goes into this test is that the observations must be independent. Otherwise it is a remarkably assumption-free test. Its equivalent in the non-Bayesian literature is called a sign test, too, but since it leads to a significance test, it does not give the same result as the Bayesian sign test which is based on the likelihood ratio and the prior odds. Incidentally, this test, like its non-Bayesian counterpart, is often classed as a *non-parametric* or *distribution-free* method because no assumption is made about the population of scores. Of course, the actual values of those scores is not taken into account in the test, only their relative magnitude is important, so some information contained in the original data is lost in this test. That means that this test is not very sensitive when the data are somewhat equivocal. Anyway, remember that the test only tells us that an effect is there, it does not tell us how big the effect is. Only by making an inference like the one in Exercise 12–4 do we find out what the difference in population means actually is. The Bayesian sign test would have given the same result if each person's 'after' score had been just 1 point larger than his 'before' score.

You might object, quite rightly, that the prior distribution for the alternative hypothesis in the exercise was not very realistic. Surely the statistics instructor does not really think all possible proportions are equally likely; it seems unlikely that instruction would cause the 'after' scores to be generally *less* than the 'before' scores, for example. I agree, but for this particular example the data are so overwhelming that the prior specification does not matter very much. Anyway, stable estimation applies here, too, so you can take the uniform prior for the alternative as equivalent to vagueness. As long as the prior is fairly flat in the vicinity of the data (it is) then the uniform prior will be satisfactory. That is not to say that the Bayesian approach cannot accommodate a more realistic prior for the alternative. It can, but the mathematics are beyond the scope of this book.

Testing correlations

Suppose you are interested only in whether two sets of observations are correlated or not. You wish to consider just two hypotheses:

H_0: uncorrelated, that is, $\rho = 0$

H_1: correlated, that is, $\rho \neq 0$

You have computed the Pearson correlation coefficient for the data and wish to find the posterior odds favouring H_0. Jeffreys has shown that, if we take a uniform distribution over ρ, the likelihood ratio is given by this approximation:

$$L \simeq \sqrt{\frac{2N-1}{\pi}} \, (1-r^2)^{(N-3)/2}$$

In this expression, N is the number of pairs of observations, π is the universal constant $3 \cdot 1415 \ldots$, and r is the sample correlation. The approximation is better the larger the value of N.

Exercise 14–7

It is not uncommon to read in the social science literature a report of research in which an investigator obtained a correlation of, say, $0 \cdot 35$, with a sample size of 30. By a non-Bayesian analysis, this would be reported as significant at the $0 \cdot 05$ level, that is, the null hypothesis of zero correlation can be rejected at the $0 \cdot 05$ level of significance. What would a Bayesian say about this result?

Answer

Let us assume that the prior probabilities for H_0 and H_1 are equal, so the prior odds are 1. Applying Jeffreys' equation gives us this likelihood ratio:

$$L = \sqrt{\frac{2(30)-1}{\pi}} \, (1 - 0 \cdot 1225)^{27/2} = \sqrt{18 \cdot 8} (0 \cdot 8775)^{13 \cdot 5}$$

At this point logarithms are needed to evaluate $(0 \cdot 8775)^{13 \cdot 5}$. Finally, I got $L = 0 \cdot 742$.

Converting the odds to probabilities:

$$p(H_0 | D) = \frac{0 \cdot 742}{1 \cdot 742} = 0 \cdot 43$$

Thus, a correlation of $0 \cdot 35$ obtained on 30 pairs of observations would lead a Bayesian to conclude that there is only a $0 \cdot 57$ probability that a linear relationship exists between the variables.

The 'significance' of the result is not a very useful conclusion. That is what I meant in the previous chapter when I said that non-Bayesian significance tests are sometimes misleading, and too ready to reject the null hypothesis. Even the more stringent 0·01 level of significance may lead the reader to think that the probability of the null hypothesis is 1%. But as we have seen, significance levels should not be interpreted as probabilities to be associated with the null hypothesis. For example, a correlation of 0·5 obtained on 25 pairs of observations will be deemed by the non-Bayesian as significant at the 0·01 level. Yet, applying Jeffreys' equation with equal prior odds gives a posterior probability for the null hypothesis of 0·14. There is a 14% chance of no linear relationship with these data, not 1 chance in 100.

Testing the mean of a normal population

You may find an occasion where it is reasonable to assign some prior probability to the hypothesis that a population mean is a specific value that you have in mind. The alternative hypothesis is that the mean is some other value.

H_0: $\mu = \mu^*$

H_1: $\mu \neq \mu^*$

Jeffreys has given an approximation to the likelihood ratio:

$$L \simeq \frac{\sqrt{\dfrac{\pi(N-1)}{2}}}{\left(1 + \dfrac{t^2}{N-1}\right)^{(N-2)/2}}$$

In the equation, π is the universal constant, N is the number of observations, and t is given by

$$t = \frac{M - \mu^*}{S/\sqrt{N}}$$

where M is the mean of the sample and S is the standard deviation of the sample. Note that t is the test statistic that was discussed in the previous chapter. This likelihood ratio presumes that opinion about the alternative value of μ is sufficiently vague for stable estimation to apply. The approximation is better for larger values of N. As usual, the likelihood ratio has only to be multiplied by the prior odds to give the posterior odds.

Exercise 14–8

An investigator who wishes to make an inference about the mean of a normal population whose variance is unknown obtains a sample, calculates the mean and standard deviation, and computes the value of the t-statistic. It is 2·8, which, for his sample of size 25, allows him to reject his null hypothesis by a traditional significance test ($p < 0·01$). What conclusions might a Bayesian draw?

Answer

Let us apply Jeffreys' test. Assume the prior probabilities for the two hypotheses are equal. Then the posterior odds equal the likelihood ratio, so

$$\Omega'' = \frac{\sqrt{12\pi}}{\left(1 + \dfrac{(2 \cdot 80)^2}{24}\right)^{11 \cdot 5}} = 0 \cdot 238$$

Converting to probabilities gives

$$p(H_0|D) = \frac{0 \cdot 238}{1 \cdot 238} = 0 \cdot 192$$

Thus, that 'significant' rejection of the null hypothesis leaves the Bayesian believing there is almost 1 chance in 5 that the null hypothesis is correct.

Testing the difference between means

Imagine, now, that you want to test the null hypothesis that the difference between the means of two normal populations is zero, that is, that the means are equal. Assume that the populations are normal and that their variances are equal.

$H_0 \colon \mu_1 = \mu_2$

$H_1 \colon \mu_1 \neq \mu_2$

This is a rather complicated problem because the alternative hypothesis is more complex than it looks. Jeffreys provides an approximation for the posterior odds:

$$\Omega'' \simeq \frac{\dfrac{2}{5} \sqrt{\left(\dfrac{\pi}{2}\right) \left(\dfrac{N_1 N_2}{N_1 + N_2}\right)}}{\left(1 + \dfrac{t^2}{N_1 + N_2 - 2}\right)^{(N_1 + N_2 - 1)/2}}$$

In this expression, π is the universal constant, N_1 and N_2 are the sizes of the samples from the two populations, and t is given by

$$t = \frac{M_1 - M_2}{\sqrt{\left(\dfrac{SS_{XX_1} + SS_{XX_2}}{N_1 + N_2 - 2}\right) \left(\dfrac{N_1 + N_2}{N_1 N_2}\right)}}$$

where SS_{XX_1}, SS_{XX_2}, M_1, and M_2 are all defined on page 279 of Chapter 12.

Exercise 14–9

An investigator carrying out a non-Bayesian significance test of the difference between two means (normal populations, variances assumed equal) obtains samples each of size 25 from the two populations, and calculates a *t*-value of 2·5. He declares the result significant at the 0·02 level (it did not quite make it to 0·01). Thus, he rejects the null hypothesis ($p < 0 \cdot 02$). What conclusion would be reached by a Bayesian?

Answer

A Bayesian would probably prefer to find a posterior credible interval for the difference between means, report that, and leave the reader to draw his own conclusion. That applies as well to the previous three exercises. But if he insists on carrying out a test of the null hypothesis, he might apply Jeffreys' approximation.

$$\Omega'' = \frac{\frac{2}{5}\sqrt{\left(\frac{\pi}{2}\right)\left(\frac{625}{50}\right)}}{\left(1 + \frac{6 \cdot 25}{48}\right)^{49/2}} = 0 \cdot 0883$$

Those odds give a posterior probability of

$$p(\mathrm{H_0|D}) = \frac{0 \cdot 0883}{1 \cdot 0883} = 0 \cdot 081$$

Even after 50 observations, the Bayesian still assigns better than 8% of his opinion to the null hypothesis.

These past few exercises should give adequate illustration of the Bayesian's claim that traditional significance tests are too ready to reject the null hypothesis.

Jeffreys gives many more methods for testing null hypotheses against alternatives, but I think the applications given here are sufficient to show the general approach. There is just one more kind of test that I want to discuss, one that is particularly useful in the early stages of an investigation when the scientist is still trying to discover what goes with what. We turn to it next.

Tests of independence

Much of the social science literature is concerned with discovering whether or not an independent variable has any relationship at all to a dependent variable. We have seen that correlation provides one approach to answering such questions; we can enquire about the value of the population correlation coefficient between variables X and Y, or we can test to see if the correlation is zero, implying no relationship, at least of a linear sort. But what do you do if you think the relationship may not be linear, or if the variables admit of no more than categorical measurement?

The two methods to be presented in this section make almost no assumptions about the data, require only that observations be classified in categories (numerical measurement is not required, though it can be carried out and used as a basis for classification), can be applied to a great many experimental situations, and are very easy to work out. But these advantages are bought at a cost: the methods tell you only whether X and Y are independent in the statistical sense discussed at the end of Chapter 3. That is not very much information, for if you carry out one of the tests and conclude that X and Y are *not* likely to be independent, then you are left knowing nothing whatsoever about the nature of the dependency. You do not know whether it is linear or nonlinear, whether it will allow meaningful predictions to be made or not, whether it is a small relationship or a large one.

In spite of these rather severe limitations, the methods are useful when an investigation is just beginning and the researcher wants to weed out independent variables that do not have any influence on his dependent variable. They may also be useful later in the study if it turns out that the assumptions that go into the tests mentioned up to now simply cannot be met. And the tests are very useful if only categorical measurement is possible on the data.

The first approach has a traditional counterpart; it is called a *Chi-squared test of independence*. It is a significance test, with all the attendant difficulties of that type of test. The second method is a Bayesian null-hypothesis test of independence due to Jeffreys. For both of these methods the experimental situation is the same. A random sample of size N is selected, and each observation is classified in only one of the X categories and in only one of the Y categories. An allowable variant on this procedure is to fix ahead of time the numbers of observations falling in either the X or the Y category.

As an example, suppose you are interested in finding out if there is any connection between the social class of parents and the age at which they wean their babies. You might set out to sample randomly middle and working class families, or you might decide ahead of time to observe, say, 50 middle class families and 30 working class. Let us suppose you tried to sample 60 families in each category, but ended up with less than that because some families dropped out of your study before it was finished. You followed these families over a period of time so you can observe when the child was weaned. Then you classified each family in one of the four cells of the following table (often called a 2-by-2 contingency table):

Weaning

		Early	Late		
Social	Middle	33	22	55	Observed
Class	Working	17	31	48	data
		50	53	103	

(These data were adapted from Miller and Swanson, 1960.)

In words, 33 middle class families weaned early while 22 weaned late. Early weaning was observed in 17 working class families, while 31 working class families weaned late. The marginal totals tell us that 55 families were middle class and 48 were working class, and that 50 families weaned early while 53 weaned late. A total of 103 families were observed. These data will be called the *observed* data.

The next step is to calculate for each cell frequencies that would be *expected* if the variables were independent. At this point, it may be helpful to re-read the discussion at the end of Chapter 3 on independence. Recall that there we said that if two events were independent, then the probability of their joint occurrence is equal to the product of their individual probabilities.

$$p(\text{E and F}) = p(\text{E})\,p(\text{F})$$

Let us apply that to the upper left cell of the 2×2 table. The probabilities of observing a middle class family that weans early, *if* those events are independent is

$$p(\text{middle class and early weaning}) = p(\text{middle class})\,p(\text{early weaning})$$

The probabilities on the right side of the equation can be obtained from the marginals; 55 families out of 103 are middle class, and 50 families out of 103 weaned early. Thus,

$$p(\text{middle class}) \quad = \frac{55}{103} = 0{\cdot}534$$

$$p(\text{early weaning}) = \frac{50}{103} = 0{\cdot}485$$

Now we can find the probability of the joint event:

$$p(\text{middle class and early weaning}) = 0{\cdot}534 \times 0{\cdot}485 = 0{\cdot}259$$

Now we repeat that process for the remaining three cells. The result is the probabilities of each joint event *given* pairwise independence.

	Early	Late	
Middle	0·259	0·275	Joint probabilities expected
Working	0·226	0·240	given independence
		1·000	

Notice that the probabilities sum to one as they should.

From that table we can construct one that gives expected frequencies. All we have to do is multiply each joint probability by 103. Here is the result:

	Early	Late		
Middle	26·7	28·3	55	
Working	23·3	24·7	48	Expected data
	50	53	103	

We call these cell frequencies *expected* data. Of course, they can be computed more easily than I have done; each expected frequency can be obtained by multiplying the appropriate marginal frequencies and dividing by the total. For example, the expected frequency in the upper left cell, 26·7, is obtained by multiplying the corresponding row marginal, 55, by the column marginal, 50, and then dividing that product by the total frequency, 103: $(55 \times 50)/103 = 26{\cdot}7$. The more cumbersome method I used above was only intended to show the logic used in arriving at expected frequencies.

At this point we have a set of observed data and a set of data we might have obtained under the hypothesis of independence. The question we must answer is whether each observed cell frequency deviates from the corresponding expected cell frequency only because chance is operating or because X and Y are really *not* independent. To answer that question we must first compute the chi-squared statistic:

$$\chi^2 = \sum \frac{(\text{O} - \text{E})^2}{\text{E}}$$

You take the difference between each observed and expected frequency, square the difference, divide by the expected frequency, and sum. Here is the calculation for these data:

$$\chi^2 = \frac{(33-26\cdot7)^2}{26\cdot7} + \frac{(22-28\cdot3)^2}{28\cdot3} + \frac{(17-23\cdot3)^2}{23\cdot3} + \frac{(31-24\cdot7)^2}{24\cdot7}$$
$$= 1\cdot49 + 1\cdot40 + 1\cdot70 + 1\cdot61 = 6\cdot2$$

Obviously the bigger that number is, the more likely it is that the null hypothesis of independence is wrong, for large values are obtained only when observed and expected frequencies differ considerably.

A Bayesian analysis tells us that the posterior distribution of the χ^2 statistic has a chi-squared distribution with $df'' = (R-1)(C-1)$, where R is the number of rows in the contingency table, and C is the number of columns. The chi-squared distribution is a very close relative of IG2, and so has a similar shape. It extends from 0 to $+\infty$, and is skewed with a long right tail.

As applied to tests of independence, the posterior distribution is *conditional* on the assumptions that went into calculating the expected frequencies, so for this problem we can use the Chi-squared distribution to give us the probability of obtaining our particular value of χ^2 or greater, *given* that independence between the two variables holds. If we find that probability is small, then we reject the assumption of independence. Thus, the posterior distribution is used to make a significance test. A non-Bayesian would arrive at the same conclusion but by a different route.

Specifically, we say that the departure of observed data from the data expected under independence is statistically significant (not due to chance) if the calculated value of χ^2 is bigger than the tabled value found in Appendix C. Since the larger χ^2 is, the more likely it is that the null hypothesis of independence is wrong, we put all of the rejection region in the right tail. The table gives, for the level of significance desired, the value of χ^2 at the borderline of the right-tail rejection region. The table is entered with the level of significance (along the top) and with $(R-1)(C-1)$ degrees of freedom (along the left edge). For a 2×2 table there is just $(2-1)(2-1) = 1$ degree of freedom.

For the example, we enter the table with 1 degree of freedom. We see that at the 0·05 level, the tabled value is only 3·84; our value of 6·20 is larger, so we can declare the result significant at the 0·05 level. Moving farther to the right we see that the result is not quite significant at the 0·01 level, but is at the 0·025 level. So, we might reject the null hypothesis of independence at the 0·025 level. There would appear to be some relationship between social class and age of weaning; the data indicate that middle class mothers tend to wean earlier than working class mothers.

This test is an approximation, valid for moderate to large values of N. It should not be used if any of the *expected* cell frequencies is less than 5. You must ensure that all the observations are independent of each other and that each observation appears only once in the table.

The procedure given above applies also to tables larger than 2×2. If, for example, you are investigating the relationship between social class and voting preference, you might have five categories of social class, and four categories of voting preference. Your 5×4 table would contain 20 cells, there would then be 20 terms to sum in calculating the χ^2 statistic, and the posterior distribution would have $(5-1)(4-1) = 12$ degrees of freedom.

For a 2×2 table, calculating the χ^2 statistic is often easier if you use this formula:

Observed frequencies

$$\chi^2 = \frac{(ad - bc)^2(a + b + c + d)}{(a + b)(c + d)(a + c)(b + d)}$$

a	b	$a+b$
c	d	$c+d$
$a+c$ $b+d$		$a+b+c+d$

That formula, which can be derived from the general expression given earlier, is particularly useful if you are making your calculations on an electronic calculator. For the problem given here, applying the formula gives the same result as before:

$$\chi^2 = \frac{[(33)(31) - (22)(17)]^2(103)}{(55)(48)(50)(53)} = \frac{43,383,703}{6,996,000} = 6 \cdot 20$$

Of course, the significance level should not be interpreted as the probability to be associated with the null hypothesis. It is difficult to devise a Bayesian procedure that will yield a posterior probability for the null hypothesis because it is very difficult to specify what the alternative is to independence. There are all sorts of possibilities, and it is not clear just how opinion should be distributed over them. Jeffreys has given one solution but it only applies to a 2×2 table:

$$L \simeq \frac{(\text{smallest marginal frequency} + 1)! \prod (\text{other marginal frequency})!}{(\text{total frequency})! \prod (\text{cell frequency})!}$$

Remember that the $\prod$ symbol means 'multiply'. L is $\dfrac{p(D|\text{independence})}{p(D|\text{dependence})}$.

Let us apply Jeffreys' procedure to the example. Suppose the prior odds are 1. Then,

$$\Omega'' \simeq \frac{(48 + 1)! \, 55! \, 50! \, 53!}{103! \, 33! \, 22! \, 17! \, 31!}$$

Logarithms of factorials are needed to evaluate this.

log (49!) =	62·7841	log (103!) =	163·9958
log (55!) =	73·1037	log (33!) =	36·9387
log (50!) =	64·4831	log (22!) =	21·0508
log (53!) =	69·6309	log (17!) =	14·5511
		log (31!) =	33·9150
	270·0018		
			270·4514

$$\log \Omega'' = 270 \cdot 0018 - 270 \cdot 4514 = -0 \cdot 4496$$

Taking the antilog,

$$\Omega'' = 0 \cdot 355$$

and converting to a probability gives

$$p(H_0|D) = \frac{0\cdot355}{1\cdot355} = 0\cdot262$$

Thus, there is better than 1 chance in 4 that independence is true. We may reject independence at the 0·025 level of significance, but there is still a 0·262 probability that social class and age of weaning are independent.

Difference between proportions

At the end of Chapter 12 in Section 12–5, I mentioned that chi-squared tests are often used to make inferences about the difference between the proportions. The method should be clear—it is just an application of the chi-squared significance test for a 2×2 table discussed in the previous section. An example should provide sufficient explanation.

Exercise 14–10

In a survey of Vassar College alumnae, M. B. Freedman (1961) found that 51% of 200 respondents from the Class of 1956 and 77% of 77 respondents from the Class of 1940–43 rejected the following item on the Public Opinion Survey that they filled out:

> 'Obedience and respect for authority are the most important virtues that children should learn.'

If those samples are taken as representative of their respective Classes, what inference could you make regarding the change in attitude reflected in the response to that one item?

Answer

One approach would be to make an inference concerning the difference in proportions between the two groups of alumnae. With such large samples, the normal approximation methods discussed in Section 12–1 are to be preferred, but any of the approaches in Section 12–5 could be used.

A chi-squared significance test requires first a table of observed frequencies. The proportions given in the problem are first translated into frequencies:

Number rejecting item in Class of 1956 = 0·51 × 200 = 102
Number rejecting item in Classes of 1940–43 = 0·77 × 77 = 59

Now a 2×2 table can be constructed.

		Item rejected	accepted	
Class	1956	102	98	200
	1940–43	59	18	77
		161	116	277

Next, we apply the special formula that enables us to find χ^2 for a 2×2 table:

$$\chi^2 = \frac{\{(102)(18) - (98)(59)\}^2 277}{(200)(77)(161)(116)} = \frac{4{,}313{,}143{,}732}{287{,}610{,}400} = 15\cdot0$$

The chi-squared table, for 1 degree of freedom, shows that 15·0 is well out in the tail, far enough that we can reject the hypothesis of independence beyond a significance level of 0·001. We could conclude that the change in attitude from 1940–43 to 1956 is real, and most likely not due to chance.

Goodness-of-fit

Another application of the chi-squared significance test is in comparing whole distributions. Suppose, for illustration, that a survey is conducted and the sample is taken from women who are passing by the main shopping area of a community and who are willing to participate in the survey. The marital status of each respondent is recorded along with the answers to the survey. Later the investigator wishes to see if his sample is representative, with regard to marital status only, of women in the community. The recent census for the area gives these percentages for adult women:

Never married	21%
Widowed	4%
Married	63%
Divorced	10%
Separated	2%

The distribution in his sample of 100 is as follows:

Never married	9
Widowed	7
Married	72
Divorced	11
Separated	1

To find out if this distribution is different from the population, we calculate expected frequencies from the census data and then compute the chi-squared statistic:

$$\chi^2 = \sum \frac{(O - E)^2}{E}$$

	Expected	*Observed*
Never married	21	9
Widowed	4	7
Married	63	72
Divorced	10	11
Separated	2	1

$$\chi^2 = \frac{(21-9)^2}{21} + \frac{(4-7)^2}{4} + \frac{(63-72)^2}{63} + \frac{(10-11)^2}{10} + \frac{(2-1)^2}{2}$$

$$= 6·86 + 2·25 + 1·29 + 0·10 + 0·50 = 11·0$$

The degrees of freedom are equal to $J-1$, where J equals the number of categories. For this problem, we have $5-1 = 4$ degrees of freedom. Next we consult the chi-squared table for 4 degrees of freedom. We see that our obtained value of 11 is not quite significant at the 0·025 level, but is significant at the 0·05 level. Thus, we might declare the obtained distribution as significantly different

($p < 0.05$) from the population, though the result is a marginal one. You can see that the distributions are fairly similar; declaring them as 'significantly different' means only that the difference is not likely due to chance.

Goodness-of-fit tests can also be used to compare one continuous distribution with another. The procedures are more involved than those given here for discrete distributions; the reader is advised to consult an advanced textbook such as Hays (1963) for the details.

Chi-squared: A warning!

It is worth repeating that the chi-squared tests are not immune from the criticisms made in the previous chapter about significance tests. The null hypotheses of independence, or of exact identity between distributions, are probably untrue right from the start. At least a minute connection can probably be found between almost any two variables, and most likely no two distributions are precisely alike. Given enough data we can always reject those null hypotheses; you will have little trouble finding in the literature chi-squared tests on very large samples that yielded significant results—but not important ones. We do not want to know only 'Is there an effect?' We want to know 'How big is the effect?' The latter question is *not* answered by the significance level. Significance at the 0·001 level does not necessarily mean that the effect is bigger or more sure or more substantial than significance at the 0·05 level. Quite the reverse could be true if the 0·001 level rejection occurred with a large sample and the 0·05 result with a small sample.

My value judgements should by now be abundantly clear. Whenever possible, I think the investigator should frame his statistical hypotheses around uncertain quantities so that he can make interval estimates of those quantities. If this cannot be done, or if interest centres on a genuine null hypothesis, then tests of null hypotheses against alternatives are much to be favoured over significance tests. In any event, adoption of conventions or blind applications of statistical procedures should never be a substitute for careful thought.

Finally, let me repeat that two assumptions must be met in applying chi-squared methods:

a   Observations must be independent. Repeated measures on the same person are not independent, so contingency tables based on such measures should not be analysed by chi-squared methods.

b   Each observation must find a unique place when it is classified. An observation must fall in only one cell of a contingency table, or be placed in only one category of a distribution.

Failure to meet these assumptions may lead you to reject the null hypothesis even though it is true.

14.4 Summary

Inferences about hypotheses that relate to an uncertain quantity are usually carried out as a test of an interval hypothesis, as a significance test, or as a test of a null hypothesis.

If we wish to find the probability that the true value of some uncertain quantity is either less than or more than some specific value, then it is only necessary to determine the area under the posterior distribution to the left and to the right of that value. Tables of the relevant cumulative distribution facilitate this task.

In a Bayesian significance test a point null hypothesis is declared rejected at the $(100 - C)$ per cent level of significance if it falls outside the C per cent credible interval. This procedure does not allow a posterior probability to be associated with the null hypothesis or its alternative; certainly the significance level cannot be so interpreted. For this reason, significance tests are not fully consistent with the general Bayesian approach.

In a null-hypothesis test a sharp null hypothesis is usually compared to a diffuse alternative. The methods discussed, mostly due to Jeffreys, allow posterior probabilities to be assigned to the hypotheses. In comparing these approaches with the non-Bayesian significance test, the latter appear to be too ready to reject the null hypothesis.

Two methods for testing the independence between two variables are the chi-squared test, which is a significance test, and a null-hypothesis test due to Jeffreys. chi-squared significance tests are also useful in testing goodness-of-fit.

Problems

14–1 (Refers to Problem 2–5)

a Use a Jeffreys approach to test the hypothesis of no difference between the two standard devices against a diffuse alternative hypothesis. Compare your result with that obtained in Problem 1 of Chapter 12.

b Test the hypothesis that using the urn gives higher probability assessments than using the spinner.

14–2 (Refers to Problem 8–5) Test the goodness-of-fit of the obtained sample to the expected distribution given the assumption that sampling is random.

14–3 (Refers to Problem 9–4) Suppose that extensive previous research has established that the mean score on the field dependence–independence task is 15 for the general population of people in Western countries. Test the hypothesis that the investigator's sample of 35 subjects is a representative sample, with respect to this task, of the general population.

14–4 (Refers to Problem 10–1) Test the hypothesis that there is zero correlation between debilitating and facilitating anxiety scores.

14–5 (Refers to Problem 11–4) Test the hypothesis that my wife and I are equal in ability to play 'Score-Four'.

14–6 (Refers to Problem 12–2) Test the hypothesis that computer-assisted instruction is superior to traditional classroom instruction.

14–7 (Refers to Problem 12–6) Answer part **c** from one or more of the points of view developed in Chapter 14.

14–8 (Refers to Problem 12–10) Test the hypothesis that first-borns marry earlier than later-borns.

14–9 *Some Correlates of Primary Recidivism* (*Psychologists Monograph No. 17*, Office of Chief Psychologist, Prison Department, Home Office, June 1966) reports an attempt to find out if there are any personality differences between first offenders and primary recidivists (individuals convicted of a criminal offence for a second time). One part of the study looks at the differences in neuroticism as measured by the 'N' scale of the Maudsley Personality Inventory. Here are the results for 636 imprisoned men aged 21 years or over:

	First offenders	Primary recidivists
Mean 'N' score	25·3	27·7
Standard deviation	10·96	11·22
Number in group	413	223

a   Find the posterior probability associated with the null hypothesis of no difference between the population means. Assume that half your prior opinion is on the null hypothesis of no difference and that the other half is spread out uniformly under the diffuse alternative hypothesis.

b   Find the posterior 99% credible interval for the difference between the population means, assuming uniform priors and normal populations.

c   Compare **a** and **b**.

14–10 Karlins and Lamm (1967) hypothesized that people who are high in integrative complexity ask more questions in a problem-solving task than people of low integrative complexity. They say that 'Higher integrative complexity refers to a greater number of perceptual categories for receiving information about the world and more conceptual or combinatory rules for organizing such units of information.' Integrative complexity is measured by a semi-projective test. In their experiment, a complex problem was given to subjects who were either high or low in integrative complexity. The solution required that questions be asked of the experimenters; the number of questions asked was tallied for each subject. Here are the results: (Since their reported standard deviations were calculated by dividing the sums of squares by N rather than $N - 1$, the values below are re-calculations to conform with the definition of a standard deviation used in this book.)

	Integrative complexity	
	Low	High
Mean no. of questions asked	56·60	69·26
Standard deviation	20·84	21·14
Number of subjects	30	30

a   Find the posterior probability associated with the null hypothesis of no difference between the population means. Assume that half your prior opinion is on the null hypothesis of no difference and that the other half is spread out uniformly under the diffuse alternative hypothesis.

b   Find the posterior 99% credible interval for the difference between the population means, assuming uniform priors and normal populations.

c   Compare **a** and **b**.

14–11 Orme (1972) hypothesizes that extraverted personalities give longer estimates in a time estimation task than introverted personalities. He tested his theory on psychiatric patients, for paranoid schizophrenics display extroverted personalities while non-paranoid schizophrenics are more introverted. Here are the numbers of patients whose time estimates were less than 25 minutes, or 25 minutes and above.

	Time estimates	
	less than 25 min.	25 min. or more
Non-paranoid schizophrenic	27	18
Paranoid schizophrenic	3	14

a Use both the Jeffreys and chi-squared approaches to test the hypothesis that there is no difference between the two groups in their time estimates.

b What conclusion would you draw regarding Orme's hypothesis?

14-12 In a survey of attitudes to traffic, residents of an area were asked: We have a certain amount of traffic which must use existing roads. If the only two ways of handling it were those shown opposite, which one would you choose?
The two alternatives given opposite the question were:

a Most of the traffic going on main roads which are usually shopping streets (making them more crowded) and only a little allowed where people live.

b Traffic evenly spread on both main roads and residential streets.

Responses to **a** and **b** were categorized according to whether the respondent was a car owner or not. Of the 245 car owners, 162 preferred **a**, while of the 194 non-car owners, 123 preferred **a**. Do these data favour the notion that an individual is less likely to favour restrictions on traffic if he owns a car?

14-13 Do a Jeffreys null-hypothesis test for Exercise 14-4. Compare your answer to the conclusions of Exercise 14-4 and of Exercise 12-3.

References

Starred (*) items are specifically concerned with Bayesian statistics.

Alpert, R. and Haber, R. N. Anxiety in academic achievement situations. *Journal of Abnormal and Social Psychology*, 1960, **61**, 207–215.

Bakan, D. The test of significance in psychological research. *Psychological Bulletin*, 1966, **66**, 423–437.

Beach, L. R. Accuracy and consistency in the revision of subjective probabilities. *IEEE Transactions on Human Factors in Electronics*, 1966, **HFE-7**, 29–37.

* Christ, D., Isaacs, G., Jackson, P. H. and Novick, M. R. *Tables for Bayesian Statistics*, Iowa City: Iowa Testing Program, 1973.

Clore, G. L. and Baldridge, B. Interpersonal attraction: the role of agreement and topic interest. *Journal of Personality and Social Psychology*, 1968, **9** (4), 340–346.

Coombs, C. H. Thurstone's measurement of social values revisited forty years later. *Journal of Personality and Social Psychology*, 1967, **6**, 85–91.

Coombs, C. H., Dawes, R. M. and Tversky, A. *Mathematical Psychology: An Elementary Introduction*. Englewood Cliffs, N. J.: Prentice-Hall, 1970.

Davidson, D., Suppes, P. and Siegel, S. *Decision Making: An Experimental Approach*. Stanford, California: Stanford University, 1957.

DuCharme, W. M. A response bias explanation of conservative human inference. *Journal of Experimental Psychology*, 1970, **85**, 66–74.

Edwards, W. Conservatism in human information processing. In: B. Kleinmuntz (ed.), *Formal Representation of Human Judgment*, New York: Wiley, 1968.

* Edwards, W., Lindman, H. and Savage, L. J. Bayesian statistical inference for psychological research. *Psychological Review*, 1963, **70**, 193–242.

Edwards, W., Phillips, L. D., Hays, W. L. and Goodman, B. C. Probabilistic information processing systems: design and evaluation. *IEEE Transactions on Systems Science and Cybernetics*, SSC-4, 1968, 248–265.

Fisher, R. A. and Yates, F. *Statistical Tables for Biological, Agricultural and Medical Research*, 6th edition. Edinburgh: Oliver and Boyd, 1963.

Fitts, P. M. and Peterson, J. R. Information capacity of discrete motor responses. *Journal of Experimental Psychology*, 1964, **67**, 103–112.

Freedman, M. B. Changes in attitudes and values over six decades, *Journal of Social Issues*, 1961, **17**, 19–28. Reprinted in *Attitudes*, M. Jahoda and N. Warren (eds), London: Penguin, 1966.

* Good, I. J., *Probability and the Weighing of Evidence*. London: Griffin; New York: Hafner, 1950.

* Good, I. J., *The Estimation of Probabilities: An Essay on Modern Bayesian Methods*. Research Monograph No. 30, Cambridge, Massachusetts: The M.I.T. Press, 1965.

Gough, H. Appraisal of social maturity by means of the CPI. *Journal of Abnormal Psychology*, 1966, **71**, 189–195.

Gustafson, D. H., Edwards, W., Phillips, L. D. and Slack, W. V. Subjective probabilities in medical diagnosis. *IEEE Transactions on Man-Machine Systems*, 1969, **MMS-10**, 61–65.

Hays, W. L. *Statistics for Psychologists*. New York: Holt, Rinehart and Winston, 1963.

Hays, W. L. *Quantification in psychology*. Belmont, California: Brooks/Cole, 1967.

Heywood, A. *A First Program in Mathematics*. Belmont, California: Dickenson, 1967.

Huff, D. *How to Lie with Statistics*. New York: W. W. Norton & Co. 1954.

* Jeffreys, H. *Theory of Probability*, 3rd edition. Oxford: Clarendon Press, 1961.

Jensen, A. R. Note on why genetic correlations are not squared. *Psychological Bulletin*, 1971, **75**, 223–224.

Karlins, M. and Lamm, H. Information search as a function of conceptual structure in a complex problem-solving task. *Journal of Personality and Social Psychology*, 1967, **5**, 456–459.

* Lindley, D. V. A statistical paradox. *Biometrika*, 1957, **44**, 187–192.

* Lindley, D. V. *Introduction to Probability and Statistics from a Bayesian Viewpoint*. Cambridge University Press, 1965.

Lindley, D. V. *Making Decisions*. London: John Wiley, 1971.

McKeachie, W. J. *Teaching Tips: A guidebook for the beginning college teacher*. Lexington, Mass.: D.C. Heath, 1969.

Miller, D. R. and Swanson, G. E. *Inner Conflict and Defense*. New York: Henry Holt, 1960; Schocken, 1966.

Moskos, C. C. and Bell, W. Attitudes towards democracy. *British Journal of Sociology*, 1964, **15**, 317–337. Reprinted in *Attitudes*, M. Jahoda and N. Warren (eds.), London: Penguin, 1966.

* Mosteller, F. and Wallace, D. *Inference and Disputed Authorship: The Federalist*. Reading, Massachusetts: Addison-Wesley, 1964.

Murdoch, P. H. J. and Smith, G. F. Birth order and affiliation. *British Journal of Social and Clinical Psychology*, 1969, **8**, 235–245.

Murphy, A. H. and Winkler, R. L. Forecasters and probability forecasts: Some current problems. *Bulletin of the American Meteorological Society*, 1971, **52**, 239–247.

* Novick, M. R. and Jackson, P. E. *Statistical Methods for Educational and Psychological Research*. New York: McGraw-Hill, 1974.

Orme, J. E. Duration of sleep and its relationship to age, personality and psychiatric illness. *British Journal of Social and Clinical Psychology*, 1972, **11**, 70–72.

Page, H. A., Rakita, G., Kaplan, H. K. and Smith, N. B. Another application of the spiral aftereffect in the determination of brain damage. *Journal of Consulting Psychology*, 1957, **21**, 89–91.

* Pankoff, L. D. and Roberts, H. V. Bayesian synthesis of clinical and statistical prediction. *Psychological Bulletin*, 1968, **70**, 762–773.

Pearson, E. S. and Hartley, H. O. *Biometrika Tables for Statisticians*, Vol. 1. Cambridge University Press, 1966.

Peterson, C. and Beach, L. R. Man as an intuitive statistician. *Psychological Bulletin*, 1967, **68**, 29–46.

Peterson, C. R., Ulehla, Z. J., Miller, A. J., Bourne, L. K., Jr. and Stilson, D. W. Internal consistency of subjective probabilities. *Journal of Experimental Psychology*, 1965, **70**, 526–533.

* Pitz, G. An example of Bayesian hypothesis testing: The perception of rotary motion in depth. *Psychological Bulletin*, 1968, **70**, 252–255.

* Pratt, J. W., Raiffa, H. and Schlaiffer, R. *Introduction to Statistical Decision Theory*. New York: McGraw-Hill, 1965. (This is a preliminary edition still in manuscript form).

Raiffa, H. *Decision Analysis: Introductory Lectures on Choices Under Uncertainty*. Reading Massachusetts: Addison-Wesley, 1968.

* Savage, L. J. *The Foundations of Statistical Inference*. London: Methuen, 1962.

* Schlaifer, R. *Probability and Statistics for Business Decisions: An Introduction to Managerial Economics Under Uncertainty*. New York: McGraw-Hill, 1959.

Schlaifer, R. *Analysis of Decisions Under Uncertainty*. New York: McGraw-Hill, 1969.

* Schlaifer, R. *Computer Programs for Elementary Decision Analysis*. Boston: Division of Research, Graduate School of Business Administration, Harvard University, 1971.

* Schmitt, S. A. *Measuring Uncertainty: An elementary introduction to Bayesian statistics*. Reading, Massachusetts: Addison-Wesley, 1969.

Siegel, S. *Nonparametric Statistics for the Behavioral Sciences*. New York: McGraw-Hill, 1956.

Sillitoe, A. F. *Britain in Figures. A handbook of social statistics*. London: Penguin, 1971.

Slovic, P. and Lichtenstein, S. Comparison of Bayesian and regression approaches to the study of information processing in judgment. *Organizational Behavior and Human Performance*, 1971, **6**, 649–744.

Stevens, S. S. The surprising simplicity of sensory metrics. *American Psychologist*, 1962, **17**, 29–39.

Stevens, S. S. On the psychological law. *Psychological Review*, 1957, **64**, 153–181.

Stevens, S. S. Operations or words? *Psychological Monographs*, 1966, **80**, (19, Whole No. 627, Part 2).

Thurstone, L. L. Method of paired comparisons for social values. *Journal of Abnormal and Social Psychology*, 1927, **21**, 384–400.

Tversky, A. and Kahneman, D. Belief in the law of small numbers. *Psychological Bulletin*, 1971, **76**, 105–110.

Wakeford, J. *The Strategy of Social Enquiry: A new programme in methods and measurement for the student of sociology*. London: Macmillan, 1968.

Walker, H. *Mathematics Essential for Elementary Statistics*. New York: Holt, Rinehart and Winston, 1957.

Wilson, G. D. and Patterson, J. R. A new measure of conservatism. *British Journal of Social and Clinical Psychology*, 1968, **7**, 264–269.

* Winkler, R. The assessment of prior distributions in Bayesian analysis. *Journal of the American Statistical Association*, 1967, **62**, 776–800.

Index of Symbols

a	a constant; the y-intercept of a linear function, 95	h	precision (see 'primes'), 237
$A_{X\mid Y}$	X-intercept of the linear regression line for predicting X from Y, 221	IG2	denotes the inverted gamma-2 distribution, 254
$A_{Y\mid X}$	Y-intercept of the linear regression line for predicting Y from X, 216	L	a likelihood ratio, 79
$\alpha_{Y\mid X}$	Y-intercept of the population regression line for predicting Y from X, 294	m	mean of prior or posterior distribution (see 'primes'), 123, 237
b	a constant; the slope of a linear function, 95	M	mean of a set of data, 176
$B_{X\mid Y}$	slope of the linear regression line for predicting X from Y, 221	μ	one of the parameters of a normal distribution; used to denote the unknown mean of a normal population, 130
$B_{Y\mid X}$	slope of the linear regression line for predicting Y from X, 216	μ_M	mean of the sampling distribution of means, 312
$\beta_{Y\mid X}$	slope of the population regression line for predicting Y from X, 294	μ_t	one of the parameters of the Student-t distribution; used to denote the mean of the prior or posterior Student-t distribution (see 'primes'), 248
C	a percentage denoting the area of the curve included within the credible interval, 114		
	the number of columns in a contingency table, 360	n	the number of events on a list, 32
χ^2	chi-squared: the distribution or the statistic, 349	n' or n''	prior or posterior n: the equivalent number of observations on which the prior or posterior is based, 237, 238
CR	critical ratio, 328	$n!$	n-factorial: $n \times (n-1) \times (n-2) \times (n-3) \times \ldots \times 3 \times 2 \times 1$, 124
D	a difference between correlated scores, 283		
df	degrees of freedom, 248	N	number of observations in a sample, 80, 182
δ	the difference between population means, 272	v	degrees of freedom, 248
e	the constant, $2\cdot7182\ldots$, 93	σ	one of the parameters of a normal distribution; used to denote the standard deviation of a normal population, 130
E	an event, 24		
Ē	the complement of E; 'not-E', 24		
$E_1, E_2, \ldots$	events on a list: the first event, the second event, etc., 32	σ_t	one of the parameters of a Student-t distribution (see 'primes'), 248
E_n	the nth event on a list, 32		
est σ_M	estimate of the standard error of the mean, 319	σ_M	standard error of estimate of the mean, 315
f	number of failures, 128	$\sigma_{Y\mid X}$	population standard error of estimate for Y in regression problems, 294
$F(df_1, df_2)$	denotes the F distribution with df_1 and df_2 degrees of freedom, 286		

Ω	odds, 24	$\bar{s}$	number of successes, 128
$\Omega(E)$	odds favouring E over $\bar{E}$, 24	S	standard deviation of a set of data, 176
p	one of the parameters of the Beta distribution, 124	Σ	an operator meaning 'add', 33
$p(D|H)$	a likelihood; the probability associated with the data given the truth of the hypothesis, 59	ΣX	sum of the X-scores, 182
		ΣX^2	sum of the squares of the X-scores, 182
$p(E)$	probability of event E, 24, 30	ΣXY	sum of the cross-products of X and Y, 200
$p(E|P,I)$	probability of event E given the person carrying out the assessment and the state of information available to him, 30	ΣY	sum of the Y-scores, 200
		ΣY^2	sum of the squares of the Y-scores, 200
$p(F|E)$	probability of event F given that E has occurred, 38	SS	sum of squares, 221
		S_X	standard deviation of X-scores, 208
$p(H)$	probability of hypothesis H before observing data; the prior probability, 59	S_Y	standard deviation of Y-scores, 208, 218
$p(H|D)$	probability of hypothesis H after observing data; the posterior probability, 59	$S_{Y|X}$	standard error of estimate in predicting Y from X, 218
		x	independent variable, 95
π	the constant 3·1415..., 93 population proportion, 258	x_{low} x_{high}	lower and upper limits of a credible interval, 113
π^*	hypothesized value of a population proportion, 340	X	a score; a numerical measurement, 182
Π	an operator meaning 'multiply', 80	y	dependent variable, 95
primes	used to denote prior or posterior: usually associated with parameters or statistics, a single prime denotes prior and a double prime denotes posterior, 79	Y	a score; a numerical measurement, 198
		$\tilde{Y}$	predicted value of Y, 216
		z	the Fisher-z transformation of r, 290
q	one of the parameters of a Beta distribution, 124		the independent variable for the standard normal distribution, 133
r	Pearson correlation coefficient, 207	Z	a standard score, 195
r_{rho}	Spearman correlation coefficient, 214	Z_X	an X-score expressed as a standard score, 208
R	number of rows in a contingency table, 360	$\tilde{Z}$	a predicted standard score, 224
		Z_Y	a Y-score expressed as a standard score, 208
ρ	population value of the correlation coefficient, 288	ζ	the Fisher-z transformation of ρ, the population correlation coefficient, 290
s	standard deviation of prior or posterior (see 'primes'), 123		

Index

Absolute scales, 155
Achievement Anxiety Test, 227, 233
Acta Psychologica, 76
Alpert, R., 227, 233, 312
Archimedes spiral after-effect illusion, 61–62
Association
  statistical, 198–199
  strength of, 212
Averages, law of, 22
Axiomatic systems, 153

Bakan, D., 332, 334
Baldridge, B., 104
Bayes' theorem
  additivity of evidence, 84
  automatic weighting of prior and sample, 241
  general form, 63
  log-odds log-likelihood ratio form, 83–84
  odds-likelihood ratio form, 79–83
  for several items of data, 64–68
  for student's driving problem, 56–58
  in tabular form, 60
  for two hypotheses, 58–60
Bayesian criticism
  of null-hypothesis testing, 333–334
  of significance tests, 328
Bayesian interpretation of traditional results
  for inferences concerning correlations, 294
  for inferences concerning the difference between two means, 285–286
  for inferences concerning means, 245–247, 259–260
  for inferences concerning proportions, 262
  for inferences concerning regression coefficients, 303
  for inferences concerning standard deviations, 260–261
  for inferences concerning the standard error of estimate in regression, 303

Bayesian interpretation of traditional results
  for inferences concerning the true and predicted values of Y in regression, 305
  significance tests, 341–342
Bayesian sign test, 345–346
Beach, L. R., 22, 53, 70, 76
Behrens distribution, 283
  comments on use of table in Appendix A 283, 285
  normal approximation to, 285
  Student-t approximation to, 285
Behrens–Fisher distribution, 286
Bell, W., 313
Bernoulli, Daniel, 102
Bernoulli, James, 22
Best guesses, 189
Beta distribution, 113
  assessing prior, 126–127
  comments on graphs in Appendix B, 125–126
  comments on tables in Appendix B, 128, 262
  credible intervals, 128–129
  equation for, 123
  normal approximation to, 138–139
  parameters, 124
  statistics, 127
BETADIF computer program, 306
Bivariate data, 200
Bivariate frequency distribution, 201–202
Bivariate histogram, 202
Bivariate-normal distribution, 291–292
Blind trials, 282
Bourne, L. K., Jr., 76
Brain damage, 61–62

Calculators, automatic, 181–182
California Psychological Inventory, 89
Causation, 95, 199
Central limit theorem, 318

Appendices

Appendix A

Behrens distribution
Highest density regions

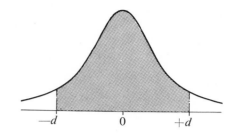

95 percent	df_2	ω						
		0°	15°	30°	45°	60°	75°	90°
$df_1=6$	6	2.45	2.44	2.43	2.43	2.43	2.44	2.45
	8	2.31	2.31	2.33	2.36	2.40	2.43	2.45
	12	2.18	2.19	2.24	2.30	2.37	2.42	2.45
	24	2.06	2.09	2.15	2.24	2.34	2.42	2.45
	∞	1.96	1.99	2.08	2.20	2.32	2.41	2.45
$df_1=8$	6	2.45	2.43	2.40	2.36	2.33	2.31	2.31
	8	2.31	2.30	2.29	2.29	2.29	2.30	2.31
	12	2.18	2.18	2.20	2.23	2.26	2.29	2.31
	24	2.06	2.08	2.12	2.17	2.24	2.29	2.31
	∞	1.96	1.98	2.04	2.13	2.21	2.28	2.31
$df_1=12$	6	2.45	2.42	2.37	2.30	2.24	2.19	2.18
	8	2.31	2.29	2.26	2.23	2.20	2.18	2.18
	12	2.18	2.17	2.17	2.17	2.17	2.17	2.18
	24	2.06	2.07	2.09	2.11	2.14	2.17	2.18
	∞	1.96	1.97	2.01	2.06	2.12	2.16	2.18
$df_1=24$	6	2.45	2.42	2.34	2.25	2.15	2.09	2.06
	8	2.31	2.29	2.24	2.18	2.12	2.08	2.06
	12	2.18	2.17	2.14	2.11	2.09	2.07	2.06
	24	2.06	2.06	2.06	2.06	2.06	2.06	2.06
	∞	1.96	1.97	1.98	2.01	2.03	2.06	2.06
$df_1=\infty$	6	2.45	2.41	2.32	2.20	2.08	1.99	1.96
	8	2.31	2.28	2.21	2.13	2.04	1.98	1.96
	12	2.18	2.16	2.12	2.06	2.01	1.97	1.96
	24	2.06	2.06	2.03	2.01	1.98	1.97	1.96
	∞	1.96	1.96	1.96	1.96	1.96	1.96	1.96

SOURCE: for the 95 % intervals: Novick and Jackson (1974) whose source is a more comprehensive table in Christ, Isaacs, Jackson and Novick (1973).

Behrens distribution
Highest density regions

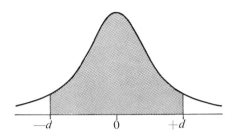

99 percent	df_2	ω						
		$0°$	$15°$	$30°$	$45°$	$60°$	$75°$	$90°$
$df_1=6$	6	3.71	3.65	3.56	3.51	3.56	3.65	3.71
	8	3.36	3.33	3.31	3.36	3.50	3.64	3.71
	12	3.06	3.05	3.10	3.25	3.45	3.64	3.71
	24	2.80	2.82	2.94	3.16	3.42	3.63	3.71
	∞	2.58	2.63	2.80	3.09	3.40	3.63	3.71
$df_1=8$	6	3.71	3.64	3.50	3.36	3.31	3.33	3.36
	8	3.36	3.32	3.24	3.21	3.24	3.32	3.36
	12	3.06	3.04	3.03	3.08	3.19	3.31	3.36
	24	2.80	2.81	2.86	2.99	3.16	3.30	3.36
	∞	2.58	2.61	2.72	2.92	3.13	3.30	3.36
$df_1=12$	6	3.71	3.64	3.45	3.25	3.10	3.05	3.06
	8	3.36	3.31	3.19	3.08	3.03	3.04	3.06
	12	3.06	3.03	2.98	2.95	2.98	3.03	3.06
	24	2.80	2.79	2.80	2.85	2.94	3.02	3.06
	∞	2.58	2.60	2.66	2.78	2.91	3.01	3.06
$df_1=24$	6	3.71	3.63	3.42	3.16	2.94	2.82	2.80
	8	3.36	3.30	3.16	2.99	2.86	2.81	2.80
	12	3.06	3.02	2.94	2.85	2.80	2.79	2.80
	24	2.80	2.79	2.76	2.75	2.76	2.79	2.80
	∞	2.58	2.59	2.61	2.66	2.73	2.78	2.80
$df_1=∞$	6	3.71	3.63	3.40	3.09	2.80	2.63	2.58
	8	3.36	3.30	3.13	2.92	2.72	2.61	2.58
	12	3.06	3.01	2.91	2.78	2.66	2.60	2.58
	24	2.80	2.78	2.73	2.66	2.61	2.59	2.58
	∞	2.58	2.58	2.58	2.58	2.58	2.58	2.58

SOURCE: for the 99% intervals: Fisher and Yates (1963).

Appendix B

Beta density functions
Mode = 0.5 (including uniform prior)

A3

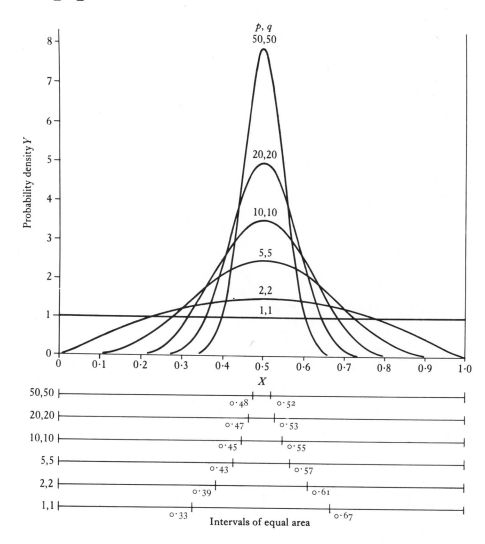

SOURCE: Drawn for this volume.

Beta density functions

Mode = 0.6

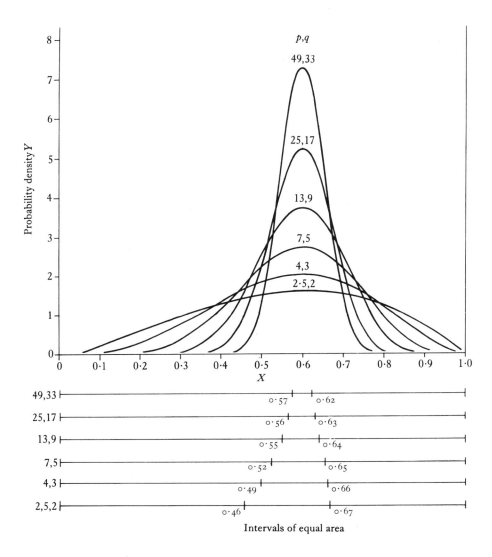

Intervals of equal area

Beta density functions

Mode $= 0.7$

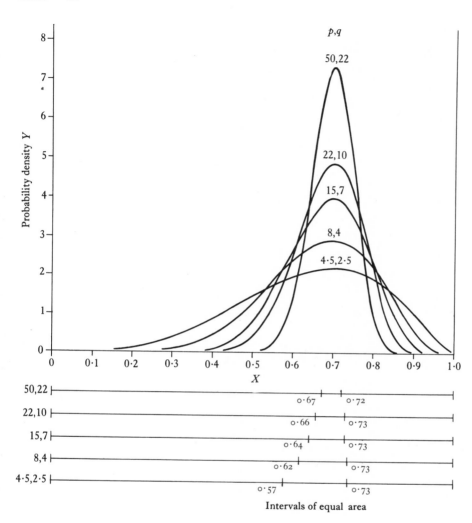

Intervals of equal area

Beta density functions

Mode = 0.8

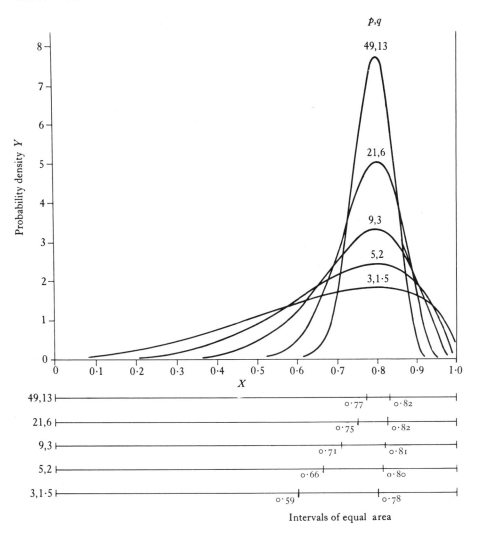

# Beta density functions
Mode = 0.9

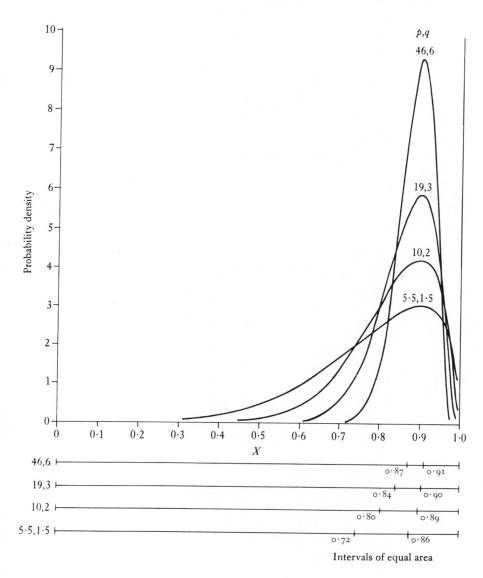

Intervals of equal area

Appendix B

Beta distribution
Highest density regions
95 per cent intervals

Q =		2		3		4	
		LOW	HIGH	LOW	HIGH	LOW	HIGH
P =	2	0.0943	0.9057	0.0438	0.7724	0.0260	0.6702
P =	3	0.2276	0.9562	0.1466	0.8534	0.1048	0.7613
P =	4	0.3298	0.9740	0.2387	0.8952	0.1840	0.8160
P =	5	0.4094	0.9822	0.3154	0.9195	0.2536	0.8515
P =	6	0.4730	0.9867	0.3790	0.9350	0.3146	0.8755
P =	7	0.5244	0.9895	0.4324	0.9458	0.3668	0.8932
P =	8	0.5665	0.9914	0.4776	0.9536	0.4120	0.9066
P =	9	0.6022	0.9927	0.5163	0.9594	0.4515	0.9171
P =	10	0.6325	0.9937	0.5497	0.9640	0.4862	0.9255
P =	11	0.6587	0.9945	0.5790	0.9677	0.5168	0.9324
P =	12	0.6813	0.9951	0.6047	0.9707	0.5441	0.9381
P =	13	0.7012	0.9955	0.6274	0.9732	0.5685	0.9430
P =	14	0.7187	0.9960	0.6478	0.9754	0.5905	0.9471
P =	15	0.7343	0.9963	0.6660	0.9772	0.6103	0.9507
P =	16	0.7482	0.9966	0.6825	0.9787	0.6284	0.9539
P =	17	0.7607	0.9968	0.6974	0.9801	0.6449	0.9567
P =	18	0.7721	0.9970	0.7110	0.9813	0.6599	0.9591
P =	19	0.7825	0.9972	0.7236	0.9824	0.6738	0.9613
P =	20	0.7916	0.9974	0.7349	0.9833	0.6866	0.9633
P =	21	0.8010	0.9975	0.7454	0.9842	0.6984	0.9651
P =	22	0.8087	0.9977	0.7551	0.9850	0.7094	0.9667
P =	23	0.8160	0.9978	0.7641	0.9857	0.7196	0.9682
P =	24	0.8227	0.9979	0.7724	0.9863	0.7291	0.9695
P =	25	0.8291	0.9980	0.7802	0.9869	0.7380	0.9708
P =	26	0.8350	0.9981	0.7875	0.9874	0.7464	0.9719
P =	27	0.8406	0.9982	0.7943	0.9879	0.7542	0.9730
P =	28	0.8458	0.9982	0.8007	0.9884	0.7616	0.9739
P =	29	0.8506	0.9983	0.8067	0.9888	0.7685	0.9749
P =	30	0.8552	0.9984	0.8123	0.9892	0.7750	0.9757
P =	31	0.8594	0.9984	0.8177	0.9896	0.7811	0.9765
P =	32	0.8637	0.9985	0.8227	0.9899	0.7870	0.9773
P =	33	0.8673	0.9985	0.8275	0.9902	0.7925	0.9780
P =	34	0.8710	0.9986	0.8320	0.9906	0.7978	0.9786
P =	35	0.8744	0.9986	0.8363	0.9908	0.8028	0.9792
P =	36	0.8776	0.9987	0.8404	0.9911	0.8076	0.9798
P =	37	0.8806	0.9987	0.8443	0.9914	0.8121	0.9804
P =	38	0.8836	0.9987	0.8479	0.9916	0.8165	0.9809
P =	39	0.8863	0.9988	0.8515	0.9918	0.8206	0.9814
P =	40	0.8890	0.9988	0.8548	0.9920	0.8245	0.9819
P =	41	0.8915	0.9989	0.8581	0.9922	0.8283	0.9823
P =	42	0.8939	0.9989	0.8611	0.9924	0.8320	0.9828
P =	43	0.8962	0.9989	0.8541	0.9926	0.8354	0.9832
P =	44	0.8984	0.9989	0.8669	0.9928	0.8388	0.9836
P =	45	0.9005	0.9990	0.8696	0.9930	0.8420	0.9839
P =	46	0.9026	0.9990	0.8722	0.9931	0.8450	0.9843
P =	47	0.9045	0.9990	0.8747	0.9933	0.8480	0.9846
P =	48	0.9064	0.9990	0.8771	0.9934	0.8509	0.9849
P =	49	0.9082	0.9991	0.8794	0.9936	0.8536	0.9853
P =	50	0.9099	0.9991	0.8817	0.9937	0.8562	0.9856
P =	51	0.9116	0.9991	0.8838	0.9938	0.8588	0.9858
P =	52	0.9132	0.9991	0.8859	0.9939	0.8613	0.9861
P =	53	0.9148	0.9991	0.8878	0.9941	0.8636	0.9864
P =	54	0.9163	0.9991	0.8898	0.9942	0.8659	0.9866
P =	55	0.9177	0.9992	0.8916	0.9943	0.8682	0.9869
P =	56	0.9191	0.9992	0.8934	0.9944	0.8703	0.9871
P =	57	0.9204	0.9992	0.8952	0.9945	0.8724	0.9873
P =	58	0.9218	0.9992	0.8969	0.9946	0.8744	0.9876
P =	59	0.9230	0.9992	0.8985	0.9947	0.8764	0.9878
P =	60	0.9242	0.9992	0.9001	0.9948	0.8782	0.9880

SOURCE: Computed for this volume.

5 LOW	5 HIGH	6 LOW	6 HIGH	7 LOW	7 HIGH	8 LOW	8 HIGH
0.0178	0.5906	0.0133	0.5270	0.0105	0.4756	0.0086	0.4335
0.0805	0.6846	0.0650	0.6210	0.0542	0.5676	0.0464	0.5224
0.1485	0.7464	0.1245	0.6854	0.1068	0.6332	0.0934	0.5880
0.2120	0.7880	0.1814	0.7318	0.1583	0.6822	0.1404	0.6382
0.2682	0.8186	0.2338	0.7662	0.2069	0.7192	0.1854	0.6770
0.3178	0.8417	0.2808	0.7931	0.2513	0.7487	0.2273	0.7084
0.3618	0.8596	0.3230	0.8146	0.2916	0.7727	0.2659	0.7341
0.4008	0.8740	0.3609	0.8320	0.3283	0.7926	0.3011	0.7559
0.4355	0.8857	0.3951	0.8465	0.3617	0.8093	0.3335	0.7743
0.4671	0.8952	0.4261	0.8587	0.3921	0.8235	0.3633	0.7902
0.4951	0.9034	0.4541	0.8691	0.4199	0.8357	0.3907	0.8040
0.5203	0.9105	0.4796	0.8781	0.4454	0.8464	0.4159	0.8161
0.5432	0.9166	0.5029	0.8860	0.4688	0.8558	0.4392	0.8267
0.5640	0.9219	0.5242	0.8929	0.4904	0.8541	0.4609	0.8363
0.5830	0.9266	0.5438	0.8990	0.5103	0.8715	0.4809	0.8448
0.6005	0.9308	0.5619	0.9045	0.5288	0.8782	0.4996	0.8525
0.6166	0.9345	0.5791	0.9092	0.5460	0.8842	0.5170	0.8594
0.6314	0.9378	0.5947	0.9136	0.5619	0.8896	0.5332	0.8658
0.6452	0.9409	0.6091	0.9176	0.5768	0.8945	0.5484	0.8716
0.6580	0.9436	0.6225	0.9213	0.5908	0.8991	0.5627	0.8769
0.6699	0.9461	0.6351	0.9247	0.6038	0.9032	0.5761	0.8818
0.6810	0.9484	0.6469	0.9277	0.6161	0.9070	0.5887	0.8863
0.6913	0.9505	0.6579	0.9306	0.6276	0.9106	0.6006	0.8905
0.7011	0.9524	0.6683	0.9332	0.6385	0.9139	0.6119	0.8944
0.7102	0.9542	0.6781	0.9356	0.6487	0.9159	0.6225	0.8980
0.7188	0.9559	0.6873	0.9379	0.6588	0.9196	0.6326	0.9014
0.7269	0.9574	0.6960	0.9400	0.6680	0.9222	0.6421	0.9046
0.7346	0.9589	0.7042	0.9420	0.6767	0.9247	0.6512	0.9075
0.7418	0.9602	0.7120	0.9438	0.6849	0.9270	0.6598	0.9103
0.7487	0.9615	0.7194	0.9456	0.6928	0.9292	0.6681	0.9129
0.7552	0.9627	0.7265	0.9472	0.7002	0.9313	0.6759	0.9154
0.7613	0.9638	0.7331	0.9487	0.7074	0.9332	0.6834	0.9178
0.7673	0.9649	0.7395	0.9502	0.7142	0.9351	0.6905	0.9200
0.7729	0.9658	0.7456	0.9516	0.7206	0.9368	0.6973	0.9221
0.7782	0.9668	0.7514	0.9528	0.7268	0.9385	0.7038	0.9241
0.7833	0.9677	0.7569	0.9541	0.7328	0.9400	0.7101	0.9260
0.7881	0.9685	0.7622	0.9552	0.7384	0.9415	0.7161	0.9278
0.7928	0.9693	0.7673	0.9563	0.7439	0.9429	0.7219	0.9295
0.7972	0.9701	0.7722	0.9574	0.7491	0.9443	0.7274	0.9311
0.8015	0.9708	0.7768	0.9584	0.7541	0.9456	0.7330	0.9325
0.8056	0.9715	0.7813	0.9594	0.7589	0.9468	0.7381	0.9340
0.8095	0.9721	0.7856	0.9603	0.7636	0.9480	0.7430	0.9355
0.8133	0.9728	0.7898	0.9612	0.7680	0.9491	0.7478	0.9368
0.8169	0.9734	0.7937	0.9620	0.7723	0.9502	0.7523	0.9381
0.8204	0.9739	0.7976	0.9628	0.7765	0.9512	0.7567	0.9394
0.8237	0.9745	0.8013	0.9636	0.7805	0.9522	0.7610	0.9406
0.8270	0.9750	0.8049	0.9643	0.7843	0.9532	0.7651	0.9418
0.8301	0.9755	0.8083	0.9650	0.7880	0.9541	0.7691	0.9429
0.8331	0.9760	0.8116	0.9657	0.7916	0.9549	0.7729	0.9440
0.8360	0.9765	0.8148	0.9664	0.7951	0.9558	0.7766	0.9450
0.8388	0.9769	0.8179	0.9670	0.7985	0.9566	0.7802	0.9460
0.8415	0.9773	0.8209	0.9676	0.8017	0.9574	0.7837	0.9470
0.8441	0.9778	0.8238	0.9682	0.8049	0.9582	0.7870	0.9479
0.8467	0.9782	0.8266	0.9687	0.8079	0.9589	0.7903	0.9488
0.8491	0.9785	0.8294	0.9693	0.8109	0.9596	0.7935	0.9497
0.8515	0.9789	0.8320	0.9698	0.8138	0.9603	0.7966	0.9505
0.8537	0.9793	0.8346	0.9703	0.8165	0.9609	0.7995	0.9513
0.8560	0.9796	0.8370	0.9708	0.8192	0.9616	0.8024	0.9521
0.8581	0.9800	0.8394	0.9713	0.8219	0.9622	0.8053	0.9528

Q =		9		10		11	
		LOW	HIGH	LOW	HIGH	LOW	HIGH
P =	2	0.0073	0.3978	0.0063	0.3675	0.0055	0.3413
P =	3	0.0406	0.4837	0.0360	0.4503	0.0323	0.4210
P =	4	0.0829	0.5485	0.0745	0.5138	0.0676	0.4832
P =	5	0.1260	0.5992	0.1143	0.5645	0.1048	0.5329
P =	6	0.1680	0.6391	0.1535	0.6049	0.1413	0.5739
P =	7	0.2074	0.6717	0.1907	0.6383	0.1765	0.6079
P =	8	0.2441	0.6989	0.2257	0.6665	0.2098	0.6367
P =	9	0.2781	0.7219	0.2583	0.6905	0.2411	0.6616
P =	10	0.3095	0.7417	0.2886	0.7114	0.2704	0.6832
P =	11	0.3384	0.7589	0.3168	0.7296	0.2978	0.7022
P =	12	0.3653	0.7739	0.3430	0.7457	0.3234	0.7191
P =	13	0.3902	0.7872	0.3675	0.7599	0.3473	0.7341
P =	14	0.4133	0.7990	0.3903	0.7726	0.3697	0.7477
P =	15	0.4348	0.8096	0.4116	0.7841	0.3908	0.7599
P =	16	0.4548	0.8191	0.4315	0.7944	0.4105	0.7710
P =	17	0.4735	0.8277	0.4502	0.8038	0.4291	0.7811
P =	18	0.4910	0.8355	0.4677	0.8124	0.4465	0.7903
P =	19	0.5074	0.8426	0.4842	0.8203	0.4630	0.7988
P =	20	0.5229	0.8492	0.4997	0.8275	0.4786	0.8066
P =	21	0.5374	0.8552	0.5143	0.8342	0.4933	0.8139
P =	22	0.5510	0.8608	0.5281	0.8404	0.5072	0.8206
P =	23	0.5639	0.8659	0.5412	0.8461	0.5204	0.8268
P =	24	0.5761	0.8707	0.5536	0.8514	0.5329	0.8327
P =	25	0.5876	0.8752	0.5653	0.8564	0.5448	0.8381
P =	26	0.5985	0.8793	0.5765	0.8611	0.5561	0.8432
P =	27	0.6089	0.8832	0.5871	0.8654	0.5669	0.8480
P =	28	0.6187	0.8869	0.5972	0.8695	0.5771	0.8525
P =	29	0.6281	0.8903	0.6068	0.8734	0.5859	0.8568
P =	30	0.6370	0.8935	0.6159	0.8770	0.5963	0.8608
P =	31	0.6456	0.8966	0.6247	0.8804	0.6052	0.8646
P =	32	0.6537	0.8995	0.6331	0.8837	0.6138	0.8682
P =	33	0.6615	0.9022	0.6411	0.8867	0.6220	0.8716
P =	34	0.6689	0.9047	0.6487	0.8897	0.6299	0.8748
P =	35	0.6760	0.9072	0.6561	0.8924	0.6374	0.8779
P =	36	0.6828	0.9095	0.6631	0.8951	0.6447	0.8808
P =	37	0.6893	0.9117	0.6699	0.8976	0.6517	0.8836
P =	38	0.6956	0.9138	0.6764	0.9000	0.6584	0.8863
P =	39	0.7016	0.9158	0.6827	0.9022	0.6648	0.8888
P =	40	0.7074	0.9177	0.6887	0.9044	0.6710	0.8912
P =	41	0.7130	0.9196	0.6945	0.9065	0.6770	0.8936
P =	42	0.7184	0.9213	0.7001	0.9085	0.6828	0.8958
P =	43	0.7235	0.9230	0.7055	0.9104	0.6884	0.8979
P =	44	0.7285	0.9246	0.7107	0.9122	0.6938	0.9000
P =	45	0.7333	0.9261	0.7157	0.9140	0.6990	0.9020
P =	46	0.7380	0.9276	0.7205	0.9157	0.7040	0.9038
P =	47	0.7424	0.9290	0.7252	0.9173	0.7089	0.9057
P =	48	0.7468	0.9304	0.7297	0.9189	0.7136	0.9074
P =	49	0.7510	0.9317	0.7341	0.9204	0.7181	0.9091
P =	50	0.7550	0.9330	0.7384	0.9218	0.7226	0.9108
P =	51	0.7589	0.9342	0.7425	0.9232	0.7268	0.9123
P =	52	0.7627	0.9354	0.7465	0.9246	0.7310	0.9138
P =	53	0.7664	0.9365	0.7503	0.9259	0.7350	0.9153
P =	54	0.7700	0.9376	0.7541	0.9272	0.7389	0.9167
P =	55	0.7735	0.9387	0.7577	0.9284	0.7427	0.9181
P =	56	0.7768	0.9397	0.7613	0.9296	0.7464	0.9194
P =	57	0.7801	0.9407	0.7647	0.9307	0.7500	0.9207
P =	58	0.7832	0.9416	0.7680	0.9318	0.7535	0.9220
P =	59	0.7863	0.9426	0.7713	0.9329	0.7569	0.9232
P =	60	0.7895	0.9434	0.7744	0.9339	0.7602	0.9243

12		13		14		15	
LOW	HIGH	LOW	HIGH	LOW	HIGH	LOW	HIGH
0.0049	0.3187	0.0045	0.2988	0.0040	0.2813	0.0037	0.2657
0.0293	0.3953	0.0268	0.3726	0.0246	0.3522	0.0228	0.3340
0.0619	0.4559	0.0570	0.4315	0.0529	0.4095	0.0493	0.3897
0.0966	0.5049	0.0895	0.4797	0.0834	0.4568	0.0781	0.4360
0.1309	0.5459	0.1219	0.5204	0.1140	0.4971	0.1071	0.4758
0.1643	0.5801	0.1536	0.5546	0.1442	0.5312	0.1359	0.5096
0.1960	0.6093	0.1839	0.5841	0.1733	0.5608	0.1637	0.5391
0.2261	0.6347	0.2128	0.6098	0.2010	0.5857	0.1904	0.5652
0.2543	0.6570	0.2401	0.6325	0.2274	0.6097	0.2159	0.5884
0.2809	0.6766	0.2659	0.6527	0.2523	0.6303	0.2401	0.6092
0.3059	0.6941	0.2902	0.6707	0.2760	0.6487	0.2631	0.6280
0.3293	0.7098	0.3131	0.6869	0.2983	0.6654	0.2850	0.6450
0.3513	0.7240	0.3346	0.7017	0.3195	0.6805	0.3057	0.6605
0.3720	0.7369	0.3550	0.7150	0.3395	0.6943	0.3253	0.6747
0.3915	0.7486	0.3742	0.7273	0.3584	0.7070	0.3440	0.6877
0.4099	0.7593	0.3924	0.7385	0.3764	0.7187	0.3617	0.6998
0.4273	0.7691	0.4096	0.7488	0.3934	0.7294	0.3785	0.7109
0.4437	0.7781	0.4260	0.7583	0.4096	0.7394	0.3945	0.7212
0.4592	0.7865	0.4414	0.7672	0.4250	0.7486	0.4098	0.7308
0.4739	0.7943	0.4561	0.7754	0.4396	0.7572	0.4243	0.7398
0.4879	0.8015	0.4701	0.7830	0.4536	0.7653	0.4382	0.7482
0.5012	0.8082	0.4834	0.7902	0.4668	0.7728	0.4514	0.7560
0.5138	0.8145	0.4960	0.7969	0.4795	0.7799	0.4641	0.7634
0.5257	0.8203	0.5081	0.8031	0.4916	0.7865	0.4762	0.7704
0.5372	0.8259	0.5196	0.8090	0.5031	0.7927	0.4878	0.7769
0.5481	0.8311	0.5306	0.8146	0.5142	0.7986	0.4989	0.7831
0.5585	0.8359	0.5411	0.8198	0.5248	0.8041	0.5095	0.7889
0.5684	0.8406	0.5511	0.8248	0.5349	0.8094	0.5197	0.7945
0.5780	0.8449	0.5608	0.8294	0.5447	0.8144	0.5295	0.7997
0.5871	0.8490	0.5700	0.8339	0.5540	0.8191	0.5389	0.8047
0.5958	0.8530	0.5789	0.8381	0.5630	0.8236	0.5479	0.8095
0.6042	0.8567	0.5874	0.8421	0.5716	0.8279	0.5566	0.8140
0.6122	0.8602	0.5956	0.8459	0.5799	0.8320	0.5650	0.8183
0.6199	0.8636	0.6034	0.8495	0.5878	0.8358	0.5731	0.8224
0.6274	0.8668	0.6110	0.8530	0.5955	0.8395	0.5809	0.8264
0.6345	0.8698	0.6183	0.8563	0.6029	0.8431	0.5884	0.8301
0.6414	0.8727	0.6253	0.8595	0.6101	0.8465	0.5957	0.8337
0.6480	0.8755	0.6321	0.8625	0.6170	0.8497	0.6027	0.8372
0.6544	0.8782	0.6386	0.8654	0.6236	0.8528	0.6094	0.8405
0.6605	0.8808	0.6449	0.8682	0.6301	0.8558	0.6160	0.8437
0.6665	0.8832	0.6510	0.8709	0.6363	0.8587	0.6223	0.8457
0.6722	0.8856	0.6569	0.8734	0.6423	0.8614	0.6284	0.8497
0.6778	0.8878	0.6626	0.8759	0.6481	0.8641	0.6343	0.8525
0.6831	0.8900	0.6681	0.8782	0.6538	0.8666	0.6401	0.8552
0.6883	0.8921	0.6734	0.8805	0.6592	0.8691	0.6457	0.8578
0.6934	0.8941	0.6786	0.8827	0.6645	0.8715	0.6511	0.8604
0.6982	0.8961	0.6836	0.8848	0.6696	0.8737	0.6563	0.8628
0.7029	0.8979	0.6885	0.8869	0.6746	0.8759	0.6614	0.8652
0.7075	0.8997	0.6932	0.8888	0.6794	0.8781	0.6663	0.8675
0.7119	0.9015	0.6977	0.8907	0.6841	0.8801	0.6711	0.8697
0.7162	0.9032	0.7022	0.8926	0.6887	0.8821	0.6758	0.8718
0.7204	0.9048	0.7065	0.8944	0.6931	0.8840	0.6803	0.8738
0.7245	0.9064	0.7107	0.8961	0.6974	0.8859	0.6847	0.8758
0.7284	0.9079	0.7147	0.8977	0.7016	0.8877	0.6890	0.8778
0.7322	0.9093	0.7187	0.8993	0.7057	0.8894	0.6932	0.8797
0.7360	0.9108	0.7225	0.9009	0.7096	0.8911	0.6973	0.8815
0.7396	0.9122	0.7263	0.9024	0.7135	0.8928	0.7012	0.8832
0.7431	0.9135	0.7299	0.9039	0.7173	0.8944	0.7051	0.8849
0.7465	0.9148	0.7335	0.9053	0.7209	0.8959	0.7088	0.8866

Q =		16		17		18	
		LOW	HIGH	LOW	HIGH	LOW	HIGH
P =	2	0.0034	0.2518	0.0032	0.2393	0.0030	0.2279
P =	3	0.0213	0.3175	0.0199	0.3026	0.0187	0.2890
P =	4	0.0461	0.3716	0.0433	0.3551	0.0409	0.3401
P =	5	0.0734	0.4170	0.0692	0.3995	0.0655	0.3834
P =	6	0.1010	0.4562	0.0955	0.4381	0.0908	0.4209
P =	7	0.1285	0.4897	0.1218	0.4712	0.1158	0.4540
P =	8	0.1552	0.5191	0.1475	0.5004	0.1406	0.4830
P =	9	0.1809	0.5452	0.1723	0.5265	0.1645	0.5090
P =	10	0.2056	0.5685	0.1962	0.5498	0.1876	0.5323
P =	11	0.2290	0.5895	0.2189	0.5709	0.2097	0.5535
P =	12	0.2514	0.6085	0.2407	0.5901	0.2309	0.5727
P =	13	0.2727	0.6258	0.2615	0.6076	0.2512	0.5904
P =	14	0.2930	0.6416	0.2813	0.6236	0.2706	0.6066
P =	15	0.3123	0.6560	0.3002	0.6383	0.2891	0.6215
P =	16	0.3306	0.6694	0.3183	0.6519	0.3068	0.6353
P =	17	0.3481	0.6817	0.3354	0.6646	0.3237	0.6482
P =	18	0.3647	0.6932	0.3518	0.6763	0.3399	0.6601
P =	19	0.3805	0.7039	0.3675	0.6872	0.3554	0.6713
P =	20	0.3956	0.7138	0.3825	0.6974	0.3702	0.6817
P =	21	0.4101	0.7231	0.3968	0.7070	0.3843	0.6915
P =	22	0.4239	0.7318	0.4105	0.7159	0.3979	0.7007
P =	23	0.4371	0.7399	0.4236	0.7244	0.4109	0.7094
P =	24	0.4497	0.7476	0.4361	0.7323	0.4234	0.7176
P =	25	0.4618	0.7548	0.4482	0.7398	0.4354	0.7253
P =	26	0.4733	0.7616	0.4598	0.7469	0.4470	0.7326
P =	27	0.4844	0.7681	0.4709	0.7536	0.4580	0.7395
P =	28	0.4951	0.7742	0.4815	0.7599	0.4687	0.7461
P =	29	0.5053	0.7800	0.4918	0.7660	0.4790	0.7523
P =	30	0.5152	0.7855	0.5016	0.7717	0.4888	0.7583
P =	31	0.5246	0.7908	0.5111	0.7772	0.4984	0.7640
P =	32	0.5337	0.7957	0.5203	0.7824	0.5075	0.7694
P =	33	0.5425	0.8005	0.5291	0.7873	0.5164	0.7745
P =	34	0.5510	0.8050	0.5376	0.7921	0.5250	0.7795
P =	35	0.5591	0.8094	0.5458	0.7966	0.5332	0.7842
P =	36	0.5670	0.8135	0.5538	0.8009	0.5412	0.7887
P =	37	0.5746	0.8175	0.5614	0.8051	0.5489	0.7930
P =	38	0.5819	0.8213	0.5689	0.8091	0.5564	0.7972
P =	39	0.5890	0.8249	0.5760	0.8129	0.5636	0.8012
P =	40	0.5959	0.8284	0.5830	0.8166	0.5706	0.8050
P =	41	0.6025	0.8318	0.5897	0.8201	0.5774	0.8087
P =	42	0.6089	0.8350	0.5962	0.8235	0.5840	0.8123
P =	43	0.6152	0.8381	0.6025	0.8268	0.5904	0.8157
P =	44	0.6212	0.8411	0.6086	0.8300	0.5965	0.8190
P =	45	0.6270	0.8440	0.6145	0.8330	0.6025	0.8222
P =	46	0.6327	0.8468	0.6203	0.8359	0.6084	0.8253
P =	47	0.6382	0.8495	0.6259	0.8388	0.6140	0.8283
P =	48	0.6435	0.8521	0.6313	0.8415	0.6195	0.8311
P =	49	0.6487	0.8546	0.6366	0.8442	0.6249	0.8339
P =	50	0.6538	0.8570	0.6417	0.8467	0.6301	0.8366
P =	51	0.6587	0.8593	0.6467	0.8492	0.6352	0.8392
P =	52	0.6634	0.8616	0.6515	0.8516	0.6401	0.8417
P =	53	0.6680	0.8638	0.6562	0.8539	0.6449	0.8442
P =	54	0.6725	0.8659	0.6608	0.8562	0.6496	0.8465
P =	55	0.6769	0.8680	0.6653	0.8583	0.6541	0.8488
P =	56	0.6812	0.8700	0.6697	0.8605	0.6585	0.8511
P =	57	0.6854	0.8719	0.6739	0.8625	0.6629	0.8532
P =	58	0.6894	0.8738	0.6780	0.8645	0.6671	0.8553
P =	59	0.6934	0.8756	0.6821	0.8664	0.6712	0.8574
P =	60	0.6972	0.8774	0.6860	0.8683	0.6752	0.8594

19		20		21		22	
LOW	HIGH	LOW	HIGH	LOW	HIGH	LOW	HIGH
0.0028	0.2175	0.0026	0.2084	0.0025	0.1990	0.0023	0.1913
0.0176	0.2764	0.0167	0.2651	0.0158	0.2546	0.0150	0.2449
0.0387	0.3262	0.0367	0.3134	0.0349	0.3016	0.0333	0.2906
0.0622	0.3686	0.0591	0.3548	0.0564	0.3420	0.0539	0.3301
0.0864	0.4053	0.0824	0.3909	0.0787	0.3775	0.0753	0.3649
0.1104	0.4381	0.1055	0.4232	0.1009	0.4092	0.0968	0.3962
0.1342	0.4668	0.1284	0.4516	0.1231	0.4373	0.1182	0.4239
0.1574	0.4926	0.1508	0.4771	0.1448	0.4626	0.1392	0.4490
0.1797	0.5158	0.1725	0.5003	0.1658	0.4857	0.1596	0.4719
0.2012	0.5370	0.1934	0.5214	0.1861	0.5067	0.1794	0.4928
0.2219	0.5563	0.2135	0.5408	0.2057	0.5261	0.1985	0.5121
0.2417	0.5740	0.2328	0.5586	0.2246	0.5439	0.2170	0.5299
0.2606	0.5904	0.2514	0.5750	0.2428	0.5604	0.2347	0.5464
0.2788	0.6055	0.2692	0.5902	0.2602	0.5757	0.2518	0.5618
0.2961	0.6195	0.2862	0.6044	0.2769	0.5899	0.2682	0.5761
0.3128	0.6325	0.3026	0.6175	0.2930	0.6032	0.2841	0.5895
0.3287	0.6446	0.3183	0.6298	0.3085	0.6157	0.2993	0.6021
0.3440	0.6560	0.3333	0.6414	0.3233	0.6273	0.3139	0.6139
0.3586	0.6667	0.3478	0.6522	0.3376	0.6383	0.3280	0.6250
0.3727	0.6767	0.3617	0.6624	0.3513	0.6487	0.3416	0.6355
0.3861	0.6861	0.3750	0.6720	0.3645	0.6584	0.3546	0.6454
0.3990	0.6950	0.3878	0.6810	0.3772	0.6676	0.3672	0.6547
0.4115	0.7033	0.4002	0.6896	0.3895	0.6764	0.3794	0.6636
0.4234	0.7113	0.4120	0.6977	0.4013	0.6847	0.3911	0.6720
0.4349	0.7188	0.4234	0.7054	0.4126	0.6925	0.4023	0.6800
0.4459	0.7259	0.4345	0.7127	0.4236	0.7000	0.4132	0.6877
0.4566	0.7327	0.4451	0.7197	0.4341	0.7071	0.4237	0.6949
0.4668	0.7391	0.4553	0.7263	0.4443	0.7139	0.4339	0.7019
0.4767	0.7453	0.4652	0.7326	0.4542	0.7204	0.4437	0.7085
0.4862	0.7511	0.4747	0.7387	0.4637	0.7266	0.4532	0.7148
0.4954	0.7567	0.4839	0.7444	0.4729	0.7325	0.4624	0.7209
0.5043	0.7621	0.4928	0.7499	0.4818	0.7382	0.4713	0.7267
0.5129	0.7672	0.5014	0.7552	0.4904	0.7436	0.4799	0.7323
0.5212	0.7721	0.5097	0.7603	0.4987	0.7488	0.4883	0.7376
0.5292	0.7768	0.5178	0.7651	0.5068	0.7538	0.4963	0.7427
0.5370	0.7813	0.5256	0.7698	0.5146	0.7586	0.5042	0.7477
0.5445	0.7856	0.5331	0.7743	0.5222	0.7632	0.5118	0.7524
0.5518	0.7897	0.5404	0.7786	0.5296	0.7676	0.5192	0.7570
0.5588	0.7937	0.5475	0.7827	0.5367	0.7719	0.5263	0.7614
0.5657	0.7976	0.5544	0.7867	0.5436	0.7760	0.5333	0.7656
0.5723	0.8013	0.5611	0.7905	0.5504	0.7800	0.5400	0.7697
0.5787	0.8049	0.5676	0.7943	0.5569	0.7839	0.5466	0.7737
0.5850	0.8083	0.5739	0.7978	0.5632	0.7876	0.5530	0.7775
0.5911	0.8116	0.5800	0.8013	0.5694	0.7911	0.5592	0.7812
0.5970	0.8149	0.5860	0.8046	0.5754	0.7946	0.5653	0.7848
0.6027	0.8180	0.5918	0.8079	0.5813	0.7980	0.5711	0.7882
0.6083	0.8210	0.5974	0.8110	0.5869	0.8012	0.5769	0.7916
0.6137	0.8239	0.6029	0.8140	0.5925	0.8043	0.5825	0.7948
0.6189	0.8267	0.6082	0.8169	0.5979	0.8074	0.5879	0.7980
0.6241	0.8294	0.6134	0.8198	0.6031	0.8103	0.5932	0.8010
0.6291	0.8320	0.6185	0.8225	0.6082	0.8132	0.5984	0.8040
0.6339	0.8346	0.6234	0.8252	0.6132	0.8159	0.6034	0.8069
0.6387	0.8371	0.6282	0.8278	0.6181	0.8186	0.6083	0.8097
0.6433	0.8395	0.6329	0.8303	0.6228	0.8212	0.6131	0.8124
0.6478	0.8418	0.6375	0.8327	0.6275	0.8238	0.6178	0.8150
0.6522	0.8441	0.6419	0.8351	0.6320	0.8263	0.6223	0.8176
0.6565	0.8463	0.6463	0.8374	0.6364	0.8287	0.6268	0.8200
0.6607	0.8484	0.6505	0.8396	0.6407	0.8310	0.6312	0.8225
0.6648	0.8505	0.6547	0.8418	0.6449	0.8333	0.6354	0.8248

Q =		23		24		25	
		LOW	HIGH	LOW	HIGH	LOW	HIGH
P =	2	0.0022	0.1840	0.0021	0.1773	0.0020	0.1709
P =	3	0.0143	0.2359	0.0137	0.2276	0.0131	0.2198
P =	4	0.0318	0.2804	0.0305	0.2709	0.0292	0.2620
P =	5	0.0516	0.3190	0.0495	0.3087	0.0476	0.2989
P =	6	0.0723	0.3531	0.0594	0.3421	0.0668	0.3317
P =	7	0.0930	0.3839	0.0894	0.3724	0.0861	0.3615
P =	8	0.1137	0.4113	0.1095	0.3994	0.1056	0.3881
P =	9	0.1341	0.4361	0.1293	0.4239	0.1248	0.4124
P =	10	0.1539	0.4588	0.1486	0.4464	0.1436	0.4347
P =	11	0.1732	0.4796	0.1573	0.4671	0.1619	0.4552
P =	12	0.1918	0.4988	0.1855	0.4862	0.1797	0.4743
P =	13	0.2098	0.5166	0.2031	0.5040	0.1969	0.4919
P =	14	0.2272	0.5332	0.2201	0.5205	0.2135	0.5084
P =	15	0.2440	0.5486	0.2366	0.5359	0.2296	0.5238
P =	16	0.2601	0.5629	0.2524	0.5503	0.2452	0.5382
P =	17	0.2756	0.5764	0.2577	0.5639	0.2602	0.5518
P =	18	0.2906	0.5891	0.2824	0.5766	0.2747	0.5646
P =	19	0.3050	0.6010	0.2967	0.5885	0.2887	0.5766
P =	20	0.3190	0.6122	0.3104	0.5998	0.3023	0.5880
P =	21	0.3324	0.6228	0.3236	0.6105	0.3153	0.5987
P =	22	0.3453	0.6328	0.3364	0.6206	0.3280	0.6089
P =	23	0.3577	0.6423	0.3487	0.6302	0.3402	0.6186
P =	24	0.3698	0.6513	0.3606	0.6394	0.3520	0.6279
P =	25	0.3814	0.6598	0.3721	0.6480	0.3634	0.6366
P =	26	0.3926	0.6680	0.3833	0.6563	0.3744	0.6450
P =	27	0.4034	0.6757	0.3940	0.6642	0.3851	0.6530
P =	28	0.4139	0.6831	0.4044	0.6717	0.3954	0.6606
P =	29	0.4240	0.6902	0.4145	0.6789	0.4054	0.6679
P =	30	0.4338	0.6970	0.4242	0.6858	0.4151	0.6749
P =	31	0.4432	0.7034	0.4337	0.6923	0.4245	0.6816
P =	32	0.4524	0.7096	0.4428	0.6986	0.4336	0.6880
P =	33	0.4613	0.7155	0.4517	0.7047	0.4425	0.6942
P =	34	0.4699	0.7212	0.4603	0.7105	0.4510	0.7001
P =	35	0.4782	0.7267	0.4686	0.7161	0.4594	0.7058
P =	36	0.4863	0.7320	0.4767	0.7215	0.4674	0.7113
P =	37	0.4942	0.7370	0.4845	0.7267	0.4753	0.7165
P =	38	0.5018	0.7419	0.4922	0.7316	0.4829	0.7216
P =	39	0.5092	0.7466	0.4996	0.7364	0.4903	0.7265
P =	40	0.5164	0.7511	0.5068	0.7411	0.4975	0.7313
P =	41	0.5233	0.7555	0.5138	0.7455	0.5045	0.7358
P =	42	0.5301	0.7597	0.5206	0.7499	0.5114	0.7403
P =	43	0.5367	0.7638	0.5272	0.7540	0.5180	0.7445
P =	44	0.5431	0.7677	0.5336	0.7581	0.5245	0.7487
P =	45	0.5494	0.7715	0.5399	0.7620	0.5308	0.7527
P =	46	0.5555	0.7752	0.5460	0.7658	0.5369	0.7565
P =	47	0.5614	0.7787	0.5520	0.7694	0.5429	0.7603
P =	48	0.5672	0.7822	0.5578	0.7730	0.5487	0.7639
P =	49	0.5728	0.7855	0.5634	0.7764	0.5544	0.7675
P =	50	0.5783	0.7888	0.5590	0.7798	0.5600	0.7709
P =	51	0.5836	0.7919	0.5743	0.7830	0.5654	0.7742
P =	52	0.5888	0.7950	0.5796	0.7861	0.5706	0.7775
P =	53	0.5939	0.7979	0.5847	0.7892	0.5758	0.7806
P =	54	0.5988	0.8008	0.5897	0.7922	0.5808	0.7837
P =	55	0.6037	0.8036	0.5946	0.7950	0.5858	0.7866
P =	56	0.6084	0.8063	0.5994	0.7979	0.5906	0.7895
P =	57	0.6130	0.8090	0.6040	0.8006	0.5953	0.7923
P =	58	0.6175	0.8116	0.6086	0.8032	0.5999	0.7951
P =	59	0.6219	0.8141	0.6130	0.8058	0.6043	0.7977
P =	60	0.6263	0.8165	0.6174	0.8084	0.6087	0.8003

26		27		28		29	
LOW	HIGH	LOW	HIGH	LOW	HIGH	LOW	HIGH
0.0019	0.1650	0.0018	0.1594	0.0018	0.1542	0.0017	0.1494
0.0126	0.2125	0.0121	0.2057	0.0116	0.1993	0.0112	0.1933
0.0281	0.2536	0.0270	0.2458	0.0261	0.2384	0.0251	0.2315
0.0458	0.2898	0.0441	0.2812	0.0426	0.2731	0.0411	0.2654
0.0644	0.3219	0.0621	0.3127	0.0600	0.3040	0.0580	0.2958
0.0831	0.3513	0.0804	0.3412	0.0778	0.3320	0.0753	0.3233
0.1020	0.3775	0.0986	0.3674	0.0954	0.3579	0.0925	0.3488
0.1207	0.4015	0.1168	0.3911	0.1131	0.3813	0.1097	0.3719
0.1389	0.4235	0.1346	0.4129	0.1305	0.4028	0.1266	0.3932
0.1568	0.4439	0.1520	0.4331	0.1475	0.4229	0.1432	0.4131
0.1741	0.4628	0.1689	0.4519	0.1641	0.4415	0.1594	0.4316
0.1910	0.4804	0.1854	0.4694	0.1802	0.4589	0.1752	0.4489
0.2073	0.4969	0.2014	0.4858	0.1959	0.4752	0.1906	0.4651
0.2231	0.5122	0.2169	0.5011	0.2111	0.4905	0.2055	0.4803
0.2384	0.5267	0.2319	0.5156	0.2258	0.5049	0.2200	0.4947
0.2531	0.5402	0.2464	0.5291	0.2401	0.5185	0.2340	0.5082
0.2674	0.5530	0.2605	0.5420	0.2539	0.5313	0.2477	0.5210
0.2812	0.5651	0.2741	0.5541	0.2673	0.5434	0.2609	0.5332
0.2946	0.5766	0.2873	0.5655	0.2803	0.5549	0.2737	0.5447
0.3075	0.5874	0.3000	0.5764	0.2929	0.5659	0.2861	0.5557
0.3200	0.5977	0.3123	0.5868	0.3051	0.5763	0.2981	0.5661
0.3320	0.6074	0.3243	0.5966	0.3169	0.5861	0.3098	0.5760
0.3437	0.6167	0.3358	0.6060	0.3283	0.5956	0.3211	0.5855
0.3550	0.6256	0.3470	0.6149	0.3394	0.6046	0.3321	0.5946
0.3660	0.6340	0.3579	0.6234	0.3502	0.6132	0.3428	0.6032
0.3766	0.6421	0.3684	0.6316	0.3606	0.6214	0.3531	0.6115
0.3868	0.6498	0.3786	0.6394	0.3707	0.6293	0.3631	0.6195
0.3968	0.6572	0.3885	0.6469	0.3805	0.6369	0.3729	0.6271
0.4064	0.6643	0.3981	0.6541	0.3901	0.6441	0.3824	0.6344
0.4158	0.6711	0.4074	0.6609	0.3993	0.6511	0.3916	0.6415
0.4248	0.6776	0.4164	0.6676	0.4083	0.6578	0.4005	0.6482
0.4336	0.6839	0.4252	0.6739	0.4170	0.6642	0.4092	0.6547
0.4422	0.6899	0.4337	0.6800	0.4255	0.6704	0.4177	0.6610
0.4505	0.6957	0.4420	0.6859	0.4338	0.6764	0.4259	0.6671
0.4586	0.7013	0.4500	0.6916	0.4418	0.6821	0.4339	0.6729
0.4664	0.7067	0.4578	0.6971	0.4496	0.6877	0.4417	0.6785
0.4740	0.7119	0.4655	0.7023	0.4572	0.6930	0.4493	0.6840
0.4814	0.7169	0.4729	0.7074	0.4646	0.6982	0.4567	0.6892
0.4886	0.7217	0.4801	0.7123	0.4718	0.7032	0.4638	0.6943
0.4957	0.7264	0.4871	0.7171	0.4788	0.7081	0.4709	0.6992
0.5025	0.7309	0.4939	0.7217	0.4857	0.7127	0.4777	0.7040
0.5092	0.7352	0.5006	0.7262	0.4924	0.7173	0.4844	0.7086
0.5156	0.7395	0.5071	0.7305	0.4989	0.7217	0.4909	0.7130
0.5220	0.7436	0.5134	0.7346	0.5052	0.7259	0.4972	0.7174
0.5281	0.7475	0.5196	0.7387	0.5114	0.7300	0.5034	0.7216
0.5341	0.7514	0.5256	0.7426	0.5174	0.7340	0.5095	0.7257
0.5400	0.7551	0.5315	0.7464	0.5233	0.7379	0.5154	0.7296
0.5457	0.7587	0.5372	0.7501	0.5291	0.7417	0.5211	0.7335
0.5513	0.7622	0.5428	0.7537	0.5347	0.7454	0.5268	0.7372
0.5567	0.7656	0.5483	0.7572	0.5402	0.7489	0.5323	0.7408
0.5620	0.7689	0.5536	0.7606	0.5455	0.7524	0.5376	0.7444
0.5672	0.7722	0.5588	0.7639	0.5508	0.7558	0.5429	0.7478
0.5723	0.7753	0.5639	0.7671	0.5559	0.7590	0.5480	0.7511
0.5772	0.7783	0.5689	0.7702	0.5609	0.7622	0.5531	0.7544
0.5821	0.7813	0.5738	0.7733	0.5658	0.7653	0.5580	0.7576
0.5868	0.7842	0.5786	0.7762	0.5706	0.7684	0.5628	0.7607
0.5914	0.7870	0.5832	0.7791	0.5753	0.7713	0.5675	0.7637
0.5959	0.7897	0.5878	0.7819	0.5798	0.7742	0.5721	0.7666
0.6004	0.7924	0.5922	0.7846	0.5843	0.7770	0.5766	0.7695

Q =		30		31		32	
		LOW	HIGH	LOW	HIGH	LOW	HIGH
P =	2	0.0016	0.1448	0.0016	0.1406	0.0015	0.1363
P =	3	0.0108	0.1877	0.0104	0.1823	0.0101	0.1773
P =	4	0.0243	0.2250	0.0235	0.2189	0.0227	0.2130
P =	5	0.0398	0.2582	0.0385	0.2513	0.0373	0.2448
P =	6	0.0562	0.2880	0.0544	0.2806	0.0528	0.2735
P =	7	0.0730	0.3151	0.0708	0.3072	0.0687	0.2998
P =	8	0.0897	0.3402	0.0871	0.3319	0.0846	0.3241
P =	9	0.1065	0.3630	0.1034	0.3544	0.1005	0.3463
P =	10	0.1230	0.3841	0.1196	0.3753	0.1163	0.3669
P =	11	0.1392	0.4037	0.1354	0.3948	0.1318	0.3862
P =	12	0.1551	0.4220	0.1510	0.4129	0.1470	0.4042
P =	13	0.1706	0.4392	0.1661	0.4300	0.1619	0.4211
P =	14	0.1856	0.4553	0.1809	0.4460	0.1764	0.4370
P =	15	0.2003	0.4705	0.1953	0.4611	0.1905	0.4521
P =	16	0.2145	0.4848	0.2092	0.4754	0.2043	0.4663
P =	17	0.2283	0.4984	0.2228	0.4889	0.2176	0.4797
P =	18	0.2417	0.5112	0.2360	0.5016	0.2306	0.4925
P =	19	0.2547	0.5233	0.2489	0.5138	0.2433	0.5046
P =	20	0.2674	0.5348	0.2613	0.5253	0.2556	0.5161
P =	21	0.2796	0.5458	0.2734	0.5363	0.2675	0.5271
P =	22	0.2915	0.5563	0.2852	0.5468	0.2791	0.5376
P =	23	0.3030	0.5662	0.2966	0.5568	0.2904	0.5476
P =	24	0.3142	0.5758	0.3077	0.5663	0.3014	0.5572
P =	25	0.3251	0.5849	0.3184	0.5755	0.3120	0.5664
P =	26	0.3357	0.5936	0.3289	0.5842	0.3224	0.5752
P =	27	0.3459	0.6019	0.3391	0.5926	0.3324	0.5836
P =	28	0.3559	0.6099	0.3489	0.6007	0.3422	0.5917
P =	29	0.3656	0.6176	0.3585	0.6084	0.3518	0.5995
P =	30	0.3750	0.6250	0.3679	0.6159	0.3610	0.6070
P =	31	0.3841	0.6321	0.3770	0.6230	0.3701	0.6142
P =	32	0.3930	0.6390	0.3858	0.6299	0.3789	0.6211
P =	33	0.4017	0.6455	0.3944	0.6366	0.3874	0.6278
P =	34	0.4101	0.6519	0.4028	0.6430	0.3958	0.6343
P =	35	0.4183	0.6580	0.4109	0.6492	0.4039	0.6405
P =	36	0.4263	0.6639	0.4189	0.6551	0.4118	0.6466
P =	37	0.4340	0.6696	0.4266	0.6609	0.4195	0.6524
P =	38	0.4416	0.6751	0.4342	0.6665	0.4270	0.6580
P =	39	0.4490	0.6804	0.4415	0.6719	0.4343	0.6635
P =	40	0.4561	0.6856	0.4487	0.6771	0.4415	0.6688
P =	41	0.4632	0.6906	0.4557	0.6821	0.4485	0.6739
P =	42	0.4700	0.6954	0.4625	0.6870	0.4553	0.6788
P =	43	0.4767	0.7001	0.4692	0.6918	0.4620	0.6836
P =	44	0.4832	0.7046	0.4757	0.6964	0.4684	0.6883
P =	45	0.4895	0.7090	0.4820	0.7008	0.4748	0.6928
P =	46	0.4957	0.7133	0.4882	0.7052	0.4810	0.6972
P =	47	0.5018	0.7174	0.4943	0.7094	0.4870	0.7015
P =	48	0.5077	0.7215	0.5002	0.7135	0.4930	0.7056
P =	49	0.5134	0.7254	0.5060	0.7174	0.4988	0.7097
P =	50	0.5191	0.7292	0.5116	0.7213	0.5044	0.7136
P =	51	0.5246	0.7329	0.5172	0.7251	0.5100	0.7174
P =	52	0.5300	0.7365	0.5226	0.7287	0.5154	0.7211
P =	53	0.5353	0.7400	0.5279	0.7323	0.5207	0.7248
P =	54	0.5404	0.7434	0.5330	0.7358	0.5259	0.7283
P =	55	0.5455	0.7467	0.5381	0.7392	0.5309	0.7317
P =	56	0.5504	0.7499	0.5431	0.7425	0.5359	0.7351
P =	57	0.5553	0.7531	0.5479	0.7457	0.5408	0.7384
P =	58	0.5600	0.7562	0.5527	0.7488	0.5456	0.7416
P =	59	0.5646	0.7592	0.5573	0.7519	0.5502	0.7447
P =	60	0.5692	0.7621	0.5619	0.7548	0.5548	0.7477

33		34		35		36	
LOW	HIGH	LOW	HIGH	LOW	HIGH	LOW	HIGH
0.0015	0.1327	0.0014	0.1290	0.0014	0.1256	0.0013	0.1224
0.0098	0.1725	0.0094	0.1680	0.0092	0.1637	0.0089	0.1596
0.0220	0.2075	0.0214	0.2022	0.0208	0.1972	0.0202	0.1924
0.0362	0.2387	0.0351	0.2327	0.0342	0.2271	0.0332	0.2218
0.0513	0.2669	0.0498	0.2605	0.0484	0.2544	0.0472	0.2486
0.0668	0.2926	0.0649	0.2858	0.0632	0.2794	0.0615	0.2732
0.0822	0.3166	0.0800	0.3095	0.0779	0.3027	0.0759	0.2962
0.0978	0.3385	0.0953	0.3311	0.0928	0.3240	0.0905	0.3172
0.1133	0.3589	0.1103	0.3513	0.1076	0.3439	0.1049	0.3369
0.1284	0.3780	0.1252	0.3701	0.1221	0.3626	0.1192	0.3553
0.1433	0.3958	0.1398	0.3878	0.1364	0.3801	0.1332	0.3726
0.1579	0.4126	0.1541	0.4044	0.1505	0.3966	0.1470	0.3890
0.1721	0.4284	0.1680	0.4201	0.1642	0.4122	0.1605	0.4045
0.1860	0.4434	0.1817	0.4350	0.1776	0.4269	0.1736	0.4191
0.1995	0.4575	0.1950	0.4490	0.1906	0.4409	0.1865	0.4330
0.2127	0.4709	0.2079	0.4624	0.2034	0.4542	0.1991	0.4462
0.2255	0.4836	0.2205	0.4750	0.2158	0.4668	0.2113	0.4588
0.2379	0.4957	0.2328	0.4871	0.2279	0.4788	0.2232	0.4708
0.2501	0.5072	0.2448	0.4986	0.2397	0.4903	0.2349	0.4822
0.2618	0.5182	0.2564	0.5096	0.2512	0.5013	0.2462	0.4932
0.2733	0.5287	0.2677	0.5201	0.2624	0.5117	0.2573	0.5037
0.2845	0.5387	0.2788	0.5301	0.2733	0.5218	0.2680	0.5137
0.2953	0.5483	0.2895	0.5397	0.2839	0.5314	0.2785	0.5233
0.3058	0.5575	0.2999	0.5490	0.2942	0.5406	0.2887	0.5326
0.3161	0.5664	0.3101	0.5578	0.3043	0.5495	0.2987	0.5414
0.3261	0.5748	0.3200	0.5663	0.3141	0.5580	0.3084	0.5500
0.3358	0.5830	0.3296	0.5745	0.3236	0.5662	0.3179	0.5582
0.3453	0.5908	0.3390	0.5823	0.3329	0.5741	0.3271	0.5661
0.3545	0.5983	0.3481	0.5899	0.3420	0.5817	0.3361	0.5737
0.3634	0.6056	0.3570	0.5972	0.3508	0.5891	0.3449	0.5811
0.3722	0.6126	0.3657	0.6042	0.3595	0.5961	0.3534	0.5882
0.3807	0.6193	0.3742	0.6110	0.3679	0.6030	0.3618	0.5951
0.3890	0.6258	0.3824	0.6176	0.3761	0.6096	0.3699	0.6017
0.3970	0.6321	0.3904	0.6239	0.3841	0.6159	0.3779	0.6081
0.4049	0.6382	0.3983	0.6301	0.3919	0.6221	0.3857	0.6143
0.4126	0.6441	0.4059	0.6360	0.3995	0.6281	0.3932	0.6204
0.4201	0.6498	0.4134	0.6417	0.4069	0.6339	0.4006	0.6262
0.4274	0.6553	0.4207	0.6473	0.4142	0.6395	0.4079	0.6318
0.4345	0.6606	0.4278	0.6527	0.4213	0.6449	0.4149	0.6373
0.4415	0.6658	0.4347	0.6579	0.4282	0.6502	0.4218	0.6426
0.4483	0.6708	0.4415	0.6630	0.4349	0.6553	0.4286	0.6478
0.4549	0.6757	0.4481	0.6679	0.4416	0.6603	0.4352	0.6528
0.4614	0.6804	0.4546	0.6727	0.4480	0.6651	0.4416	0.6577
0.4678	0.6850	0.4610	0.6773	0.4543	0.6698	0.4479	0.6624
0.4740	0.6894	0.4671	0.6818	0.4605	0.6743	0.4541	0.6670
0.4800	0.6938	0.4732	0.6862	0.4666	0.6788	0.4601	0.6715
0.4859	0.6980	0.4791	0.6905	0.4725	0.6831	0.4661	0.6759
0.4917	0.7021	0.4849	0.6946	0.4783	0.6873	0.4718	0.6801
0.4974	0.7060	0.4906	0.6986	0.4839	0.6914	0.4775	0.6842
0.5029	0.7099	0.4961	0.7026	0.4895	0.6953	0.4830	0.6883
0.5084	0.7137	0.5016	0.7064	0.4949	0.6992	0.4885	0.6922
0.5137	0.7174	0.5069	0.7101	0.5002	0.7030	0.4938	0.6960
0.5189	0.7210	0.5121	0.7138	0.5055	0.7067	0.4990	0.6997
0.5240	0.7245	0.5172	0.7173	0.5106	0.7103	0.5041	0.7034
0.5289	0.7279	0.5222	0.7208	0.5156	0.7138	0.5091	0.7069
0.5338	0.7312	0.5271	0.7241	0.5205	0.7172	0.5141	0.7104
0.5386	0.7344	0.5319	0.7274	0.5253	0.7206	0.5189	0.7138
0.5433	0.7376	0.5366	0.7306	0.5300	0.7238	0.5236	0.7171
0.5479	0.7407	0.5412	0.7338	0.5346	0.7270	0.5282	0.7203

Q =		37		38		39	
		LOW	HIGH	LOW	HIGH	LOW	HIGH
P =	2	0.0013	0.1194	0.0013	0.1164	0.0012	0.1137
P =	3	0.0086	0.1557	0.0084	0.1521	0.0082	0.1485
P =	4	0.0196	0.1879	0.0191	0.1835	0.0186	0.1794
P =	5	0.0323	0.2167	0.0315	0.2119	0.0307	0.2072
P =	6	0.0459	0.2431	0.0448	0.2378	0.0437	0.2327
P =	7	0.0600	0.2672	0.0585	0.2616	0.0571	0.2561
P =	8	0.0740	0.2899	0.0722	0.2839	0.0705	0.2781
P =	9	0.0883	0.3107	0.0862	0.3044	0.0842	0.2984
P =	10	0.1024	0.3301	0.1000	0.3236	0.0978	0.3173
P =	11	0.1164	0.3483	0.1137	0.3416	0.1112	0.3352
P =	12	0.1302	0.3655	0.1273	0.3586	0.1245	0.3520
P =	13	0.1437	0.3817	0.1405	0.3747	0.1375	0.3679
P =	14	0.1569	0.3971	0.1535	0.3899	0.1503	0.3830
P =	15	0.1699	0.4116	0.1663	0.4043	0.1628	0.3973
P =	16	0.1825	0.4254	0.1787	0.4181	0.1751	0.4110
P =	17	0.1949	0.4386	0.1909	0.4311	0.1871	0.4240
P =	18	0.2070	0.4511	0.2028	0.4436	0.1988	0.4364
P =	19	0.2187	0.4630	0.2144	0.4555	0.2103	0.4482
P =	20	0.2302	0.4744	0.2257	0.4669	0.2214	0.4596
P =	21	0.2414	0.4854	0.2368	0.4778	0.2324	0.4704
P =	22	0.2523	0.4958	0.2476	0.4882	0.2430	0.4808
P =	23	0.2630	0.5058	0.2581	0.4982	0.2534	0.4908
P =	24	0.2733	0.5155	0.2684	0.5078	0.2636	0.5004
P =	25	0.2835	0.5247	0.2784	0.5171	0.2735	0.5097
P =	26	0.2933	0.5336	0.2881	0.5260	0.2831	0.5186
P =	27	0.3029	0.5422	0.2977	0.5345	0.2926	0.5271
P =	28	0.3123	0.5504	0.3070	0.5428	0.3018	0.5354
P =	29	0.3215	0.5583	0.3160	0.5507	0.3108	0.5433
P =	30	0.3304	0.5660	0.3249	0.5584	0.3196	0.5510
P =	31	0.3391	0.5734	0.3335	0.5658	0.3281	0.5585
P =	32	0.3476	0.5805	0.3420	0.5730	0.3365	0.5657
P =	33	0.3559	0.5874	0.3502	0.5799	0.3447	0.5726
P =	34	0.3640	0.5941	0.3583	0.5866	0.3527	0.5793
P =	35	0.3719	0.6005	0.3661	0.5931	0.3605	0.5858
P =	36	0.3796	0.6068	0.3738	0.5994	0.3682	0.5921
P =	37	0.3872	0.6128	0.3813	0.6055	0.3756	0.5983
P =	38	0.3945	0.6187	0.3887	0.6113	0.3829	0.6042
P =	39	0.4017	0.6244	0.3958	0.6171	0.3901	0.6099
P =	40	0.4088	0.6299	0.4028	0.6226	0.3970	0.6155
P =	41	0.4157	0.6353	0.4097	0.6280	0.4039	0.6210
P =	42	0.4224	0.6405	0.4164	0.6333	0.4105	0.6262
P =	43	0.4290	0.6455	0.4229	0.6384	0.4171	0.6314
P =	44	0.4354	0.6504	0.4293	0.6433	0.4235	0.6364
P =	45	0.4417	0.6552	0.4356	0.6481	0.4297	0.6412
P =	46	0.4479	0.6599	0.4418	0.6528	0.4359	0.6459
P =	47	0.4539	0.6644	0.4478	0.6574	0.4419	0.6505
P =	48	0.4598	0.6688	0.4537	0.6618	0.4478	0.6550
P =	49	0.4656	0.6731	0.4595	0.6662	0.4535	0.6594
P =	50	0.4712	0.6772	0.4651	0.6704	0.4592	0.6637
P =	51	0.4768	0.6813	0.4707	0.6745	0.4647	0.6678
P =	52	0.4822	0.6853	0.4761	0.6785	0.4701	0.6719
P =	53	0.4875	0.6892	0.4814	0.6824	0.4755	0.6758
P =	54	0.4927	0.6929	0.4866	0.6862	0.4807	0.6797
P =	55	0.4979	0.6966	0.4917	0.6900	0.4858	0.6834
P =	56	0.5029	0.7002	0.4968	0.6936	0.4908	0.6871
P =	57	0.5078	0.7037	0.5017	0.6971	0.4957	0.6907
P =	58	0.5126	0.7071	0.5065	0.7006	0.5006	0.6942
P =	59	0.5173	0.7105	0.5112	0.7040	0.5053	0.6976
P =	60	0.5220	0.7138	0.5159	0.7073	0.5100	0.7010

40		41		42		43	
LOW	HIGH	LOW	HIGH	LOW	HIGH	LOW	HIGH
0.0012	0.1110	0.0011	0.1085	0.0011	0.1051	0.0011	0.1038
0.0080	0.1452	0.0078	0.1419	0.0076	0.1389	0.0074	0.1359
0.0181	0.1755	0.0177	0.1717	0.0172	0.1680	0.0168	0.1645
0.0299	0.2028	0.0292	0.1985	0.0285	0.1944	0.0279	0.1905
0.0426	0.2278	0.0416	0.2232	0.0406	0.2187	0.0397	0.2144
0.0557	0.2509	0.0544	0.2459	0.0532	0.2411	0.0520	0.2364
0.0689	0.2726	0.0675	0.2670	0.0660	0.2619	0.0645	0.2570
0.0823	0.2926	0.0804	0.2870	0.0787	0.2816	0.0770	0.2765
0.0956	0.3113	0.0935	0.3055	0.0915	0.2999	0.0896	0.2945
0.1088	0.3290	0.1064	0.3230	0.1042	0.3172	0.1021	0.3116
0.1218	0.3456	0.1192	0.3395	0.1168	0.3335	0.1144	0.3278
0.1346	0.3614	0.1318	0.3551	0.1291	0.3490	0.1266	0.3431
0.1472	0.3764	0.1442	0.3699	0.1413	0.3637	0.1386	0.3577
0.1595	0.3906	0.1563	0.3840	0.1533	0.3777	0.1503	0.3715
0.1716	0.4041	0.1682	0.3975	0.1650	0.3911	0.1619	0.3848
0.1834	0.4170	0.1799	0.4103	0.1765	0.4038	0.1732	0.3975
0.1950	0.4294	0.1913	0.4226	0.1877	0.4150	0.1843	0.4096
0.2063	0.4412	0.2024	0.4343	0.1987	0.4277	0.1951	0.4213
0.2173	0.4525	0.2133	0.4456	0.2095	0.4389	0.2057	0.4324
0.2281	0.4633	0.2240	0.4564	0.2200	0.4496	0.2161	0.4431
0.2386	0.4737	0.2344	0.4667	0.2303	0.4600	0.2263	0.4534
0.2489	0.4836	0.2445	0.4767	0.2403	0.4699	0.2362	0.4633
0.2589	0.4932	0.2545	0.4862	0.2501	0.4794	0.2460	0.4728
0.2687	0.5025	0.2642	0.4955	0.2597	0.4886	0.2555	0.4820
0.2783	0.5114	0.2736	0.5043	0.2691	0.4975	0.2648	0.4908
0.2877	0.5199	0.2829	0.5129	0.2783	0.5061	0.2738	0.4994
0.2968	0.5282	0.2919	0.5212	0.2873	0.5143	0.2827	0.5076
0.3057	0.5362	0.3008	0.5291	0.2960	0.5223	0.2914	0.5156
0.3144	0.5439	0.3094	0.5368	0.3046	0.5300	0.2999	0.5233
0.3229	0.5513	0.3179	0.5443	0.3130	0.5375	0.3082	0.5308
0.3312	0.5585	0.3261	0.5515	0.3212	0.5447	0.3164	0.5380
0.3394	0.5655	0.3342	0.5585	0.3292	0.5517	0.3243	0.5451
0.3473	0.5722	0.3421	0.5653	0.3370	0.5585	0.3321	0.5519
0.3551	0.5787	0.3498	0.5718	0.3447	0.5651	0.3397	0.5584
0.3627	0.5851	0.3574	0.5782	0.3522	0.5714	0.3472	0.5648
0.3701	0.5912	0.3647	0.5843	0.3595	0.5776	0.3545	0.5710
0.3774	0.5972	0.3720	0.5903	0.3667	0.5836	0.3616	0.5771
0.3845	0.6030	0.3790	0.5961	0.3738	0.5895	0.3686	0.5829
0.3914	0.6086	0.3859	0.6018	0.3806	0.5951	0.3755	0.5886
0.3982	0.6141	0.3928	0.6072	0.3874	0.6007	0.3822	0.5942
0.4049	0.6194	0.3993	0.6126	0.3940	0.6060	0.3885	0.5998
0.4114	0.6245	0.4058	0.6178	0.4002	0.6115	0.3952	0.6048
0.4178	0.6296	0.4122	0.6229	0.4068	0.6163	0.4013	0.6101
0.4240	0.6344	0.4184	0.6278	0.4130	0.6213	0.4077	0.6149
0.4301	0.6392	0.4245	0.6326	0.4191	0.6251	0.4138	0.6197
0.4361	0.6438	0.4305	0.6373	0.4250	0.6308	0.4197	0.6245
0.4420	0.6484	0.4364	0.6418	0.4309	0.6354	0.4255	0.6291
0.4477	0.6528	0.4421	0.6462	0.4366	0.6398	0.4312	0.6336
0.4534	0.6570	0.4477	0.6506	0.4422	0.6442	0.4369	0.6380
0.4589	0.6612	0.4533	0.6548	0.4477	0.6485	0.4424	0.6422
0.4643	0.6653	0.4587	0.6589	0.4531	0.6526	0.4478	0.6464
0.4696	0.6693	0.4640	0.6629	0.4584	0.6567	0.4531	0.6505
0.4749	0.6732	0.4692	0.6669	0.4637	0.6606	0.4583	0.6545
0.4800	0.6770	0.4743	0.6707	0.4688	0.6645	0.4634	0.6584
0.4850	0.6807	0.4793	0.6744	0.4738	0.6683	0.4684	0.6622
0.4899	0.6843	0.4842	0.6781	0.4787	0.6720	0.4733	0.6659
0.4947	0.6879	0.4891	0.6817	0.4835	0.6756	0.4781	0.6696
0.4995	0.6913	0.4938	0.6852	0.4883	0.6791	0.4829	0.6731
0.5042	0.6947	0.4985	0.6886	0.4929	0.6826	0.4875	0.6765

Q =		44		45		46	
		LOW	HIGH	LOW	HIGH	LOW	HIGH
P =	2	0.0011	0.1015	0.0010	0.0995	0.0010	0.0974
P =	3	0.0072	0.1331	0.0070	0.1304	0.0069	0.1278
P =	4	0.0164	0.1612	0.0161	0.1580	0.0157	0.1550
P =	5	0.0272	0.1867	0.0266	0.1831	0.0261	0.1796
P =	6	0.0388	0.2102	0.0380	0.2063	0.0372	0.2024
P =	7	0.0509	0.2320	0.0498	0.2277	0.0488	0.2235
P =	8	0.0632	0.2522	0.0619	0.2477	0.0606	0.2433
P =	9	0.0754	0.2715	0.0739	0.2667	0.0724	0.2620
P =	10	0.0878	0.2893	0.0860	0.2843	0.0843	0.2795
P =	11	0.1000	0.3062	0.0980	0.3010	0.0962	0.2960
P =	12	0.1122	0.3222	0.1100	0.3169	0.1079	0.3117
P =	13	0.1241	0.3374	0.1218	0.3319	0.1195	0.3266
P =	14	0.1359	0.3519	0.1334	0.3462	0.1309	0.3408
P =	15	0.1475	0.3657	0.1448	0.3599	0.1422	0.3543
P =	16	0.1589	0.3788	0.1560	0.3730	0.1532	0.3673
P =	17	0.1700	0.3914	0.1670	0.3855	0.1641	0.3797
P =	18	0.1810	0.4035	0.1778	0.3975	0.1747	0.3916
P =	19	0.1917	0.4150	0.1884	0.4089	0.1851	0.4030
P =	20	0.2022	0.4261	0.1987	0.4200	0.1954	0.4140
P =	21	0.2124	0.4368	0.2089	0.4306	0.2054	0.4246
P =	22	0.2225	0.4470	0.2138	0.4408	0.2152	0.4347
P =	23	0.2323	0.4569	0.2285	0.4506	0.2248	0.4445
P =	24	0.2419	0.4564	0.2380	0.4601	0.2342	0.4540
P =	25	0.2513	0.4755	0.2473	0.4692	0.2435	0.4631
P =	26	0.2605	0.4844	0.2564	0.4780	0.2525	0.4719
P =	27	0.2695	0.4929	0.2654	0.4866	0.2613	0.4804
P =	28	0.2783	0.5011	0.2741	0.4948	0.2700	0.4886
P =	29	0.2870	0.5091	0.2826	0.5028	0.2784	0.4966
P =	30	0.2954	0.5168	0.2910	0.5105	0.2867	0.5043
P =	31	0.3036	0.5243	0.2992	0.5180	0.2948	0.5118
P =	32	0.3117	0.5316	0.3072	0.5252	0.3028	0.5190
P =	33	0.3196	0.5386	0.3150	0.5322	0.3106	0.5260
P =	34	0.3273	0.5454	0.3227	0.5390	0.3182	0.5329
P =	35	0.3349	0.5520	0.3302	0.5457	0.3257	0.5395
P =	36	0.3423	0.5584	0.3376	0.5521	0.3330	0.5459
P =	37	0.3496	0.5646	0.3448	0.5583	0.3401	0.5521
P =	38	0.3567	0.5707	0.3519	0.5644	0.3472	0.5582
P =	39	0.3636	0.5765	0.3588	0.5703	0.3541	0.5641
P =	40	0.3704	0.5822	0.3656	0.5760	0.3608	0.5699
P =	41	0.3771	0.5878	0.3722	0.5816	0.3674	0.5755
P =	42	0.3837	0.5932	0.3787	0.5870	0.3739	0.5809
P =	43	0.3899	0.5987	0.3851	0.5923	0.3803	0.5862
P =	44	0.3964	0.6036	0.3912	0.5977	0.3865	0.5914
P =	45	0.4023	0.6088	0.3976	0.6024	0.3924	0.5967
P =	46	0.4086	0.6135	0.4033	0.6076	0.3987	0.6013
P =	47	0.4145	0.6183	0.4094	0.6122	0.4043	0.6064
P =	48	0.4203	0.6229	0.4152	0.6168	0.4103	0.6109
P =	49	0.4260	0.6274	0.4209	0.6214	0.4160	0.6154
P =	50	0.4316	0.6318	0.4265	0.6258	0.4215	0.6199
P =	51	0.4371	0.6361	0.4320	0.6302	0.4270	0.6243
P =	52	0.4425	0.6404	0.4374	0.6344	0.4324	0.6285
P =	53	0.4478	0.6445	0.4426	0.6385	0.4376	0.6327
P =	54	0.4530	0.6485	0.4478	0.6426	0.4428	0.6368
P =	55	0.4581	0.6524	0.4529	0.6465	0.4479	0.6407
P =	56	0.4631	0.6563	0.4579	0.6504	0.4529	0.6446
P =	57	0.4680	0.6500	0.4528	0.6542	0.4578	0.6484
P =	58	0.4728	0.6637	0.4677	0.6579	0.4626	0.6522
P =	59	0.4776	0.6673	0.4724	0.6615	0.4673	0.6558
P =	60	0.4822	0.6708	0.4771	0.6650	0.4720	0.6594

|—— 47 ——|		|—— 48 ——|		|—— 49 ——|		|—— 50 ——|	
LOW	HIGH	LOW	HIGH	LOW	HIGH	LOW	HIGH
0.0010	0.0955	0.0010	0.0936	0.0009	0.0918	0.0009	0.0901
0.0067	0.1253	0.0066	0.1229	0.0064	0.1206	0.0063	0.1183
0.0154	0.1520	0.0151	0.1491	0.0147	0.1454	0.0144	0.1438
0.0255	0.1763	0.0250	0.1730	0.0245	0.1699	0.0240	0.1669
0.0364	0.1987	0.0357	0.1951	0.0350	0.1917	0.0343	0.1884
0.0478	0.2195	0.0468	0.2157	0.0459	0.2120	0.0451	0.2084
0.0594	0.2390	0.0582	0.2349	0.0571	0.2309	0.0560	0.2271
0.0710	0.2576	0.0696	0.2532	0.0683	0.2490	0.0670	0.2450
0.0827	0.2748	0.0811	0.2703	0.0796	0.2659	0.0782	0.2616
0.0943	0.2911	0.0926	0.2864	0.0909	0.2819	0.0892	0.2774
0.1059	0.3066	0.1039	0.3018	0.1021	0.2971	0.1003	0.2925
0.1173	0.3214	0.1152	0.3164	0.1131	0.3115	0.1112	0.3068
0.1285	0.3355	0.1263	0.3304	0.1241	0.3254	0.1219	0.3206
0.1396	0.3489	0.1372	0.3437	0.1348	0.3386	0.1325	0.3337
0.1505	0.3618	0.1479	0.3565	0.1454	0.3513	0.1430	0.3462
0.1612	0.3741	0.1585	0.3687	0.1558	0.3634	0.1533	0.3583
0.1717	0.3860	0.1689	0.3805	0.1661	0.3751	0.1634	0.3699
0.1820	0.3973	0.1790	0.3917	0.1761	0.3863	0.1733	0.3811
0.1921	0.4082	0.1890	0.4026	0.1860	0.3971	0.1831	0.3918
0.2020	0.4187	0.1988	0.4131	0.1957	0.4075	0.1926	0.4021
0.2118	0.4289	0.2084	0.4231	0.2052	0.4175	0.2020	0.4121
0.2213	0.4386	0.2178	0.4328	0.2145	0.4272	0.2112	0.4217
0.2306	0.4480	0.2270	0.4422	0.2236	0.4366	0.2202	0.4310
0.2397	0.4571	0.2361	0.4513	0.2325	0.4456	0.2291	0.4400
0.2486	0.4659	0.2449	0.4600	0.2413	0.4543	0.2378	0.4487
0.2574	0.4744	0.2536	0.4685	0.2499	0.4628	0.2463	0.4572
0.2660	0.4826	0.2621	0.4767	0.2583	0.4709	0.2546	0.4653
0.2743	0.4905	0.2704	0.4846	0.2665	0.4789	0.2628	0.4732
0.2826	0.4982	0.2785	0.4923	0.2746	0.4866	0.2708	0.4809
0.2906	0.5057	0.2865	0.4998	0.2826	0.4940	0.2787	0.4884
0.2985	0.5130	0.2944	0.5070	0.2903	0.5012	0.2864	0.4956
0.3062	0.5200	0.3020	0.5141	0.2979	0.5083	0.2940	0.5026
0.3138	0.5268	0.3095	0.5209	0.3054	0.5151	0.3014	0.5094
0.3212	0.5334	0.3169	0.5275	0.3127	0.5217	0.3086	0.5161
0.3285	0.5399	0.3241	0.5339	0.3199	0.5282	0.3158	0.5225
0.3356	0.5461	0.3312	0.5402	0.3269	0.5344	0.3228	0.5288
0.3426	0.5522	0.3382	0.5463	0.3338	0.5405	0.3296	0.5349
0.3495	0.5581	0.3450	0.5522	0.3406	0.5465	0.3363	0.5408
0.3562	0.5639	0.3516	0.5580	0.3472	0.5523	0.3430	0.5466
0.3627	0.5695	0.3582	0.5636	0.3538	0.5579	0.3494	0.5523
0.3692	0.5750	0.3646	0.5691	0.3602	0.5634	0.3558	0.5578
0.3755	0.5803	0.3709	0.5745	0.3664	0.5688	0.3620	0.5631
0.3817	0.5855	0.3771	0.5797	0.3726	0.5740	0.3682	0.5684
0.3878	0.5906	0.3832	0.5848	0.3786	0.5791	0.3742	0.5735
0.3936	0.5957	0.3891	0.5897	0.3846	0.5840	0.3801	0.5785
0.3997	0.6003	0.3948	0.5947	0.3904	0.5889	0.3859	0.5834
0.4053	0.6052	0.4008	0.5992	0.3959	0.5938	0.3916	0.5881
0.4111	0.6096	0.4062	0.6041	0.4018	0.5982	0.3970	0.5929
0.4166	0.6141	0.4119	0.6084	0.4071	0.6030	0.4027	0.5973
0.4221	0.6185	0.4173	0.6128	0.4127	0.6072	0.4079	0.6019
0.4275	0.6228	0.4227	0.6171	0.4178	0.6118	0.4134	0.6061
0.4327	0.6270	0.4279	0.6213	0.4232	0.6158	0.4184	0.6105
0.4379	0.6311	0.4331	0.6254	0.4284	0.6199	0.4238	0.6145
0.4429	0.6351	0.4381	0.6295	0.4334	0.6240	0.4286	0.6188
0.4479	0.6390	0.4431	0.6334	0.4384	0.6279	0.4338	0.6225
0.4528	0.6428	0.4480	0.6373	0.4433	0.6318	0.4386	0.6264
0.4576	0.6466	0.4528	0.6410	0.4481	0.6356	0.4434	0.6303
0.4624	0.6502	0.4575	0.6447	0.4528	0.6393	0.4481	0.6340
0.4670	0.6538	0.4622	0.6484	0.4574	0.6430	0.4528	0.6377

Q =	51 LOW	51 HIGH	52 LOW	52 HIGH	53 LOW	53 HIGH
P = 2	0.0009	0.0884	0.0009	0.0868	0.0009	0.0852
P = 3	0.0062	0.1162	0.0061	0.1141	0.0059	0.1122
P = 4	0.0142	0.1412	0.0139	0.1387	0.0136	0.1364
P = 5	0.0235	0.1640	0.0231	0.1612	0.0227	0.1585
P = 6	0.0336	0.1852	0.0330	0.1821	0.0324	0.1791
P = 7	0.0442	0.2049	0.0434	0.2015	0.0426	0.1983
P = 8	0.0550	0.2234	0.0540	0.2198	0.0530	0.2163
P = 9	0.0658	0.2411	0.0646	0.2373	0.0635	0.2336
P = 10	0.0768	0.2575	0.0754	0.2535	0.0741	0.2497
P = 11	0.0877	0.2732	0.0862	0.2690	0.0847	0.2650
P = 12	0.0985	0.2881	0.0968	0.2838	0.0952	0.2796
P = 13	0.1093	0.3023	0.1074	0.2978	0.1056	0.2935
P = 14	0.1199	0.3159	0.1179	0.3113	0.1160	0.3069
P = 15	0.1303	0.3289	0.1282	0.3242	0.1262	0.3197
P = 16	0.1407	0.3413	0.1384	0.3366	0.1362	0.3320
P = 17	0.1508	0.3533	0.1484	0.3485	0.1461	0.3438
P = 18	0.1608	0.3548	0.1533	0.3599	0.1558	0.3551
P = 19	0.1706	0.3759	0.1680	0.3709	0.1654	0.3661
P = 20	0.1802	0.3866	0.1775	0.3815	0.1748	0.3766
P = 21	0.1897	0.3969	0.1868	0.3918	0.1841	0.3868
P = 22	0.1990	0.4068	0.1960	0.4016	0.1931	0.3966
P = 23	0.2081	0.4164	0.2050	0.4112	0.2021	0.4061
P = 24	0.2170	0.4257	0.2139	0.4204	0.2108	0.4153
P = 25	0.2258	0.4346	0.2225	0.4294	0.2194	0.4242
P = 26	0.2344	0.4433	0.2311	0.4380	0.2278	0.4328
P = 27	0.2428	0.4517	0.2394	0.4464	0.2361	0.4412
P = 28	0.2511	0.4598	0.2476	0.4545	0.2442	0.4493
P = 29	0.2592	0.4677	0.2556	0.4624	0.2522	0.4571
P = 30	0.2671	0.4754	0.2635	0.4700	0.2600	0.4647
P = 31	0.2749	0.4828	0.2713	0.4774	0.2677	0.4721
P = 32	0.2826	0.4900	0.2789	0.4846	0.2752	0.4793
P = 33	0.2901	0.4971	0.2863	0.4916	0.2826	0.4863
P = 34	0.2974	0.5039	0.2936	0.4984	0.2899	0.4931
P = 35	0.3047	0.5105	0.3008	0.5051	0.2970	0.4998
P = 36	0.3117	0.5170	0.3078	0.5115	0.3040	0.5062
P = 37	0.3187	0.5232	0.3147	0.5178	0.3108	0.5125
P = 38	0.3255	0.5293	0.3215	0.5239	0.3176	0.5186
P = 39	0.3322	0.5353	0.3281	0.5299	0.3242	0.5245
P = 40	0.3388	0.5411	0.3347	0.5357	0.3307	0.5304
P = 41	0.3452	0.5467	0.3411	0.5413	0.3371	0.5360
P = 42	0.3515	0.5523	0.3474	0.5469	0.3433	0.5416
P = 43	0.3578	0.5576	0.3536	0.5522	0.3495	0.5469
P = 44	0.3639	0.5629	0.3596	0.5575	0.3555	0.5522
P = 45	0.3698	0.5680	0.3656	0.5626	0.3615	0.5574
P = 46	0.3757	0.5730	0.3715	0.5676	0.3673	0.5624
P = 47	0.3815	0.5779	0.3772	0.5725	0.3730	0.5673
P = 48	0.3872	0.5827	0.3829	0.5773	0.3787	0.5721
P = 49	0.3928	0.5873	0.3882	0.5822	0.3842	0.5768
P = 50	0.3981	0.5921	0.3939	0.5866	0.3895	0.5816
P = 51	0.4037	0.5963	0.3991	0.5912	0.3950	0.5859
P = 52	0.4088	0.6009	0.4046	0.5954	0.4001	0.5904
P = 53	0.4141	0.6050	0.4096	0.5999	0.4055	0.5945
P = 54	0.4191	0.6094	0.4149	0.6039	0.4104	0.5989
P = 55	0.4243	0.6132	0.4197	0.6082	0.4155	0.6029
P = 56	0.4290	0.6174	0.4248	0.6120	0.4203	0.6071
P = 57	0.4341	0.6212	0.4295	0.6162	0.4253	0.6109
P = 58	0.4387	0.6252	0.4344	0.6198	0.4299	0.6149
P = 59	0.4436	0.6288	0.4389	0.6238	0.4348	0.6185
P = 60	0.4482	0.6324	0.4438	0.6273	0.4392	0.6224

54 LOW	54 HIGH	55 LOW	55 HIGH	56 LOW	56 HIGH	57 LOW	57 HIGH
0.0009	0.0837	0.0008	0.0823	0.0008	0.0809	0.0008	0.0796
0.0058	0.1102	0.0057	0.1084	0.0056	0.1066	0.0055	0.1048
0.0134	0.1341	0.0131	0.1318	0.0129	0.1297	0.0127	0.1276
0.0222	0.1559	0.0218	0.1533	0.0215	0.1509	0.0211	0.1485
0.0318	0.1762	0.0313	0.1734	0.0307	0.1706	0.0302	0.1680
0.0418	0.1951	0.0411	0.1921	0.0404	0.1891	0.0397	0.1862
0.0521	0.2130	0.0512	0.2097	0.0503	0.2065	0.0495	0.2034
0.0624	0.2300	0.0613	0.2265	0.0603	0.2232	0.0593	0.2199
0.0728	0.2459	0.0716	0.2423	0.0704	0.2387	0.0693	0.2353
0.0833	0.2611	0.0819	0.2573	0.0806	0.2536	0.0793	0.2500
0.0936	0.2755	0.0921	0.2716	0.0907	0.2578	0.0892	0.2640
0.1039	0.2893	0.1023	0.2853	0.1007	0.2813	0.0991	0.2775
0.1141	0.3026	0.1123	0.2984	0.1106	0.2943	0.1089	0.2904
0.1242	0.3153	0.1222	0.3110	0.1203	0.3068	0.1185	0.3027
0.1341	0.3275	0.1320	0.3231	0.1300	0.3188	0.1281	0.3146
0.1438	0.3392	0.1417	0.3347	0.1395	0.3303	0.1375	0.3261
0.1535	0.3504	0.1512	0.3459	0.1489	0.3415	0.1468	0.3371
0.1629	0.3613	0.1605	0.3567	0.1582	0.3522	0.1559	0.3478
0.1722	0.3718	0.1697	0.3671	0.1673	0.3525	0.1649	0.3581
0.1814	0.3819	0.1788	0.3772	0.1762	0.3725	0.1737	0.3680
0.1903	0.3917	0.1876	0.3869	0.1850	0.3822	0.1824	0.3777
0.1992	0.4012	0.1964	0.3963	0.1937	0.3916	0.1910	0.3870
0.2078	0.4103	0.2050	0.4054	0.2021	0.4006	0.1994	0.3960
0.2163	0.4192	0.2134	0.4142	0.2105	0.4094	0.2077	0.4047
0.2247	0.4277	0.2217	0.4228	0.2187	0.4179	0.2158	0.4132
0.2329	0.4361	0.2298	0.4311	0.2267	0.4262	0.2238	0.4214
0.2410	0.4441	0.2378	0.4391	0.2347	0.4342	0.2316	0.4294
0.2489	0.4520	0.2456	0.4469	0.2424	0.4420	0.2393	0.4372
0.2566	0.4596	0.2533	0.4545	0.2501	0.4496	0.2469	0.4447
0.2642	0.4670	0.2608	0.4619	0.2575	0.4569	0.2543	0.4521
0.2717	0.4741	0.2683	0.4691	0.2649	0.4641	0.2616	0.4592
0.2790	0.4811	0.2755	0.4760	0.2721	0.4711	0.2688	0.4662
0.2862	0.4879	0.2827	0.4828	0.2792	0.4778	0.2759	0.4729
0.2933	0.4945	0.2897	0.4894	0.2862	0.4844	0.2828	0.4795
0.3003	0.5010	0.2966	0.4959	0.2931	0.4909	0.2896	0.4859
0.3071	0.5073	0.3034	0.5021	0.2998	0.4971	0.2963	0.4922
0.3138	0.5134	0.3100	0.5083	0.3064	0.5032	0.3029	0.4983
0.3203	0.5193	0.3166	0.5142	0.3129	0.5092	0.3093	0.5043
0.3268	0.5251	0.3230	0.5200	0.3193	0.5150	0.3157	0.5101
0.3331	0.5308	0.3293	0.5257	0.3256	0.5207	0.3219	0.5158
0.3394	0.5363	0.3355	0.5312	0.3317	0.5252	0.3280	0.5213
0.3455	0.5417	0.3416	0.5366	0.3378	0.5316	0.3341	0.5267
0.3515	0.5470	0.3476	0.5419	0.3437	0.5369	0.3400	0.5320
0.3574	0.5522	0.3535	0.5471	0.3496	0.5421	0.3458	0.5372
0.3632	0.5572	0.3593	0.5521	0.3554	0.5471	0.3516	0.5422
0.3689	0.5621	0.3649	0.5571	0.3610	0.5521	0.3572	0.5472
0.3746	0.5669	0.3705	0.5619	0.3666	0.5569	0.3627	0.5520
0.3801	0.5716	0.3760	0.5666	0.3721	0.5616	0.3682	0.5567
0.3855	0.5762	0.3812	0.5714	0.3775	0.5662	0.3736	0.5614
0.3906	0.5809	0.3868	0.5757	0.3826	0.5710	0.3788	0.5659
0.3961	0.5851	0.3918	0.5803	0.3880	0.5752	0.3838	0.5705
0.4011	0.5896	0.3971	0.5845	0.3929	0.5797	0.3891	0.5747
0.4063	0.5937	0.4020	0.5889	0.3981	0.5838	0.3940	0.5791
0.4111	0.5980	0.4072	0.5928	0.4029	0.5881	0.3991	0.5831
0.4162	0.6019	0.4119	0.5971	0.4080	0.5920	0.4038	0.5874
0.4209	0.6060	0.4169	0.6009	0.4126	0.5962	0.4088	0.5912
0.4258	0.6097	0.4215	0.6049	0.4175	0.5999	0.4134	0.5953
0.4303	0.6137	0.4263	0.6086	0.4220	0.6039	0.4182	0.5990
0.4351	0.6173	0.4307	0.6125	0.4268	0.6075	0.4226	0.6029

Q =		58		59		60	
		LOW	HIGH	LOW	HIGH	LOW	HIGH
P =	2	0.0008	0.0782	0.0008	0.0770	0.0008	0.0758
P =	3	0.0054	0.1031	0.0053	0.1015	0.0052	0.0999
P =	4	0.0124	0.1256	0.0122	0.1236	0.0120	0.1218
P =	5	0.0207	0.1463	0.0204	0.1440	0.0200	0.1419
P =	6	0.0297	0.1654	0.0292	0.1630	0.0287	0.1606
P =	7	0.0391	0.1835	0.0384	0.1808	0.0378	0.1781
P =	8	0.0487	0.2005	0.0479	0.1976	0.0472	0.1947
P =	9	0.0584	0.2168	0.0574	0.2137	0.0566	0.2105
P =	10	0.0682	0.2320	0.0671	0.2287	0.0661	0.2256
P =	11	0.0780	0.2465	0.0768	0.2431	0.0757	0.2398
P =	12	0.0878	0.2504	0.0865	0.2569	0.0852	0.2535
P =	13	0.0976	0.2737	0.0961	0.2701	0.0947	0.2665
P =	14	0.1072	0.2865	0.1056	0.2827	0.1041	0.2791
P =	15	0.1168	0.2988	0.1151	0.2949	0.1134	0.2912
P =	16	0.1262	0.3106	0.1244	0.3066	0.1226	0.3028
P =	17	0.1355	0.3220	0.1336	0.3179	0.1317	0.3140
P =	18	0.1447	0.3329	0.1426	0.3288	0.1406	0.3248
P =	19	0.1537	0.3435	0.1516	0.3393	0.1495	0.3352
P =	20	0.1626	0.3537	0.1604	0.3495	0.1582	0.3453
P =	21	0.1713	0.3636	0.1690	0.3593	0.1667	0.3551
P =	22	0.1800	0.3732	0.1775	0.3688	0.1752	0.3646
P =	23	0.1884	0.3825	0.1859	0.3781	0.1835	0.3737
P =	24	0.1968	0.3914	0.1942	0.3870	0.1916	0.3826
P =	25	0.2049	0.4001	0.2023	0.3957	0.1997	0.3913
P =	26	0.2130	0.4086	0.2103	0.4041	0.2076	0.3996
P =	27	0.2209	0.4168	0.2181	0.4122	0.2154	0.4078
P =	28	0.2287	0.4247	0.2258	0.4202	0.2230	0.4157
P =	29	0.2363	0.4325	0.2334	0.4279	0.2305	0.4234
P =	30	0.2438	0.4400	0.2408	0.4354	0.2379	0.4308
P =	31	0.2512	0.4473	0.2481	0.4427	0.2452	0.4381
P =	32	0.2584	0.4544	0.2553	0.4498	0.2523	0.4452
P =	33	0.2656	0.4614	0.2624	0.4567	0.2593	0.4521
P =	34	0.2726	0.4681	0.2694	0.4634	0.2662	0.4588
P =	35	0.2794	0.4747	0.2762	0.4700	0.2730	0.4654
P =	36	0.2862	0.4811	0.2829	0.4764	0.2797	0.4718
P =	37	0.2929	0.4874	0.2895	0.4827	0.2862	0.4780
P =	38	0.2994	0.4935	0.2960	0.4888	0.2927	0.4841
P =	39	0.3058	0.4994	0.3024	0.4947	0.2990	0.4900
P =	40	0.3121	0.5053	0.3087	0.5005	0.3053	0.4958
P =	41	0.3183	0.5109	0.3148	0.5062	0.3114	0.5015
P =	42	0.3244	0.5165	0.3209	0.5117	0.3174	0.5071
P =	43	0.3304	0.5219	0.3259	0.5171	0.3234	0.5125
P =	44	0.3363	0.5272	0.3327	0.5224	0.3292	0.5178
P =	45	0.3421	0.5323	0.3385	0.5276	0.3350	0.5229
P =	46	0.3478	0.5374	0.3442	0.5327	0.3406	0.5280
P =	47	0.3534	0.5424	0.3498	0.5376	0.3462	0.5330
P =	48	0.3590	0.5472	0.3553	0.5425	0.3516	0.5378
P =	49	0.3644	0.5519	0.3607	0.5472	0.3570	0.5426
P =	50	0.3697	0.5566	0.3660	0.5519	0.3623	0.5472
P =	51	0.3748	0.5613	0.3712	0.5564	0.3676	0.5518
P =	52	0.3802	0.5656	0.3762	0.5611	0.3727	0.5562
P =	53	0.3851	0.5701	0.3815	0.5652	0.3776	0.5608
P =	54	0.3903	0.5742	0.3863	0.5697	0.3827	0.5649
P =	55	0.3951	0.5785	0.3914	0.5737	0.3875	0.5693
P =	56	0.4001	0.5825	0.3961	0.5780	0.3925	0.5732
P =	57	0.4047	0.5866	0.4010	0.5818	0.3971	0.5774
P =	58	0.4096	0.5904	0.4056	0.5859	0.4019	0.5812
P =	59	0.4141	0.5944	0.4103	0.5897	0.4064	0.5852
P =	60	0.4188	0.5981	0.4148	0.5936	0.4111	0.5889

Beta distribution

Highest density regions
99 per cent intervals

Q =		2		3		4	
		LOW	HIGH	LOW	HIGH	LOW	HIGH
P =	2	0.0414	0.9586	0.0159	0.8668	0.0083	0.7820
P =	3	0.1332	0.9841	0.0828	0.9172	0.0567	0.8441
P =	4	0.2180	0.9917	0.1559	0.9433	0.1177	0.8823
P =	5	0.2917	0.9948	0.2231	0.9579	0.1773	0.9066
P =	6	0.3548	0.9963	0.2826	0.9669	0.2321	0.9231
P =	7	0.4087	0.9972	0.3349	0.9729	0.2816	0.9348
P =	8	0.4549	0.9978	0.3807	0.9771	0.3259	0.9436
P =	9	0.4947	0.9982	0.4212	0.9803	0.3656	0.9503
P =	10	0.5294	0.9984	0.4569	0.9827	0.4013	0.9557
P =	11	0.5598	0.9987	0.4887	0.9846	0.4334	0.9600
P =	12	0.5866	0.9988	0.5171	0.9861	0.4624	0.9636
P =	13	0.6104	0.9989	0.5426	0.9874	0.4887	0.9666
P =	14	0.6316	0.9990	0.5657	0.9885	0.5126	0.9692
P =	15	0.6507	0.9991	0.5865	0.9894	0.5344	0.9713
P =	16	0.6680	0.9992	0.6055	0.9901	0.5545	0.9733
P =	17	0.6836	0.9993	0.6229	0.9908	0.5729	0.9749
P =	18	0.6979	0.9993	0.6388	0.9914	0.5899	0.9764
P =	19	0.7109	0.9994	0.6534	0.9919	0.6056	0.9777
P =	20	0.7229	0.9994	0.6669	0.9924	0.6202	0.9789
P =	21	0.7339	0.9994	0.6794	0.9928	0.6337	0.9800
P =	22	0.7441	0.9995	0.6911	0.9931	0.6463	0.9809
P =	23	0.7535	0.9995	0.7019	0.9935	0.6581	0.9818
P =	24	0.7623	0.9995	0.7120	0.9938	0.6692	0.9826
P =	25	0.7705	0.9996	0.7214	0.9941	0.6795	0.9833
P =	26	0.7781	0.9996	0.7302	0.9943	0.6893	0.9840
P =	27	0.7852	0.9996	0.7385	0.9945	0.6984	0.9846
P =	28	0.7919	0.9996	0.7463	0.9948	0.7071	0.9852
P =	29	0.7982	0.9996	0.7537	0.9950	0.7152	0.9857
P =	30	0.8042	0.9996	0.7606	0.9951	0.7230	0.9862
P =	31	0.8097	0.9997	0.7672	0.9953	0.7303	0.9867
P =	32	0.8150	0.9997	0.7734	0.9955	0.7372	0.9871
P =	33	0.8200	0.9997	0.7793	0.9956	0.7438	0.9875
P =	34	0.8248	0.9997	0.7849	0.9958	0.7501	0.9879
P =	35	0.8292	0.9997	0.7902	0.9959	0.7561	0.9883
P =	36	0.8335	0.9997	0.7953	0.9960	0.7618	0.9886
P =	37	0.8376	0.9997	0.8001	0.9961	0.7673	0.9889
P =	38	0.8414	0.9997	0.8047	0.9962	0.7725	0.9892
P =	39	0.8451	0.9997	0.8091	0.9963	0.7774	0.9895
P =	40	0.8487	0.9997	0.8133	0.9964	0.7822	0.9898
P =	41	0.8520	0.9998	0.8173	0.9965	0.7867	0.9900
P =	42	0.8552	0.9998	0.8212	0.9966	0.7911	0.9903
P =	43	0.8583	0.9998	0.8249	0.9967	0.7953	0.9905
P =	44	0.8613	0.9998	0.8285	0.9968	0.7993	0.9907
P =	45	0.8641	0.9998	0.8318	0.9969	0.8032	0.9910
P =	46	0.8668	0.9998	0.8351	0.9969	0.8070	0.9912
P =	47	0.8694	0.9998	0.8383	0.9970	0.8105	0.9914
P =	48	0.8720	0.9998	0.8413	0.9971	0.8140	0.9915
P =	49	0.8744	0.9998	0.8442	0.9971	0.8174	0.9917
P =	50	0.8767	0.9998	0.8470	0.9972	0.8206	0.9919
P =	51	0.8789	0.9998	0.8498	0.9972	0.8237	0.9921
P =	52	0.8811	0.9998	0.8524	0.9973	0.8267	0.9922
P =	53	0.8832	0.9998	0.8549	0.9974	0.8296	0.9924
P =	54	0.8852	0.9998	0.8573	0.9974	0.8324	0.9925
P =	55	0.8871	0.9998	0.8597	0.9975	0.8351	0.9926
P =	56	0.8890	0.9998	0.8620	0.9975	0.8378	0.9928
P =	57	0.8909	0.9998	0.8642	0.9976	0.8403	0.9929
P =	58	0.8926	0.9998	0.8664	0.9976	0.8428	0.9930
P =	59	0.8943	0.9998	0.8684	0.9976	0.8452	0.9932
P =	60	0.8960	0.9998	0.8705	0.9977	0.8475	0.9933

SOURCE: Computed for this volume.

Q=		5		6		7	
		LOW	HIGH	LOW	HIGH	LOW	HIGH
P=	2	0.0052	0.7083	0.0037	0.6452	0.0028	0.5913
P=	3	0.0421	0.7769	0.0331	0.7174	0.0271	0.6651
P=	4	0.0934	0.8227	0.0769	0.7679	0.0652	0.7184
P=	5	0.1461	0.8539	0.1237	0.8039	0.1071	0.7578
P=	6	0.1961	0.8763	0.1693	0.8307	0.1488	0.7876
P=	7	0.2422	0.8929	0.2122	0.8512	0.1887	0.8113
P=	8	0.2844	0.9058	0.2521	0.8674	0.2262	0.8302
P=	9	0.3227	0.9159	0.2888	0.8805	0.2612	0.8458
P=	10	0.3576	0.9241	0.3225	0.8913	0.2937	0.8587
P=	11	0.3893	0.9309	0.3535	0.9003	0.3238	0.8697
P=	12	0.4183	0.9366	0.3820	0.9080	0.3517	0.8791
P=	13	0.4448	0.9415	0.4083	0.9146	0.3776	0.8873
P=	14	0.4690	0.9456	0.4326	0.9203	0.4016	0.8944
P=	15	0.4914	0.9492	0.4551	0.9253	0.4240	0.9007
P=	16	0.5120	0.9524	0.4759	0.9297	0.4448	0.9063
P=	17	0.5310	0.9552	0.4952	0.9336	0.4642	0.9113
P=	18	0.5486	0.9577	0.5132	0.9372	0.4824	0.9158
P=	19	0.5650	0.9599	0.5300	0.9403	0.4994	0.9199
P=	20	0.5803	0.9620	0.5457	0.9432	0.5154	0.9236
P=	21	0.5945	0.9638	0.5605	0.9458	0.5304	0.9269
P=	22	0.6079	0.9654	0.5743	0.9482	0.5446	0.9300
P=	23	0.6204	0.9669	0.5873	0.9504	0.5579	0.9329
P=	24	0.6321	0.9683	0.5995	0.9524	0.5705	0.9355
P=	25	0.6431	0.9696	0.6110	0.9542	0.5824	0.9379
P=	26	0.6535	0.9708	0.6219	0.9559	0.5937	0.9402
P=	27	0.6634	0.9719	0.6323	0.9575	0.6044	0.9422
P=	28	0.6726	0.9729	0.6420	0.9590	0.6145	0.9442
P=	29	0.6814	0.9738	0.6513	0.9604	0.6242	0.9460
P=	30	0.6898	0.9747	0.6601	0.9617	0.6334	0.9477
P=	31	0.6977	0.9755	0.6685	0.9629	0.6421	0.9493
P=	32	0.7052	0.9763	0.6765	0.9640	0.6505	0.9508
P=	33	0.7124	0.9770	0.6841	0.9651	0.6584	0.9523
P=	34	0.7192	0.9777	0.6914	0.9661	0.6661	0.9536
P=	35	0.7257	0.9783	0.6983	0.9670	0.6734	0.9549
P=	36	0.7319	0.9789	0.7049	0.9679	0.6803	0.9561
P=	37	0.7379	0.9795	0.7113	0.9688	0.6870	0.9572
P=	38	0.7435	0.9801	0.7174	0.9696	0.6934	0.9583
P=	39	0.7490	0.9806	0.7232	0.9704	0.6996	0.9593
P=	40	0.7542	0.9811	0.7288	0.9711	0.7055	0.9603
P=	41	0.7592	0.9815	0.7342	0.9718	0.7112	0.9612
P=	42	0.7641	0.9820	0.7394	0.9724	0.7167	0.9621
P=	43	0.7687	0.9824	0.7444	0.9731	0.7220	0.9630
P=	44	0.7731	0.9828	0.7491	0.9737	0.7271	0.9638
P=	45	0.7774	0.9832	0.7538	0.9742	0.7320	0.9646
P=	46	0.7815	0.9836	0.7582	0.9748	0.7367	0.9653
P=	47	0.7855	0.9839	0.7625	0.9753	0.7413	0.9660
P=	48	0.7893	0.9842	0.7666	0.9758	0.7457	0.9667
P=	49	0.7930	0.9846	0.7706	0.9763	0.7500	0.9674
P=	50	0.7966	0.9849	0.7745	0.9768	0.7541	0.9680
P=	51	0.8000	0.9852	0.7783	0.9772	0.7581	0.9686
P=	52	0.8034	0.9855	0.7819	0.9777	0.7619	0.9692
P=	53	0.8066	0.9857	0.7854	0.9781	0.7657	0.9698
P=	54	0.8097	0.9860	0.7888	0.9785	0.7693	0.9703
P=	55	0.8127	0.9863	0.7921	0.9789	0.7728	0.9708
P=	56	0.8156	0.9865	0.7953	0.9793	0.7762	0.9713
P=	57	0.8185	0.9868	0.7984	0.9796	0.7796	0.9718
P=	58	0.8212	0.9870	0.8013	0.9800	0.7828	0.9723
P=	59	0.8239	0.9872	0.8042	0.9803	0.7859	0.9728
P=	60	0.8265	0.9874	0.8071	0.9806	0.7889	0.9732

8		9		10		11	
LOW	HIGH	LOW	HIGH	LOW	HIGH	LOW	HIGH
0.0022	0.5451	0.0018	0.5053	0.0016	0.4706	0.0013	0.4402
0.0229	0.6193	0.0197	0.5788	0.0173	0.5431	0.0154	0.5113
0.0564	0.6741	0.0497	0.6344	0.0443	0.5987	0.0400	0.5666
0.0942	0.7156	0.0841	0.6773	0.0759	0.6424	0.0691	0.6107
0.1326	0.7479	0.1195	0.7112	0.1087	0.6775	0.0997	0.6465
0.1698	0.7738	0.1542	0.7388	0.1413	0.7063	0.1303	0.6762
0.2051	0.7949	0.1876	0.7616	0.1728	0.7304	0.1601	0.7013
0.2384	0.8124	0.2193	0.7807	0.2030	0.7508	0.1889	0.7228
0.2696	0.8272	0.2492	0.7970	0.2316	0.7684	0.2164	0.7413
0.2987	0.8399	0.2772	0.8111	0.2587	0.7836	0.2424	0.7576
0.3259	0.8508	0.3036	0.8234	0.2842	0.7970	0.2672	0.7719
0.3512	0.8603	0.3283	0.8341	0.3083	0.8088	0.2906	0.7846
0.3749	0.8688	0.3515	0.8437	0.3310	0.8193	0.3128	0.7959
0.3970	0.8762	0.3733	0.8522	0.3524	0.8288	0.3338	0.8062
0.4177	0.8829	0.3938	0.8598	0.3726	0.8373	0.3536	0.8154
0.4371	0.8889	0.4131	0.8667	0.3916	0.8449	0.3724	0.8238
0.4553	0.8943	0.4312	0.8729	0.4096	0.8519	0.3902	0.8315
0.4724	0.8992	0.4483	0.8786	0.4267	0.8583	0.4071	0.8385
0.4885	0.9037	0.4645	0.8838	0.4428	0.8642	0.4231	0.8450
0.5037	0.9078	0.4797	0.8886	0.4581	0.8696	0.4384	0.8510
0.5181	0.9115	0.4942	0.8930	0.4726	0.8746	0.4528	0.8565
0.5316	0.9150	0.5079	0.8970	0.4863	0.8792	0.4666	0.8616
0.5445	0.9182	0.5209	0.9008	0.4994	0.8835	0.4798	0.8664
0.5566	0.9212	0.5332	0.9043	0.5119	0.8875	0.4923	0.8709
0.5682	0.9239	0.5450	0.9076	0.5237	0.8912	0.5042	0.8750
0.5791	0.9265	0.5561	0.9106	0.5351	0.8947	0.5157	0.8789
0.5896	0.9289	0.5668	0.9135	0.5459	0.8980	0.5266	0.8826
0.5995	0.9312	0.5770	0.9161	0.5562	0.9011	0.5370	0.8861
0.6090	0.9333	0.5867	0.9187	0.5661	0.9040	0.5470	0.8893
0.6180	0.9353	0.5959	0.9210	0.5755	0.9067	0.5566	0.8924
0.6267	0.9372	0.6048	0.9233	0.5846	0.9093	0.5658	0.8953
0.6350	0.9390	0.6133	0.9254	0.5933	0.9117	0.5747	0.8981
0.6429	0.9406	0.6215	0.9274	0.6016	0.9140	0.5832	0.9007
0.6504	0.9422	0.6293	0.9293	0.6096	0.9162	0.5913	0.9032
0.6577	0.9437	0.6368	0.9311	0.6173	0.9183	0.5992	0.9055
0.6647	0.9451	0.6440	0.9328	0.6247	0.9203	0.6067	0.9078
0.6714	0.9465	0.6509	0.9344	0.6319	0.9222	0.6140	0.9099
0.6778	0.9478	0.6576	0.9360	0.6387	0.9240	0.6211	0.9120
0.6840	0.9490	0.6640	0.9375	0.6453	0.9257	0.6278	0.9140
0.6900	0.9502	0.6702	0.9389	0.6517	0.9274	0.6344	0.9158
0.6957	0.9513	0.6762	0.9402	0.6579	0.9290	0.6407	0.9176
0.7013	0.9524	0.6819	0.9415	0.6638	0.9305	0.6468	0.9193
0.7066	0.9534	0.6875	0.9427	0.6696	0.9319	0.6527	0.9210
0.7117	0.9544	0.6928	0.9439	0.6751	0.9333	0.6584	0.9226
0.7167	0.9553	0.6980	0.9451	0.6805	0.9346	0.6639	0.9241
0.7215	0.9562	0.7030	0.9462	0.6857	0.9359	0.6693	0.9255
0.7262	0.9571	0.7079	0.9472	0.6907	0.9371	0.6745	0.9270
0.7307	0.9579	0.7126	0.9482	0.6956	0.9383	0.6795	0.9283
0.7350	0.9587	0.7172	0.9492	0.7003	0.9395	0.6844	0.9296
0.7392	0.9595	0.7216	0.9501	0.7049	0.9406	0.6891	0.9309
0.7433	0.9603	0.7258	0.9510	0.7093	0.9416	0.6937	0.9321
0.7473	0.9610	0.7300	0.9519	0.7136	0.9426	0.6982	0.9333
0.7511	0.9617	0.7340	0.9527	0.7178	0.9436	0.7025	0.9344
0.7548	0.9623	0.7379	0.9536	0.7219	0.9446	0.7067	0.9355
0.7585	0.9630	0.7417	0.9543	0.7259	0.9455	0.7108	0.9365
0.7620	0.9636	0.7454	0.9551	0.7297	0.9464	0.7148	0.9376
0.7654	0.9642	0.7490	0.9558	0.7334	0.9473	0.7187	0.9386
0.7687	0.9648	0.7525	0.9565	0.7371	0.9481	0.7225	0.9395
0.7719	0.9654	0.7558	0.9572	0.7406	0.9489	0.7261	0.9405

Q =		12		13		14	
		LOW	HIGH	LOW	HIGH	LOW	HIGH
P =	2	0.0012	0.4134	0.0011	0.3896	0.0010	0.3684
P =	3	0.0139	0.4829	0.0126	0.4574	0.0115	0.4343
P =	4	0.0364	0.5376	0.0334	0.5113	0.03C8	0.4874
P =	5	0.0634	0.5817	0.0585	0.5552	0.0544	0.5310
P =	6	0.0920	0.618C	0.0854	0.5917	C.C797	0.5674
P =	7	0.1209	0.6483	0.1127	0.6224	0.1C56	0.5984
P =	8	0.1492	C.6741	0.1397	0.6488	0.1312	0.6251
P =	9	0.1766	0.6964	0.1659	0.6717	C.1563	0.6485
P =	10	0.2030	0.7158	0.1912	0.6917	0.1807	0.6690
P =	11	0.2281	0.7328	0.2154	0.7094	0.2041	0.6872
P =	12	0.2521	0.7479	0.2386	C.7251	0.2265	0.7C35
P =	13	0.2749	0.7614	0.2607	0.7393	0.2480	0.7182
P =	14	0.2965	C.7735	C.2818	0.752C	0.2686	0.7314
P =	15	0.3170	0.7844	0.3019	0.7635	0.2882	0.7435
P =	16	0.3365	C.7943	0.3210	0.7740	0.3069	0.7545
P =	17	0.3550	0.8034	0.3392	0.7836	0.3248	0.7646
P =	18	0.3726	0.8116	0.3565	0.7925	C.3418	0.7739
P =	19	0.3893	C.8193	0.3730	C.8006	0.3581	0.7825
P =	20	0.4052	0.8263	0.3888	C.8C81	C.3737	0.7905
P =	21	0.4203	0.8328	0.4038	0.8151	0.3886	0.7979
P =	22	0.4348	0.8388	C.4182	0.8215	0.4028	0.8048
P =	23	0.4485	0.8444	0.4319	0.8276	0.4164	0.8112
P =	24	0.4617	0.8496	0.4450	0.8332	0.4295	0.8172
P =	25	0.4742	0.8545	0.4575	C.8385	C.442C	0.8229
P =	26	0.4862	0.8591	0.4695	0.8435	0.454C	0.8282
P =	27	0.4977	0.8634	0.4810	C.8481	0.4655	0.8332
P =	28	0.5087	0.8674	0.4920	C.8525	C.4765	0.8379
P =	29	0.5192	0.8713	0.5026	C.8567	0.4871	0.8423
P =	30	0.5293	0.8749	0.5128	0.8606	0.4973	0.8465
P =	31	0.5390	0.8783	0.5226	0.8643	0.5072	0.8505
P =	32	0.5483	0.8815	0.5320	0.8678	0.5166	0.8543
P =	33	0.5573	C.8845	C.5410	C.8711	C.5257	0.8579
P =	34	0.5659	0.8874	0.5497	0.8743	0.5345	0.8614
P =	35	0.5742	C.8902	0.5581	0.8773	0.5430	0.8646
P =	36	0.5822	0.8928	0.5662	0.8802	0.5511	0.8678
P =	37	0.5899	0.8953	0.5740	0.8830	0.5590	0.8707
P =	38	0.5973	0.8977	0.5815	0.8856	0.5667	0.8736
P =	39	0.6045	0.9000	0.5888	C.8881	C.5740	0.8763
P =	40	0.6114	0.9022	0.5958	0.8905	0.5812	0.8789
P =	41	0.6180	0.9043	0.6026	0.8928	0.5881	0.8814
P =	42	0.6245	0.9063	0.6092	0.8950	0.5947	0.8838
P =	43	0.63C8	C.9082	0.6156	0.8971	0.6012	0.8861
P =	44	0.6368	0.9101	0.6217	0.8992	0.6075	0.8883
P =	45	0.6426	0.9118	0.6277	0.9011	0.6135	0.8905
P =	46	0.6483	0.9135	0.6335	0.9030	0.6194	0.8925
P =	47	0.6538	0.9152	C.6391	0.9048	C.6251	0.8945
P =	48	0.6591	0.9167	0.6446	0.9065	0.6307	0.8964
P =	49	0.6643	0.9183	0.6498	0.9082	0.6361	0.8982
P =	50	0.6693	0.9197	0.6550	0.9098	0.6413	0.9000
P =	51	0.6742	0.9211	0.6600	0.9114	0.6464	0.9017
P =	52	0.6789	0.9225	0.6648	0.9129	0.6514	0.9034
P =	53	0.6835	0.9238	0.6695	0.9144	0.6562	0.9050
P =	54	0.6880	0.9251	0.6741	0.9158	0.6609	0.9065
P =	55	0.6923	0.9263	0.6786	0.9172	0.6654	0.9080
P =	56	0.6965	0.9275	0.6829	0.9185	0.6699	0.9095
P =	57	0.7006	C.9287	0.6871	0.9198	0.6742	0.9109
P =	58	0.7046	0.9298	0.6912	0.9210	0.6784	0.9122
P =	59	C.7085	0.9309	0.6952	0.9222	0.6825	0.9135
P =	60	0.7123	C.9319	0.6991	0.9234	C.6865	0.9148

15		16		17		18	
LOW	HIGH	LOW	HIGH	LOW	HIGH	LOW	HIGH
0.0009	0.3493	0.0008	0.3320	0.0007	0.3164	0.0007	0.3021
0.0106	0.4135	0.0099	0.3945	0.0092	0.3771	0.0086	0.3612
0.0287	0.4656	0.0267	0.4455	0.0251	0.4271	0.0236	0.4101
0.0508	0.5086	0.0476	0.4880	0.0448	0.4690	0.0423	0.4514
0.0747	0.5449	0.0703	0.5241	0.0664	0.5048	0.0628	0.4868
0.0993	0.5760	0.0937	0.5552	0.0887	0.5358	0.0842	0.5176
0.1238	0.6030	0.1171	0.5823	0.1111	0.5629	0.1057	0.5447
0.1478	0.6267	0.1402	0.6062	0.1333	0.5869	0.1271	0.5688
0.1712	0.6476	0.1627	0.6274	0.1551	0.6084	0.1481	0.5904
0.1938	0.6662	0.1846	0.6464	0.1762	0.6276	0.1685	0.6098
0.2156	0.6830	0.2057	0.6635	0.1966	0.6450	0.1884	0.6274
0.2365	0.6981	0.2260	0.6790	0.2164	0.6608	0.2075	0.6435
0.2565	0.7118	0.2455	0.6931	0.2354	0.6752	0.2261	0.6582
0.2757	0.7243	0.2642	0.7060	0.2536	0.6885	0.2439	0.6717
0.2940	0.7358	0.2822	0.7178	0.2712	0.7007	0.2611	0.6842
0.3115	0.7464	0.2993	0.7288	0.2881	0.7119	0.2777	0.6957
0.3283	0.7561	0.3158	0.7389	0.3043	0.7223	0.2936	0.7064
0.3444	0.7651	0.3317	0.7482	0.3199	0.7320	0.3089	0.7164
0.3597	0.7734	0.3468	0.7570	0.3348	0.7411	0.3236	0.7257
0.3745	0.7812	0.3614	0.7651	0.3492	0.7495	0.3378	0.7344
0.3886	0.7885	0.3753	0.7727	0.3630	0.7574	0.3514	0.7426
0.4021	0.7953	0.3887	0.7798	0.3763	0.7648	0.3646	0.7503
0.4151	0.8016	0.4016	0.7865	0.3891	0.7718	0.3773	0.7575
0.4275	0.8076	0.4140	0.7928	0.4013	0.7783	0.3895	0.7643
0.4395	0.8132	0.4259	0.7987	0.4132	0.7845	0.4012	0.7708
0.4509	0.8185	0.4373	0.8043	0.4246	0.7904	0.4125	0.7769
0.4620	0.8236	0.4484	0.8096	0.4356	0.7959	0.4235	0.7826
0.4726	0.8283	0.4590	0.8146	0.4461	0.8012	0.4340	0.7881
0.4828	0.8328	0.4692	0.8193	0.4564	0.8062	0.4442	0.7933
0.4927	0.8371	0.4791	0.8239	0.4662	0.8109	0.4541	0.7983
0.5022	0.8411	0.4886	0.8281	0.4757	0.8154	0.4636	0.8030
0.5113	0.8450	0.4978	0.8322	0.4849	0.8198	0.4728	0.8075
0.5202	0.8486	0.5066	0.8361	0.4938	0.8239	0.4817	0.8119
0.5287	0.8521	0.5152	0.8399	0.5024	0.8278	0.4903	0.8160
0.5369	0.8555	0.5235	0.8434	0.5107	0.8315	0.4986	0.8199
0.5449	0.8587	0.5315	0.8468	0.5188	0.8351	0.5067	0.8237
0.5526	0.8617	0.5393	0.8501	0.5266	0.8386	0.5146	0.8273
0.5600	0.8647	0.5468	0.8532	0.5342	0.8419	0.5221	0.8308
0.5672	0.8675	0.5540	0.8562	0.5415	0.8451	0.5295	0.8341
0.5742	0.8702	0.5611	0.8590	0.5486	0.8481	0.5367	0.8373
0.5810	0.8727	0.5679	0.8618	0.5555	0.8510	0.5436	0.8404
0.5875	0.8752	0.5745	0.8645	0.5622	0.8538	0.5503	0.8434
0.5939	0.8776	0.5810	0.8670	0.5686	0.8566	0.5569	0.8462
0.6001	0.8799	0.5872	0.8695	0.5749	0.8592	0.5632	0.8490
0.6060	0.8821	0.5933	0.8718	0.5811	0.8617	0.5694	0.8517
0.6118	0.8843	0.5992	0.8741	0.5870	0.8641	0.5754	0.8542
0.6175	0.8863	0.6049	0.8763	0.5928	0.8665	0.5813	0.8567
0.6230	0.8883	0.6104	0.8785	0.5985	0.8687	0.5870	0.8591
0.6283	0.8902	0.6158	0.8805	0.6039	0.8709	0.5925	0.8614
0.6335	0.8921	0.6211	0.8825	0.6093	0.8730	0.5979	0.8637
0.6385	0.8939	0.6262	0.8844	0.6145	0.8751	0.6032	0.8658
0.6434	0.8956	0.6312	0.8863	0.6195	0.8771	0.6083	0.8679
0.6482	0.8973	0.6361	0.8881	0.6245	0.8790	0.6133	0.8700
0.6529	0.8989	0.6408	0.8898	0.6293	0.8809	0.6182	0.8720
0.6574	0.9005	0.6454	0.8915	0.6340	0.8827	0.6229	0.8739
0.6618	0.9020	0.6499	0.8932	0.6385	0.8844	0.6276	0.8757
0.6661	0.9035	0.6543	0.8948	0.6430	0.8861	0.6321	0.8775
0.6703	0.9049	0.6586	0.8963	0.6473	0.8878	0.6365	0.8793
0.6744	0.9063	0.6628	0.8978	0.6516	0.8894	0.6408	0.8810

Q=		19		20		21
	LOW	HIGH	LOW	HIGH	LOW	HIGH
P= 2	0.0006	0.2891	0.0006	0.2771	0.0006	0.2661
P= 3	0.0081	0.3466	0.0076	0.3331	0.0072	0.3206
P= 4	0.0223	0.3944	0.0211	0.3798	0.0200	0.3663
P= 5	0.0401	0.4350	0.0380	0.4197	0.0362	0.4055
P= 6	0.0597	0.4700	0.0568	0.4543	0.0542	0.4395
P= 7	0.0801	0.5006	0.0764	0.4846	0.0731	0.4696
P= 8	0.1008	0.5276	0.0963	0.5115	0.0922	0.4963
P= 9	0.1214	0.5517	0.1162	0.5355	0.1114	0.5203
P= 10	0.1417	0.5733	0.1358	0.5572	0.1304	0.5419
P= 11	0.1615	0.5929	0.1550	0.5769	0.1490	0.5616
P= 12	0.1807	0.6107	0.1737	0.5948	0.1672	0.5797
P= 13	0.1994	0.6270	0.1919	0.6112	0.1849	0.5962
P= 14	0.2175	0.6419	0.2095	0.6263	0.2021	0.6114
P= 15	0.2349	0.6556	0.2266	0.6403	0.2188	0.6255
P= 16	0.2518	0.6683	0.2430	0.6532	0.2349	0.6386
P= 17	0.2680	0.6801	0.2589	0.6652	0.2505	0.6508
P= 18	0.2836	0.6911	0.2743	0.6764	0.2656	0.6622
P= 19	0.2987	0.7013	0.2891	0.6868	0.2801	0.6728
P= 20	0.3132	0.7109	0.3034	0.6966	0.2942	0.6828
P= 21	0.3272	0.7199	0.3172	0.7058	0.3078	0.6922
P= 22	0.3406	0.7283	0.3305	0.7144	0.3209	0.7010
P= 23	0.3536	0.7362	0.3434	0.7225	0.3337	0.7093
P= 24	0.3662	0.7437	0.3558	0.7302	0.3459	0.7172
P= 25	0.3783	0.7507	0.3677	0.7375	0.3578	0.7247
P= 26	0.3899	0.7574	0.3793	0.7444	0.3692	0.7317
P= 27	0.4012	0.7637	0.3905	0.7509	0.3803	0.7385
P= 28	0.4121	0.7697	0.4013	0.7571	0.3911	0.7448
P= 29	0.4226	0.7754	0.4117	0.7630	0.4014	0.7509
P= 30	0.4327	0.7808	0.4219	0.7686	0.4115	0.7567
P= 31	0.4426	0.7860	0.4316	0.7739	0.4213	0.7622
P= 32	0.4521	0.7909	0.4411	0.7790	0.4307	0.7675
P= 33	0.4613	0.7956	0.4503	0.7839	0.4399	0.7725
P= 34	0.4702	0.8001	0.4592	0.7886	0.4487	0.7773
P= 35	0.4788	0.8044	0.4678	0.7931	0.4573	0.7820
P= 36	0.4871	0.8085	0.4762	0.7973	0.4657	0.7864
P= 37	0.4952	0.8125	0.4843	0.8015	0.4738	0.7907
P= 38	0.5031	0.8162	0.4921	0.8054	0.4817	0.7948
P= 39	0.5107	0.8199	0.4998	0.8092	0.4893	0.7987
P= 40	0.5181	0.8234	0.5072	0.8128	0.4967	0.8025
P= 41	0.5253	0.8267	0.5144	0.8163	0.5040	0.8061
P= 42	0.5322	0.8300	0.5214	0.8197	0.5110	0.8096
P= 43	0.5390	0.8331	0.5282	0.8230	0.5178	0.8130
P= 44	0.5456	0.8361	0.5348	0.8261	0.5245	0.8163
P= 45	0.5520	0.8390	0.5413	0.8291	0.5310	0.8195
P= 46	0.5582	0.8418	0.5475	0.8321	0.5373	0.8225
P= 47	0.5643	0.8445	0.5536	0.8349	0.5434	0.8254
P= 48	0.5702	0.8471	0.5596	0.8376	0.5494	0.8283
P= 49	0.5760	0.8496	0.5654	0.8403	0.5552	0.8311
P= 50	0.5816	0.8521	0.5710	0.8428	0.5609	0.8337
P= 51	0.5870	0.8544	0.5765	0.8453	0.5664	0.8363
P= 52	0.5923	0.8567	0.5819	0.8477	0.5718	0.8388
P= 53	0.5975	0.8589	0.5871	0.8500	0.5771	0.8413
P= 54	0.6026	0.8611	0.5922	0.8523	0.5823	0.8436
P= 55	0.6075	0.8632	0.5972	0.8545	0.5873	0.8459
P= 56	0.6123	0.8652	0.6021	0.8566	0.5922	0.8481
P= 57	0.6170	0.8672	0.6068	0.8587	0.5970	0.8503
P= 58	0.6216	0.8691	0.6115	0.8607	0.6017	0.8524
P= 59	0.6261	0.8709	0.6160	0.8626	0.6063	0.8544
P= 60	0.6304	0.8727	0.6204	0.8645	0.6107	0.8564

22		23		24		25	
LOW	HIGH	LOW	HIGH	LOW	HIGH	LOW	HIGH
0.0005	0.2559	0.0005	0.2465	0.0005	0.2377	0.0004	0.2295
0.0069	0.3089	0.0065	0.2981	0.0062	0.2880	0.0059	0.2786
0.0191	0.3537	0.0182	0.3419	0.0174	0.3308	0.0167	0.3205
0.0346	0.3921	0.0331	0.3796	0.0317	0.3679	0.0304	0.3569
0.0518	0.4257	0.0496	0.4127	0.0476	0.4005	0.0458	0.3890
0.0700	0.4554	0.0671	0.4421	0.0645	0.4295	0.0621	0.4176
0.0885	0.4819	0.0850	0.4684	0.0818	0.4555	0.0788	0.4434
0.1070	0.5058	0.1030	0.4921	0.0992	0.4791	0.0957	0.4668
0.1254	0.5274	0.1208	0.5137	0.1165	0.5006	0.1125	0.4881
0.1435	0.5472	0.1384	0.5334	0.1336	0.5202	0.1291	0.5077
0.1612	0.5652	0.1556	0.5515	0.1504	0.5383	0.1455	0.5258
0.1785	0.5818	0.1724	0.5681	0.1668	0.5550	0.1615	0.5425
0.1952	0.5972	0.1888	0.5836	0.1828	0.5705	0.1771	0.5580
0.2115	0.6114	0.2047	0.5979	0.1984	0.5849	0.1924	0.5725
0.2273	0.6247	0.2202	0.6113	0.2135	0.5984	0.2072	0.5860
0.2426	0.6370	0.2352	0.6237	0.2282	0.6109	0.2217	0.5987
0.2574	0.6486	0.2497	0.6354	0.2425	0.6227	0.2357	0.6105
0.2717	0.6594	0.2638	0.6464	0.2563	0.6338	0.2493	0.6217
0.2856	0.6695	0.2775	0.6566	0.2698	0.6442	0.2625	0.6323
0.2990	0.6791	0.2907	0.6663	0.2828	0.6541	0.2753	0.6422
0.3120	0.6880	0.3034	0.6755	0.2954	0.6634	0.2878	0.6516
0.3245	0.6966	0.3158	0.6842	0.3076	0.6722	0.2998	0.6606
0.3366	0.7046	0.3278	0.6924	0.3195	0.6805	0.3115	0.6690
0.3484	0.7122	0.3394	0.7002	0.3310	0.6885	0.3229	0.6771
0.3597	0.7195	0.3507	0.7075	0.3421	0.6960	0.3339	0.6847
0.3707	0.7263	0.3616	0.7146	0.3529	0.7032	0.3446	0.6921
0.3814	0.7329	0.3722	0.7213	0.3634	0.7100	0.3550	0.6990
0.3917	0.7391	0.3824	0.7277	0.3736	0.7165	0.3651	0.7057
0.4017	0.7451	0.3923	0.7338	0.3834	0.7228	0.3749	0.7120
0.4114	0.7508	0.4020	0.7396	0.3930	0.7287	0.3844	0.7181
0.4208	0.7562	0.4113	0.7452	0.4023	0.7344	0.3937	0.7240
0.4299	0.7614	0.4204	0.7505	0.4114	0.7399	0.4027	0.7296
0.4387	0.7664	0.4292	0.7556	0.4201	0.7452	0.4114	0.7349
0.4474	0.7711	0.4378	0.7606	0.4287	0.7502	0.4199	0.7401
0.4557	0.7757	0.4461	0.7653	0.4370	0.7550	0.4282	0.7450
0.4638	0.7801	0.4542	0.7698	0.4450	0.7597	0.4362	0.7498
0.4717	0.7844	0.4621	0.7742	0.4529	0.7642	0.4441	0.7544
0.4793	0.7884	0.4697	0.7784	0.4605	0.7685	0.4517	0.7588
0.4868	0.7923	0.4772	0.7824	0.4680	0.7727	0.4591	0.7631
0.4940	0.7961	0.4844	0.7863	0.4752	0.7767	0.4664	0.7672
0.5010	0.7998	0.4915	0.7901	0.4823	0.7805	0.4734	0.7712
0.5079	0.8033	0.4983	0.7937	0.4891	0.7843	0.4803	0.7751
0.5146	0.8067	0.5050	0.7972	0.4958	0.7879	0.4870	0.7788
0.5211	0.8099	0.5115	0.8006	0.5024	0.7914	0.4935	0.7824
0.5274	0.8131	0.5179	0.8039	0.5087	0.7948	0.4999	0.7859
0.5336	0.8162	0.5241	0.8070	0.5149	0.7980	0.5061	0.7892
0.5396	0.8191	0.5301	0.8101	0.5210	0.8012	0.5122	0.7925
0.5454	0.8220	0.5360	0.8131	0.5269	0.8043	0.5182	0.7956
0.5511	0.8248	0.5417	0.8159	0.5327	0.8073	0.5239	0.7987
0.5567	0.8275	0.5474	0.8187	0.5383	0.8101	0.5296	0.8017
0.5622	0.8301	0.5528	0.8214	0.5438	0.8129	0.5351	0.8046
0.5675	0.8326	0.5582	0.8241	0.5492	0.8157	0.5405	0.8074
0.5727	0.8351	0.5634	0.8266	0.5545	0.8183	0.5458	0.8101
0.5777	0.8374	0.5685	0.8291	0.5596	0.8209	0.5510	0.8128
0.5827	0.8398	0.5735	0.8315	0.5646	0.8234	0.5560	0.8153
0.5875	0.8420	0.5784	0.8338	0.5695	0.8258	0.5609	0.8179
0.5923	0.8442	0.5831	0.8361	0.5743	0.8282	0.5658	0.8203
0.5969	0.8463	0.5878	0.8383	0.5790	0.8304	0.5705	0.8227
0.6014	0.8484	0.5924	0.8405	0.5836	0.8327	0.5751	0.8250

Q=		26		27		28	
		LOW	HIGH	LOW	HIGH	LOW	HIGH
P=	2	C.0004	0.2219	0.0004	0.2148	0.0004	0.2081
P=	3	0.0057	0.2698	C.0055	C.2615	C.0C52	0.2537
P=	4	0.0160	0.3107	0.0154	0.3016	0.0148	C.2929
P=	5	C.0292	0.3465	0.0281	0.3366	0.0271	0.3274
P=	6	0.0441	0.3781	0.0425	C.3677	C.0410	0.3580
P=	7	0.0598	0.4063	0.0578	0.3956	0.0558	0.3855
P=	8	0.0761	C.4318	C.0735	C.4209	0.0711	0.4104
P=	9	0.0924	0.4550	0.0894	0.4439	0.0865	0.4332
P=	10	0.1088	C.4763	0.1053	0.4649	0.1020	0.4541
P=	11	0.1250	C.4958	0.1211	0.4843	0.1174	0.4734
P=	12	0.1409	0.5138	0.1366	0.5023	0.1326	0.4913
P=	13	0.1565	C.5305	0.1519	C.5190	0.1475	0.5080
P=	14	0.1718	0.5460	C.1668	0.5345	C.1621	0.5235
P=	15	0.1868	0.5605	0.1815	0.5491	0.1764	0.5380
P=	16	0.2013	0.5741	C.1957	0.5627	0.1904	0.5516
P=	17	0.2155	0.5868	C.2096	0.5754	0.2041	0.5644
P=	18	0.2292	0.5988	0.2231	0.5875	0.2174	0.5765
P=	19	0.2426	C.6101	C.2363	0.5988	C.2303	0.5879
P=	20	0.2556	0.6207	0.2491	0.6095	C.2429	0.5987
P=	21	0.2683	0.6308	0.2615	0.6197	0.2552	0.6089
P=	22	0.2805	0.6403	0.2737	0.6293	0.2671	0.6186
P=	23	0.2925	0.6493	0.2854	0.6384	0.2787	0.6278
P=	24	0.3040	0.6579	0.2968	0.6471	0.2900	0.6366
P=	25	0.3153	0.6661	C.3079	C.6554	C.3010	0.6450
P=	26	0.3262	0.6738	0.3187	0.6632	0.3117	0.6529
P=	27	0.3368	0.6813	0.3293	0.6707	0.3221	0.6606
P=	28	0.3471	0.6883	0.3394	0.6779	0.3322	0.6678
P=	29	0.3571	C.6951	0.3494	0.6848	0.3420	0.6748
P=	30	0.3668	0.7016	0.3590	C.6914	C.3516	0.6815
P=	31	0.3762	0.7078	0.3684	0.6977	C.3609	0.6879
P=	32	0.3855	0.7137	0.3775	0.7038	0.3700	0.6941
P=	33	0.3944	0.7194	0.3864	0.7096	0.3788	0.7000
P=	34	0.4031	0.7249	0.3951	0.7152	0.3874	0.7057
P=	35	0.4115	C.7302	0.4035	0.7205	0.3958	0.7111
P=	36	0.4198	0.7353	0.4117	0.7257	0.4039	0.7164
P=	37	C.4278	0.7402	0.4197	0.7307	0.4119	0.7215
P=	38	0.4356	C.7449	C.4275	C.7355	C.4197	C.7264
P=	39	0.4432	0.7494	0.4351	0.7401	0.4272	0.7311
P=	40	0.4506	0.7538	0.4425	0.7446	0.4346	0.7356
P=	41	0.4579	0.7580	0.4497	0.7489	0.4418	0.7401
P=	42	0.4649	0.7621	0.4567	0.7531	0.4488	0.7443
P=	43	0.4718	C.7660	0.4636	0.7571	0.4557	0.7484
P=	44	0.4785	C.7698	C.4703	C.7611	0.4624	0.7524
P=	45	0.4850	0.7735	0.4768	0.7648	0.4689	0.7563
P=	46	0.4914	C.7771	0.4832	0.7685	0.4753	0.7601
P=	47	0.4976	0.7806	0.4894	0.7720	0.4815	0.7637
P=	48	0.5037	C.7839	0.4955	0.7755	0.4876	0.7672
P=	49	0.5097	0.7872	0.5015	0.7788	0.4936	0.7706
P=	50	0.5155	0.7903	0.5073	0.7821	0.4994	0.7740
P=	51	0.5211	0.7934	0.5130	0.7852	0.5051	0.7772
P=	52	0.5267	0.7964	0.5185	0.7883	C.5107	0.7803
P=	53	0.5321	C.7992	0.5240	0.7912	0.5161	0.7834
P=	54	0.5374	C.8021	0.5293	0.7941	0.5215	0.7863
P=	55	0.5426	0.8048	0.5345	0.7969	0.5267	0.7892
P=	56	0.5477	0.8074	0.5396	0.7997	0.5318	0.7920
P=	57	0.5526	0.8100	0.5446	C.8023	0.5368	0.7947
P=	58	0.5575	0.8125	0.5495	0.8049	0.5417	0.7974
P=	59	0.5622	C.8150	0.5542	C.8074	0.5465	0.8000
P=	60	0.5669	0.8174	0.5589	C.8099	0.5512	0.8025

	29		30		31		32
LOW	HIGH	LOW	HIGH	LOW	HIGH	LOW	HIGH
0.0004	0.2018	0.0004	0.1958	0.0003	0.1903	0.0003	0.1850
0.0050	0.2463	0.0049	0.2394	0.0047	0.2328	0.0045	0.2266
0.0143	0.2848	0.0138	0.2770	0.0133	0.2697	0.0129	0.2628
0.0262	0.3186	0.0253	0.3102	0.0245	0.3023	0.0237	0.2948
0.0396	0.3487	0.0383	0.3399	0.0371	0.3315	0.0360	0.3235
0.0540	0.3758	0.0523	0.3666	0.0507	0.3579	0.0492	0.3495
0.0688	0.4005	0.0667	0.3910	0.0647	0.3820	0.0628	0.3733
0.0839	0.4230	0.0813	0.4133	0.0790	0.4041	0.0767	0.3952
0.0989	0.4438	0.0960	0.4339	0.0933	0.4245	0.0907	0.4154
0.1139	0.4630	0.1107	0.4530	0.1076	0.4434	0.1047	0.4342
0.1287	0.4808	0.1251	0.4707	0.1217	0.4610	0.1185	0.4517
0.1433	0.4974	0.1394	0.4872	0.1357	0.4774	0.1322	0.4680
0.1577	0.5129	0.1535	0.5027	0.1495	0.4928	0.1457	0.4834
0.1717	0.5274	0.1672	0.5172	0.1629	0.5073	0.1589	0.4978
0.1854	0.5410	0.1807	0.5308	0.1761	0.5209	0.1719	0.5114
0.1988	0.5539	0.1938	0.5436	0.1891	0.5338	0.1846	0.5243
0.2119	0.5660	0.2067	0.5558	0.2017	0.5459	0.1970	0.5364
0.2246	0.5774	0.2192	0.5673	0.2140	0.5574	0.2091	0.5479
0.2370	0.5883	0.2314	0.5781	0.2261	0.5684	0.2210	0.5589
0.2491	0.5986	0.2433	0.5885	0.2378	0.5787	0.2325	0.5693
0.2609	0.6083	0.2549	0.5983	0.2492	0.5886	0.2438	0.5792
0.2723	0.6176	0.2662	0.6077	0.2604	0.5980	0.2548	0.5887
0.2835	0.6264	0.2772	0.6166	0.2713	0.6070	0.2656	0.5977
0.2943	0.6349	0.2880	0.6251	0.2819	0.6156	0.2760	0.6063
0.3049	0.6429	0.2984	0.6332	0.2922	0.6238	0.2863	0.6145
0.3152	0.6506	0.3086	0.6410	0.3023	0.6316	0.2962	0.6225
0.3252	0.6580	0.3185	0.6484	0.3121	0.6391	0.3059	0.6300
0.3350	0.6650	0.3282	0.6556	0.3217	0.6463	0.3154	0.6373
0.3444	0.6718	0.3376	0.6624	0.3310	0.6532	0.3247	0.6443
0.3537	0.6783	0.3468	0.6690	0.3401	0.6599	0.3337	0.6510
0.3627	0.6846	0.3557	0.6753	0.3490	0.6663	0.3425	0.6575
0.3715	0.6906	0.3644	0.6814	0.3576	0.6725	0.3511	0.6637
0.3800	0.6963	0.3729	0.6873	0.3661	0.6784	0.3595	0.6697
0.3883	0.7019	0.3812	0.6929	0.3743	0.6841	0.3677	0.6755
0.3965	0.7073	0.3893	0.6983	0.3823	0.6896	0.3757	0.6811
0.4044	0.7124	0.3972	0.7036	0.3902	0.6949	0.3835	0.6865
0.4121	0.7174	0.4048	0.7087	0.3978	0.7001	0.3911	0.6917
0.4197	0.7222	0.4124	0.7135	0.4053	0.7051	0.3985	0.6967
0.4270	0.7269	0.4197	0.7183	0.4126	0.7099	0.4058	0.7016
0.4342	0.7314	0.4269	0.7228	0.4198	0.7145	0.4129	0.7063
0.4412	0.7357	0.4338	0.7273	0.4267	0.7190	0.4198	0.7109
0.4480	0.7399	0.4407	0.7316	0.4335	0.7234	0.4266	0.7153
0.4547	0.7440	0.4473	0.7357	0.4402	0.7276	0.4333	0.7196
0.4613	0.7479	0.4539	0.7397	0.4467	0.7317	0.4398	0.7238
0.4676	0.7518	0.4602	0.7436	0.4531	0.7357	0.4461	0.7278
0.4739	0.7555	0.4665	0.7474	0.4593	0.7395	0.4524	0.7317
0.4800	0.7591	0.4726	0.7511	0.4654	0.7433	0.4584	0.7356
0.4859	0.7626	0.4785	0.7547	0.4713	0.7469	0.4644	0.7393
0.4918	0.7660	0.4844	0.7581	0.4772	0.7504	0.4702	0.7429
0.4975	0.7693	0.4901	0.7615	0.4829	0.7539	0.4759	0.7464
0.5030	0.7725	0.4956	0.7648	0.4885	0.7572	0.4815	0.7498
0.5085	0.7756	0.5011	0.7680	0.4939	0.7605	0.4870	0.7531
0.5138	0.7786	0.5065	0.7711	0.4993	0.7636	0.4923	0.7563
0.5191	0.7816	0.5117	0.7741	0.5045	0.7667	0.4976	0.7595
0.5242	0.7845	0.5168	0.7770	0.5097	0.7697	0.5027	0.7625
0.5292	0.7873	0.5219	0.7799	0.5147	0.7726	0.5078	0.7655
0.5341	0.7900	0.5268	0.7827	0.5197	0.7755	0.5127	0.7684
0.5389	0.7926	0.5316	0.7854	0.5245	0.7783	0.5176	0.7713
0.5437	0.7952	0.5364	0.7881	0.5293	0.7810	0.5224	0.7740

Q=		33		34		35	
		LOW	HIGH	LOW	HIGH	LCW	HIGH
P =	2	0.0003	0.1800	0.0003	0.1752	0.0003	0.1708
P =	3	0.0044	0.2207	0.0042	0.2151	0.0041	0.2098
P =	4	0.0125	0.2562	0.0121	0.2499	0.0117	0.2439
P =	5	0.0230	0.2876	0.0223	0.2808	0.0217	0.2743
P =	6	0.0349	0.3159	0.0339	0.3086	0.0330	0.3017
P =	7	0.0477	0.3416	0.0464	0.3339	0.0451	0.3266
P =	8	0.0610	0.3650	0.0594	0.3571	0.0578	0.3496
P =	9	0.0746	0.3867	0.0726	0.3785	0.0707	0.3707
P =	10	0.0883	0.4067	0.0860	0.3984	0.0838	0.3904
P =	11	0.1019	0.4253	0.0993	0.4168	0.0968	0.4087
P =	12	0.1155	0.4427	0.1126	0.4341	0.1098	0.4258
P =	13	0.1289	0.4590	0.1257	0.4503	0.1227	0.4419
P =	14	0.1421	0.4743	0.1386	0.4655	0.1354	0.4570
P =	15	0.1550	0.4887	0.1514	0.4798	0.1479	0.4713
P =	16	0.1678	0.5022	0.1639	0.4934	0.1601	0.4848
P =	17	0.1802	0.5151	0.1761	0.5062	0.1722	0.4976
P =	18	0.1925	0.5272	0.1881	0.5183	0.1840	0.5097
P =	19	0.2044	0.5387	0.1999	0.5298	0.1956	0.5212
P =	20	0.2161	0.5497	0.2114	0.5408	0.2069	0.5322
P =	21	0.2275	0.5601	0.2227	0.5513	0.2180	0.5427
P =	22	0.2386	0.5701	0.2336	0.5613	0.2289	0.5526
P =	23	0.2495	0.5796	0.2444	0.5708	0.2394	0.5622
P =	24	0.2601	0.5886	0.2548	0.5799	0.2498	0.5713
P =	25	0.2704	0.5973	0.2651	0.5886	0.2599	0.5801
P =	26	0.2806	0.6056	0.2751	0.5969	0.2698	0.5885
P =	27	0.2904	0.6136	0.2848	0.6049	0.2795	0.5965
P =	28	0.3000	0.6212	0.2943	0.6126	0.2889	0.6042
P =	29	0.3094	0.6285	0.3037	0.6200	0.2981	0.6117
P =	30	0.3186	0.6356	0.3127	0.6271	0.3071	0.6188
P =	31	0.3275	0.6424	0.3216	0.6339	0.3159	0.6257
P =	32	0.3363	0.6489	0.3303	0.6405	0.3245	0.6323
P =	33	0.3448	0.6552	0.3387	0.6469	0.3329	0.6387
P =	34	0.3531	0.6613	0.3470	0.6530	0.3411	0.6449
P =	35	0.3613	0.6671	0.3551	0.6589	0.3491	0.6509
P =	36	0.3692	0.6728	0.3630	0.6646	0.3570	0.6566
P =	37	0.3770	0.6782	0.3707	0.6701	0.3646	0.6622
P =	38	0.3845	0.6835	0.3782	0.6755	0.3721	0.6676
P =	39	0.3920	0.6886	0.3856	0.6806	0.3795	0.6728
P =	40	0.3992	0.6935	0.3928	0.6856	0.3866	0.6779
P =	41	0.4063	0.6983	0.3999	0.6905	0.3937	0.6828
P =	42	0.4132	0.7030	0.4068	0.6952	0.4005	0.6875
P =	43	0.4200	0.7075	0.4135	0.6997	0.4072	0.6922
P =	44	0.4266	0.7118	0.4201	0.7041	0.4138	0.6966
P =	45	0.4331	0.7160	0.4266	0.7084	0.4203	0.7010
P =	46	0.4394	0.7201	0.4329	0.7126	0.4266	0.7052
P =	47	0.4456	0.7241	0.4391	0.7166	0.4327	0.7093
P =	48	0.4517	0.7280	0.4452	0.7206	0.4388	0.7133
P =	49	0.4576	0.7318	0.4511	0.7244	0.4447	0.7172
P =	50	0.4635	0.7354	0.4569	0.7281	0.4505	0.7209
P =	51	0.4692	0.7390	0.4626	0.7317	0.4562	0.7246
P =	52	0.4748	0.7425	0.4682	0.7353	0.4618	0.7282
P =	53	0.4802	0.7458	0.4737	0.7387	0.4673	0.7317
P =	54	0.4856	0.7491	0.4790	0.7420	0.4726	0.7351
P =	55	0.4908	0.7523	0.4843	0.7453	0.4779	0.7384
P =	56	0.4960	0.7554	0.4894	0.7485	0.4831	0.7416
P =	57	0.5011	0.7585	0.4945	0.7516	0.4881	0.7448
P =	58	0.5060	0.7615	0.4995	0.7546	0.4931	0.7478
P =	59	0.5109	0.7643	0.5043	0.7575	0.4979	0.7508
P =	60	0.5156	0.7672	0.5091	0.7604	0.5027	0.7538

36 LOW	36 HIGH	37 LOW	37 HIGH	38 LOW	38 HIGH	39 LOW	39 HIGH
0.0003	0.1665	0.0003	0.1624	0.0003	0.1586	0.0003	0.1549
0.0040	0.2047	0.0039	0.1999	0.0038	0.1953	0.0037	0.1909
0.0114	0.2382	0.0111	0.2327	0.0108	0.2275	0.0105	0.2226
0.0211	0.2681	0.0205	0.2621	0.0199	0.2565	0.0194	0.2510
0.0321	0.2951	0.0312	0.2887	0.0304	0.2826	0.0296	0.2768
0.0439	0.3197	0.0428	0.3130	0.0417	0.3066	0.0407	0.3004
0.0563	0.3423	0.0549	0.3353	0.0535	0.3286	0.0522	0.3222
0.0689	0.3632	0.0672	0.3560	0.0656	0.3491	0.0640	0.3424
0.0817	0.3827	0.0797	0.3753	0.0778	0.3681	0.0760	0.3613
0.0945	0.4008	0.0922	0.3933	0.0901	0.3860	0.0880	0.3789
0.1072	0.4178	0.1047	0.4101	0.1023	0.4027	0.1000	0.3955
0.1198	0.4338	0.1170	0.4260	0.1144	0.4185	0.1119	0.4112
0.1322	0.4489	0.1293	0.4410	0.1264	0.4333	0.1237	0.4260
0.1445	0.4631	0.1413	0.4551	0.1383	0.4474	0.1353	0.4400
0.1566	0.4765	0.1532	0.4685	0.1499	0.4607	0.1468	0.4532
0.1685	0.4893	0.1649	0.4812	0.1614	0.4734	0.1581	0.4658
0.1801	0.5014	0.1763	0.4933	0.1727	0.4854	0.1692	0.4779
0.1915	0.5129	0.1875	0.5048	0.1838	0.4969	0.1801	0.4893
0.2027	0.5238	0.1985	0.5157	0.1946	0.5079	0.1908	0.5002
0.2136	0.5343	0.2093	0.5262	0.2052	0.5183	0.2013	0.5107
0.2243	0.5443	0.2199	0.5362	0.2156	0.5283	0.2116	0.5207
0.2347	0.5539	0.2302	0.5458	0.2258	0.5379	0.2216	0.5303
0.2450	0.5630	0.2403	0.5550	0.2358	0.5471	0.2315	0.5395
0.2550	0.5718	0.2502	0.5638	0.2456	0.5559	0.2412	0.5483
0.2647	0.5802	0.2598	0.5722	0.2551	0.5644	0.2506	0.5568
0.2743	0.5883	0.2693	0.5803	0.2645	0.5725	0.2599	0.5649
0.2836	0.5961	0.2785	0.5881	0.2736	0.5803	0.2689	0.5728
0.2927	0.6035	0.2876	0.5956	0.2826	0.5879	0.2778	0.5803
0.3017	0.6107	0.2964	0.6028	0.2913	0.5952	0.2865	0.5876
0.3104	0.6177	0.3051	0.6098	0.2999	0.6022	0.2949	0.5947
0.3189	0.6243	0.3135	0.6165	0.3083	0.6089	0.3033	0.6015
0.3272	0.6308	0.3218	0.6230	0.3165	0.6155	0.3114	0.6080
0.3354	0.6370	0.3299	0.6293	0.3245	0.6218	0.3194	0.6144
0.3434	0.6430	0.3378	0.6354	0.3324	0.6279	0.3272	0.6205
0.3512	0.6488	0.3455	0.6412	0.3401	0.6338	0.3348	0.6265
0.3588	0.6545	0.3531	0.6469	0.3476	0.6395	0.3423	0.6322
0.3662	0.6599	0.3605	0.6524	0.3550	0.6450	0.3496	0.6378
0.3735	0.6652	0.3678	0.6577	0.3622	0.6504	0.3568	0.6432
0.3807	0.6703	0.3749	0.6629	0.3693	0.6556	0.3638	0.6485
0.3876	0.6753	0.3818	0.6679	0.3762	0.6607	0.3707	0.6536
0.3945	0.6801	0.3886	0.6727	0.3829	0.6656	0.3774	0.6585
0.4012	0.6847	0.3953	0.6775	0.3896	0.6703	0.3840	0.6633
0.4077	0.6893	0.4018	0.6820	0.3961	0.6749	0.3905	0.6680
0.4142	0.6937	0.4082	0.6865	0.4025	0.6794	0.3969	0.6725
0.4204	0.6979	0.4145	0.6908	0.4087	0.6838	0.4031	0.6769
0.4266	0.7021	0.4206	0.6950	0.4148	0.6881	0.4092	0.6812
0.4326	0.7061	0.4266	0.6991	0.4208	0.6922	0.4152	0.6854
0.4386	0.7101	0.4325	0.7031	0.4267	0.6962	0.4210	0.6895
0.4443	0.7139	0.4383	0.7070	0.4325	0.7002	0.4268	0.6935
0.4500	0.7176	0.4440	0.7107	0.4382	0.7040	0.4324	0.6973
0.4556	0.7212	0.4496	0.7144	0.4437	0.7077	0.4380	0.7011
0.4611	0.7248	0.4550	0.7180	0.4492	0.7113	0.4434	0.7048
0.4664	0.7282	0.4604	0.7215	0.4545	0.7149	0.4488	0.7084
0.4717	0.7316	0.4656	0.7249	0.4597	0.7183	0.4540	0.7119
0.4768	0.7349	0.4708	0.7282	0.4649	0.7217	0.4592	0.7153
0.4819	0.7381	0.4759	0.7315	0.4700	0.7250	0.4642	0.7186
0.4869	0.7412	0.4808	0.7346	0.4749	0.7282	0.4692	0.7218
0.4917	0.7442	0.4857	0.7377	0.4798	0.7313	0.4740	0.7250
0.4965	0.7472	0.4905	0.7408	0.4846	0.7344	0.4788	0.7281

Q =		40		41		42	
		LOW	HIGH	LOW	HIGH	LOW	HIGH
P =	2	0.0003	0.1513	0.0002	0.1480	0.0002	0.1448
P =	3	0.0036	0.1867	0.0035	0.1827	0.0034	0.1788
P =	4	0.0102	0.2178	0.0100	0.2133	0.0097	0.2089
P =	5	0.0189	0.2458	0.0185	0.2408	0.0180	0.2359
P =	6	0.0289	0.2712	0.0282	0.2658	0.0276	0.2606
P =	7	0.0397	0.2945	0.0388	0.2888	0.0379	0.2833
P =	8	0.0510	0.3160	0.0498	0.3100	0.0487	0.3043
P =	9	0.0625	0.3360	0.0611	0.3298	0.0598	0.3238
P =	10	0.0743	0.3547	0.0726	0.3483	0.0710	0.3421
P =	11	0.0860	0.3722	0.0842	0.3656	0.0824	0.3593
P =	12	0.0978	0.3886	0.0957	0.3820	0.0937	0.3755
P =	13	0.1095	0.4042	0.1072	0.3974	0.1050	0.3908
P =	14	0.1211	0.4188	0.1186	0.4119	0.1162	0.4053
P =	15	0.1325	0.4328	0.1298	0.4258	0.1273	0.4190
P =	16	0.1438	0.4460	0.1410	0.4389	0.1382	0.4321
P =	17	0.1549	0.4585	0.1519	0.4514	0.1490	0.4445
P =	18	0.1659	0.4705	0.1627	0.4633	0.1596	0.4564
P =	19	0.1766	0.4819	0.1733	0.4747	0.1700	0.4678
P =	20	0.1872	0.4928	0.1837	0.4856	0.1803	0.4786
P =	21	0.1975	0.5033	0.1939	0.4960	0.1904	0.4890
P =	22	0.2077	0.5132	0.2039	0.5060	0.2002	0.4990
P =	23	0.2176	0.5228	0.2137	0.5156	0.2099	0.5085
P =	24	0.2273	0.5320	0.2233	0.5248	0.2195	0.5177
P =	25	0.2369	0.5409	0.2328	0.5336	0.2288	0.5266
P =	26	0.2462	0.5494	0.2420	0.5421	0.2379	0.5351
P =	27	0.2554	0.5575	0.2511	0.5503	0.2469	0.5433
P =	28	0.2644	0.5654	0.2599	0.5582	0.2557	0.5512
P =	29	0.2731	0.5730	0.2686	0.5658	0.2643	0.5588
P =	30	0.2817	0.5803	0.2772	0.5731	0.2727	0.5662
P =	31	0.2901	0.5874	0.2855	0.5802	0.2810	0.5733
P =	32	0.2984	0.5942	0.2937	0.5871	0.2891	0.5802
P =	33	0.3065	0.6008	0.3017	0.5937	0.2970	0.5868
P =	34	0.3144	0.6072	0.3095	0.6001	0.3048	0.5932
P =	35	0.3221	0.6134	0.3172	0.6063	0.3125	0.5995
P =	36	0.3297	0.6193	0.3247	0.6124	0.3199	0.6055
P =	37	0.3371	0.6251	0.3321	0.6182	0.3273	0.6114
P =	38	0.3444	0.6307	0.3393	0.6238	0.3344	0.6171
P =	39	0.3515	0.6362	0.3464	0.6293	0.3415	0.6226
P =	40	0.3585	0.6415	0.3534	0.6346	0.3484	0.6279
P =	41	0.3654	0.6466	0.3602	0.6398	0.3552	0.6331
P =	42	0.3721	0.6516	0.3669	0.6448	0.3618	0.6382
P =	43	0.3787	0.6564	0.3734	0.6497	0.3683	0.6431
P =	44	0.3851	0.6612	0.3798	0.6545	0.3747	0.6479
P =	45	0.3914	0.6657	0.3861	0.6591	0.3810	0.6525
P =	46	0.3976	0.6702	0.3923	0.6636	0.3871	0.6571
P =	47	0.4037	0.6745	0.3984	0.6680	0.3932	0.6615
P =	48	0.4097	0.6788	0.4043	0.6722	0.3991	0.6658
P =	49	0.4155	0.6829	0.4101	0.6764	0.4049	0.6700
P =	50	0.4213	0.6869	0.4159	0.6804	0.4106	0.6741
P =	51	0.4269	0.6908	0.4215	0.6844	0.4162	0.6781
P =	52	0.4324	0.6946	0.4270	0.6882	0.4217	0.6819
P =	53	0.4379	0.6983	0.4324	0.6920	0.4271	0.6857
P =	54	0.4432	0.7019	0.4377	0.6956	0.4324	0.6894
P =	55	0.4484	0.7055	0.4430	0.6992	0.4376	0.6931
P =	56	0.4536	0.7089	0.4481	0.7027	0.4428	0.6966
P =	57	0.4586	0.7123	0.4531	0.7061	0.4478	0.7000
P =	58	0.4636	0.7156	0.4581	0.7095	0.4528	0.7034
P =	59	0.4684	0.7188	0.4630	0.7127	0.4576	0.7067
P =	60	0.4732	0.7220	0.4677	0.7159	0.4624	0.7099

43		44		45		46	
LOW	HIGH	LOW	HIGH	LOW	HIGH	LOW	HIGH
0.0002	0.1417	0.0002	0.1387	0.0002	0.1359	0.0002	0.1332
0.0033	0.1751	0.0032	0.1715	0.0031	0.1682	0.0031	0.1649
0.0095	0.2047	0.0093	0.2007	0.0090	0.1968	0.0088	0.1930
0.0176	0.2313	0.0172	0.2269	0.0168	0.2226	0.0164	0.2185
0.0269	0.2556	0.0263	0.2509	0.0258	0.2462	0.0252	0.2418
0.0370	0.2780	0.0362	0.2729	0.0354	0.2680	0.0347	0.2633
0.0476	0.2987	0.0466	0.2934	0.0456	0.2883	0.0447	0.2833
0.0585	0.3181	0.0573	0.3125	0.0561	0.3072	0.0549	0.3020
0.0695	0.3362	0.0681	0.3304	0.0667	0.3249	0.0654	0.3195
0.0807	0.3532	0.0790	0.3473	0.0774	0.3416	0.0759	0.3361
0.0918	0.3692	0.0899	0.3632	0.0882	0.3574	0.0865	0.3517
0.1029	0.3844	0.1008	0.3783	0.0989	0.3723	0.0970	0.3665
0.1139	0.3988	0.1117	0.3925	0.1095	0.3865	0.1075	0.3806
0.1248	0.4125	0.1224	0.4061	0.1201	0.3999	0.1179	0.3940
0.1355	0.4255	0.1330	0.4190	0.1305	0.4128	0.1282	0.4067
0.1462	0.4378	0.1434	0.4314	0.1408	0.4251	0.1383	0.4189
0.1566	0.4497	0.1538	0.4431	0.1510	0.4368	0.1483	0.4306
0.1669	0.4610	0.1639	0.4544	0.1610	0.4480	0.1582	0.4418
0.1770	0.4718	0.1739	0.4652	0.1709	0.4587	0.1679	0.4525
0.1870	0.4822	0.1837	0.4755	0.1805	0.4690	0.1775	0.4627
0.1967	0.4921	0.1933	0.4854	0.1901	0.4789	0.1869	0.4726
0.2063	0.5017	0.2028	0.4950	0.1994	0.4885	0.1961	0.4821
0.2157	0.5109	0.2121	0.5042	0.2086	0.4976	0.2052	0.4913
0.2249	0.5197	0.2212	0.5130	0.2176	0.5065	0.2141	0.5001
0.2340	0.5282	0.2302	0.5215	0.2265	0.5150	0.2229	0.5086
0.2429	0.5364	0.2389	0.5297	0.2352	0.5232	0.2315	0.5168
0.2516	0.5443	0.2476	0.5376	0.2437	0.5311	0.2399	0.5247
0.2601	0.5520	0.2560	0.5453	0.2521	0.5387	0.2482	0.5324
0.2684	0.5593	0.2643	0.5527	0.2603	0.5461	0.2564	0.5398
0.2766	0.5665	0.2724	0.5598	0.2683	0.5533	0.2643	0.5469
0.2847	0.5734	0.2804	0.5667	0.2762	0.5602	0.2722	0.5539
0.2925	0.5800	0.2882	0.5734	0.2840	0.5669	0.2799	0.5606
0.3003	0.5865	0.2959	0.5799	0.2916	0.5734	0.2874	0.5671
0.3078	0.5928	0.3034	0.5862	0.2990	0.5797	0.2948	0.5734
0.3153	0.5988	0.3107	0.5923	0.3063	0.5858	0.3021	0.5796
0.3225	0.6047	0.3180	0.5982	0.3135	0.5918	0.3092	0.5855
0.3297	0.6104	0.3251	0.6039	0.3206	0.5975	0.3162	0.5913
0.3367	0.6160	0.3320	0.6095	0.3275	0.6031	0.3231	0.5969
0.3436	0.6213	0.3388	0.6149	0.3343	0.6086	0.3298	0.6024
0.3503	0.6266	0.3455	0.6202	0.3409	0.6139	0.3364	0.6077
0.3569	0.6317	0.3521	0.6253	0.3475	0.6190	0.3429	0.6129
0.3634	0.6366	0.3586	0.6303	0.3539	0.6240	0.3493	0.6179
0.3697	0.6414	0.3649	0.6351	0.3602	0.6289	0.3556	0.6228
0.3760	0.6461	0.3711	0.6398	0.3664	0.6336	0.3617	0.6276
0.3821	0.6507	0.3772	0.6444	0.3724	0.6383	0.3678	0.6322
0.3881	0.6551	0.3832	0.6489	0.3784	0.6428	0.3737	0.6368
0.3940	0.6595	0.3891	0.6533	0.3842	0.6472	0.3795	0.6412
0.3998	0.6637	0.3948	0.6575	0.3900	0.6515	0.3853	0.6455
0.4055	0.6678	0.4005	0.6617	0.3956	0.6557	0.3909	0.6497
0.4111	0.6718	0.4061	0.6657	0.4012	0.6597	0.3964	0.6538
0.4166	0.6758	0.4115	0.6697	0.4066	0.6637	0.4019	0.6579
0.4220	0.6796	0.4169	0.6736	0.4120	0.6676	0.4072	0.6618
0.4273	0.6833	0.4222	0.6773	0.4173	0.6714	0.4125	0.6656
0.4325	0.6870	0.4274	0.6810	0.4224	0.6751	0.4176	0.6694
0.4376	0.6906	0.4325	0.6846	0.4275	0.6788	0.4227	0.6730
0.4426	0.6940	0.4375	0.6881	0.4325	0.6823	0.4277	0.6766
0.4475	0.6974	0.4425	0.6916	0.4375	0.6858	0.4326	0.6801
0.4524	0.7008	0.4473	0.6949	0.4423	0.6892	0.4374	0.6835
0.4572	0.7040	0.4521	0.6982	0.4471	0.6925	0.4422	0.6869

Q=		47		48		49	
		LOW	HIGH	LOW	HIGH	LCW	HIGH
P=	2	0.0002	0.1306	0.0002	0.1280	0.0002	0.1256
P=	3	0.0030	0.1617	0.0029	0.1587	0.0029	0.1558
P=	4	0.0086	0.1895	0.0085	0.1860	0.CC83	0.1826
P=	5	0.0161	0.2145	0.0158	0.2107	0.0154	0.2070
P=	6	0.0247	0.2375	0.0242	0.2334	0.0237	0.2294
P=	7	0.0340	0.2587	0.0333	0.2543	0.0326	0.250C
P=	8	0.0438	0.2785	0.0429	0.2738	0.0421	0.2693
P=	9	0.0538	0.2S7C	0.0528	0.2921	0.C518	0.2874
P=	10	0.0641	0.3143	0.0629	0.3093	0.0617	0.3044
P=	11	0.0745	0.3307	0.0730	0.3255	0.0717	0.3205
P=	12	0.0848	0.3462	0.0833	0.34C9	0.0817	0.3357
P=	13	0.0952	0.3609	0.0935	0.3554	0.0918	0.3502
P=	14	0.1055	0.3749	0.1036	0.3693	0.1018	0.3639
P=	15	0.1157	0.3882	0.1137	0.3825	0.1117	0.377C
P=	16	0.1259	0.4008	0.1237	0.3951	0.1215	0.3896
P=	17	0.1359	0.413C	0.1335	0.4C72	0.1313	0.4015
P=	18	0.1458	0.4246	0.1433	0.4187	0.1409	0.413C
P=	19	0.1555	0.4357	0.1529	0.4298	0.1504	0.4240
P=	20	0.1651	0.4464	0.1624	0.4404	0.1597	0.4346
P=	21	0.1746	0.4566	0.1717	0.4506	0.1689	0.4448
P=	22	0.1838	0.4664	0.1809	0.4604	0.1780	0.4546
P=	23	0.1930	0.4759	0.1899	0.4699	0.1869	0.464C
P=	24	0.2020	0.4851	0.1988	0.4790	0.1957	0.4731
P=	25	0.2108	0.4939	0.2075	0.4878	0.2044	0.4818
P=	26	0.2194	0.5024	0.2161	0.4963	0.2128	0.4903
P=	27	0.2280	0.5106	0.2245	0.5045	0.2212	0.4985
P=	28	0.2363	0.5185	0.2328	0.5124	0.2294	0.5064
P=	29	0.2445	0.5261	0.2409	0.5200	0.2374	0.5141
P=	30	0.2526	0.5335	0.2489	0.5274	0.2453	0.5215
P=	31	0.2605	0.5407	0.2567	0.5346	0.2531	0.5287
P=	32	0.2683	0.5476	0.2644	0.5416	0.2607	0.5356
P=	33	0.2759	0.5544	0.2720	0.5483	0.2682	0.5424
P=	34	0.2834	0.5609	0.2794	0.5548	0.C2756	0.5489
P=	35	0.2907	0.5673	0.2867	0.5612	0.2828	0.5553
P=	36	0.2979	0.5734	0.2939	0.5674	0.2899	0.5614
P=	37	0.3050	0.5794	0.3009	0.5734	0.2969	0.5675
P=	38	0.3119	0.5852	0.3078	0.5792	0.3038	0.5733
P=	39	0.3188	0.5908	0.3146	0.5848	0.3105	0.5790
P=	40	0.3255	0.5963	0.3212	0.5903	0.3171	0.5845
P=	41	0.3320	0.6C16	0.3278	0.5957	0.3236	0.5899
P=	42	0.3385	0.6068	0.3342	0.60C9	0.C3300	0.5951
P=	43	0.3449	0.6119	0.3405	0.6060	0.3363	0.6002
P=	44	0.3511	0.6168	0.3467	0.6109	0.3425	0.6052
P=	45	0.3572	0.6216	0.3528	0.6158	0.3485	0.6100
P=	46	0.3632	0.6263	0.3588	0.6205	0.3545	0.6147
P=	47	0.3691	0.6309	0.3647	0.6251	0.C3603	0.6194
P=	48	0.3749	0.6353	0.3705	0.6295	0.3661	0.6239
P=	49	0.3806	0.6397	0.3761	0.6339	0.3718	0.6282
P=	50	0.3863	0.6439	0.3817	0.6382	0.C3773	0.6325
P=	51	0.3918	0.6480	0.3872	0.6423	0.3828	0.6367
P=	52	0.3972	0.6521	0.3926	0.6464	0.3882	0.6408
P=	53	0.4025	0.656C	0.3979	0.6504	0.3935	0.6448
P=	54	0.4078	0.6599	0.4032	0.6543	0.3987	0.6487
P=	55	0.4129	0.6637	0.4083	0.6581	0.4038	0.6526
P=	56	0.4180	0.6674	0.4133	0.6618	0.4C88	0.6563
P=	57	0.4230	0.6710	0.4183	0.6654	0.4138	0.6600
P=	58	0.4279	0.6745	0.4232	0.6690	0.4187	0.6636
P=	59	0.4327	0.6780	0.4280	0.6725	0.4235	0.6671
P=	60	0.4374	0.6813	0.4328	0.6759	0.4282	0.6705

50		51		52		53	
LOW	HIGH	LOW	HIGH	LOW	HIGH	LOW	HIGH
0.0002	0.1233	0.0002	0.1211	0.0002	0.1189	0.0002	0.1168
0.0028	0.1530	0.0028	0.1502	0.0027	0.1476	0.0026	0.1451
0.0081	0.1794	0.0079	0.1763	0.0078	0.1733	0.0076	0.1704
0.0151	0.2034	0.0148	0.2000	0.0145	0.1966	0.0143	0.1934
0.0232	0.2255	0.0228	0.2217	0.0223	0.2181	0.0219	0.2146
0.0320	0.2459	0.0314	0.2419	0.0308	0.2381	0.0302	0.2343
0.0413	0.2650	0.0405	0.2608	0.0397	0.2567	0.0390	0.2527
0.0508	0.2828	0.0499	0.2784	0.0490	0.2742	0.0481	0.2700
0.0605	0.2997	0.0594	0.2951	0.0584	0.2907	0.0574	0.2864
0.0704	0.3156	0.0691	0.3109	0.0679	0.3063	0.0667	0.3018
0.0803	0.3307	0.0789	0.3258	0.0775	0.3211	0.0762	0.3165
0.0902	0.3450	0.0886	0.3400	0.0871	0.3352	0.0856	0.3305
0.1000	0.3587	0.0983	0.3536	0.0966	0.3486	0.0950	0.3438
0.1098	0.3717	0.1079	0.3665	0.1061	0.3615	0.1044	0.3566
0.1195	0.3842	0.1175	0.3789	0.1156	0.3738	0.1137	0.3688
0.1291	0.3961	0.1270	0.3907	0.1249	0.3855	0.1229	0.3805
0.1386	0.4075	0.1363	0.4021	0.1342	0.3968	0.1321	0.3917
0.1479	0.4184	0.1456	0.4130	0.1433	0.4077	0.1411	0.4025
0.1572	0.4290	0.1547	0.4235	0.1523	0.4181	0.1500	0.4129
0.1663	0.4391	0.1637	0.4336	0.1612	0.4282	0.1587	0.4229
0.1752	0.4489	0.1725	0.4433	0.1699	0.4378	0.1674	0.4325
0.1841	0.4583	0.1813	0.4526	0.1786	0.4472	0.1759	0.4418
0.1927	0.4673	0.1899	0.4617	0.1871	0.4562	0.1843	0.4508
0.2013	0.4761	0.1983	0.4704	0.1954	0.4649	0.1926	0.4595
0.2097	0.4845	0.2066	0.4789	0.2036	0.4733	0.2008	0.4679
0.2179	0.4927	0.2148	0.4870	0.2117	0.4815	0.2088	0.4760
0.2260	0.5006	0.2228	0.4949	0.2197	0.4893	0.2166	0.4839
0.2340	0.5082	0.2307	0.5025	0.2275	0.4970	0.2244	0.4915
0.2419	0.5156	0.2385	0.5099	0.2352	0.5044	0.2320	0.4989
0.2496	0.5228	0.2461	0.5171	0.2428	0.5115	0.2395	0.5061
0.2571	0.5298	0.2536	0.5241	0.2502	0.5185	0.2469	0.5130
0.2646	0.5365	0.2610	0.5308	0.2575	0.5252	0.2542	0.5198
0.2719	0.5431	0.2683	0.5374	0.2647	0.5318	0.2613	0.5263
0.2791	0.5495	0.2754	0.5438	0.2718	0.5382	0.2683	0.5327
0.2861	0.5557	0.2824	0.5500	0.2788	0.5444	0.2752	0.5389
0.2930	0.5617	0.2893	0.5560	0.2856	0.5504	0.2820	0.5450
0.2998	0.5675	0.2960	0.5618	0.2923	0.5563	0.2887	0.5508
0.3065	0.5732	0.3027	0.5676	0.2989	0.5620	0.2952	0.5566
0.3131	0.5787	0.3092	0.5731	0.3054	0.5676	0.3017	0.5621
0.3196	0.5841	0.3156	0.5785	0.3118	0.5730	0.3080	0.5676
0.3259	0.5894	0.3219	0.5838	0.3181	0.5783	0.3143	0.5729
0.3322	0.5945	0.3282	0.5889	0.3242	0.5834	0.3204	0.5780
0.3383	0.5995	0.3343	0.5939	0.3303	0.5885	0.3264	0.5831
0.3443	0.6044	0.3403	0.5988	0.3363	0.5934	0.3324	0.5880
0.3503	0.6091	0.3462	0.6036	0.3421	0.5981	0.3382	0.5928
0.3561	0.6137	0.3520	0.6082	0.3479	0.6028	0.3440	0.5975
0.3618	0.6183	0.3577	0.6128	0.3536	0.6074	0.3496	0.6021
0.3675	0.6227	0.3633	0.6172	0.3592	0.6118	0.3552	0.6065
0.3730	0.6270	0.3688	0.6215	0.3647	0.6162	0.3607	0.6109
0.3785	0.6312	0.3742	0.6258	0.3701	0.6204	0.3660	0.6152
0.3838	0.6353	0.3796	0.6299	0.3754	0.6246	0.3713	0.6194
0.3891	0.6393	0.3848	0.6340	0.3806	0.6287	0.3766	0.6234
0.3943	0.6433	0.3900	0.6379	0.3858	0.6326	0.3817	0.6274
0.3994	0.6471	0.3951	0.6418	0.3909	0.6365	0.3867	0.6314
0.4044	0.6509	0.4001	0.6456	0.3959	0.6403	0.3917	0.6352
0.4094	0.6546	0.4050	0.6493	0.4008	0.6441	0.3966	0.6389
0.4142	0.6582	0.4099	0.6529	0.4056	0.6477	0.4015	0.6426
0.4190	0.6617	0.4147	0.6565	0.4104	0.6513	0.4062	0.6462
0.4237	0.6652	0.4194	0.6600	0.4151	0.6548	0.4109	0.6497

Q =		54		55		56	
		LOW	HIGH	LOW	HIGH	LOW	HIGH
P =	2	0.0002	0.1148	0.0002	0.1129	0.0002	0.1110
P =	3	0.0026	0.1427	0.0025	0.1403	0.0025	0.1380
P =	4	0.0075	0.1676	0.0074	0.1649	0.0072	0.1622
P =	5	0.0140	0.1903	0.0137	0.1873	0.0135	0.1844
P =	6	0.0215	0.2112	0.0211	0.2079	0.0207	0.2047
P =	7	0.0297	0.2307	0.0292	0.2272	0.0287	0.2238
P =	8	0.0383	0.2489	0.0377	0.2452	0.0370	0.2415
P =	9	0.0473	0.2660	0.0464	0.2621	0.0457	0.2583
P =	10	0.0564	0.2822	0.0554	0.2781	0.0545	0.2741
P =	11	0.0656	0.2975	0.0645	0.2933	0.0635	0.2892
P =	12	0.0749	0.3120	0.0737	0.3077	0.0725	0.3035
P =	13	0.0842	0.3259	0.0828	0.3214	0.0815	0.3171
P =	14	0.0935	0.3391	0.0920	0.3346	0.0905	0.3301
P =	15	0.1027	0.3518	0.1011	0.3471	0.0995	0.3426
P =	16	0.1119	0.3639	0.1102	0.3592	0.1085	0.3546
P =	17	0.1210	0.3755	0.1191	0.3707	0.1173	0.3660
P =	18	0.1300	0.3867	0.1280	0.3818	0.1261	0.3771
P =	19	0.1389	0.3974	0.1368	0.3925	0.1348	0.3877
P =	20	0.1477	0.4078	0.1455	0.4028	0.1434	0.3979
P =	21	0.1564	0.4177	0.1541	0.4127	0.1519	0.4078
P =	22	0.1649	0.4273	0.1626	0.4223	0.1602	0.4173
P =	23	0.1734	0.4366	0.1709	0.4315	0.1685	0.4265
P =	24	0.1817	0.4455	0.1791	0.4404	0.1766	0.4354
P =	25	0.1899	0.4542	0.1872	0.4490	0.1847	0.4440
P =	26	0.1979	0.4626	0.1952	0.4574	0.1926	0.4523
P =	27	0.2059	0.4707	0.2031	0.4655	0.2003	0.4604
P =	28	0.2137	0.4785	0.2108	0.4733	0.2080	0.4682
P =	29	0.2214	0.4862	0.2184	0.4809	0.2155	0.4758
P =	30	0.2289	0.4935	0.2259	0.4883	0.2230	0.4832
P =	31	0.2364	0.5007	0.2333	0.4955	0.2303	0.4903
P =	32	0.2437	0.5077	0.2405	0.5024	0.2375	0.4973
P =	33	0.2509	0.5144	0.2477	0.5092	0.2446	0.5040
P =	34	0.2580	0.5210	0.2547	0.5157	0.2515	0.5106
P =	35	0.2649	0.5274	0.2616	0.5221	0.2584	0.5169
P =	36	0.2718	0.5336	0.2684	0.5283	0.2651	0.5232
P =	37	0.2785	0.5396	0.2751	0.5344	0.2718	0.5292
P =	38	0.2851	0.5455	0.2817	0.5403	0.2783	0.5351
P =	39	0.2916	0.5512	0.2881	0.5460	0.2847	0.5408
P =	40	0.2981	0.5568	0.2945	0.5516	0.2911	0.5464
P =	41	0.3044	0.5623	0.3008	0.5570	0.2973	0.5519
P =	42	0.3106	0.5676	0.3069	0.5624	0.3034	0.5572
P =	43	0.3167	0.5727	0.3130	0.5675	0.3094	0.5624
P =	44	0.3227	0.5778	0.3190	0.5726	0.3154	0.5675
P =	45	0.3286	0.5827	0.3249	0.5776	0.3212	0.5725
P =	46	0.3344	0.5875	0.3306	0.5824	0.3270	0.5773
P =	47	0.3401	0.5922	0.3363	0.5871	0.3326	0.5820
P =	48	0.3457	0.5968	0.3419	0.5917	0.3382	0.5867
P =	49	0.3513	0.6013	0.3474	0.5962	0.3437	0.5912
P =	50	0.3567	0.6057	0.3529	0.6006	0.3491	0.5956
P =	51	0.3621	0.6100	0.3582	0.6049	0.3544	0.5999
P =	52	0.3674	0.6142	0.3635	0.6091	0.3597	0.6041
P =	53	0.3726	0.6183	0.3686	0.6133	0.3648	0.6083
P =	54	0.3777	0.6223	0.3737	0.6173	0.3699	0.6123
P =	55	0.3827	0.6263	0.3788	0.6212	0.3749	0.6163
P =	56	0.3877	0.6301	0.3837	0.6251	0.3798	0.6202
P =	57	0.3926	0.6339	0.3886	0.6289	0.3847	0.6240
P =	58	0.3974	0.6376	0.3934	0.6326	0.3895	0.6277
P =	59	0.4021	0.6412	0.3981	0.6362	0.3942	0.6314
P =	60	0.4068	0.6447	0.4028	0.6398	0.3988	0.6350

	57		58		59		60
LOW	HIGH	LOW	HIGH	LCW	HIGH	LCW	HIGH
0.0002	0.1091	0.0002	0.1074	0.0002	0.1057	0.0002	0.1040
0.0024	0.1358	0.0024	0.1336	0.0024	0.1316	0.0023	0.1295
0.0071	0.1597	0.0070	0.1572	0.0068	0.1548	0.0067	0.1525
0.0132	0.1815	0.0130	0.1788	0.0128	0.1761	0.0126	0.1735
0.0204	0.2016	0.0200	0.1987	0.0197	0.1958	0.0194	0.1929
0.0282	0.2204	0.0277	0.2172	0.0272	0.2141	0.0268	0.2111
0.0364	0.2380	0.0358	0.2346	0.0352	0.2313	0.0346	0.2281
0.0449	0.2546	0.0442	0.2510	0.0435	0.2475	0.0428	0.2442
0.0536	0.2703	0.0527	0.2666	0.0519	0.2629	0.0511	0.2594
0.0624	0.2852	0.0614	0.2813	0.0605	0.2775	0.0595	0.2739
0.0713	0.2994	0.0702	0.2954	0.0691	0.2915	0.0681	0.2877
0.0802	0.3129	0.0790	0.3088	0.0778	0.3048	0.0766	0.3009
0.0891	0.3258	0.0878	0.3216	0.0865	0.3175	0.0852	0.3135
0.0980	0.3382	0.0965	0.3339	0.0951	0.3297	0.0937	0.3256
0.1068	0.3501	0.1052	0.3457	0.1037	0.3414	0.1022	0.3372
0.1156	0.3615	0.1139	0.3570	0.1122	0.3527	0.1106	0.3484
0.1243	0.3724	0.1225	0.3679	0.1207	0.3635	0.1190	0.3592
0.1328	0.3830	0.1309	0.3784	0.1291	0.3739	0.1273	0.3696
0.1413	0.3932	0.1393	0.3885	0.1374	0.3840	0.1355	0.3796
0.1497	0.4030	0.1476	0.3983	0.1456	0.3937	0.1436	0.3893
0.1580	0.4125	0.1558	0.4077	0.1537	0.4031	0.1516	0.3986
0.1662	0.4216	0.1639	0.4169	0.1617	0.4122	0.1595	0.4076
0.1742	0.4305	0.1718	0.4257	0.1696	0.4210	0.1673	0.4164
0.1821	0.4391	0.1797	0.4342	0.1773	0.4295	0.1750	0.4249
0.1900	0.4474	0.1875	0.4425	0.1850	0.4378	0.1826	0.4331
0.1977	0.4554	0.1951	0.4505	0.1926	0.4458	0.1901	0.4411
0.2053	0.4632	0.2026	0.4583	0.2000	0.4535	0.1975	0.4488
0.2127	0.4708	0.2100	0.4659	0.2074	0.4611	0.2048	0.4563
0.2201	0.4781	0.2173	0.4732	0.2146	0.4684	0.2119	0.4636
0.2274	0.4853	0.2245	0.4803	0.2217	0.4755	0.2190	0.4707
0.2345	0.4922	0.2316	0.4873	0.2287	0.4824	0.2260	0.4776
0.2415	0.4989	0.2385	0.4940	0.2357	0.4891	0.2328	0.4844
0.2484	0.5055	0.2454	0.5005	0.2425	0.4957	0.2396	0.4909
0.2552	0.5119	0.2522	0.5069	0.2492	0.5021	0.2462	0.4973
0.2619	0.5181	0.2588	0.5131	0.2558	0.5083	0.2528	0.5035
0.2685	0.5241	0.2654	0.5192	0.2623	0.5143	0.2592	0.5095
0.2750	0.5300	0.2718	0.5251	0.2687	0.5202	0.2656	0.5154
0.2814	0.5358	0.2782	0.5308	0.2750	0.5260	0.2719	0.5212
0.2877	0.5414	0.2844	0.5364	0.2812	0.5316	0.2780	0.5268
0.2939	0.5469	0.2905	0.5419	0.2873	0.5370	0.2841	0.5323
0.3000	0.5522	0.2966	0.5472	0.2933	0.5424	0.2901	0.5376
0.3060	0.5574	0.3026	0.5525	0.2992	0.5476	0.2960	0.5428
0.3119	0.5625	0.3084	0.5575	0.3051	0.5527	0.3018	0.5479
0.3177	0.5675	0.3142	0.5625	0.3108	0.5577	0.3075	0.5529
0.3234	0.5723	0.3199	0.5674	0.3165	0.5626	0.3131	0.5578
0.3290	0.5770	0.3255	0.5721	0.3220	0.5673	0.3187	0.5626
0.3346	0.5817	0.3310	0.5768	0.3275	0.5720	0.3241	0.5672
0.3400	0.5862	0.3364	0.5813	0.3329	0.5765	0.3295	0.5718
0.3454	0.5906	0.3418	0.5858	0.3383	0.5810	0.3348	0.5763
0.3507	0.5950	0.3471	0.5901	0.3435	0.5853	0.3400	0.5806
0.3559	0.5992	0.3523	0.5944	0.3487	0.5896	0.3452	0.5849
0.3611	0.6034	0.3574	0.5985	0.3538	0.5938	0.3503	0.5891
0.3661	0.6074	0.3624	0.6026	0.3588	0.5979	0.3553	0.5932
0.3711	0.6114	0.3674	0.6066	0.3638	0.6019	0.3602	0.5972
0.3760	0.6153	0.3723	0.6105	0.3686	0.6058	0.3650	0.6012
0.3809	0.6191	0.3771	0.6144	0.3734	0.6097	0.3698	0.6050
0.3856	0.6229	0.3819	0.6181	0.3782	0.6135	0.3746	0.6088
0.3903	0.6266	0.3865	0.6218	0.3829	0.6171	0.3792	0.6126
0.3950	0.6302	0.3912	0.6254	0.3874	0.6208	0.3838	0.6162

Appendix C

Chi-squared distribution

Values of χ^2 for which indicated area lies to the right.

df	Area in right tail						
	0·250	0·100	0·050	0·025	0·010	0·005	0·001
1	1·32330	2·70554	3·84146	5·02389	6·63490	7·87944	10·828
2	2·77259	4·60517	5·99146	7·37776	9·21034	10·5966	13·816
3	4·10834	6·25139	7·81473	9·34840	11·3449	12·8382	16·266
4	5·38527	7·77944	9·48773	11·1433	13·2767	14·8603	18·467
5	6·62568	9·23636	11·0705	12·8325	15·0863	16·7496	20·515
6	7·84080	10·6446	12·5916	14·4494	16·8119	18·5476	22·458
7	9·03715	12·0170	14·0671	16·0128	18·4753	20·2777	24·322
8	10·2189	13·3616	15·5073	17·5345	20·0902	21·9550	26·125
9	11·3888	14·6837	16·9190	19·0228	21·6660	23·5894	27·877
10	12·5489	15·9872	18·3070	20·4832	23·2093	25·1882	29·588
11	13·7007	17·2750	19·6751	21·9200	24·7250	26·7568	31·264
12	14·8454	18·5493	21·0261	23·3367	26·2170	28·2995	32·909
13	15·9839	19·8119	22·3620	24·7356	27·6882	29·8195	34·528
14	17·1169	21·0641	23·6848	26·1189	29·1412	31·3194	36·123
15	18·2451	22·3071	24·9958	27·4884	30·5779	32·8013	37·697
16	19·3689	23·5418	26·2962	28·8454	31·9999	34·2672	39·252
17	20·4887	24·7690	27·5871	30·1910	33·4087	35·7185	40·790
18	21·6049	25·9894	28·8693	31·5264	34·8053	37·1565	42·312
19	22·7178	27·2036	30·1435	32·8523	36·1909	38·5823	43·820
20	23·8277	28·4120	31·4104	34·1696	37·5662	39·9968	45·315
21	24·9348	29·6151	32·6706	35·4789	38·9322	41·4011	46·797
22	26·0393	30·8133	33·9244	36·7807	40·2894	42·7957	48·268
23	27·1413	32·0069	35·1725	38·0756	41·6384	44·1813	49·728
24	28·2412	33·1962	36·4150	39·3641	42·9798	45·5585	51·179
25	29·3389	34·3816	37·6525	40·6465	44·3141	46·9279	52·618
26	30·4346	35·5632	38·8851	41·9232	45·6417	48·2899	54·052
27	31·5284	36·7412	40·1133	43·1945	46·9629	49·6449	55·476
28	32·6205	37·9159	41·3371	44·4608	48·2782	50·9934	56·892
29	33·7109	39·0875	42·5570	45·7223	49·5879	52·3356	58·301
30	34·7997	40·2560	43·7730	46·9792	50·8922	53·6720	59·703
40	45·6160	51·8051	55·7585	59·3417	63·6907	66·7660	73·402
50	56·3336	63·1671	67·5048	71·4202	76·1539	79·4900	86·661
60	66·9815	74·3970	79·0819	83·2977	88·3794	91·9517	99·607
70	77·5767	85·5270	90·5312	95·0232	100·425	104·215	112·317
80	88·1303	96·5782	101·879	106·629	112·329	116·321	124·839
90	98·6499	107·565	113·145	118·136	124·116	128·299	137·208
100	109·141	118·498	124·342	129·561	135·807	140·169	149·449

SOURCE: Pearson and Hartley (1966).

Appendix D

F distribution

Values of F_{high} for which indicated area lies to the right

0.05 in right tail (use for 90 per cent credible interval)

df_2 \ df_1	1	2	3	4	5	6	7	8	9	10	12	15	20	24	30	40	60	120	∞
1	161.4	199.5	215.7	224.6	230.2	234.0	236.8	238.9	240.5	241.9	243.9	245.9	248.0	249.1	250.1	251.1	252.2	253.3	254.3
2	18.51	19.00	19.16	19.25	19.30	19.33	19.35	19.37	19.38	19.40	19.41	19.43	19.45	19.45	19.46	19.47	19.48	19.49	19.50
3	10.13	9.55	9.28	9.12	9.01	8.94	8.89	8.85	8.81	8.79	8.74	8.70	8.66	8.64	8.62	8.59	8.57	8.55	8.53
4	7.71	6.94	6.59	6.39	6.26	6.16	6.09	6.04	6.00	5.96	5.91	5.86	5.80	5.77	5.75	5.72	5.69	5.66	5.63
5	6.61	5.79	5.41	5.19	5.05	4.95	4.88	4.82	4.77	4.74	4.68	4.62	4.56	4.53	4.50	4.46	4.43	4.40	4.36
6	5.99	5.14	4.76	4.53	4.39	4.28	4.21	4.15	4.10	4.06	4.00	3.94	3.87	3.84	3.81	3.77	3.74	3.70	3.67
7	5.59	4.74	4.35	4.12	3.97	3.87	3.79	3.73	3.68	3.64	3.57	3.51	3.44	3.41	3.38	3.34	3.30	3.27	3.23
8	5.32	4.46	4.07	3.84	3.69	3.58	3.50	3.44	3.39	3.35	3.28	3.22	3.15	3.12	3.08	3.04	3.01	2.97	2.93
9	5.12	4.26	3.86	3.63	3.48	3.37	3.29	3.23	3.18	3.14	3.07	3.01	2.94	2.90	2.86	2.83	2.79	2.75	2.71
10	4.96	4.10	3.71	3.48	3.33	3.22	3.14	3.07	3.02	2.98	2.91	2.85	2.77	2.74	2.70	2.66	2.62	2.58	2.54
11	4.84	3.98	3.59	3.36	3.20	3.09	3.01	2.95	2.90	2.85	2.79	2.72	2.65	2.61	2.57	2.53	2.49	2.45	2.40
12	4.75	3.89	3.49	3.26	3.11	3.00	2.91	2.85	2.80	2.75	2.69	2.62	2.54	2.51	2.47	2.43	2.38	2.34	2.30
13	4.67	3.81	3.41	3.18	3.03	2.92	2.83	2.77	2.71	2.67	2.60	2.53	2.46	2.42	2.38	2.34	2.30	2.25	2.21
14	4.60	3.74	3.34	3.11	2.96	2.85	2.76	2.70	2.65	2.60	2.53	2.46	2.39	2.35	2.31	2.27	2.22	2.18	2.13
15	4.54	3.68	3.29	3.06	2.90	2.79	2.71	2.64	2.59	2.54	2.48	2.40	2.33	2.29	2.25	2.20	2.16	2.11	2.07
16	4.49	3.63	3.24	3.01	2.85	2.74	2.66	2.59	2.54	2.49	2.42	2.35	2.28	2.24	2.19	2.15	2.11	2.06	2.01
17	4.45	3.59	3.20	2.96	2.81	2.70	2.61	2.55	2.49	2.45	2.38	2.31	2.23	2.19	2.15	2.10	2.06	2.01	1.96
18	4.41	3.55	3.16	2.93	2.77	2.66	2.58	2.51	2.46	2.41	2.34	2.27	2.19	2.15	2.11	2.06	2.02	1.97	1.92
19	4.38	3.52	3.13	2.90	2.74	2.63	2.54	2.48	2.42	2.38	2.31	2.23	2.16	2.11	2.07	2.03	1.98	1.93	1.88
20	4.35	3.49	3.10	2.87	2.71	2.60	2.51	2.45	2.39	2.35	2.28	2.20	2.12	2.08	2.04	1.99	1.95	1.90	1.84
21	4.32	3.47	3.07	2.84	2.68	2.57	2.49	2.42	2.37	2.32	2.25	2.18	2.10	2.05	2.01	1.96	1.92	1.87	1.81
22	4.30	3.44	3.05	2.82	2.66	2.55	2.46	2.40	2.34	2.30	2.23	2.15	2.07	2.03	1.98	1.94	1.89	1.84	1.78
23	4.28	3.42	3.03	2.80	2.64	2.53	2.44	2.37	2.32	2.27	2.20	2.13	2.05	2.01	1.96	1.91	1.86	1.81	1.76
24	4.26	3.40	3.01	2.78	2.62	2.51	2.42	2.36	2.30	2.25	2.18	2.11	2.03	1.98	1.94	1.89	1.84	1.79	1.73
25	4.24	3.39	2.99	2.76	2.60	2.49	2.40	2.34	2.28	2.24	2.16	2.09	2.01	1.96	1.92	1.87	1.82	1.77	1.71
26	4.23	3.37	2.98	2.74	2.59	2.47	2.39	2.32	2.27	2.22	2.15	2.07	1.99	1.95	1.90	1.85	1.80	1.75	1.69
27	4.21	3.35	2.96	2.73	2.57	2.46	2.37	2.31	2.25	2.20	2.13	2.06	1.97	1.93	1.88	1.84	1.79	1.73	1.67
28	4.20	3.34	2.95	2.71	2.56	2.45	2.36	2.29	2.24	2.19	2.12	2.04	1.96	1.91	1.87	1.82	1.77	1.71	1.65
29	4.18	3.33	2.93	2.70	2.55	2.43	2.35	2.28	2.22	2.18	2.10	2.03	1.94	1.90	1.85	1.81	1.75	1.70	1.64
30	4.17	3.32	2.92	2.69	2.53	2.42	2.33	2.27	2.21	2.16	2.09	2.01	1.93	1.89	1.84	1.79	1.74	1.68	1.62
40	4.08	3.23	2.84	2.61	2.45	2.34	2.25	2.18	2.12	2.08	2.00	1.92	1.84	1.79	1.74	1.69	1.64	1.58	1.51
60	4.00	3.15	2.76	2.53	2.37	2.25	2.17	2.10	2.04	1.99	1.92	1.84	1.75	1.70	1.65	1.59	1.53	1.47	1.39
120	3.92	3.07	2.68	2.45	2.29	2.17	2.09	2.02	1.96	1.91	1.83	1.75	1.66	1.61	1.55	1.50	1.43	1.35	1.25
∞	3.84	3.00	2.60	2.37	2.21	2.10	2.01	1.94	1.88	1.83	1.75	1.67	1.57	1.52	1.46	1.39	1.32	1.22	1.00

SOURCE: Pearson and Hartley (1966).

0.025 in right tail (use for 95 per cent credible interval)

df_2 \ df_1	1	2	3	4	5	6	7	8	9	10	12	15	20	24	30	40	60	120	∞
1	647·8	799·5	864·2	899·6	921·8	937·1	948·2	956·7	963·3	968·6	976·7	984·9	993·1	997·2	1001	1006	1010	1014	1018
2	38·51	39·00	39·17	39·25	39·30	39·33	39·36	39·37	39·39	39·40	39·41	39·43	39·45	39·46	39·46	39·47	39·48	39·49	39·50
3	17·44	16·04	15·44	15·10	14·88	14·73	14·62	14·54	14·47	14·42	14·34	14·25	14·17	14·12	14·08	14·04	13·99	13·95	13·90
4	12·22	10·65	9·98	9·60	9·36	9·20	9·07	8·98	8·90	8·84	8·75	8·66	8·56	8·51	8·46	8·41	8·36	8·31	8·26
5	10·01	8·43	7·76	7·39	7·15	6·98	6·85	6·76	6·68	6·62	6·52	6·43	6·33	6·28	6·23	6·18	6·12	6·07	6·02
6	8·81	7·26	6·60	6·23	5·99	5·82	5·70	5·60	5·52	5·46	5·37	5·27	5·17	5·12	5·07	5·01	4·96	4·90	4·85
7	8·07	6·54	5·89	5·52	5·29	5·12	4·99	4·90	4·82	4·76	4·67	4·57	4·47	4·42	4·36	4·31	4·25	4·20	4·14
8	7·57	6·06	5·42	5·05	4·82	4·65	4·53	4·43	4·36	4·30	4·20	4·10	4·00	3·95	3·89	3·84	3·78	3·73	3·67
9	7·21	5·71	5·08	4·72	4·48	4·32	4·20	4·10	4·03	3·96	3·87	3·77	3·67	3·61	3·56	3·51	3·45	3·39	3·33
10	6·94	5·46	4·83	4·47	4·24	4·07	3·95	3·85	3·78	3·72	3·62	3·52	3·42	3·37	3·31	3·26	3·20	3·14	3·08
11	6·72	5·26	4·63	4·28	4·04	3·88	3·76	3·66	3·59	3·53	3·43	3·33	3·23	3·17	3·12	3·06	3·00	2·94	2·88
12	6·55	5·10	4·47	4·12	3·89	3·73	3·61	3·51	3·44	3·37	3·28	3·18	3·07	3·02	2·96	2·91	2·85	2·79	2·72
13	6·41	4·97	4·35	4·00	3·77	3·60	3·48	3·39	3·31	3·25	3·15	3·05	2·95	2·89	2·84	2·78	2·72	2·66	2·60
14	6·30	4·86	4·24	3·89	3·66	3·50	3·38	3·29	3·21	3·15	3·05	2·95	2·84	2·79	2·73	2·67	2·61	2·55	2·49
15	6·20	4·77	4·15	3·80	3·58	3·41	3·29	3·20	3·12	3·06	2·96	2·86	2·76	2·70	2·64	2·59	2·52	2·46	2·40
16	6·12	4·69	4·08	3·73	3·50	3·34	3·22	3·12	3·05	2·99	2·89	2·79	2·68	2·63	2·57	2·51	2·45	2·38	2·32
17	6·04	4·62	4·01	3·66	3·44	3·28	3·16	3·06	2·98	2·92	2·82	2·72	2·62	2·56	2·50	2·44	2·38	2·32	2·25
18	5·98	4·56	3·95	3·61	3·38	3·22	3·10	3·01	2·93	2·87	2·77	2·67	2·56	2·50	2·44	2·38	2·32	2·26	2·19
19	5·92	4·51	3·90	3·56	3·33	3·17	3·05	2·96	2·88	2·82	2·72	2·62	2·51	2·45	2·39	2·33	2·27	2·20	2·13
20	5·87	4·46	3·86	3·51	3·29	3·13	3·01	2·91	2·84	2·77	2·68	2·57	2·46	2·41	2·35	2·29	2·22	2·16	2·09
21	5·83	4·42	3·82	3·48	3·25	3·09	2·97	2·87	2·80	2·73	2·64	2·53	2·42	2·37	2·31	2·25	2·18	2·11	2·04
22	5·79	4·38	3·78	3·44	3·22	3·05	2·93	2·84	2·76	2·70	2·60	2·50	2·39	2·33	2·27	2·21	2·14	2·08	2·00
23	5·75	4·35	3·75	3·41	3·18	3·02	2·90	2·81	2·73	2·67	2·57	2·47	2·36	2·30	2·24	2·18	2·11	2·04	1·97
24	5·72	4·32	3·72	3·38	3·15	2·99	2·87	2·78	2·70	2·64	2·54	2·44	2·33	2·27	2·21	2·15	2·08	2·01	1·94
25	5·69	4·29	3·69	3·35	3·13	2·97	2·85	2·75	2·68	2·61	2·51	2·41	2·30	2·24	2·18	2·12	2·05	1·98	1·91
26	5·66	4·27	3·67	3·33	3·10	2·94	2·82	2·73	2·65	2·59	2·49	2·39	2·28	2·22	2·16	2·09	2·03	1·95	1·88
27	5·63	4·24	3·65	3·31	3·08	2·92	2·80	2·71	2·63	2·57	2·47	2·36	2·25	2·19	2·13	2·07	2·00	1·93	1·85
28	5·61	4·22	3·63	3·29	3·06	2·90	2·78	2·69	2·61	2·55	2·45	2·34	2·23	2·17	2·11	2·05	1·98	1·91	1·83
29	5·59	4·20	3·61	3·27	3·04	2·88	2·76	2·67	2·59	2·53	2·43	2·32	2·21	2·15	2·09	2·03	1·96	1·89	1·81
30	5·57	4·18	3·59	3·25	3·03	2·87	2·75	2·65	2·57	2·51	2·41	2·31	2·20	2·14	2·07	2·01	1·94	1·87	1·79
40	5·42	4·05	3·46	3·13	2·90	2·74	2·62	2·53	2·45	2·39	2·29	2·18	2·07	2·01	1·94	1·88	1·80	1·72	1·64
60	5·29	3·93	3·34	3·01	2·79	2·63	2·51	2·41	2·33	2·27	2·17	2·06	1·94	1·88	1·82	1·74	1·67	1·58	1·48
120	5·15	3·80	3·23	2·89	2·67	2·52	2·39	2·30	2·22	2·16	2·05	1·94	1·82	1·76	1·69	1·61	1·53	1·43	1·31
∞	5·02	3·69	3·12	2·79	2·57	2·41	2·29	2·19	2·11	2·05	1·94	1·83	1·71	1·64	1·57	1·48	1·39	1·27	1·00

0.005 in right tail (use for 99 per cent credible interval)

df_2 \ df_1	1	2	3	4	5	6	7	8	9	10	12	15	20	24	30	40	60	120	∞
1	16211	20000	21615	22500	23056	23437	23715	23925	24091	24224	24426	24630	24836	24940	25044	25148	25253	25359	25465
2	198·5	199·0	199·2	199·2	199·3	199·3	199·4	199·4	199·4	199·4	199·4	199·4	199·4	199·5	199·5	199·5	199·5	199·5	199·5
3	55·55	49·80	47·47	46·19	45·39	44·84	44·43	44·13	43·88	43·69	43·39	43·08	42·78	42·62	42·47	42·31	42·15	41·99	41·83
4	31·33	26·28	24·26	23·15	22·46	21·97	21·62	21·35	21·14	20·97	20·70	20·44	20·17	20·03	19·89	19·75	19·61	19·47	19·32
5	22·78	18·31	16·53	15·56	14·94	14·51	14·20	13·96	13·77	13·62	13·38	13·15	12·90	12·78	12·66	12·53	12·40	12·27	12·14
6	18·63	14·54	12·92	12·03	11·46	11·07	10·79	10·57	10·39	10·25	10·03	9·81	9·59	9·47	9·36	9·24	9·12	9·00	8·88
7	16·24	12·40	10·88	10·05	9·52	9·16	8·89	8·68	8·51	8·38	8·18	7·97	7·75	7·65	7·53	7·42	7·31	7·19	7·08
8	14·69	11·04	9·60	8·81	8·30	7·95	7·69	7·50	7·34	7·21	7·01	6·81	6·61	6·50	6·40	6·29	6·18	6·06	5·95
9	13·61	10·11	8·72	7·96	7·47	7·13	6·88	6·69	6·54	6·42	6·23	6·03	5·83	5·73	5·62	5·52	5·41	5·30	5·19
10	12·83	9·43	8·08	7·34	6·87	6·54	6·30	6·12	5·97	5·85	5·66	5·47	5·27	5·17	5·07	4·97	4·86	4·75	4·64
11	12·23	8·91	7·60	6·88	6·42	6·10	5·86	5·68	5·54	5·42	5·24	5·05	4·86	4·76	4·65	4·55	4·44	4·34	4·23
12	11·75	8·51	7·23	6·52	6·07	5·76	5·52	5·35	5·20	5·09	4·91	4·72	4·53	4·43	4·33	4·23	4·12	4·01	3·90
13	11·37	8·19	6·93	6·23	5·79	5·48	5·25	5·08	4·94	4·82	4·64	4·46	4·27	4·17	4·07	3·97	3·87	3·76	3·65
14	11·06	7·92	6·68	6·00	5·56	5·26	5·03	4·86	4·72	4·60	4·43	4·25	4·06	3·96	3·86	3·76	3·66	3·55	3·44
15	10·80	7·70	6·48	5·80	5·37	5·07	4·85	4·67	4·54	4·42	4·25	4·07	3·88	3·79	3·69	3·58	3·48	3·37	3·26
16	10·58	7·51	6·30	5·64	5·21	4·91	4·69	4·52	4·38	4·27	4·10	3·92	3·73	3·64	3·54	3·44	3·33	3·22	3·11
17	10·38	7·35	6·16	5·50	5·07	4·78	4·56	4·39	4·25	4·14	3·97	3·79	3·61	3·51	3·41	3·31	3·21	3·10	2·98
18	10·22	7·21	6·03	5·37	4·96	4·66	4·44	4·28	4·14	4·03	3·86	3·68	3·50	3·40	3·30	3·20	3·10	2·99	2·87
19	10·07	7·09	5·92	5·27	4·85	4·56	4·34	4·18	4·04	3·93	3·76	3·59	3·40	3·31	3·21	3·11	3·00	2·89	2·78
20	9·94	6·99	5·82	5·17	4·76	4·47	4·26	4·09	3·96	3·85	3·68	3·50	3·32	3·22	3·12	3·02	2·92	2·81	2·69
21	9·83	6·89	5·73	5·09	4·68	4·39	4·18	4·01	3·88	3·77	3·60	3·43	3·24	3·15	3·05	2·95	2·84	2·73	2·61
22	9·73	6·81	5·65	5·02	4·61	4·32	4·11	3·94	3·81	3·70	3·54	3·36	3·18	3·08	2·98	2·88	2·77	2·66	2·55
23	9·63	6·73	5·58	4·95	4·54	4·26	4·05	3·88	3·75	3·64	3·47	3·30	3·12	3·02	2·92	2·82	2·71	2·60	2·48
24	9·55	6·66	5·52	4·89	4·49	4·20	3·99	3·83	3·69	3·59	3·42	3·25	3·06	2·97	2·87	2·77	2·66	2·55	2·43
25	9·48	6·60	5·46	4·84	4·43	4·15	3·94	3·78	3·64	3·54	3·37	3·20	3·01	2·92	2·82	2·72	2·61	2·50	2·38
26	9·41	6·54	5·41	4·79	4·38	4·10	3·89	3·73	3·60	3·49	3·33	3·15	2·97	2·87	2·77	2·67	2·56	2·45	2·33
27	9·34	6·49	5·36	4·74	4·34	4·06	3·85	3·69	3·56	3·45	3·28	3·11	2·93	2·83	2·73	2·63	2·52	2·41	2·29
28	9·28	6·44	5·32	4·70	4·30	4·02	3·81	3·65	3·52	3·41	3·25	3·07	2·89	2·79	2·69	2·59	2·48	2·37	2·25
29	9·23	6·40	5·28	4·66	4·26	3·98	3·77	3·61	3·48	3·38	3·21	3·04	2·86	2·76	2·66	2·56	2·45	2·33	2·21
30	9·18	6·35	5·24	4·62	4·23	3·95	3·74	3·58	3·45	3·34	3·18	3·01	2·82	2·73	2·63	2·52	2·42	2·30	2·18
40	8·83	6·07	4·98	4·37	3·99	3·71	3·51	3·35	3·22	3·12	2·95	2·78	2·60	2·50	2·40	2·30	2·18	2·06	1·93
60	8·49	5·79	4·73	4·14	3·76	3·49	3·29	3·13	3·01	2·90	2·74	2·57	2·39	2·29	2·19	2·08	1·96	1·83	1·69
120	8·18	5·54	4·50	3·92	3·55	3·28	3·09	2·93	2·81	2·71	2·54	2·37	2·19	2·09	1·98	1·87	1·75	1·61	1·43
∞	7·88	5·30	4·28	3·72	3·35	3·09	2·90	2·74	2·62	2·52	2·36	2·19	2·00	1·90	1·79	1·67	1·53	1·36	1·00

Appendix E

Inverted gamma-2 distribution
Highest density regions

D.F.	Area within HDR 0.95 LCW	0.95 HIGH	0.99 LCW	0.99 HIGH	0.999 LCW	0.999 HIGH
2	0.445	5.437	0.379	12.235	0.323	33.588
3	0.507	3.406	0.437	5.924	0.376	12.842
4	0.549	2.688	0.478	4.126	0.416	7.436
5	0.582	2.326	0.511	3.315	0.447	5.359
6	0.607	2.106	0.537	2.859	0.473	4.303
7	0.628	1.959	0.559	2.567	0.495	3.671
8	0.646	1.852	0.578	2.364	0.514	3.258
9	0.661	1.771	0.594	2.214	0.530	2.964
10	0.674	1.708	0.608	2.099	0.545	2.745
11	0.685	1.656	0.621	2.008	0.558	2.577
12	0.696	1.613	0.632	1.934	0.570	2.441
13	0.705	1.577	0.642	1.872	0.581	2.333
14	0.713	1.546	0.652	1.819	0.591	2.239
15	0.721	1.519	0.660	1.774	0.600	2.161
16	0.728	1.495	0.668	1.735	0.609	2.094
17	0.735	1.474	0.675	1.700	0.617	2.037
18	0.741	1.456	0.682	1.670	0.624	1.986
19	0.746	1.439	0.688	1.643	0.631	1.941
20	0.751	1.423	0.694	1.618	0.637	1.901
21	0.756	1.410	0.700	1.596	0.643	1.865
22	0.761	1.397	0.705	1.576	0.649	1.832
23	0.765	1.385	0.710	1.557	0.655	1.802
24	0.769	1.374	0.715	1.540	0.660	1.775
25	0.773	1.364	0.719	1.525	0.665	1.751
26	0.777	1.355	0.724	1.510	0.669	1.728
27	0.780	1.346	0.728	1.497	0.674	1.707
28	0.783	1.338	0.732	1.484	0.678	1.687
29	0.787	1.331	0.735	1.472	0.682	1.669
30	0.790	1.324	0.739	1.461	0.686	1.652
31	0.793	1.317	0.742	1.451	0.690	1.636
32	0.795	1.311	0.745	1.441	0.694	1.621
33	0.798	1.305	0.748	1.432	0.697	1.607
34	0.800	1.299	0.751	1.423	0.701	1.594
35	0.803	1.293	0.754	1.415	0.704	1.581
36	0.805	1.288	0.757	1.408	0.707	1.569
37	0.807	1.283	0.760	1.400	0.710	1.558
38	0.810	1.279	0.762	1.393	0.713	1.547
39	0.812	1.274	0.765	1.386	0.716	1.537
40	0.814	1.270	0.767	1.380	0.718	1.528
41	0.816	1.266	0.769	1.374	0.721	1.519
42	0.818	1.262	0.772	1.368	0.724	1.510
43	0.819	1.258	0.774	1.362	0.726	1.501
44	0.821	1.255	0.776	1.357	0.729	1.493
45	0.823	1.251	0.778	1.352	0.731	1.486
46	0.825	1.248	0.780	1.347	0.733	1.478
47	0.826	1.245	0.782	1.342	0.735	1.471
48	0.828	1.241	0.784	1.337	0.738	1.465
49	0.829	1.238	0.786	1.333	0.740	1.458

SOURCE: Computed for this volume.

		Area within HDR			
	0.95		0.99		0.999

D.F.	LOW	HIGH	LOW	HIGH	LOW	HIGH
54	0.836	1.225	0.794	1.313	0.749	1.429
59	0.843	1.213	0.802	1.296	0.758	1.404
64	0.848	1.203	0.808	1.281	0.766	1.383
69	0.853	1.195	0.814	1.269	0.773	1.365
74	0.858	1.187	0.820	1.258	0.779	1.348
79	0.862	1.180	0.825	1.248	0.785	1.334
84	0.865	1.174	0.829	1.239	0.790	1.321
89	0.869	1.168	0.833	1.230	0.795	1.310
94	0.872	1.163	0.837	1.223	0.800	1.300
99	0.875	1.158	0.841	1.216	0.804	1.290
104	0.878	1.154	0.844	1.210	0.808	1.281
109	0.880	1.150	0.848	1.204	0.812	1.273
114	0.883	1.146	0.850	1.199	0.816	1.266
119	0.885	1.142	0.853	1.194	0.819	1.259
124	0.887	1.139	0.856	1.190	0.822	1.253
129	0.889	1.136	0.858	1.185	0.825	1.247
134	0.891	1.133	0.861	1.181	0.828	1.241
139	0.893	1.131	0.863	1.177	0.831	1.236
144	0.894	1.128	0.865	1.174	0.833	1.231
149	0.896	1.126	0.867	1.171	0.836	1.226
154	0.898	1.123	0.869	1.167	0.838	1.222
159	0.899	1.121	0.871	1.164	0.840	1.218
164	0.901	1.119	0.873	1.161	0.842	1.214
169	0.902	1.117	0.874	1.159	0.844	1.210
174	0.903	1.115	0.876	1.156	0.846	1.207
179	0.905	1.114	0.878	1.154	0.848	1.203
184	0.906	1.112	0.879	1.151	0.850	1.200
189	0.907	1.110	0.881	1.149	0.852	1.197
194	0.908	1.109	0.882	1.147	0.853	1.194
199	0.909	1.107	0.883	1.145	0.855	1.191
204	0.910	1.106	0.885	1.143	0.857	1.188
209	0.911	1.104	0.886	1.141	0.858	1.186
214	0.912	1.103	0.887	1.139	0.860	1.183
219	0.913	1.102	0.888	1.137	0.861	1.181
224	0.914	1.100	0.889	1.136	0.862	1.178
229	0.915	1.099	0.891	1.134	0.864	1.176
234	0.916	1.098	0.892	1.132	0.865	1.174
239	0.917	1.097	0.893	1.131	0.866	1.172
244	0.917	1.096	0.894	1.129	0.868	1.170
249	0.918	1.095	0.895	1.128	0.869	1.168

Appendix F

Standardized normal distribution
Areas

z	left tail	right tail	centre	z	left tail	right tail	centre
.00	.5000	.5000	.0000	.46	.6772	.3228	.3545
.01	.5040	.4960	.0080	.47	.6808	.3192	.3616
.02	.5080	.4920	.0160	.48	.6844	.3156	.3688
.03	.5120	.4880	.0239	.49	.6879	.3121	.3759
.04	.5160	.4840	.0319	.50	.6915	.3085	.3829
.05	.5199	.4801	.0399				
				.51	.6950	.3050	.3899
.06	.5239	.4761	.0478	.52	.6985	.3015	.3969
.07	.5279	.4721	.0558	.53	.7019	.2981	.4039
.08	.5319	.4681	.0638	.54	.7054	.2946	.4108
.09	.5359	.4641	.0717	.55	.7088	.2912	.4177
.10	.5398	.4602	.0797				
				.56	.7123	.2877	.4245
.11	.5438	.4562	.0876	.57	.7157	.2843	.4313
.12	.5478	.4522	.0955	.58	.7190	.2810	.4381
.13	.5517	.4483	.1034	.59	.7224	.2776	.4448
.14	.5557	.4443	.1113	.60	.7257	.2743	.4515
.15	.5596	.4404	.1192				
				.61	.7291	.2709	.4581
.16	.5636	.4364	.1271	.62	.7324	.2676	.4647
.17	.5675	.4325	.1350	.63	.7357	.2643	.4713
.18	.5714	.4286	.1428	.64	.7389	.2611	.4778
.19	.5753	.4247	.1507	.65	.7422	.2578	.4843
.20	.5793	.4207	.1585				
.21	.5832	.4168	.1663	.66	.7454	.2546	.4907
.22	.5871	.4129	.1741	.67	.7486	.2514	.4971
.23	.5910	.4090	.1819	.68	.7517	.2483	.5035
.24	.5948	.4052	.1897	.69	.7549	.2451	.5098
.25	.5987	.4013	.1974	.70	.7580	.2420	.5161
.26	.6026	.3974	.2051	.71	.7611	.2389	.5223
.27	.6064	.3936	.2128	.72	.7642	.2358	.5285
.28	.6103	.3897	.2205	.73	.7673	.2327	.5346
.29	.6141	.3859	.2282	.74	.7704	.2296	.5407
.30	.6179	.3821	.2358	.75	.7734	.2266	.5467
.31	.6217	.3783	.2434	.76	.7764	.2236	.5527
.32	.6255	.3745	.2510	.77	.7793	.2207	.5587
.33	.6293	.3707	.2586	.78	.7823	.2177	.5646
.34	.6331	.3669	.2661	.79	.7852	.2148	.5705
.35	.6368	.3632	.2737	.80	.7881	.2119	.5763
.36	.6406	.3594	.2812	.81	.7910	.2090	.5821
.37	.6443	.3557	.2886	.82	.7939	.2061	.5878
.38	.6480	.3520	.2961	.83	.7967	.2033	.5935
.39	.6517	.3483	.3035	.84	.7995	.2005	.5991
.40	.6554	.3446	.3108	.85	.8023	.1977	.6047
.41	.6591	.3409	.3182	.86	.8051	.1949	.6102
.42	.6628	.3372	.3255	.87	.8078	.1922	.6157
.43	.6664	.3336	.3328	.88	.8106	.1894	.6211
.44	.6700	.3300	.3401	.89	.8133	.1867	.6265
.45	.6736	.3264	.3473	.90	.8159	.1841	.6319

SOURCE: Computed for this volume.

z	left tail	right tail	centre	z	left tail	right tail	centre
·91	·8186	·1814	·6372	1·36	·9131	·0869	·8262
·92	·8212	·1788	·6424	1·37	·9147	·0853	·8293
·93	·8238	·1762	·6476	1·38	·9162	·0838	·8324
·94	·8264	·1736	·6528	1·39	·9177	·0823	·8355
·95	·8289	·1711	·6579	1·40	·9192	·0808	·8385
·96	·8315	·1685	·6629	1·41	·9207	·0793	·8415
·97	·8340	·1660	·6680	1·42	·9222	·0778	·8444
·98	·8365	·1635	·6729	1·43	·9236	·0764	·8473
·99	·8389	·1611	·6778	1·44	·9251	·0749	·8501
1·00	·8413	·1587	·6827	1·45	·9265	·0735	·8529
1·01	·8438	·1562	·6875	1·46	·9279	·0721	·8557
1·02	·8461	·1539	·6923	1·47	·9292	·0708	·8584
1·03	·8485	·1515	·6970	1·48	·9306	·0694	·8611
1·04	·8508	·1492	·7017	1·49	·9319	·0681	·8638
1·05	·8531	·1469	·7063	1·50	·9332	·0668	·8664
1·06	·8554	·1446	·7109	1·51	·9345	·0655	·8690
1·07	·8577	·1423	·7154	1·52	·9357	·0643	·8715
1·08	·8599	·1401	·7199	1·53	·9370	·0630	·8740
1·09	·8621	·1379	·7243	1·54	·9382	·0618	·8764
1·10	·8643	·1357	·7287	1·55	·9394	·0606	·8789
1·11	·8665	·1335	·7330	1·56	·9406	·0594	·8812
1·12	·8686	·1314	·7373	1·57	·9418	·0582	·8836
1·13	·8708	·1292	·7415	1·58	·9429	·0571	·8859
1·14	·8729	·1271	·7457	1·59	·9441	·0559	·8882
1·15	·8749	·1251	·7499	1·60	·9452	·0548	·8904
1·16	·8770	·1230	·7539	1·61	·9463	·0537	·8926
1·17	·8790	·1210	·7580	1·62	·9474	·0526	·8948
1·18	·8810	·1190	·7620	1·63	·9484	·0516	·8969
1·19	·8830	·1170	·7660	1·64	·9495	·0505	·8990
1·20	·8849	·1151	·7699	1·65	·9505	·0495	·9011
1·21	·8869	·1131	·7737	1·66	·9515	·0485	·9031
1·22	·8888	·1112	·7775	1·67	·9525	·0475	·9051
1·23	·8907	·1093	·7813	1·68	·9535	·0465	·9070
1·24	·8925	·1075	·7850	1·69	·9545	·0455	·9090
1·25	·8944	·1056	·7887	1·70	·9554	·0446	·9109
1·26	·8962	·1038	·7923	1·71	·9564	·0436	·9127
1·27	·8980	·1020	·7959	1·72	·9573	·0427	·9146
1·28	·8997	·1003	·7995	1·73	·9582	·0418	·9164
1·29	·9015	·0985	·8029	1·74	·9591	·0409	·9181
1·30	·9032	·0968	·8064	1·75	·9599	·0401	·9199
1·31	·9049	·0951	·8098	1·76	·9608	·0392	·9216
1·32	·9066	·0934	·8132	1·77	·9616	·0384	·9233
1·33	·9082	·0918	·8165	1·78	·9625	·0375	·9249
1·34	·9099	·0901	·8198	1·79	·9633	·0367	·9265
1·35	·9115	·0885	·8230	1·80	·9641	·0359	·9281

z	left tail	right tail	centre	z	left tail	right tail	centre
1.81	.9649	.0351	.9297	2.26	.9881	.0119	.9762
1.82	.9656	.0344	.9312	2.27	.9884	.0116	.9768
1.83	.9664	.0336	.9327	2.28	.9887	.0113	.9774
1.84	.9671	.0329	.9342	2.29	.9890	.0110	.9780
1.85	.9678	.0322	.9357	2.30	.9893	.0107	.9785
1.86	.9686	.0314	.9371	2.31	.9896	.0104	.9791
1.87	.9693	.0307	.9385	2.32	.9898	.0102	.9797
1.88	.9699	.0301	.9399	2.33	.9901	.0099	.9802
1.89	.9706	.0294	.9412	2.34	.9904	.0096	.9807
1.90	.9713	.0287	.9426	2.35	.9906	.0094	.9812
1.91	.9719	.0281	.9439	2.36	.9909	.0091	.9817
1.92	.9726	.0274	.9451	2.37	.9911	.0089	.9822
1.93	.9732	.0268	.9464	2.38	.9913	.0087	.9827
1.94	.9738	.0262	.9476	2.39	.9916	.0084	.9831
1.95	.9744	.0256	.9488	2.40	.9918	.0082	.9836
1.96	.9750	.0250	.9500	2.41	.9920	.0080	.9840
1.97	.9756	.0244	.9512	2.42	.9922	.0078	.9845
1.98	.9761	.0239	.9523	2.43	.9925	.0075	.9849
1.99	.9767	.0233	.9534	2.44	.9927	.0073	.9853
2.00	.9772	.0228	.9545	2.45	.9929	.0071	.9857
2.01	.9778	.0222	.9556	2.46	.9931	.0069	.9861
2.02	.9783	.0217	.9566	2.47	.9932	.0068	.9865
2.03	.9788	.0212	.9576	2.48	.9934	.0066	.9869
2.04	.9793	.0207	.9586	2.49	.9936	.0064	.9872
2.05	.9798	.0202	.9596	2.50	.9938	.0062	.9876
2.06	.9803	.0197	.9606	2.51	.9940	.0060	.9879
2.07	.9808	.0192	.9615	2.52	.9941	.0059	.9883
2.08	.9812	.0188	.9625	2.53	.9943	.0057	.9886
2.09	.9817	.0183	.9634	2.54	.9945	.0055	.9889
2.10	.9821	.0179	.9643	2.55	.9946	.0054	.9892
2.11	.9826	.0174	.9651	2.56	.9948	.0052	.9895
2.12	.9830	.0170	.9660	2.57	.9949	.0051	.9898
2.13	.9834	.0166	.9668	2.58	.9951	.0049	.9901
2.14	.9838	.0162	.9676	2.59	.9952	.0048	.9904
2.15	.9842	.0158	.9684	2.60	.9953	.0047	.9907
2.16	.9846	.0154	.9692	2.61	.9955	.0045	.9909
2.17	.9850	.0150	.9700	2.62	.9956	.0044	.9912
2.18	.9854	.0146	.9707	2.63	.9957	.0043	.9915
2.19	.9857	.0143	.9715	2.64	.9959	.0041	.9917
2.20	.9861	.0139	.9722	2.65	.9960	.0040	.9919
2.21	.9864	.0136	.9729	2.66	.9961	.0039	.9922
2.22	.9868	.0132	.9736	2.67	.9962	.0038	.9924
2.23	.9871	.0129	.9743	2.68	.9963	.0037	.9926
2.24	.9875	.0125	.9749	2.69	.9964	.0036	.9929
2.25	.9878	.0122	.9755	2.70	.9965	.0035	.9931

z	left tail	right tail	centre	z	left tail	right tail	centre
2.71	.9966	.0034	.9933	3.01	.9987	.0013	.9974
2.72	.9967	.0033	.9935	3.02	.9987	.0013	.9975
2.73	.9968	.0032	.9937	3.03	.9988	.0012	.9976
2.74	.9969	.0031	.9939	3.04	.9988	.0012	.9976
2.75	.9970	.0030	.9940	3.05	.9989	.0011	.9977
2.76	.9971	.0029	.9942	3.06	.9989	.0011	.9978
2.77	.9972	.0028	.9944	3.07	.9989	.0011	.9979
2.78	.9973	.0027	.9946	3.08	.9990	.0010	.9979
2.79	.9974	.0026	.9947	3.09	.9990	.0010	.9980
2.80	.9974	.0026	.9949	3.10	.9990	.0010	.9981
2.81	.9975	.0025	.9950	3.11	.9991	.0009	.9981
2.82	.9976	.0024	.9952	3.12	.9991	.0009	.9982
2.83	.9977	.0023	.9953	3.13	.9991	.0009	.9983
2.84	.9977	.0023	.9955	3.14	.9992	.0008	.9983
2.85	.9978	.0022	.9956	3.15	.9992	.0008	.9984
2.86	.9979	.0021	.9958	3.16	.9992	.0008	.9984
2.87	.9979	.0021	.9959	3.17	.9992	.0008	.9985
2.88	.9980	.0020	.9960	3.18	.9993	.0007	.9985
2.89	.9981	.0019	.9961	3.19	.9993	.0007	.9986
2.90	.9981	.0019	.9963	3.20	.9993	.0007	.9986
2.91	.9982	.0018	.9964	3.21	.9993	.0007	.9987
2.92	.9982	.0018	.9965	3.22	.9994	.0006	.9987
2.93	.9983	.0017	.9966	3.23	.9994	.0006	.9988
2.94	.9984	.0016	.9967	3.24	.9994	.0006	.9988
2.95	.9984	.0016	.9968	3.25	.9994	.0006	.9988
2.96	.9985	.0015	.9969	3.26	.9994	.0006	.9989
2.97	.9985	.0015	.9970	3.27	.9995	.0005	.9989
2.98	.9986	.0014	.9971	3.28	.9995	.0005	.9990
2.99	.9986	.0014	.9972	3.29	.9995	.0005	.9990
3.00	.9987	.0014	.9973	3.30	.9995	.0005	.9990

Appendix G

Student-_t_ distribution
Highest density regions

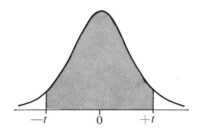

df	Area within interval									
	0.20	0.50	0.80	0.90	0.95	0.98	0.99	0.995	0.998	0.999
1	0·325	1·000	3·078	6·314	12·706	31·821	63·657	127·32	318·31	636·62
2	·289	0·816	1·886	2·920	4·303	6·965	9·925	14·089	22·327	31·598
3	·277	·765	1·638	2·353	3·182	4·541	5·841	7·453	10·214	12·924
4	·271	·741	1·533	2·132	2·776	3·747	4·604	5·598	7·173	8·610
5	0·267	0·727	1·476	2·015	2·571	3·365	4·032	4·773	5·893	6·869
6	·265	·718	1·440	1·943	2·447	3·143	3·707	4·317	5·208	5·959
7	·263	·711	1·415	1·895	2·365	2·998	3·499	4·029	4·785	5·408
8	·262	·706	1·397	1·860	2·306	2·896	3·355	3·833	4·501	5·041
9	·261	·703	1·383	1·833	2·262	2·821	3·250	3·690	4·297	4·781
10	0·260	0·700	1·372	1·812	2·228	2·764	3·169	3·581	4·144	4·587
11	·260	·697	1·363	1·796	2·201	2·718	3·106	3·497	4·025	4·437
12	·259	·695	1·356	1·782	2·179	2·681	3·055	3·428	3·930	4·318
13	·259	·694	1·350	1·771	2·160	2·650	3·012	3·372	3·852	4·221
14	·258	·692	1·345	1·761	2·145	2·624	2·977	3·326	3·787	4·140
15	0·258	0·691	1·341	1·753	2·131	2·602	2·947	3·286	3·733	4·073
16	·258	·690	1·337	1·746	2·120	2·583	2·921	3·252	3·686	4·015
17	·257	·689	1·333	1·740	2·110	2·567	2·898	3·222	3·646	3·965
18	·257	·688	1·330	1·734	2·101	2·552	2·878	3·197	3·610	3·922
19	·257	·688	1·328	1·729	2·093	2·539	2·861	3·174	3·579	3·883
20	0·257	0·687	1·325	1·725	2·086	2·528	2·845	3·153	3·552	3·850
21	·257	·686	1·323	1·721	2·080	2·518	2·831	3·135	3·527	3·819
22	·256	·686	1·321	1·717	2·074	2·508	2·819	3·119	3·505	3·792
23	·256	·685	1·319	1·714	2·069	2·500	2·807	3·104	3·485	3·767
24	·256	·685	1·318	1·711	2·064	2·492	2·797	3·091	3·467	3·745
25	0·256	0·684	1·316	1·708	2·060	2·485	2·787	3·078	3·450	3·725
26	·256	·684	1·315	1·706	2·056	2·479	2·779	3·067	3·435	3·707
27	·256	·684	1·314	1·703	2·052	2·473	2·771	3·057	3·421	3·690
28	·256	·683	1·313	1·701	2·048	2·467	2·763	3·047	3·408	3·674
29	·256	·683	1·311	1·699	2·045	2·462	2·756	3·038	3·396	3·659
30	0·256	0·683	1·310	1·697	2·042	2·457	2·750	3·030	3·385	3·646
40	·255	·681	1·303	1·684	2·021	2·423	2·704	2·971	3·307	3·551
60	·254	·679	1·296	1·671	2·000	2·390	2·660	2·915	3·232	3·460
120	·254	·677	1·289	1·658	1·980	2·358	2·617	2·860	3·160	3·373
∞	·253	·674	1·282	1·645	1·960	2·326	2·576	2·807	3·090	3·291

SOURCE: Pearson and Hartley (1966).

Appendix G   Student-*t* distribution
Cumulative areas

	(area to left of +*t*)									
df \ t	1	2	3	4	5	6	7	8	9	10
0·0	0·50000	0·50000	0·50000	0·50000	0·50000	0·50000	0·50000	0·50000	0·50000	0·50000
0·1	·53173	·53527	·53667	·53742	·53788	·53820	·53843	·53860	·53873	·53884
0·2	·56283	·57002	·57286	·57438	·57532	·57596	·57642	·57676	·57704	·57726
0·3	·59277	·60376	·60812	·61044	·61188	·61285	·61356	·61409	·61450	·61484
0·4	·62112	·63608	·64203	·64520	·64716	·64850	·64946	·65019	·65076	·65122
0·5	0·64758	0·66667	0·67428	0·67834	0·68085	0·68256	0·68380	0·68473	0·68546	0·68605
0·6	·67202	·69529	·70460	·70958	·71267	·71477	·71629	·71745	·71835	·71907
0·7	·69440	·72181	·73284	·73875	·74243	·74493	·74674	·74811	·74919	·75006
0·8	·71478	·74618	·75890	·76574	·76999	·77289	·77500	·77659	·77784	·77885
0·9	·73326	·76845	·78277	·79050	·79531	·79860	·80099	·80280	·80422	·80536
1·0	0·75000	0·78868	0·80450	0·81305	0·81839	0·82204	0·82469	0·82670	0·82828	0·82955
1·1	·76515	·80698	·82416	·83346	·83927	·84325	·84614	·84834	·85006	·85145
1·2	·77886	·82349	·84187	·85182	·85805	·86232	·86541	·86777	·86961	·87110
1·3	·79129	·83838	·85777	·86827	·87485	·87935	·88262	·88510	·88705	·88862
1·4	·80257	·85177	·87200	·88295	·88980	·89448	·89788	·90046	·90249	·90412
1·5	0·81283	0·86380	0·88471	0·89600	0·90305	0·90786	0·91135	0·91400	0·91608	0·91775
1·6	·82219	·87464	·89605	·90758	·91475	·91964	·92318	·92587	·92797	·92966
1·7	·83075	·88439	·90615	·91782	·92506	·92998	·93354	·93622	·93833	·94002
1·8	·83859	·89317	·91516	·92688	·93412	·93902	·94256	·94522	·94731	·94897
1·9	·84579	·90109	·92318	·93488	·94207	·94691	·95040	·95302	·95506	·95669
2·0	0·85242	0·90825	0·93034	0·94194	0·94903	0·95379	0·95719	0·95974	0·96172	0·96331
2·1	·85854	·91473	·93672	·94817	·95512	·95976	·96306	·96553	·96744	·96896
2·2	·86420	·92060	·94241	·95367	·96045	·96495	·96813	·97050	·97233	·97378
2·3	·86945	·92593	·94751	·95853	·96511	·96945	·97250	·97476	·97650	·97787
2·4	·87433	·93077	·95206	·96282	·96919	·97335	·97627	·97841	·98005	·98134
2·5	0·87888	0·93519	0·95615	0·96662	0·97275	0·97674	0·97950	0·98153	0·98307	0·98428
2·6	·88313	·93923	·95981	·96998	·97587	·97967	·98229	·98419	·98563	·98675
2·7	·88709	·94292	·96311	·97295	·97861	·98221	·98468	·98646	·98780	·98884
2·8	·89081	·94630	·96607	·97559	·98100	·98442	·98674	·98840	·98964	·99060
2·9	·89430	·94941	·96875	·97794	·98310	·98633	·98851	·99005	·99120	·99208
3·0	0·89758	0·95227	0·97116	0·98003	0·98495	0·98800	0·99003	0·99146	0·99252	0·99333
3·1	·90067	·95490	·97335	·98189	·98657	·98944	·99134	·99267	·99364	·99437
3·2	·90359	·95733	·97533	·98355	·98800	·99070	·99247	·99369	·99459	·99525
3·3	·90634	·95958	·97713	·98503	·98926	·99180	·99344	·99457	·99539	·99599
3·4	·90895	·96166	·97877	·98636	·99037	·99275	·99428	·99532	·99606	·99661
3·5	0·91141	0·96358	0·98026	0·98755	0·99136	0·99359	0·99500	0·99596	0·99664	0·99714
3·6	·91376	·96538	·98162	·98862	·99223	·99432	·99562	·99651	·99713	·99758
3·7	·91598	·96705	·98286	·98958	·99300	·99496	·99617	·99698	·99754	·99795
3·8	·91809	·96860	·98400	·99045	·99369	·99552	·99664	·99738	·99789	·99826
3·9	·92010	·97005	·98504	·99123	·99430	·99601	·99705	·99773	·99819	·99852
4·0	0·92202	0·97141	0·98600	0·99193	0·99484	0·99644	0·99741	0·99803	0·99845	0·99874
4·2	·92560	·97386	·98768	·99315	·99575	·99716	·99798	·99850	·99885	·99909
4·4	·92887	·97602	·98912	·99415	·99649	·99772	·99842	·99886	·99914	·99933
4·6	·93186	·97792	·99034	·99498	·99708	·99815	·99876	·99912	·99936	·99951
4·8	·93462	·97962	·99140	·99568	·99756	·99850	·99902	·99932	·99951	·99964
5·0	0·93717	0·98113	0·99230	0·99625	0·99795	0·99877	0·99922	0·99947	0·99963	0·99973
5·2	·93952	·98248	·99309	·99674	·99827	·99899	·99937	·99959	·99972	·99980
5·4	·94171	·98369	·99378	·99715	·99853	·99917	·99950	·99968	·99978	·99985
5·6	·94375	·98478	·99437	·99750	·99875	·99931	·99959	·99975	·99983	·99989
5·8	·94565	·98577	·99490	·99780	·99893	·99942	·99967	·99980	·99987	·99991
6·0	0·94743	0·98666	0·99536	0·99806	0·99908	0·99952	0·99973	0·99984	0·99990	0·99993
6·2	·94910	·98748	·99577	·99828	·99920	·99959	·99978	·99987	·99992	·99995
6·4	·95066	·98822	·99614	·99847	·99931	·99966	·99982	·99990	·99994	·99996
6·6	·95214	·98890	·99646	·99863	·99940	·99971	·99985	·99992	·99995	·99997
6·8	·95352	·98953	·99675	·99878	·99948	·99975	·99987	·99993	·99996	·99998
7·0	0·95483	0·99010	0·99701	0·99890	0·99954	0·99979	0·99990	0·99994	0·99997	0·99998
7·2	·95607	·99063	·99724	·99901	·99960	·99982	·99991	·99995	·99997	·99999
7·4	·95724	·99111	·99745	·99911	·99964	·99984	·99993	·99996	·99998	·99999
7·6	·95836	·99156	·99764	·99920	·99969	·99986	·99994	·99997	·99998	·99999
7·8	·95941	·99198	·99781	·99927	·99972	·99988	·99995	·99997	·99999	·99999
8·0	0·96042	0·99237	0·99796	0·99934	0·99975	0·99990	0·99996	0·99998	0·99999	0·99999

SOURCE: Pearson and Hartley (1966).

	(area to left of $+t$)									
df $\diagdown$ t	11	12	13	14	15	16	17	18	19	20
0·0	0·50000	0·50000	0·50000	0·50000	0·50000	0·50000	0·50000	0·50000	0·50000	0·50000
0·1	·53893	·53900	·53907	·53912	·53917	·53921	·53924	·53928	·53930	·53933
0·2	·57744	·57759	·57771	·57782	·57792	·57800	·57807	·57814	·57820	·57825
0·3	·61511	·61534	·61554	·61571	·61585	·61598	·61609	·61619	·61628	·61636
0·4	·65159	·65191	·65217	·65240	·65260	·65278	·65293	·65307	·65319	·65330
0·5	0·68654	0·68694	0·68728	0·68758	0·68783	0·68806	0·68826	0·68843	0·68859	0·68873
0·6	·71967	·72017	·72059	·72095	·72127	·72155	·72179	·72201	·72220	·72238
0·7	·75077	·75136	·75187	·75230	·75268	·75301	·75330	·75356	·75380	·75400
0·8	·77968	·78037	·78096	·78146	·78190	·78229	·78263	·78293	·78320	·78344
0·9	·80630	·80709	·80776	·80833	·80883	·80927	·80965	·81000	·81031	·81058
1·0	0·83060	0·83148	0·83222	0·83286	0·83341	0·83390	0·83433	0·83472	0·83506	0·83537
1·1	·85259	·85355	·85436	·85506	·85566	·85620	·85667	·85709	·85746	·85780
1·2	·87233	·87335	·87422	·87497	·87562	·87620	·87670	·87715	·87756	·87792
1·3	·88991	·89099	·89191	·89270	·89339	·89399	·89452	·89500	·89542	·89581
1·4	·90546	·90658	·90754	·90836	·90907	·90970	·91025	·91074	·91118	·91158
1·5	0·91912	0·92027	0·92125	0·92209	0·92282	0·92346	0·92402	0·92452	0·92498	0·92538
1·6	·93105	·93221	·93320	·93404	·93478	·93542	·93599	·93650	·93695	·93736
1·7	·94140	·94256	·94354	·94439	·94512	·94576	·94632	·94683	·94728	·94768
1·8	·95034	·95148	·95245	·95328	·95400	·95463	·95518	·95568	·95612	·95652
1·9	·95802	·95914	·96008	·96089	·96158	·96220	·96273	·96321	·96364	·96403
2·0	0·96460	0·96567	0·96658	0·96736	0·96803	0·96861	0·96913	0·96959	0·97000	0·97037
2·1	·97020	·97123	·97209	·97283	·97347	·97403	·97452	·97495	·97534	·97569
2·2	·97496	·97593	·97675	·97745	·97805	·97858	·97904	·97945	·97981	·98014
2·3	·97898	·97990	·98067	·98132	·98189	·98238	·98281	·98319	·98352	·98383
2·4	·98238	·98324	·98396	·98457	·98509	·98554	·98594	·98629	·98660	·98688
2·5	0·98525	0·98604	0·98671	0·98727	0·98775	0·98816	0·98853	0·98885	0·98913	0·98938
2·6	·98765	·98839	·98900	·98951	·98995	·99033	·99066	·99095	·99121	·99144
2·7	·98967	·99035	·99090	·99137	·99177	·99211	·99241	·99267	·99290	·99311
2·8	·99136	·99198	·99249	·99291	·99327	·99358	·99385	·99408	·99429	·99447
2·9	·99278	·99334	·99380	·99418	·99450	·99478	·99502	·99523	·99541	·99557
3·0	0·99396	0·99447	0·99488	0·99522	0·99551	0·99576	0·99597	0·99616	0·99632	0·99646
3·1	·99495	·99541	·99578	·99608	·99634	·99656	·99675	·99691	·99705	·99718
3·2	·99577	·99618	·99652	·99679	·99702	·99721	·99738	·99752	·99764	·99775
3·3	·99646	·99683	·99713	·99737	·99757	·99774	·99789	·99801	·99812	·99821
3·4	·99703	·99737	·99763	·99784	·99802	·99817	·99830	·99840	·99850	·99858
3·5	0·99751	0·99781	0·99804	0·99823	0·99839	0·99852	0·99863	0·99872	0·99880	0·99887
3·6	·99791	·99818	·99838	·99855	·99869	·99880	·99890	·99898	·99905	·99911
3·7	·99825	·99848	·99867	·99881	·99893	·99903	·99911	·99918	·99924	·99929
3·8	·99853	·99874	·99890	·99902	·99913	·99921	·99928	·99934	·99939	·99944
3·9	·99876	·99895	·99909	·99920	·99929	·99936	·99942	·99948	·99952	·99956
4·0	0·99896	0·99912	0·99924	0·99934	0·99942	0·99948	0·99954	0·99958	0·99962	0·99965
4·2	·99926	·99938	·99948	·99955	·99961	·99966	·99970	·99973	·99976	·99978
4·4	·99947	·99957	·99964	·99970	·99974	·99978	·99980	·99983	·99985	·99986
4·6	·99962	·99969	·99975	·99979	·99983	·99985	·99987	·99989	·99990	·99991
4·8	·99972	·99978	·99983	·99986	·99988	·99990	·99992	·99993	·99994	·99995
5·0	0·99980	0·99985	0·99988	0·99990	0·99992	0·99993	0·99995	0·99995	0·99996	0·99997
5·2	·99985	·99989	·99992	·99993	·99995	·99996	·99996	·99997	·99997	·99998
5·4	·99989	·99992	·99994	·99995	·99996	·99997	·99998	·99998	·99998	·99999
5·6	·99992	·99994	·99996	·99997	·99997	·99998	·99998	·99999	·99999	·99999
5·8	·99994	·99996	·99997	·99998	·99998	·99998	·99999	·99999	·99999	·99999
6·0	0·99995	0·99997	0·99998	0·99998	0·99999	0·99999	0·99999	0·99999		
6·2	·99997	·99998	·99998	·99999	·99999	·99999				
6·4	·99997	·99998	·99998	·99999	·99999	·99999				
6·6	·99998	·99999	·99999	·99999	·99999					
6·8	·99998	·99999	·99999							
7·0	0·99999	0·99999								

	(area to left of $+t$)									
df / t	20	21	22	23	24	30	40	60	120	∞
0·00	0·50000	0·50000	0·50000	0·50000	0·50000	0·50000	0·50000	0·50000	0·50000	0·50000
0·05	·51969	·51970	·51971	·51972	·51973	·51977	·51981	·51986	·51990	·51994
0·10	·53933	·53935	·53938	·53939	·53941	·53950	·53958	·53966	·53974	·53983
0·15	·55887	·55890	·55893	·55896	·55899	·55912	·55924	·55937	·55949	·55962
0·20	·57825	·57830	·57834	·57838	·57842	·57858	·57875	·57892	·57909	·57926
0·25	0·59743	0·59749	0·59755	0·59760	0·59764	0·59785	0·59807	0·59828	0·59849	0·59871
0·30	·61636	·61644	·61650	·61656	·61662	·61688	·61713	·61739	·61765	·61791
0·35	·63500	·63509	·63517	·63524	·63530	·63561	·63591	·63622	·63652	·63683
0·40	·65330	·65340	·65349	·65358	·65365	·65400	·65436	·65471	·65507	·65542
0·45	·67122	·67134	·67144	·67154	·67163	·67203	·67243	·67283	·67324	·67364
0·50	0·68873	0·68886	0·68898	0·68909	0·68919	0·68964	0·69009	0·69055	0·69100	0·69146
0·55	·70579	·70594	·70607	·70619	·70630	·70680	·70731	·70782	·70833	·70884
0·60	·72238	·72254	·72268	·72281	·72294	·72349	·72405	·72462	·72518	·72575
0·65	·73846	·73863	·73879	·73893	·73907	·73968	·74030	·74091	·74153	·74215
0·70	·75400	·75419	·75437	·75453	·75467	·75534	·75601	·75668	·75736	·75804
0·75	0·76901	0·76921	0·76940	0·76957	0·76973	0·77045	0·77118	0·77191	0·77264	0·77337
0·80	·78344	·78367	·78387	·78405	·78422	·78500	·78578	·78657	·78735	·78814
0·85	·79731	·79754	·79776	·79796	·79814	·79897	·79981	·80065	·80149	·80234
0·90	·81058	·81084	·81107	·81128	·81147	·81236	·81325	·81414	·81504	·81594
0·95	·82327	·82354	·82378	·82401	·82421	·82515	·82609	·82704	·82799	·82894
1·00	0·83537	0·83565	0·83591	0·83614	0·83636	0·83735	0·83834	0·83934	0·84034	0·84134
1·05	·84688	·84717	·84744	·84769	·84791	·84895	·84999	·85104	·85209	·85314
1·10	·85780	·85811	·85839	·85864	·85888	·85996	·86105	·86214	·86323	·86433
1·15	·86814	·86846	·86875	·86902	·86926	·87039	·87151	·87265	·87378	·87493
1·20	·87792	·87825	·87855	·87882	·87907	·88023	·88140	·88257	·88375	·88493
1·25	0·88714	0·88747	0·88778	0·88807	0·88832	0·88952	0·89072	0·89192	0·89313	0·89435
1·30	·89581	·89616	·89647	·89676	·89703	·89825	·89948	·90071	·90195	·90320
1·35	·90395	·90431	·90463	·90492	·90644	·90770	·90896	·91022	·91149	
1·40	·91158	·91194	·91227	·91257	·91285	·91411	·91539	·91667	·91795	·91924
1·45	·91872	·91908	·91942	·91972	·92000	·92128	·92257	·92387	·92517	·92647
1·50	0·92538	0·92575	0·92608	0·92639	0·92667	0·92797	0·92927	0·93057	0·93188	0·93319
1·55	·93159	·93196	·93230	·93260	·93289	·93419	·93549	·93680	·93811	·93943
1·60	·93736	·93773	·93807	·93838	·93866	·93996	·94127	·94257	·94389	·94520
1·65	·94272	·94309	·94342	·94373	·94401	·94531	·94661	·94792	·94922	·95053
1·70	·94768	·94805	·94839	·94869	·94897	·95026	·95155	·95284	·95414	·95543
1·75	0·95228	0·95264	0·95297	0·95327	0·95355	0·95483	0·95611	0·95738	0·95866	0·95994
1·80	·95652	·95688	·95720	·95750	·95778	·95904	·96030	·96156	·96281	·96407
1·85	·96043	·96078	·96110	·96140	·96167	·96291	·96414	·96538	·96661	·96784
1·90	·96403	·96437	·96469	·96498	·96524	·96646	·96767	·96888	·97008	·97128
1·95	·96733	·96767	·96798	·96827	·96852	·96971	·97089	·97207	·97325	·97441
2·0	0·97037	0·97070	0·97100	0·97128	0·97153	0·97269	0·97384	0·97498	0·97612	0·97725
2·1	·97569	·97601	·97629	·97655	·97679	·97788	·97896	·98003	·98109	·98214
2·2	·98014	·98043	·98070	·98094	·98116	·98218	·98318	·98416	·98514	·98610
2·3	·98383	·98410	·98435	·98457	·98478	·98571	·98663	·98753	·98841	·98928
2·4	·98688	·98712	·98735	·98756	·98774	·98860	·98943	·99024	·99103	·99180
2·5	0·98938	0·98961	0·98982	0·99000	0·99017	0·99094	0·99169	0·99241	0·99312	0·99379
2·6	·99144	·99164	·99183	·99200	·99215	·99284	·99350	·99414	·99475	·99534
2·7	·99311	·99329	·99346	·99361	·99375	·99436	·99494	·99550	·99603	·99653
2·8	·99447	·99463	·99478	·99492	·99504	·99557	·99608	·99657	·99702	·99744
2·9	·99557	·99572	·99585	·99596	·99607	·99654	·99698	·99740	·99778	·99813
3·0	0·99646	0·99659	0·99670	0·99681	0·99690	0·99730	0·99768	0·99804	0·99836	0·99865
3·1	·99718	·99729	·99739	·99748	·99756	·99791	·99823	·99853	·99879	·99903
3·2	·99775	·99785	·99793	·99801	·99808	·99838	·99865	·99890	·99912	·99931
3·3	·99821	·99829	·99837	·99844	·99849	·99875	·99898	·99918	·99936	·99952
3·4	·99858	·99865	·99871	·99877	·99882	·99904	·99923	·99940	·99954	·99966
3·5	0·99887	0·99893	0·99899	0·99904	0·99908	0·99926	0·99942	0·99956	0·99967	0·99977
3·6	·99911	·99916	·99920	·99925	·99928	·99943	·99957	·99968	·99977	·99984
3·7	·99929	·99933	·99937	·99941	·99944	·99957	·99967	·99976	·99984	·99989
3·8	·99944	·99948	·99951	·99954	·99956	·99967	·99976	·99983	·99989	·99993
3·9	·99956	·99959	·99961	·99964	·99966	·99975	·99982	·99988	·99992	·99995
4·0	0·99965	0·99967	0·99970	0·99972	0·99974	0·99981	0·99987	0·99991	0·99995	0·99997
5·0	0·99997	0·99997	0·99998	0·99998	0·99998	0·99999	0·99999			

Appendix H Logarithms
$\text{Log}_{10} N$

N	0	1	2	3	4	5	6	7	8	9
10	0000	0043	0086	0128	0170	0212	0253	0294	0334	0374
11	0414	0453	0492	0531	0569	0607	0645	0682	0719	0755
12	0792	0828	0864	0899	0934	0969	1004	1038	1072	1106
13	1139	1173	1206	1239	1271	1303	1335	1367	1399	1430
14	1461	1492	1523	1553	1584	1614	1644	1673	1703	1732
15	1761	1790	1818	1847	1875	1903	1931	1959	1987	2014
16	2041	2068	2095	2122	2148	2175	2201	2227	2253	2279
17	2304	2330	2355	2380	2405	2430	2455	2480	2504	2529
18	2553	2577	2601	2625	2648	2672	2695	2718	2742	2765
19	2788	2810	2833	2856	2878	2900	2923	2945	2967	2989
20	3010	3032	3054	3075	3096	3118	3139	3160	3181	3201
21	3222	3243	3263	3284	3304	3324	3345	3365	3385	3404
22	3424	3444	3464	3483	3502	3522	3541	3560	3579	3598
23	3617	3636	3655	3674	3692	3711	3729	3747	3766	3784
24	3802	3820	3838	3856	3874	3892	3909	3927	3945	3962
25	3979	3997	4014	4031	4048	4065	4082	4099	4116	4133
26	4150	4166	4183	4200	4216	4232	4249	4265	4281	4298
27	4314	4330	4346	4362	4378	4393	4409	4425	4440	4456
28	4472	4487	4502	4518	4533	4548	4564	4579	4594	4609
29	4624	4639	4654	4669	4683	4698	4713	4728	4742	4757
30	4771	4786	4800	4814	4829	4843	4857	4871	4886	4900
31	4914	4928	4942	4955	4969	4983	4997	5011	5024	5038
32	5051	5065	5079	5092	5105	5119	5132	5145	5159	5172
33	5185	5198	5211	5224	5237	5250	5263	5276	5289	5302
34	5315	5328	5340	5353	5366	5378	5391	5403	5416	5428
35	5441	5453	5465	5478	5490	5502	5515	5527	5539	5551
36	5563	5575	5587	5599	5611	5623	5635	5647	5658	5670
37	5682	5694	5705	5717	5729	5740	5752	5763	5775	5786
38	5798	5809	5821	5832	5843	5855	5866	5877	5888	5899
39	5911	5922	5933	5944	5955	5966	5977	5988	5999	6010
40	6021	6031	6042	6053	6064	6075	6085	6096	6107	6117
41	6128	6138	6149	6160	6170	6180	6191	6201	6212	6222
42	6232	6243	6253	6263	6274	6284	6294	6304	6314	6325
43	6335	6345	6355	6365	6375	6385	6395	6405	6415	6425
44	6435	6444	6454	6464	6474	6484	6493	6503	6513	6522
45	6532	6542	6551	6561	6571	6580	6590	6599	6609	6618
46	6628	6637	6646	6656	6665	6675	6684	6693	6702	6712
47	6721	6730	6739	6749	6758	6767	6776	6785	6794	6803
48	6812	6821	6830	6839	6848	6857	6866	6875	6884	6893
49	6902	6911	6920	6928	6937	6946	6955	6964	6972	6981
50	6990	6998	7007	7016	7024	7033	7042	7050	7059	7067
51	7076	7084	7093	7101	7110	7118	7126	7135	7143	7152
52	7160	7168	7177	7185	7193	7202	7210	7218	7226	7235
53	7243	7251	7259	7267	7275	7284	7292	7300	7308	7316
54	7324	7332	7340	7348	7356	7364	7372	7380	7388	7396

SOURCE: Computed for this volume.

N	0	1	2	3	4	5	6	7	8	9
55	7404	7412	7419	7427	7435	7443	7451	7459	7466	7474
56	7482	7490	7497	7505	7513	7520	7528	7536	7543	7551
57	7559	7566	7574	7582	7589	7597	7604	7612	7619	7627
58	7634	7642	7649	7657	7664	7672	7679	7686	7694	7701
59	7709	7716	7723	7731	7738	7745	7752	7760	7767	7774
60	7782	7789	7796	7803	7810	7818	7825	7832	7839	7846
61	7853	7860	7868	7875	7882	7889	7896	7903	7910	7917
62	7924	7931	7938	7945	7952	7959	7966	7973	7980	7987
63	7993	8000	8007	8014	8021	8028	8035	8041	8048	8055
64	8062	8069	8075	8082	8089	8096	8102	8109	8116	8122
65	8129	8136	8142	8149	8156	8162	8169	8176	8182	8189
66	8195	8202	8209	8215	8222	8228	8235	8241	8248	8254
67	8261	8267	8274	8280	8287	8293	8299	8306	8312	8319
68	8325	8331	8338	8344	8351	8357	8363	8370	8376	8382
69	8388	8395	8401	8407	8414	8420	8426	8432	8439	8445
70	8451	8457	8463	8470	8476	8482	8488	8494	8500	8506
71	8513	8519	8525	8531	8537	8543	8549	8555	8561	8567
72	8573	8579	8585	8591	8597	8603	8609	8615	8621	8627
73	8633	8639	8645	8651	8657	8663	8669	8675	8681	8686
74	8692	8698	8704	8710	8716	8722	8727	8733	8739	8745
75	8751	8756	8762	8768	8774	8779	8785	8791	8797	8802
76	8808	8814	8820	8825	8831	8837	8842	8848	8854	8859
77	8865	8871	8876	8882	8887	8893	8899	8904	8910	8915
78	8921	8927	8932	8938	8943	8949	8954	8960	8965	8971
79	8976	8982	8987	8993	8998	9004	9009	9015	9020	9025
80	9031	9036	9042	9047	9053	9058	9063	9069	9074	9079
81	9085	9090	9096	9101	9106	9112	9117	9122	9128	9133
82	9138	9143	9149	9154	9159	9165	9170	9175	9180	9186
83	9191	9196	9201	9206	9212	9217	9222	9227	9232	9238
84	9243	9248	9253	9258	9263	9269	9274	9279	9284	9289
85	9294	9299	9304	9309	9315	9320	9325	9330	9335	9340
86	9345	9350	9355	9360	9365	9370	9375	9380	9385	9390
87	9395	9400	9405	9410	9415	9420	9425	9430	9435	9440
88	9445	9450	9455	9460	9465	9469	9474	9479	9484	9489
89	9494	9499	9504	9509	9513	9518	9523	9528	9533	9538
90	9542	9547	9552	9557	9562	9566	9571	9576	9581	9586
91	9590	9595	9600	9605	9609	9614	9619	9624	9628	9633
92	9638	9643	9647	9652	9657	9661	9666	9671	9675	9680
93	9685	9689	9694	9699	9703	9708	9713	9717	9722	9727
94	9731	9736	9741	9745	9750	9754	9759	9763	9768	9773
95	9777	9782	9786	9791	9795	9800	9805	9809	9814	9818
96	9823	9827	9832	9836	9841	9845	9850	9854	9859	9863
97	9868	9872	9877	9881	9886	9890	9894	9899	9903	9908
98	9912	9917	9921	9926	9930	9934	9939	9943	9948	9952
99	9956	9961	9965	9969	9974	9978	9983	9987	9991	9996

Logarithms of factorials

$\text{Log}_{10} N!$

n	$\log_{10} n!$	n	$\log_{10} n!$	n	$\log_{10} n!$	n	$\log_{10} n!$	n	$\log_{10} n!$
1	0·000 0000	51	66·190 6450	101	159·974 3250	151	264·935 8704	201	377·200 0847
2	0·301 0300	52	67·906 6484	102	161·982 9252	152	267·117 7139	202	379·505 4361
3	0·778 1513	53	69·630 9243	103	163·995 7624	153	269·302 4054	203	381·812 9321
4	1·380 2112	54	71·363 3180	104	166·012 7958	154	271·489 9261	204	384·122 5623
5	2·079 1812	55	73·103 6807	105	168·033 9851	155	273·680 2578	205	386·434 3161
6	2·857 3325	56	74·851 8687	106	170·059 2909	156	275·873 3824	206	388·748 1834
7	3·702 4305	57	76·607 7436	107	172·088 6747	157	278·069 2820	207	391·064 1537
8	4·605 5205	58	78·371 1716	108	174·122 0985	158	280·267 9391	208	393·382 2170
9	5·559 7630	59	80·142 0236	109	176·159 5250	159	282·469 3363	209	395·702 3633
10	6·559 7630	60	81·920 1748	110	178·200 9176	160	284·673 4562	210	398·024 5826
11	7·601 1557	61	83·705 5047	111	180·246 2406	161	286·880 2821	211	400·348 8651
12	8·680 3370	62	85·497 8964	112	182·295 4586	162	289·089 7971	212	402·675 2009
13	9·794 2803	63	87·297 2369	113	184·348 5371	163	291·301 9847	213	405·003 5805
14	10·940 4084	64	89·103 4169	114	186·405 4419	164	293·516 8286	214	407·333 9943
15	12·116 4996	65	90·916 3303	115	188·466 1398	165	295·734 3125	215	409·666 4328
16	13·320 6196	66	92·735 8742	116	190·530 5978	166	297·954 4206	216	412·000 8865
17	14·551 0685	67	94·561 9490	117	192·598 7836	167	300·177 1371	217	414·337 3463
18	15·806 3410	68	96·394 4579	118	194·670 6656	168	302·402 4464	218	416·675 8027
19	17·085 0946	69	98·233 3070	119	196·746 2126	169	304·630 3331	219	419·016 2469
20	18·386 1246	70	100·078 4050	120	198·825 3938	170	306·860 7820	220	421·358 6695
21	19·708 3439	71	101·929 6634	121	200·908 1792	171	309·093 7781	221	423·703 0618
22	21·050 7666	72	103·786 9959	122	202·994 5390	172	311·329 3066	222	426·049 4148
23	22·412 4944	73	105·650 3187	123	205·084 4442	173	313·567 3527	223	428·397 7197
24	23·792 7057	74	107·519 5505	124	207·177 8658	174	315·807 9019	224	430·747 9677
25	25·190 6457	75	109·394 6117	125	209·274 7759	175	318·050 9400	225	433·100 1502
26	26·605 6190	76	111·275 4253	126	211·375 1464	176	320·296 4526	226	435·454 2586
27	28·036 9828	77	113·161 9160	127	213·478 9501	177	322·544 4259	227	437·810 2845
28	29·484 1408	78	115·054 0106	128	215·586 1601	178	324·794 8459	228	440·168 2193
29	30·946 5388	79	116·951 6377	129	217·696 7498	179	327·047 6989	229	442·528 0548
30	32·423 6601	80	118·854 7277	130	219·810 6932	180	329·302 9714	230	444·889 7827
31	33·915 0218	81	120·763 2127	131	221·927 9645	181	331·560 6500	231	447·253 3946
32	35·420 1717	82	122·677 0266	132	224·048 5384	182	333·820 7214	232	449·618 8826
33	36·938 6857	83	124·596 1047	133	226·172 3900	183	336·083 1725	233	451·986 2385
34	38·470 1646	84	126·520 3840	134	228·299 4948	184	338·347 9903	234	454·355 4544
35	40·014 2326	85	128·449 8029	135	230·429 8286	185	340·615 1620	235	456·726 5223
36	41·570 5351	86	130·384 3013	136	232·563 3675	186	342·884 6750	236	459·099 4343
37	43·138 7369	87	132·323 8206	137	234·700 0881	187	345·156 5166	237	461·474 1826
38	44·718 5205	88	134·268 3033	138	236·839 9672	188	347·430 6744	238	463·850 7596
39	46·309 5851	89	136·217 6933	139	238·982 9820	189	349·707 1362	239	466·229 1575
40	47·911 6451	90	138·171 9358	140	241·129 1100	190	351·985 8898	240	468·609 3687
41	49·524 4289	91	140·130 9772	141	243·278 3291	191	354·266 9232	241	470·991 3857
42	51·147 6782	92	142·094 7650	142	245·430 6174	192	356·550 2244	242	473·375 2011
43	52·781 1467	93	144·063 2480	143	247·585 9535	193	358·835 7817	243	475·760 8074
44	54·424 5993	94	146·036 3758	144	249·744 3160	194	361·123 5835	244	478·148 1972
45	56·077 8119	95	148·014 0994	145	251·905 6840	195	363·413 6181	245	480·537 3633
46	57·740 5697	96	149·996 3707	146	254·070 0368	196	365·705 8742	246	482·928 2984
47	59·412 6676	97	151·983 1424	147	256·237 3542	197	368·000 3404	247	485·320 9954
48	61·093 9088	98	153·974 3685	148	258·407 6159	198	370·297 0056	248	487·715 4470
49	62·784 1049	99	155·970 0037	149	260·580 8022	199	372·595 8586	249	490·111 6464
50	64·483 0749	100	157·970 0037	150	262·756 8934	200	374·896 8886	250	492·509 5864

SOURCE: Pearson and Hartley (1966).

Logarithms

A Finding the logarithm of a number, N.

If $N > 1$: e.g., $\log_{10} 62.3$

Step 1 Count the number of digits to the left of the decimal place, and subtract 1.
e.g., 62 is two digits.
$2 - 1 = 1$

Step 2 Enter the log table with N, disregarding the decimal, interpolating if necessary.
e.g., enter with 623
tabled value is 7945

Step 3 $\log_{10} 62.3 = 1.7945$

If $N < 1$: e.g., $\log_{10} 0.0623$

Step 1 Enter the log table with N, disregarding the decimal, interpolating if necessary.
e.g., enter with 623
tabled value is 7945

Step 2 Count the number of zeros to the right of the decimal, and add 1.
e.g., .0623 has 1 zero $1 + 1 = 2$

Step 3 $\log_{10} 0.0623 = \quad .7945 - 2$
$= -1.2055$

B Finding the number whose logarithm is given, i.e., finding an anti-logarithm.

If N is positive: e.g., $\log N = 2.7945$

Step 1 Add 1 to this number to get the number of decimal places in the antilog.
e.g., $2 + 1 = 3$ places

Step 2 Look up this number in the *body* of the log table and read off the co-ordinates to get the antilog.
e.g., the co-ordinates for 7945 are 623.

Step 3 $N = 623.0$

If N is negative: e.g., log $N = -2.2055$

Step 1   Take the absolute value of this number to get the number of zeros in the antilog.

e.g., 2 zeros

Step 2   Take the complement of this number, look up the complement in the *body* of the log table and read off the co-ordinates.

e.g., 10000 — 2055 = 7945
the co-ordinates for 7945 are 623.

Step 3 $N = .00623$

C   Rules

1 $\log XY = \log X + \log Y$

2 $\log \dfrac{X}{Y} = \log X - \log Y$

3 $\log X^a = a \log X$
4 $\log 1 = 0$
5 $\log_{10} e = 0.4343$
6 $\log_{10} \pi = 0.4971$

Appendix I
Interpolation

Interpolation is necessary whenever you wish to enter a table with a number that falls between the table entries. Linear interpolation will be adequate for the tables in this book.

Suppose, for example, you wish to find the logarithm of 4.126. The log table in Appendix H gives

$$\log 4.12 = .6149,$$
$$\text{and } \log 4.13 = .6160,$$

but is not "fine" enough to give log 4.126. You can see that 4.126 is $\frac{6}{10}$ of the distance from 4.120 to 4.130. We assume in linear interpolation that log 4.126 is, then, $\frac{6}{10}$ of the distance from log 4.120 to log 4.130, i.e., .6 of the distance from .6149 to .6160. That distance is .0011, and .6 of it is .0011 × .6 = .00066, or .0007. If we add that distance to .6149 we get,

$$\log 4.126 = .6149 + .0007 = .6156$$

You can see this more clearly in the following interpolation diagram.

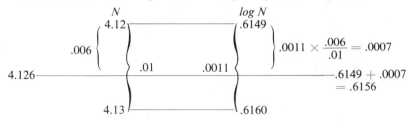

Appendix J   Powers and roots

N	N^2	$\sqrt{N}$	N	N^2	$\sqrt{N}$	N	N^2	$\sqrt{N}$
			50	2500	7.0711	100	10000	10.0000
1	1	1.0000	51	2601	7.1414	101	10201	10.0499
2	4	1.4142	52	2704	7.2111	102	10404	10.0995
3	9	1.7321	53	2809	7.2801	103	10609	10.1489
4	16	2.0000	54	2916	7.3485	104	10816	10.1980
5	25	2.2361	55	3025	7.4162	105	11025	10.2470
6	36	2.4495	56	3136	7.4833	106	11236	10.2956
7	49	2.6458	57	3249	7.5498	107	11449	10.3441
8	64	2.8284	58	3364	7.6158	108	11664	10.3923
9	81	3.0000	59	3481	7.6811	109	11881	10.4403
10	100	3.1623	60	3600	7.7460	110	12100	10.4881
11	121	3.3166	61	3721	7.8102	111	12321	10.5357
12	144	3.4641	62	3844	7.8740	112	12544	10.5830
13	169	3.6056	63	3969	7.9373	113	12769	10.6301
14	196	3.7417	64	4096	8.0000	114	12996	10.6771
15	225	3.8730	65	4225	8.0623	115	13225	10.7238
16	256	4.0000	66	4356	8.1240	116	13456	10.7703
17	289	4.1231	67	4489	8.1854	117	13689	10.8167
18	324	4.2426	68	4624	8.2462	118	13924	10.8628
19	361	4.3589	69	4761	8.3066	119	14161	10.9087
20	400	4.4721	70	4900	8.3666	120	14400	10.9545
21	441	4.5826	71	5041	8.4261	121	14641	11.0000
22	484	4.6904	72	5184	8.4853	122	14884	11.0454
23	529	4.7958	73	5329	8.5440	123	15129	11.0905
24	576	4.8990	74	5476	8.6023	124	15376	11.1355
25	625	5.0000	75	5625	8.6603	125	15625	11.1803
26	676	5.0990	76	5776	8.7178	126	15876	11.2250
27	729	5.1962	77	5929	8.7750	127	16129	11.2694
28	784	5.2915	78	6084	8.8318	128	16384	11.3137
29	841	5.3852	79	6241	8.8882	129	16641	11.3578
30	900	5.4772	80	6400	8.9443	130	16900	11.4018
31	961	5.5678	81	6561	9.0000	131	17161	11.4455
32	1024	5.6569	82	6724	9.0554	132	17424	11.4891
33	1089	5.7446	83	6889	9.1104	133	17689	11.5326
34	1156	5.8310	84	7056	9.1652	134	17956	11.5758
35	1225	5.9161	85	7225	9.2195	135	18225	11.6190
36	1296	6.0000	86	7396	9.2736	136	18496	11.6619
37	1369	6.0828	87	7569	9.3274	137	18769	11.7047
38	1444	6.1644	88	7744	9.3808	138	19044	11.7473
39	1521	6.2450	89	7921	9.4340	139	19321	11.7898
40	1600	6.3246	90	8100	9.4868	140	19600	11.8322
41	1681	6.4031	91	8281	9.5394	141	19881	11.8743
42	1764	6.4807	92	8464	9.5917	142	20164	11.9164
43	1849	6.5574	93	8649	9.6437	143	20449	11.9583
44	1936	6.6332	94	8836	9.6954	144	20736	12.0000
45	2025	6.7082	95	9025	9.7468	145	21025	12.0416
46	2116	6.7823	96	9216	9.7980	146	21316	12.0830
47	2209	6.8557	97	9409	9.8489	147	21609	12.1244
48	2304	6.9282	98	9604	9.8995	148	21904	12.1655
49	2401	7.0000	99	9801	9.9499	149	22201	12.2066

SOURCE: Computed for this volume.

N	N²	√N	N	N²	√N	N	N²	√N
150	22500	12·2474	200	40000	14·1421	250	62500	15·8114
151	22801	12·2882	201	40401	14·1774	251	63001	15·8430
152	23104	12·3288	202	40804	14·2127	252	63504	15·8745
153	23409	12·3693	203	41209	14·2478	253	64009	15·9060
154	23716	12·4097	204	41616	14·2829	254	64516	15·9374
155	24025	12·4499	205	42025	14·3178	255	65025	15·9687
156	24336	12·4900	206	42436	14·3527	256	65536	16·0000
157	24649	12·5300	207	42849	14·3875	257	66049	16·0312
158	24964	12·5698	208	43264	14·4222	258	66564	16·0624
159	25281	12·6095	209	43681	14·4568	259	67081	16·0935
160	25600	12·6491	210	44100	14·4914	260	67600	16·1245
161	25921	12·6886	211	44521	14·5258	261	68121	16·1555
162	26244	12·7279	212	44944	14·5602	262	68644	16·1864
163	26569	12·7671	213	45369	14·5945	263	69169	16·2173
164	26896	12·8062	214	45796	14·6287	264	69696	16·2481
165	27225	12·8452	215	46225	14·6629	265	70225	16·2788
166	27556	12·8841	216	46656	14·6969	266	70756	16·3095
167	27889	12·9228	217	47089	14·7309	267	71289	16·3401
168	28224	12·9615	218	47524	14·7648	268	71824	16·3707
169	28561	13·0000	219	47961	14·7986	269	72361	16·4012
170	28900	13·0384	220	48400	14·8324	270	72900	16·4317
171	29241	13·0767	221	48841	14·8661	271	73441	16·4621
172	29584	13·1149	222	49284	14·8997	272	73984	16·4924
173	29929	13·1529	223	49729	14·9332	273	74529	16·5227
174	30276	13·1909	224	50176	14·9666	274	75076	16·5529
175	30625	13·2288	225	50625	15·0000	275	75625	16·5831
176	30976	13·2665	226	51076	15·0333	276	76176	16·6132
177	31329	13·3041	227	51529	15·0665	277	76729	16·6433
178	31684	13·3417	228	51984	15·0997	278	77284	16·6733
179	32041	13·3791	229	52441	15·1327	279	77841	16·7033
180	32400	13·4164	230	52900	15·1658	280	78400	16·7332
181	32761	13·4536	231	53361	15·1987	281	78961	16·7631
182	33124	13·4907	232	53824	15·2315	282	79524	16·7929
183	33489	13·5277	233	54289	15·2643	283	80089	16·8226
184	33856	13·5647	234	54756	15·2971	284	80656	16·8523
185	34225	13·6015	235	55225	15·3297	285	81225	16·8819
186	34596	13·6382	236	55696	15·3623	286	81796	16·9115
187	34969	13·6748	237	56169	15·3948	287	82369	16·9411
188	35344	13·7113	238	56644	15·4272	288	82944	16·9706
189	35721	13·7477	239	57121	15·4596	289	83521	17·0000
190	36100	13·7840	240	57600	15·4919	290	84100	17·0294
191	36481	13·8203	241	58081	15·5242	291	84681	17·0587
192	36864	13·8564	242	58564	15·5563	292	85264	17·0880
193	37249	13·8924	243	59049	15·5885	293	85849	17·1172
194	37636	13·9284	244	59536	15·6205	294	86436	17·1464
195	38025	13·9642	245	60025	15·6525	295	87025	17·1756
196	38416	14·0000	246	60516	15·6844	296	87616	17·2047
197	38809	14·0357	247	61009	15·7162	297	88209	17·2337
198	39204	14·0712	248	61504	15·7480	298	88804	17·2627
199	39601	14·1067	249	62001	15·7797	299	89401	17·2916

N	N²	√N	N	N²	√N	N	N²	√N
300	90000	17.3205	350	122500	18.7083	400	160000	20.0000
301	90601	17.3494	351	123201	18.7350	401	160801	20.0250
302	91204	17.3781	352	123904	18.7617	402	161604	20.0499
303	91809	17.4069	353	124609	18.7883	403	162409	20.0749
304	92416	17.4356	354	125316	18.8149	404	163216	20.0998
305	93025	17.4642	355	126025	18.8414	405	164025	20.1246
306	93636	17.4929	356	126736	18.8680	406	164836	20.1494
307	94249	17.5214	357	127449	18.8944	407	165649	20.1742
308	94864	17.5499	358	128164	18.9209	408	166464	20.1990
309	95481	17.5784	359	128881	18.9473	409	167281	20.2237
310	96100	17.6068	360	129600	18.9737	410	168100	20.2485
311	96721	17.6352	361	130321	19.0000	411	168921	20.2731
312	97344	17.6635	362	131044	19.0263	412	169744	20.2978
313	97969	17.6918	363	131769	19.0526	413	170569	20.3224
314	98596	17.7200	364	132496	19.0788	414	171396	20.3470
315	99225	17.7482	365	133225	19.1050	415	172225	20.3715
316	99856	17.7764	366	133956	19.1311	416	173056	20.3961
317	100489	17.8045	367	134689	19.1572	417	173889	20.4206
318	101124	17.8326	368	135424	19.1833	418	174724	20.4450
319	101761	17.8606	369	136161	19.2094	419	175561	20.4695
320	102400	17.8885	370	136900	19.2354	420	176400	20.4939
321	103041	17.9165	371	137641	19.2614	421	177241	20.5183
322	103684	17.9444	372	138384	19.2873	422	178084	20.5426
323	104329	17.9722	373	139129	19.3132	423	178929	20.5670
324	104976	18.0000	374	139876	19.3391	424	179776	20.5913
325	105625	18.0278	375	140625	19.3649	425	180625	20.6155
326	106276	18.0555	376	141376	19.3907	426	181476	20.6398
327	106929	18.0831	377	142129	19.4165	427	182329	20.6640
328	107584	18.1108	378	142884	19.4422	428	183184	20.6882
329	108241	18.1384	379	143641	19.4679	429	184041	20.7123
330	108900	18.1659	380	144400	19.4936	430	184900	20.7364
331	109561	18.1934	381	145161	19.5192	431	185761	20.7605
332	110224	18.2209	382	145924	19.5448	432	186624	20.7846
333	110889	18.2483	383	146689	19.5704	433	187489	20.8087
334	111556	18.2757	384	147456	19.5959	434	188356	20.8327
335	112225	18.3030	385	148225	19.6214	435	189225	20.8567
336	112896	18.3303	386	148996	19.6469	436	190096	20.8806
337	113569	18.3576	387	149769	19.6723	437	190969	20.9045
338	114244	18.3848	388	150544	19.6977	438	191844	20.9284
339	114921	18.4120	389	151321	19.7231	439	192721	20.9523
340	115600	18.4391	390	152100	19.7484	440	193600	20.9762
341	116281	18.4662	391	152881	19.7737	441	194481	21.0000
342	116964	18.4932	392	153664	19.7990	442	195364	21.0238
343	117649	18.5203	393	154449	19.8242	443	196249	21.0476
344	118336	18.5472	394	155236	19.8494	444	197136	21.0713
345	119025	18.5742	395	156025	19.8746	445	198025	21.0950
346	119716	18.6011	396	156816	19.8997	446	198916	21.1187
347	120409	18.6279	397	157609	19.9249	447	199809	21.1424
348	121104	18.6548	398	158404	19.9499	448	200704	21.1660
349	121801	18.6815	399	159201	19.9750	449	201601	21.1896

N	N^2	$\sqrt{N}$	N	N^2	$\sqrt{N}$	N	N^2	$\sqrt{N}$
450	202500	21.2132	500	250000	22.3607	550	302500	23.4521
451	203401	21.2368	501	251001	22.3830	551	303601	23.4734
452	204304	21.2603	502	252004	22.4054	552	304704	23.4947
453	205209	21.2838	503	253009	22.4277	553	305809	23.5160
454	206116	21.3073	504	254016	22.4499	554	306916	23.5372
455	207025	21.3307	505	255025	22.4722	555	308025	23.5584
456	207936	21.3542	506	256036	22.4944	556	309136	23.5797
457	208849	21.3776	507	257049	22.5167	557	310249	23.6008
458	209764	21.4009	508	258064	22.5389	558	311364	23.6220
459	210681	21.4243	509	259081	22.5610	559	312481	23.6432
460	211600	21.4476	510	260100	22.5832	560	313600	23.6643
461	212521	21.4709	511	261121	22.6053	561	314721	23.6854
462	213444	21.4942	512	262144	22.6274	562	315844	23.7065
463	214369	21.5174	513	263169	22.6495	563	316969	23.7276
464	215296	21.5407	514	264196	22.6716	564	318096	23.7487
465	216225	21.5639	515	265225	22.6936	565	319225	23.7697
466	217156	21.5870	516	266256	22.7156	566	320356	23.7908
467	218089	21.6102	517	267289	22.7376	567	321489	23.8118
468	219024	21.6333	518	268324	22.7596	568	322624	23.8328
469	219961	21.6564	519	269361	22.7816	569	323761	23.8537
470	220900	21.6795	520	270400	22.8035	570	324900	23.8747
471	221841	21.7025	521	271441	22.8254	571	326041	23.8956
472	222784	21.7256	522	272484	22.8473	572	327184	23.9165
473	223729	21.7486	523	273529	22.8692	573	328329	23.9374
474	224676	21.7715	524	274576	22.8910	574	329476	23.9583
475	225625	21.7945	525	275625	22.9129	575	330625	23.9792
476	226576	21.8174	526	276676	22.9347	576	331776	24.0000
477	227529	21.8403	527	277729	22.9565	577	332929	24.0208
478	228484	21.8632	528	278784	22.9783	578	334084	24.0416
479	229441	21.8861	529	279841	23.0000	579	335241	24.0624
480	230400	21.9089	530	280900	23.0217	580	336400	24.0832
481	231361	21.9317	531	281961	23.0434	581	337561	24.1039
482	232324	21.9545	532	283024	23.0651	582	338724	24.1247
483	233289	21.9773	533	284089	23.0868	583	339889	24.1454
484	234256	22.0000	534	285156	23.1084	584	341056	24.1661
485	235225	22.0227	535	286225	23.1301	585	342225	24.1868
486	236196	22.0454	536	287296	23.1517	586	343396	24.2074
487	237169	22.0681	537	288369	23.1733	587	344569	24.2281
488	238144	22.0907	538	289444	23.1948	588	345744	24.2487
489	239121	22.1133	539	290521	23.2164	589	346921	24.2693
490	240100	22.1359	540	291600	23.2379	590	348100	24.2899
491	241081	22.1585	541	292681	23.2594	591	349281	24.3105
492	242064	22.1811	542	293764	23.2809	592	350464	24.3311
493	243049	22.2036	543	294849	23.3024	593	351649	24.3516
494	244036	22.2261	544	295936	23.3238	594	352836	24.3721
495	245025	22.2486	545	297025	23.3452	595	354025	24.3926
496	246016	22.2711	546	298116	23.3666	596	355216	24.4131
497	247009	22.2935	547	299209	23.3880	597	356409	24.4336
498	248004	22.3159	548	300304	23.4094	598	357604	24.4540
499	249001	22.3383	549	301401	23.4307	599	358801	24.4745

N	N²	√N	N	N²	√N	N	N²	√N
600	360000	24.4949	650	422500	25.4951	700	490000	26.4575
601	361201	24.5153	651	423801	25.5147	701	491401	26.4764
602	362404	24.5357	652	425104	25.5343	702	492804	26.4953
603	363609	24.5561	653	426409	25.5539	703	494209	26.5141
604	364816	24.5764	654	427716	25.5734	704	495616	26.5330
605	366025	24.5967	655	429025	25.5930	705	497025	26.5518
606	367236	24.6171	656	430336	25.6125	706	498436	26.5707
607	368449	24.6374	657	431649	25.6320	707	499849	26.5895
608	369664	24.6577	658	432964	25.6515	708	501264	26.6083
609	370881	24.6779	659	434281	25.6710	709	502681	26.6271
610	372100	24.6982	660	435600	25.6905	710	504100	26.6458
611	373321	24.7184	661	436921	25.7099	711	505521	26.6646
612	374544	24.7386	662	438244	25.7294	712	506944	26.6833
613	375769	24.7588	663	439569	25.7488	713	508369	26.7021
614	376996	24.7790	664	440896	25.7682	714	509796	26.7208
615	378225	24.7992	665	442225	25.7876	715	511225	26.7395
616	379456	24.8193	666	443556	25.8070	716	512656	26.7582
617	380689	24.8395	667	444889	25.8263	717	514089	26.7769
618	381924	24.8596	668	446224	25.8457	718	515524	26.7955
619	383161	24.8797	669	447561	25.8650	719	516961	26.8142
620	384400	24.8998	670	448900	25.8844	720	518400	26.8328
621	385641	24.9199	671	450241	25.9037	721	519841	26.8514
622	386884	24.9399	672	451584	25.9230	722	521284	26.8701
623	388129	24.9600	673	452929	25.9422	723	522729	26.8887
624	389376	24.9800	674	454276	25.9615	724	524176	26.9072
625	390625	25.0000	675	455625	25.9808	725	525625	26.9258
626	391876	25.0200	676	456976	26.0000	726	527076	26.9444
627	393129	25.0400	677	458329	26.0192	727	528529	26.9629
628	394384	25.0599	678	459684	26.0384	728	529984	26.9815
629	395641	25.0799	679	461041	26.0576	729	531441	27.0000
630	396900	25.0998	680	462400	26.0768	730	532900	27.0185
631	398161	25.1197	681	463761	26.0960	731	534361	27.0370
632	399424	25.1396	682	465124	26.1151	732	535824	27.0555
633	400689	25.1595	683	466489	26.1343	733	537289	27.0740
634	401956	25.1794	684	467856	26.1534	734	538756	27.0924
635	403225	25.1992	685	469225	26.1725	735	540225	27.1109
636	404496	25.2190	686	470596	26.1916	736	541696	27.1293
637	405769	25.2389	687	471969	26.2107	737	543169	27.1477
638	407044	25.2587	688	473344	26.2298	738	544644	27.1662
639	408321	25.2784	689	474721	26.2488	739	546121	27.1846
640	409600	25.2982	690	476100	26.2679	740	547600	27.2029
641	410881	25.3180	691	477481	26.2869	741	549081	27.2213
642	412164	25.3377	692	478864	26.3059	742	550564	27.2397
643	413449	25.3574	693	480249	26.3249	743	552049	27.2580
644	414736	25.3772	694	481636	26.3439	744	553536	27.2764
645	416025	25.3969	695	483025	26.3629	745	555025	27.2947
646	417316	25.4165	696	484416	26.3818	746	556516	27.3130
647	418609	25.4362	697	485809	26.4008	747	558009	27.3313
648	419904	25.4558	698	487204	26.4197	748	559504	27.3496
649	421201	25.4755	699	488601	26.4386	749	561001	27.3679

N	N^2	$\sqrt{N}$	N	N^2	$\sqrt{N}$	N	N^2	$\sqrt{N}$
750	562500	27.3861	800	640000	28.2843	850	722500	29.1548
751	564001	27.4044	801	641601	28.3019	851	724201	29.1719
752	565504	27.4226	802	643204	28.3196	852	725904	29.1890
753	567009	27.4408	803	644809	28.3373	853	727609	29.2062
754	568516	27.4591	804	646416	28.3549	854	729316	29.2233
755	570025	27.4773	805	648025	28.3725	855	731025	29.2404
756	571536	27.4955	806	649636	28.3901	856	732736	29.2575
757	573049	27.5136	807	651249	28.4077	857	734449	29.2746
758	574564	27.5318	808	652864	28.4253	858	736164	29.2916
759	576081	27.5500	809	654481	28.4429	859	737881	29.3087
760	577600	27.5681	810	656100	28.4605	860	739600	29.3258
761	579121	27.5862	811	657721	28.4781	861	741321	29.3428
762	580644	27.6043	812	659344	28.4956	862	743044	29.3598
763	582169	27.6225	813	660969	28.5132	863	744769	29.3769
764	583696	27.6405	814	662596	28.5307	864	746496	29.3939
765	585225	27.6586	815	664225	28.5482	865	748225	29.4109
766	586756	27.6767	816	665856	28.5657	866	749956	29.4279
767	588289	27.6948	817	667489	28.5832	867	751689	29.4449
768	589824	27.7128	818	669124	28.6007	868	753424	29.4618
769	591361	27.7308	819	670761	28.6182	869	755161	29.4788
770	592900	27.7489	820	672400	28.6356	870	756900	29.4958
771	594441	27.7669	821	674041	28.6531	871	758641	29.5127
772	595984	27.7849	822	675684	28.6705	872	760384	29.5296
773	597529	27.8029	823	677329	28.6880	873	762129	29.5466
774	599076	27.8209	824	678976	28.7054	874	763876	29.5635
775	600625	27.8388	825	680625	28.7228	875	765625	29.5804
776	602176	27.8568	826	682276	28.7402	876	767376	29.5973
777	603729	27.8747	827	683929	28.7576	877	769129	29.6142
778	605284	27.8927	828	685584	28.7750	878	770884	29.6311
779	606841	27.9106	829	687241	28.7924	879	772641	29.6479
780	608400	27.9285	830	688900	28.8097	880	774400	29.6648
781	609961	27.9464	831	690561	28.8271	881	776161	29.6816
782	611524	27.9643	832	692224	28.8444	882	777924	29.6985
783	613089	27.9821	833	693889	28.8617	883	779689	29.7153
784	614656	28.0000	834	695556	28.8791	884	781456	29.7321
785	616225	28.0179	835	697225	28.8964	885	783225	29.7489
786	617796	28.0357	836	698896	28.9137	886	784996	29.7658
787	619369	28.0535	837	700569	28.9310	887	786769	29.7825
788	620944	28.0713	838	702244	28.9482	888	788544	29.7993
789	622521	28.0891	839	703921	28.9655	889	790321	29.8161
790	624100	28.1069	840	705600	28.9828	890	792100	29.8329
791	625681	28.1247	841	707281	29.0000	891	793881	29.8496
792	627264	28.1425	842	708964	29.0172	892	795664	29.8664
793	628849	28.1603	843	710649	29.0345	893	797449	29.8831
794	630436	28.1780	844	712336	29.0517	894	799236	29.8998
795	632025	28.1957	845	714025	29.0689	895	801025	29.9166
796	633616	28.2135	846	715716	29.0861	896	802816	29.9333
797	635209	28.2312	847	717409	29.1033	897	804609	29.9500
798	636804	28.2489	848	719104	29.1204	898	806404	29.9666
799	638401	28.2666	849	720801	29.1376	899	808201	29.9833

N	N²	√N	N	N²	√N	N	N²	√N
900	810000	30.0000	950	902500	30.8221	1000	1000000	31.6228
901	811801	30.0167	951	904401	30.8383			
902	813604	30.0333	952	906304	30.8545			
903	815409	30.0500	953	908209	30.8707			
904	817216	30.0666	954	910116	30.8869			
905	819025	30.0832	955	912025	30.9031			
906	820836	30.0998	956	913936	30.9192			
907	822649	30.1164	957	915849	30.9354			
908	824464	30.1330	958	917764	30.9516			
909	826281	30.1496	959	919681	30.9677			
910	828100	30.1662	960	921600	30.9839			
911	829921	30.1828	961	923521	31.0000			
912	831744	30.1993	962	925444	31.0161			
913	833569	30.2159	963	927369	31.0322			
914	835396	30.2324	964	929296	31.0483			
915	837225	30.2490	965	931225	31.0644			
916	839056	30.2655	966	933156	31.0805			
917	840889	30.2820	967	935089	31.0966			
918	842724	30.2985	968	937024	31.1127			
919	844561	30.3150	969	938961	31.1288			
920	846400	30.3315	970	940900	31.1448			
921	848241	30.3480	971	942841	31.1609			
922	850084	30.3645	972	944784	31.1769			
923	851929	30.3809	973	946729	31.1929			
924	853776	30.3974	974	948676	31.2090			
925	855625	30.4138	975	950625	31.2250			
926	857476	30.4302	976	952576	31.2410			
927	859329	30.4467	977	954529	31.2570			
928	861184	30.4631	978	956484	31.2730			
929	863041	30.4795	979	958441	31.2890			
930	864900	30.4959	980	960400	31.3050			
931	866761	30.5123	981	962361	31.3209			
932	868624	30.5287	982	964324	31.3369			
933	870489	30.5450	983	966289	31.3528			
934	872356	30.5614	984	968256	31.3688			
935	874225	30.5778	985	970225	31.3847			
936	876096	30.5941	986	972196	31.4006			
937	877969	30.6105	987	974169	31.4166			
938	879844	30.6268	988	976144	31.4325			
939	881721	30.6431	989	978121	31.4484			
940	883600	30.6594	990	980100	31.4643			
941	885481	30.6757	991	982081	31.4802			
942	887364	30.6920	992	984064	31.4960			
943	889249	30.7083	993	986049	31.5119			
944	891136	30.7246	994	988036	31.5278			
945	893025	30.7409	995	990025	31.5436			
946	894916	30.7571	996	992016	31.5595			
947	896809	30.7734	997	994009	31.5753			
948	898704	30.7896	998	996004	31.5911			
949	900601	30.8058	999	998001	31.6070			

Appendix K

Fisher-z transformation

The function tabled is $z = \frac{1}{2}\ln\frac{1+r}{1-r}$

r	z	r	z	r	z	r	z
0·00	0·00	·25	·26	·50	·55	·75	·97
·01	·01	·26	·27	·51	·56	·76	1·00
·02	·02	·27	·28	·52	·58	·77	1·02
·03	·03	·28	·29	·53	·59	·78	1·05
·04	·04	·29	·30	·54	·60	·79	1·07
·05	·05	·30	·31	·55	·62	·80	1·10
·06	·06	·31	·32	·56	·63	·81	1·13
·07	·07	·32	·33	·57	·65	·82	1·16
·08	·08	·33	·34	·58	·66	·83	1·19
·09	·09	·34	·35	·59	·68	·84	1·22
·10	·10	·35	·37	·60	·69	·85	1·26
·11	·11	·36	·38	·61	·71	·86	1·29
·12	·12	·37	·39	·62	·73	·87	1·33
·13	·13	·38	·40	·63	·74	·88	1·38
·14	·14	·39	·41	·64	·76	·89	1·42
·15	·15	·40	·42	·65	·78	·90	1·47
·16	·16	·41	·44	·66	·79	·91	1·53
·17	·17	·42	·45	·67	·81	·92	1·59
·18	·18	·43	·46	·68	·83	·93	1·66
·19	·19	·44	·47	·69	·85	·94	1·74
·20	·20	·45	·48	·70	·87	·95	1·83
·21	·21	·46	·50	·71	·89	·96	1·95
·22	·22	·47	·51	·72	·91	·97	2·09
·23	·23	·48	·52	·73	·93	·98	2·30
·24	·24	·49	·54	·74	·95	·99	2·65

SOURCE: Computed for this volume.

Appendix L Tangents

ω	tan ω	ω	tan ω	ω	tan ω
0	0·000	30	·577	60	1·732
1	·017	31	·601	61	1·804
2	·035	32	·625	62	1·881
3	·052	33	·649	63	1·963
4	·070	34	·675	64	2·050
5	·087	35	·700	65	2·145
6	·105	36	·727	66	2·246
7	·123	37	·754	67	2·356
8	·141	38	·781	68	2·475
9	·158	39	·810	69	2·605
10	·176	40	·839	70	2·747
11	·194	41	·869	71	2·904
12	·213	42	·900	72	3·078
13	·231	43	·933	73	3·271
14	·249	44	·966	74	3·487
15	·268	45	1·000	75	3·732
16	·287	46	1·036	76	4·011
17	·306	47	1·072	77	4·331
18	·325	48	1·111	78	4·705
19	·344	49	1·150	79	5·145
20	·364	50	1·192	80	5·671
21	·384	51	1·235	81	6·314
22	·404	52	1·280	82	7·115
23	·424	53	1·327	83	8·144
24	·445	54	1·376	84	9·514
25	·466	55	1·428	85	11·430
26	·488	56	1·483	86	14·301
27	·510	57	1·540	87	19·081
28	·532	58	1·600	88	28·636
29	·554	59	1·664	89	57·290

SOURCE: Pearson and Hartley (1966).

Appendix M — Transformation of ranks to normal scores

i \ n	2	3	4	5	6	7	8	9	10	11	12
1	0·564	0·846	1·029	1·163	1·267	1·352	1·424	1·485	1·539	1·586	1·629
2		·000	0·297	0·495	0·642	0·757	0·852	0·932	1·001	1·062	1·116
3				·000	·202	·353	·473	·572	0·656	0·729	0·793
4						·000	·153	·275	·376	·462	·537
5								0·000	0·123	0·225	0·312
6										·000	·103
ΣX^2	0·636	1·431	2·294	3·195	4·117	5·051	6·002	6·953	7·915	8·878	9·849

i \ n	13	14	15	16	17	18	19	20	21	22	23	24	25
1	1·668	1·703	1·736	1·766	1·794	1·820	1·844	1·867	1·89	1·91	1·93	1·95	1·97
2	1·164	1·208	1·248	1·285	1·319	1·350	1·380	1·408	1·43	1·46	1·48	1·50	1·52
3	0·850	0·901	0·948	0·990	1·029	1·066	1·099	1·131	1·16	1·19	1·21	1·24	1·26
4	·603	·662	·715	·763	0·807	0·848	0·886	0·921	0·95	0·98	1·01	1·04	1·07
5	0·388	0·456	0·516	0·570	0·619	0·665	0·707	0·745	0·78	0·82	0·85	0·88	0·91
6	·190	·267	·335	·396	·451	·502	·548	·590	·63	·67	·70	·73	·76
7	·000	·088	·165	·234	·295	·351	·402	·448	·49	·53	·57	·60	·64
8			·000	·077	·146	·208	·264	·315	·36	·41	·45	·48	·52
9					·000	·069	·131	·187	·24	·29	·33	·37	·41
10							0·000	0·062	0·12	0·17	0·22	0·26	0·30
11									·00	·06	·11	·16	·20
12											·00	·05	·10
13													·00
ΣX^2	10·820	11·793	12·774	13·749	14·726	15·712	16·692	17·675	18·62	19·69	20·62	21·60	22·64

i \ n	26	28	30	32	34	36	38	40	42	44	46	48	50
1	1·98	2·01	2·04	2·07	2·09	2·12	2·14	2·16	2·18	2·20	2·22	2·23	2·25
2	1·54	1·58	1·62	1·65	1·68	1·70	1·73	1·75	1·78	1·80	1·82	1·84	1·85
3	1·29	1·33	1·36	1·40	1·43	1·46	1·49	1·52	1·54	1·57	1·59	1·61	1·63
4	1·09	1·14	1·18	1·22	1·25	1·28	1·32	1·34	1·37	1·40	1·42	1·44	1·46
5	0·93	0·98	1·03	1·07	1·11	1·14	1·17	1·20	1·23	1·26	1·28	1·31	1·33
6	·79	·85	0·89	0·94	0·98	1·02	1·05	1·08	1·11	1·14	1·17	1·19	1·22
7	·67	·73	·78	·82	·87	0·91	0·94	0·98	1·01	1·04	1·07	1·09	1·12
8	·55	·61	·67	·72	·76	·81	·85	·88	0·91	0·95	0·98	1·00	1·03
9	·44	·51	·57	·62	·67	·71	·75	·79	·83	·86	·89	0·92	0·95
10	0·34	0·41	0·47	0·53	0·58	0·63	0·67	0·71	0·75	0·78	0·81	0·84	0·87
11	·24	·32	·38	·44	·50	·54	·59	·63	·67	·71	·74	·77	·80
12	·14	·22	·29	·36	·41	·47	·51	·56	·60	·64	·67	·70	·74
13	·05	·13	·21	·28	·34	·39	·44	·49	·53	·57	·60	·64	·67
14		·04	·12	·20	·26	·32	·37	·42	·46	·50	·54	·58	·61
15			0·04	0·12	0·18	0·24	0·30	0·35	0·40	0·44	0·48	0·52	0·55
16				·04	·11	·17	·23	·28	·33	·38	·42	·46	·49
17					·04	·10	·16	·22	·27	·32	·36	·40	·44
18						·03	·10	·16	·21	·26	·30	·34	·38
19							·03	·09	·15	·20	·25	·29	·33
20								0·03	0·09	0·14	0·19	0·24	0·28
21									·03	·09	·14	·18	·23
22										·03	·08	·13	·18
23											·03	·08	·13
24												·03	·07
25													0·03
ΣX^2	23·55	25·58	27·55	29·80	31·52	33·49	35·48	37·43	39·47	41·58	43·49	45·36	47·38

SOURCE: Pearson and Hartley (1966). Values of ΣX^2 were computed for this volume and do not appear in the original table.